Symposium on

ORGANIC MATTER
IN
NATURAL WATERS

held at the University of Alaska
September 2-4 1968

edited by
DONALD W. HOOD

INSTITUTE OF MARINE SCIENCE
OCCASIONAL PUBLICATION NO. 1
June, 1970

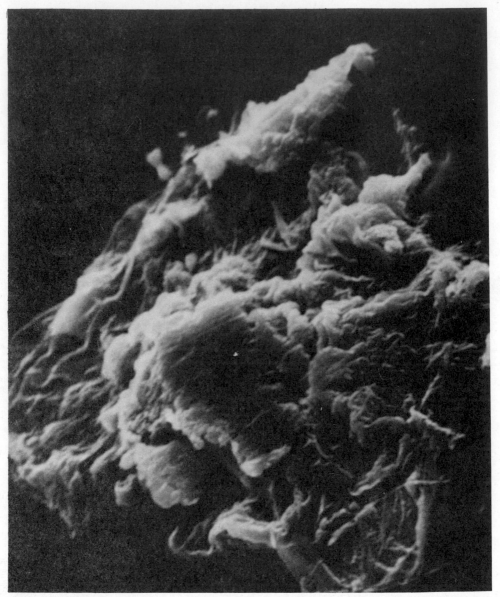

This organic aggregate was collected during a plankton bloom in the Chukchi Sea off the coast of Alaska (68°28′N, 172°20′W) in July, 1968. The denser material near the center may be either an inorganic or an organic particle. It is associated with flake-like organic material.

The aggregate was photographed with a Joelco scanning electron microscope (JSM-2) at the Bedford Institute of Oceanography, Dartmouth, Nova Scotia, by T. C. Loder. The crinkled surface is a result of the drying process used. Particle diameter: 60 - 70 μ. Magnification: 1400x.

Symposium on

ORGANIC MATTER
IN
NATURAL WATERS

held at the University of Alaska
September 2-4 1968

edited by
DONALD W. HOOD

INSTITUTE OF MARINE SCIENCE
OCCASIONAL PUBLICATION NO. 1
June, 1970

Published June 1970
Price: $10.00, paper $8.00

Order from: Institute of Marine Science
University of Alaska
College, Alaska   99701

Library of Congress Catalog Card 73-63-1866

SYMPOSIUM COMMITTEE

General Chairman
DONALD W. HOOD
Professor and Director of Marine Science

Vera Alexander .... Associate Professor of Marine Science
Mary Belle Allen .. Professor of Microbiological Sciences and Marine Science
Robert J. Barsdate .... Associate Professor of Marine Science
John J. Goering ....Professor of Marine Science
Patrick J. Kinney .... Associate Professor of Marine Science
G. D. Sharma .... Associate Professor of Marine Science

SPONSORED BY

National Science Foundation

U. S. Atomic Energy Commission

Office of Water Resources Research
U. S. Department of the Interior

Institute of Marine Science
University of Alaska

TECHNICAL EDITOR

Kathleen M. Stamm

FOREWORD

This symposium was organized by the staff of the Institute of Marine Science at the University of Alaska for two primary reasons. First, it was felt that no previous symposium had adequately covered the subject of organic matter in natural waters. It was hoped that a three-day discussion of this subject by as many specialists as possible coming from various relevant disciplines would provide material for a significant background document. Further, the interaction of the participants coupled with the resulting published papers would stimulate additional research in this important topic.

Second, the Institute of Marine Science at the University of Alaska, a relatively new center for oceanographic research, sits in the heart of a state that contains nearly half of the fresh water resources of the United States, roughly 53% of the tidal coast line and more than 70% of the continental shelf. It seemed appropriate that this symposium be held in this far northern setting to aquaint the researchers with the possibilities offered by Alaska's waters.

More than 100 participants (80 from outside the state) attended the symposium held on the University of Alaska campus in early September, 1968. Approximately half of the group participated in one of three field trips to the Southeast Alaska fiords, Barrow (on the arctic slope) or Mt. McKinley National Park.

This volume consists of papers presented at the symposium. The papers and the discussions which follow them were edited for clarity, readability and stylistic uniformity, but no effort was made to change technical content.

Two papers are missing. R. P. Collins (University of Connecticut) and J. J. Morgan (California Institute of Technology) read papers but did not submit their manuscripts for publication. To prevent confusion, discussion remarks which hinged on these two papers have been deleted.

TABLE OF CONTENTS

Session III. Organic matter and water quality

Session IV. Inorganic-organic associations in natural waters

Session V. Recent development - invited short papers

Closing Address:

Master Bibliography

INTRODUCTION

Information concerning the importance of organic matter in natural waters is limited and scattered. It is extremely difficult, if not impossible to draw quantitative conclusions at this time. Nevertheless, there is a large amount of information pointing directly to the significance of these minor organic components in the complex chemistry of the sea.

Probably the first to recognize the importance of organic components, were the biologists whose thinking was well-summarized in a paper by Lucas (1955) which emphasized the significance of the so-called "organic metabolites" on the distribution and growth of marine algae, bacteria, protozoa and larvae. Their work also focused attention on the effects of these materials on physiological responses of a large group of marine organisms. Most parameters indicate no difference between "good" and "bad" ocean waters. The discriminating factor seems to be productivity. Good waters support a heavy growth of organisms; bad waters are nearly sterile. These observations suggest other critical factors such as growth substances, toxins and trace elements which hold the key to the productivity of the sea. Several recent reviews (Hood, 1963; Johnston, 1955; Provasoli, 1963; Vallentyne, 1957; and Saunders, 1957) and many papers demonstrate the importance of dissolved organic matter in the biology of the sea from five viewpoints:

-organic compounds, even in dilute solution, serve as energy sources for algae, bacteria, yeast, fungi and larvae;

-vitamins serve as growth stimulators for algae, bacteria, yeast, fungi and larvae;

-organic toxins such as those derived from *Gymnodinium breve*, kill entire populations;

-certain organic compounds trigger feeding processes of organisms, even though these compounds are not nutrients;

-nutrient or toxic trace elements may be associated or chelated with organic compounds thus controlling the level of these elements in the aquatic medium.

Evidence for the importance of organic matter to geological and geochemical processes is becoming voluminous. The association of organics with sediment during metamorphosis and diagenesis into sedimentary rocks has been found to be involved in both the origin and migration of petroleum. Data strongly suggest that organic acids, particularly the fatty acids sorbed to clays or other particles suspended in sea water, subsequently settle to the bottom and participate in the formation and accumulation of recoverable petroleum products. Probably the most difficult and least understood aspect of clay mineralogy concerns relating the sorbed organic matter on clay minerals to the changes in cation exchange properties, physical characteristics and consolidation of these clays in sedimentary materials.

The organic materials in sedimentary deposits probably have several origins. They may be deposited as discrete particles from a marine or terrestrial source. They may be formed in place by action of macro- and micro- organisms living in these deposits. They may be a product of sorption of dissolved organic matter to the surface of settling inorganic particulate matter, or of aggregate formation from dissolved organic matter through the action of bubbles surface active phenomena or chemical fractionation by bacterial action.

Physical oceanographers have devoted little attention to the presence of dissolved or particulate organic compounds in sea water. Exceptions include Jerlov's work on particulate matter in the ocean (1959), that on the light absorbency of sea water by dissolved organic matter (Clark and James, 1939; Armstrong and Boalch, 1961) and the relatively large body of literature on the causes of sea slicks in coastal and open ocean regions. Surface tension measurements (Lumby and Folkard, 1956) using the spreading-drop method (Adam, 1937) indicate an effect of organic matter on surface tension. Further, it has been found that the surface tension of natural ocean water is always lower than that of clean water because of organic contamination. The effect of organic matter on density appears to be relatively unimportant (Lyman, 1959).

Qualitatively, the importance of organic matter to the chemistry of the oceans is self-evident. However, only quantitative data will make possible a precise evaluation of the significance of organic matter to the dynamics of ocean phenomena. There is little question that many interactions of biological organisms with organic matter in the sea are compound specific. Thus, an understanding of the stimulus, depression or activity of organisms caused by organic matter hinges on careful, detailed analysis of the constituents present, a determination of their rates of production and degradation, and a determination of their distribution in the ocean.

Technologically, we are now approaching the point where such analysis is possible. The chemical oceanographer of today has at his disposal Raman infrared and ultraviolet spectrophotometry; electron magnetic and nuclear magnetic resonance; gas chromatography coupled with mass spectrometry; thin layer, paper and column chromatography; anodic stripping polarography; radioactive and stable isotope tracer techniques; X-ray diffraction and fluorescence; electron microscopy (see frontispiece) and many other sophisticated techniques which may now be brought to bear on the organic problem in natural waters.

To understand the dynamics of ocean processes and to better use the sea, man must understand the cycle of carbon through the biological, geochemical and physical pathways of the environment. This symposium is a part of the continuing effort to achieve this understanding.

Donald W. Hood, Editor
Professor and Director
Institute of Marine Science
University of Alaska
College, Alaska   99701

IMPORTANCE AND GENERAL IMPLICATIONS OF ORGANIC MATTER IN AQUATIC ENVIRONMENTS

T. R. Parsons and H. Seki[1]
Fisheries Research Board of Canada
Pacific Oceanographic Group
Biological Station
Nanaimo, B. C.

ABSTRACT

Processes leading to the steady-state equilibrium of organic materials in aquatic environments are reviewed. Particular attention is devoted to the removal of organic material from the large reservoir of organic debris formed from the food chain. Results show the importance of the small particles produced as a result of decomposition and feeding processes in the food chain. Finally, an estimate is made of the level of particulate organic material required to support the growth and maintenance of filter feeding copepods.

INTRODUCTION

During the last decade there has been an enormous increase in the number of studies on organic materials in natural waters. One result of these studies is a new regard for the well-established principle that in any environment there must be an eventual overall balance between the processes of production and decomposition. In the case of organic materials, photosynthesis, a well-studied and biochemically-definable process, is conceived to be the starting point of the organic carbon cycle in Nature. On the other hand, descriptions of the ultimate fate of organic material are often lost in such biologically nebulous terms as "decomposition" "recycling," or "waste products."

The question of what really happens in the organic carbon cycle following the initial input by primary producers has become more complex in detail but, as Wangersky (1965) observed, it has become quantitatively easier to understand. Improved techniques have made it apparent that a fraction of the organic carbon produced annually by the food chain tends to accumulate to a steady-state value several orders of magnitude greater than the organisms from which it is derived. From this observation and from work on organic aggregates, Riley (1963) has concluded that there is a flexible system of reversible reactions allowing organisms to draw upon the reservoir of organic carbon and replenish it in a variety of ways. This in turn is suggested as a factor which has tended to stabilize the aquatic environment by providing a food source for living organisms over a longer period of time

---

[1] National Research Council Post-doctoral Fellow

than that in which a single phytoplankton bloom could be sustained by the environment.

Such a system is illustrated in Fig. 1, which has been numbered to show (1) the input into the system, (2) the steady-state equilibrium, and (3) the output. We will give a number of examples of these three processes and present some experimental results which pertain to the reutilization of organic materials (Fig. 1, 3, Output). We have limited our discussion to biological processes in the belief that these are considerably more important in magnitude than purely chemical processes in the aerobic organic carbon cycle of aquatic environments.

Input of organic materials

The only original source of energy for the carbon cycle illustrated in Fig. 1 is photosynthesis at the primary trophic level. In our discussion, however, we have labelled as (1) Input, processes by which dissolved and particulate organic carbon are discarded by the food chain — the formation of all carbon in an aquatic system which is not part of the living tissue of primary producers, or of some higher trophic level, and which has not been respired out of the cycle as carbon dioxide. Essentially there are two natural processes which contribute to the formation of these organic products in aquatic environments.

The first of these involves the decomposition of plant and animal materials. This may result in an initial 15 to 50% loss of total biomass due to post-mortem changes in the permeability of cell membranes and the effects of autolytic enzymes (Krause et al., 1961; Krause, 1961 and 1962). Products which have been reported to occur as soluble organic compounds released from dead plankton include amino acids, keto acids and fatty acids. The more refractory components of plankton are decomposed at least in part by bacterial action. In the marine environment, for example, the decomposition of one of the more abundant of these substances, chitin, has been shown to proceed quite rapidly due to the widespread occurrence of chitinoclastic bacteria (Seki and Taga, 1963; Seki, 1965a and b).

The second process involved in the formation of organic materials is the liberation of extracellular products by living plants and animals. Apart from the true excrement of animals, the term "excretion" has also been applied to the liberation of soluble organic materials by plants, although as the exact process becomes known there may be less reason to use this physiologically precise word. The subject has recently been reviewed by Fogg (1966). In some species up to 50% of the amount of photosynthetically fixed CO_2 may be released as soluble organic carbon (Allen, 1956; Fogg, 1952). Studies of some of the more common phytoplankton species as well as of natural populations have found that, in general, the release of extracellular products by healthy cells amounts to 15% or less of the total carbon fixed (Eppley and Sloan, 1965; Hellebust, 1965). Watt (1966) has suggested a maximum loss of extracellular products of up to 30%. In our own studies (Antia et al., 1963), we obtained indirect evidence for the extracellular release of about 35% of the total organic

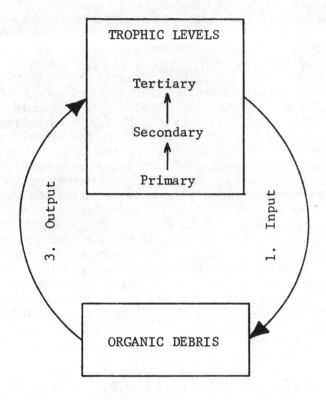

2. Steady-state

Fig. 1.   A generalized organic carbon cycle.

matter photosynthesized during an experiment with a natural phytoplankton population contained in a large plastic sphere. Substances which have been identified as resulting from the release of extracellular products include polysaccharides, polypeptides, amino acids and glycollic acid, as well as certain species-specific, biologically active compounds such as enzymes (Fogg, 1962 and 1966). The release of amino acids by healthy zooplankton has also been reported in quantities which within one month would be sufficient to replace the quantities found to occur naturally in oceanic waters (Webb and Johannes, 1967).

In conclusion, it appears that the release of organic compounds to the carbon reservoir in an aquatic environment, either through decomposition processes or from healthy plankton, could be quite appreciable. If we add a range of 5 to 30% extracellular products to 20 to 30% detrital products from the food chain [considering only one trophic level and assuming a 70 to 80% assimilation efficiency of phytoplankton by zooplankton (Conover, 1966a and b)] then the total amount of soluble and particulate materials available for reutilization in the food chain could amount to between 25 and 60% of the annual primary production of particulate phytoplankton. For an average annual marine primary production of 70[1] g C/m^2 /yr this would amount to an annual minimum input of 18 to 42 g C/m^2 /yr. Assuming that much of this material occurs as soluble compounds, the quantities are similar to the soluble organic production of 52 g C/m^2 /yr estimated by Duursma (1963). In coastal areas and in lakes the quantity of organic carbon contributed as soluble and particulate material may be much higher than this due to the addition of terrigenous material washed from the surrounding land (e.g., Stephens et al., 1967), or due to the pollution of an aquatic system by a domestic or industrial outfall.

The steady-state equilibrium

The steady-state equilibrium can be defined as the point at which the input of an element to a system is balanced by its loss. In our world of averages it has little more meaning than the statistician's "average man," but as with a comparison of different populations, so with a comparison of different environments: the steady-state equilibrium may serve to reduce processes to a common denominator in terms of which the overall activities of environments can be compared. The concept is equally applicable to shallow waters, where most of the organic carbon may be concentrated in a sediment, and to deep ocean waters, where most of the material is present as soluble organic carbon which has reached a steady-state concentration of one or two parts per million.

The kinetics of the steady-state equilibrium have been described by Olson (1963) for terrestrial environments. In the simplest case, if there is a

---

[1] If this value is 31% too low (Nielsen, 1965) then the agreement with soluble carbon production becomes even more acceptable.

continual input (L) to a standing stock of carbon (X) then the change in X with time can be described by the equation

$$X = \frac{L}{k} (1 - e^{-kt})$$

where k represents the rate (time $^{-1}$) at which the standing stock is being decomposed. In a situation in which sufficient time has been allowed (t large) the system will reach a steady-state value, X_{ss}, equal to $\frac{L}{k}$. Using these kinetic computations Skopintsev (1966) has estimated that the steady-state value of one or two parts per million of soluble organic carbon in ocean waters has been accumulated over a period of several thousand years. This result would appear to refer to deep water. The approximate value of 18 to 42 g C/m^2/yr for detrital carbon production in surface waters would require that much of this was reutilized in the surface layers, resulting in a rate of turnover one or two orders of magnitude higher than that for soluble organic carbon in deep water. Using the same approach with data from a shallow bay we have determined that the accumulation of organic carbon to a steady-state value occurred in the surface sediment within approximately 30 years (Seki et al., 1968). While these values are approximate, they do quantify differences in the level of biological activity in the two environments.

Output of organic materials

The utilization of sedimented organic materials by benthic animals has been studied by a number of authors (e.g., Jorgensen, 1966, and references cited therein). Newell (1965) has suggested that the actual food component for benthic animals may be the bacterial biomass on the surface of organic and inorganic particles, rather than organic debris per se. Considering this the first step in the output of organic material from a sediment, we assayed sedimented material using a species of bacteria commonly found in the coastal waters of British Columbia (Seki et al., 1968). Our results indicate that extracts of a marine sediment can support the growth of bacteria and that the bacteria produced can then serve as a source of food for the growth of brine shrimp up to the 4th instar. From these and other studies it is apparent that the shallow water marine sediment employed in our studies is a relatively good substrate for growth of a common bacterial species. In Nature, however, organic material is buried a few centimeters deep, which preserves it from biological attack, although the activities of large burrowing animals, especially in marine environments, tend to decrease this effect by continually turning over the sediment. As pointed out by Vallentyne (1962) the factor determining the amount of organic material in benthic communities is the balance between insoluble particles held in place by gravity and the production of dissolved substances which tend to move away from the sediment by diffusion. This situation is almost completely reversed in the pelagic zone where the bulk of the organic material is present as soluble compounds (Duursma, 1960), and the problem of achieving an output is largely one of converting it back to a particulate state suitable for filter feeding organisms or for sedimentation[1].

Earlier studies using radioactive substrates, demonstrated that the heterotrophic uptake of soluble organic material in sea water could be explained in terms of Michaelis-Menten enzyme kinetics (Parsons and Strickland, 1962). Since these kinetics explain the conversion of substances in proportion to their concentration, it is implicit that the active uptake of metabolizable compounds is a function of their concentration. Two mechanisms of heterotrophic uptake were recognized from additional studies in lakes (Hobbie and Wright, 1965; Wright and Hobbie, 1966). One of these, the active transport of substrate, is effective at concentrations below 100 μg C/liter. The second, passive uptake of substrate by diffusion, occurs at concentrations above 500 μg C/liter and was attributed to algae. In natural water the active uptake of substrates by bacteria generally keeps the level of a specific substrate below 20 μg C/liter. In experimental studies Jannasch (1967) demonstrated threshold substrate concentrations for the survival of a number of bacterial species, although he points out that the level of substrates in a complex biota under natural conditions is much lower than can be demonstrated experimentally for a single bacterium. Thus the accumulation of dissolved organic compounds must in part depend on their great dilution in large volumes of water. An unknown number of compounds resistant to biological attack may also accumulate in natural waters.

The specific nature of the compounds found in natural waters has been the subject of a number of reviews (e.g., Vallentyne, 1957; Koyama, 1962; Duursma, 1965). Among substances isolated are five-and six-carbon sugars, most of the amino acids, C_{12} to C_{22} saturated and unsaturated (C_{16} and C_{18}) fatty acids, intermediates of the citric acid cycle and vitamins. More complex compounds causing weak fluorescence in sea water, humic acids and hydrocarbons have also been reported.

The conversion of soluble organic carbon to a particulate form may not be entirely accounted for in terms of heterotrophic processes. Sutcliffe et al. (1963) showed that when air is bubbled through filtered sea water, organic particles are found in the spray droplets from bursting bubbles. It was further shown that these particles can support the growth of brine shrimp (Baylor and Sutcliffe, Jr., 1963). In a re-evaluation of these findings, Menzel (1966) concludes that bubbling per se is not a causative agent in the conversion of soluble organic carbon to a particulate form. Carlucci and Williams (1965) showed that the action of bubbling sea water tends to

---

[1] We have not attempted to discuss the early views of Pütter (1909) or more recent studies (e.g., Stephens and Schinske, 1961) which suggest some direct utilization of soluble organic materials by animals and which may, under certain circumstances, contribute to reutilization of organic material. Vallentyne suggested (personal communication) it is also possible that soluble organic compounds are adsorbed on the filtering apparatus of some animals and digested without ever passing through a particulate state. In this connection the adsorption of soluble organic material on glass fiber and silver filters has been demonstrated (Menzel, 1966).

concentrate bacteria in the foam. Barber (1966) reported that neither bacteria nor bubbling alone cause a significant increase in the amount of particulate material in sea water containing organic materials with a molecular weight of less than 100,000.

Apparently other processes are involved in the formation of particulate organic material. The role of inorganic particles should be considered. The adsorption of dissolved organic materials such as sugars, amino acids and peptone by inorganic particles in sea water has been demonstrated (Wilson, 1955; Bader et al., 1960). Recently, the occurrence of an absorbed layer of organic materials on carbonate particles in tropical and subtropical seas was demonstrated (Chave, 1965). In reviewing the recent literature on particle formation in the sea, Wangersky (1965) points out that about 70% of the naturally occurring particulate material in sea water is inorganic. He suggests that the initial step in the production of organic materials by bubbling is the formation of inorganic particles and that organic substances are then adsorbed on the inorganic surfaces.

Sieburth (1965) reports that the action of bacteria in producing local concentrations of ammonia causes a sufficient increase in pH to bring about carbonate precipitation. We found that particle formation proceeds in Millipore® filtered sea water without bubbling (see also Riley et al., 1965). The particles reach an equilibrium concentration and show some tendency to form aggregates. Microscopic examination of these particles showed that more than one type was present but it was possible to demonstrate that the aggregation process is dependent either on a particular species of bacteria or on the interaction between two or more bacterial types (Sheldon et al., 1967).

Once soluble organic materials have been converted back to a particulate form, it appears that the particles formed can re-enter the food chain to provide a food source for filter feeders (see Jorgensen, 1966, for review). It is this process by which organic carbon re-enters the food chain in a pelagic environment that we wish to discuss further.

MATERIALS AND METHODS

Particulate material was measured with a Coulter Counter® (Sheldon and Parsons, 1967a). A 50 or 400 μ aperture was used. Results were expressed as the volume of material in each particle diameter category (Sheldon and Parsons, 1967b). For particle size distributions below ca. 4 μ only the righthand part of the distribution may be shown (e.g., Fig. 2) due to limitations of the apparatus in measuring very small particles (Sheldon et al., 1967). The precision of all data reported on counts made with the Coulter Counter® was below 10% coincidence for large numbers of particles and above 10% reproducibility for small numbers of particles. Incubation of natural sea water samples (ca. 27°/∘∘ salinity) was carried out at room temperature in pyrex flasks or, for the growth of algae, at 20 C in a water bath illuminated with an incandescent light.

Field studies on the development of a natural phytoplankton bloom were carried out in Saanich Inlet, B.C., the oceanography of which has been

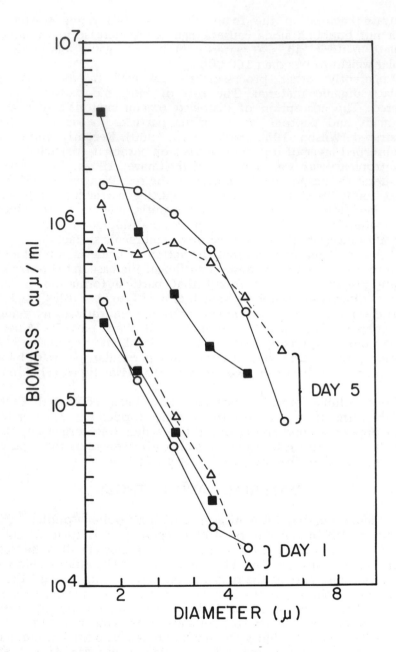

Fig. 2. Size distribution of two species of marine bacteria incubated in an enriched sea water medium for 5 days (■ — ■ *Pseudomonas* sp.; ▲ — ▲ *Chromobacterium* sp.; ○ — ○ mixture of both species).

described by Herlinveaux (1962). Zooplankton grazing experiments were carried out as described previously (Parsons et al., 1967) using euphausiids from Saanich Inlet or oyster larvae provided by Dr. N. Bourne, Biological Station, Nanaimo, B. C.

Bacterial examinations of sea water samples and filtrates were made on agar poured plates and by direct microscopic counts. The former were prepared using medium 2216 (ZoBell, 1941) for marine organisms and peptone, which has been widely used for counting fresh water bacteria (Society of American Bacteriologists, 1957). Yeasts were grown on a medium described by van Uden and Castelo-Branco (1961).

Sea water filtrates were prepared in a filter assembly sterilized as a unit in an autoclave. Filters employed were either Millipore® membrane filters (mean pore size 0.45 μ) or Seitz filters in combination with a Millipore® filter to prevent the introduction of excessive particulate material from the Seitz filter.

The weight of bacteria produced in the experiment was measured on a Cahn electrobalance. The soluble carbon in the sea water was measured by the method of Menzel and Vaccaro (1964). Both cultures were harvested after 2 days of growth when the bacteria were still growing exponentially.

RESULTS AND DISCUSSION

In an earlier report we discussed the formation of particulate material in membrane filtered sea water (Sheldon et al., 1967). It was concluded that the process is in part due to the growth of bacteria and that the clumping phenomenon can be eliminated by reducing the number of bacterial species present in the filtered sea water.

In subsequent experiments we have grown a number of species of bacteria isolated from the waters of Departure Bay, either as individual isolates or as a mixture of two or three species, in sea water enriched with 100 mg Bacto-peptone per liter. The sea water was enriched to produce a pronounced growth of bacteria from which the tendency to clump could be readily observed. An example of the type of result obtained with two motile species is shown in Fig. 2. The *Chromobacterium* sp. had a marked tendency to clump. By day 5 the maximum in the biomass of particles for this species had increased from a diameter of 2 μ or less, to nearly 4 μ. Clumping was not apparent with the *Pseudomonas* sp., which showed approximately the same slope for the size distribution of particles on days 1 and 5. When the two species were grown together the tendency to clump was not increased beyond that already apparent from the curve obtained with *Chromobacterium* sp. With combinations of four species of bacteria, certain species had a marked tendency toward clumping but there was no increased tendency toward clumping when two or more species were combined.

The aggregation of bacteria is a phenomenon which has received some attention in recent literature, particularly with respect to the disposal of waste materials. Busch and Stumm (1968) describe the aggregation of microorganisms under experimental conditions as resulting from the interaction of polymers excreted by the microbial cell or exposed at its surface. They describe the optimum conditions for flocculation as occurring when a certain fraction of the available adsorption sites on the surface of bacteria are bridged by polymers. Too little or too much polymer tends to decrease aggregation. Stanley and Rose (1967) emphasize that the tendency to clump was observed as a property of only certain bacterial species, and that this activity could be enhanced by temperature changes and by bubbling gas through cultures. The natural flocculation of bacteria must be a complex process, however, and often includes other materials such as diatom cells and inorganic materials.

From the point of view of our generalized scheme (Fig. 1) the tendency toward clumping appears to be significant in the case of removing soluble organic materials from the pelagic zone. In the first place, the sinking rate of approximately spherical particles of equal density is four times as great if the particle diameter is doubled. Thus in shallow areas the presence of species of bacteria which clump would enhance the permanent removal of organic materials from the soluble organic reservoir in the pelagic zone. Secondly, with respect to filter feeding crustaceans, the minimum particle size retained by the setae of these animals ranges from approximately 2 to 7 μ depending to some extent on the size of the animal. Thus these animals would tend to miss very small particles such as unclumped bacteria. By using a different feeding mechanism other filter feeders (e.g., *Oikopleura*) are capable of retaining particles the size of bacteria. Finally, in examining the efficiency with which soluble organic carbon is converted to bacterial biomass we found that the species which clump convert ca. 30% more carbon to a particulate form than do the species which show no tendency to clump. This is illustrated in Table 1 where the amount of carbon used in a medium originally containing 50 mg C/liter Bacto-peptone is compared with the amount of carbon produced as bacterial biomass and the amount left in the medium. Either the *Chromobacterium* sp. is more efficient at converting Bacto-peptone to bacterial biomass or it retains more of its cellular substance than does the *Pseudomonas* sp. Clumping would certainly decrease the total surface over which losses might occur through the cell walls of the bacteria.

In another series of experiments we have examined the formation of small particles in samples of sea water in which a phytoplankton bloom has been allowed to grow and then die in the dark. Fig. 3 shows the size spectrum of particulate material after 10 days in a lighted incubator at 20 C. The peak at ca. 20 μ was largely due to short chains of *Skeletonema costatum*. The spectrum 10 days after the sample had been placed in the dark shows a marked reduction in the phytoplankton peak but a very large comparative increase in the amount of particulate material less than 4 μ in diameter. The number of bacteria per ml as measured by plate counts was 18,000 on Jan. 11, 1967, and 30,000 on Jan. 22, 1967. These counts are not in the same proportion to the increase in particulate material (Fig. 3) due to the effect of clumping, which tends to disproportionately reduce the plate count while the bacterial biomass increases. Microscopic examination of the material produced on Jan. 22, 1967, revealed that the small particle peak at 2 μ was also composed of colorless flagellates which we have observed as generally occurring at the end of a large plankton bloom. The significant

Table 1. Efficiency of soluble to particulate carbon conversion by two species of marine bacteria.

	C remaining from 50 mg C/liter	C utilized (mg)	Dry wt bacteria harvested (mg)	Bacterial carbon* (mg)	% conversion
Chromobacterium sp.	25.3 ± 0.2	24.7	21.3 ± 0.3	8.5	34
Pseudomonas sp.	27.8 ± 1.0	22.2	13.3 ± 2.3	5.3	24

*Carbon content of both species assumed to be 40% of dry weight.

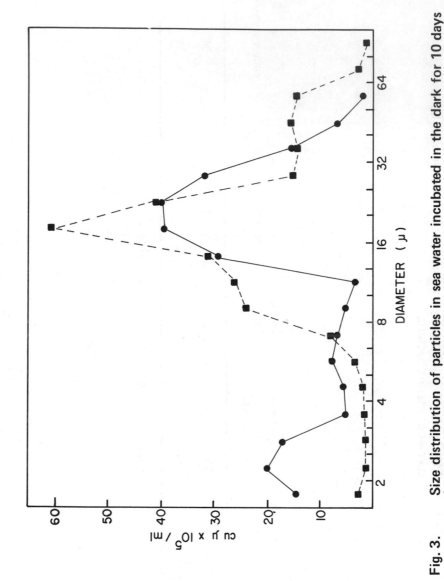

Fig. 3.   Size distribution of particles in sea water incubated in the dark for 10 days
(■ — ■ 0 time; ● — ● after 10 days).

point is the occurrence of this large population of small particles which may form a specific food size for some organisms, such as early life stages of zooplankton. Since the whole population was grown in the dark it must be considered to be entirely composed of heterotrophs (bacteria and flagellates) and to represent a major pathway for the return of soluble organic compounds (presumably derived from the dying *S. costatum*) to a particulate form useful to filter feeders. The total biomass of small particles produced by Jan. 22, 1967, amounted to approximately 20% of the biomass of phytoplankton which occurred on Jan. 11, 1967. Considerable caution is necessary in the interpretation of this conversion, however, since the carbon content per unit particle on the two dates would almost certainly be different.

A similar formation of small particles due to heterotrophic organisms is shown to occur in natural waters from data in Fig. 4 and 5. In Fig. 4 the growth of phytoplankton during a one-month period in an inlet on the coast of Vancouver Island is shown as the average increase in chlorophyll *a* for the water column, 0 to 10 m. The number of heterotrophic bacteria measured as clumps during the same period is seen to increase with the standing stock of phytoplankton and to reach a pronounced maximum at the time of the chlorophyll *a* maximum. A large increase in yeasts occurred at the same time. From the size spectrum of particulate material before (May 17, 1968) and after (May 25, 1968) the chlorophyll *a* maximum, it may be seen in Fig. 5 that there was a decrease in peak heights at approximately 8 and 70 μ. During the same interval there was a substantial increase in small particles (less than 4 μ diameter), as well as an increase in a third species of phytoplankton of ca. 25 μ diameter.

The formation of small particles is often most marked in the presence of certain filter feeders, especially euphausiids. This is shown in Fig. 6A and B for *Euphausia pacifica* feeding on a mixed bloom of *Skeletonema costatum* and *Thalassiosira* sp. The amount of food eaten by the euphausiids is shown in Fig. 6A and, on an expanded scale, the simultaneous formation of very small particles is shown in Fig. 6B. The increase in the quantity of material over the size range 1.78 to 5.66 μ was about 20%, while for the smallest size category measured it amounted to 65%. This increase in very small particles was partly due to bacterial growth and aggregation (some of it below 1.78 μ), and partly to fragments of phytoplankton cells. The mixture of bacteria and cellular debris was then fed to 48-hr-old oyster larvae and the change in the particle spectrum recorded for the next 12 hours. The result of this experiment is shown in Fig. 6C. The oyster larvae removed about half of the material less than 4 μ in diameter. After 12 hours they had grazed the standing stock of small particles to a level below that originally present in the sea water, before the addition of the euphausiids. It appears that during feeding, a large zooplankter may obtain its own ration from a large phytoplankter and simultaneously provide a greatly increased standing stock of particulate organic material for a much smaller ciliary feeder capable of extracting very small particles from the water. While these two animals are present in the inlets along the coast of British Columbia, we do not wish to imply that euphausiids would be beneficial to oyster farming! It has been

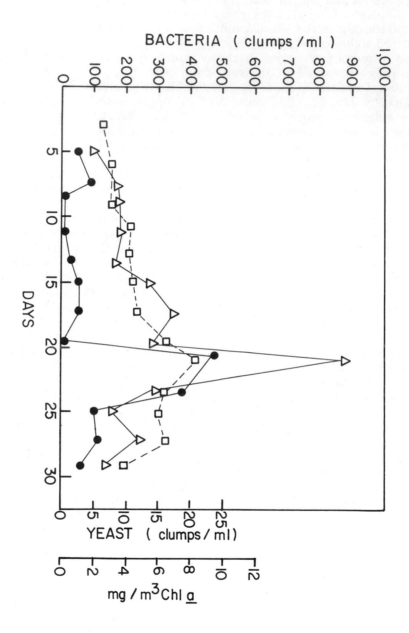

Fig. 4. Changes in autotrophs and heterotrophs in Saanich Inlet, B.C., May, 1968 (△ — △ bacteria and ● — ● yeasts from plate counts; □ — □ chlorophyll a. All values reported as average for 0 to 10 m).

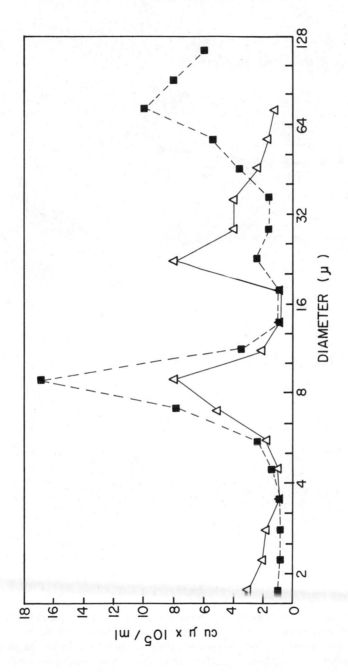

Fig. 5.   Changes in particle size spectrum at 5 m in Saanich Inlet, B.C. (■ — ■ May 17, 1968; △ — △ May 25, 1968).

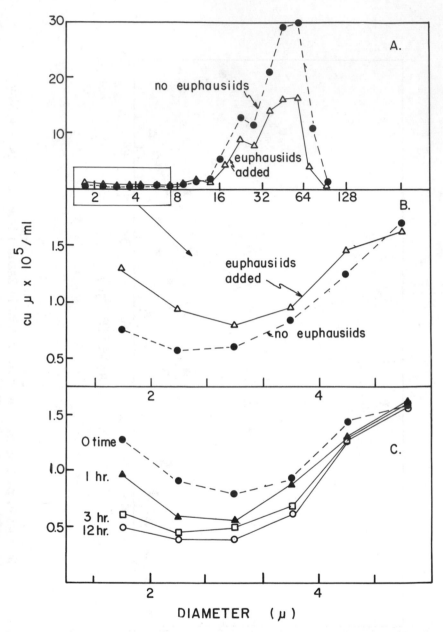

Fig. 6. Particle size spectra of euphausiids grazing and small particle production. (A) Effect of *E. pacifica* grazing on a bloom of *S. costatum* and *Thalassiosira* sp.; (B) expanded scale of previous figure to show small particle production; (C) effect of oyster larvae grazing on small particles for 12 hours.

our intention to demonstrate a mechanism which in its broader interpretation emphasizes the close association of organic debris from one animal's food chain to another's.

The question remains, at what concentration must particles be produced in order to provide sufficient food for a filter feeding organism? Obtaining an approximate answer to this question necessitates consideration of the physiological requirements of zooplankters and comparison of these with *in situ* concentrations of particulate food. While data on respiration rates and food requirements of zooplankton are diverse, the following calculation is believed to represent a realistic approximation of the food required during the growth of a common copepod, *Calanus finmarchicus*.

From data on the respiration of *Calanus* it is possible to approximate the amount of food required to maintain the various stages of *Calanus* at 10 C (Marshall and Orr, 1955 and 1958). The data in Table 2, columns one and two, have been derived from the above references and are reported for a range of animal wet weights from 0.005 to 5.0 mg. The amount of food required for growth has been determined from Winberg's (1956) equation

$$\% \text{ of body wt required per day} = [10^{\frac{1}{t}(\log W_2 - \log W_1)} - 1]100$$

where W_1 and W_2 represent an animal's weight at the beginning and end of the time period, t. For *Calanus*, $t = 100$ days for an animal to develop from a nauplius to a stage V copepod, the change in biomass during this period being 1000-fold (Cushing, 1964). From these figures an overall growth rate of 7% per day has been derived and entered in Table 2. Assuming a food assimilation efficiency of 80%, the quantity of carbon required for each weight of animal is given in the fourth column of Table 2. Filtering rates for *Calanus* nauplii and copepodites have been derived from Harvey (1937), Gauld (1951) and Marshall and Orr (1956) [for a summary see Jorgensen (1966)]. These are given for the animal weights reported in the first column of Table 2. The concentrations of particulate carbon which would then be required to support the animal's maintenance and growth are given in the last column of Table 2 and are shown as the right hand diagonal line in Fig. 7. Similar calculations for animals growing at 5 C [approximately half the maintenance requirement at 10 C; data from Petipa (1966) for *Acartia*] and animals growing at 0.7% per day at 5 and 10 C are also shown in Fig. 7 together with data on the approximate level of particulate carbon in the oceans. The latter values have been taken from Menzel and Goering (1966) Menzel (1967) and a summary of earlier values by Parsons (1963).

From Fig. 7 it may be seen that for a growth rate of 7% per day, the quantity of particulate carbon in the water must be greater than 100 μg/liter, and for the smallest creatures at 10 C the concentration should be in excess of 250 μg/liter. In one sense these may be minimum concentrations; the 80% food assimilation assumed in the calculations employed here should be considered a maximum figure. On the other hand, data in Fig. 7 do not take into account that particulate materials may occur as local aggregations (e.g.,

Table 2. Approximate food requirement for the growth and maintenance of a marine copepod at 10 C.

Copepod, wet wt (mg)	% body wt per day for maintenance	% body wt per day to double wt every 10 days	Food required assuming 80% assmiliation (µg C/animal/day)	Filtering rate (ml/day)	Concn of carbon necessary (µg C/liter)
0.005	11.8	7	0.059	0.2	295
0.05	8.6	7	0.49	2.0	245
0.5	4.6	7	3.6	20.0	180
5.0	1.4	7	26.0	'.30	130

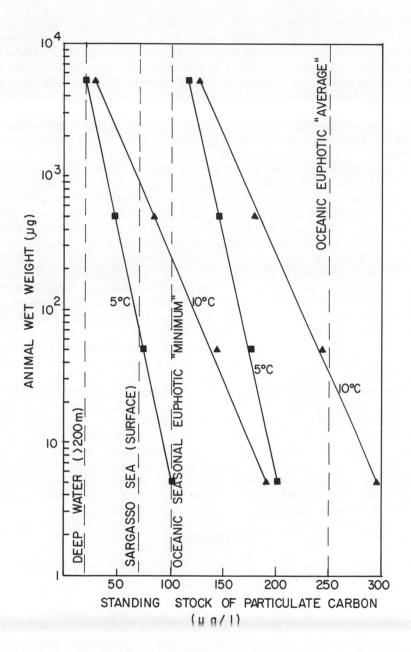

Fig. 7. Approximate standing stock of particulate carbon required by different sized zooplankton at 5 and 10 C and at two growth rates (0.7, ■ — ■; and 7%, ▲ — ▲ per day).

along a discontinuity layer). This would tend to improve the grazing for filter feeders at discrete locations within a volume of water where the average content of particulate carbon may be very low. Generally the level of carbon required will only be found in the euphotic zone of the oceans and usually during times of substantial plant growth. For animals growing at 0.7% per day, lower concentrations of particulate carbon are necessary, but for all animals shown in Fig. 7 the deep ocean particulate carbon concentration of less than 20 μg/liter (Menzel, 1967, gives some values of ca. 6 μg C/liter) is below that at which growth of these small organisms would be possible.

A separate evaluation of particulate carbon concentrations found in Nature can be obtained from recent experimental results. Adams and Steele (1966) and Parsons et al. (1967) have shown by separate techniques that the grazing of particulate material by certain zooplankters does not continue down to zero carbon concentration. There is a value — p_0, prey density at zero ration — at which filter feeding ceases (Parsons et al., 1967). The value reported by Adams and Steele (1966) for *Calanus* was ca. 70 μg C/liter and by Parsons et al. (1967) for *Pseudocalanus*, 58 μg C/liter; *Euphausia pacifica*, 131 μg C/liter; and a mixture of *Calanus pacificus* and euphausiid furcilia, 74 to 79 μg C/liter. In all these cases, the carbon concentrations at which grazing ceased are above those generally found in deep water, but are within the range of values found in the euphotic zone.

It is apparent that the output of organic materials from the steady-state reservoir in aquatic environments can in part be accomplished through bacterial action. In some cases this may be a particularly beneficial process for very young zooplankton, or for ciliary feeders, since it may result in the right size fraction of food being produced, either directly from the extracellular products of phytoplankton or through the "wasteful" feeding activity of the larger zooplankton on large phytoplankton. Finally, it is suggested that the concentration of particulate carbon in aquatic environments has to reach some threshold level for it to be physiologically possible to support a filter feeding organism. This threshold level appears to be detectable by animals and to represent the steady-state value for suspended particulate carbon in an aquatic environment.

DISCUSSION

HOLM-HANSEN: What source of food do you suggest for copepods living in the ocean between 2000 and 5000 meters?

PARSONS: I think a mechanism exists at certain locations within the supposedly uniform distribution of particulate matter in deep water. I believe (and there is some evidence in the literature) that high concentrations of particulate material, several orders of magnitude higher than indicated by Menzel's work, may exist at very brief intervals in a depth profile. These may represent particle accumulations at a small discontinuity layer. When this happens I think the deep water zooplankton, if there are such truly deep water species (and I think that the Russians have shown that there are filter feeders that do feed at great depths) are feeding off very localized particle aggregations. Certainly if you take the Hardy-Longhurst recorder, you don't find a uniform distribution of zooplankton in deep waters; you find zooplankton in patches. What I was dealing with in Fig. 7 is a uniform profile of particulate carbon which is probably the general rule, patchiness being the exception. I don't know whether you would agree with that.

HOLM-HANSEN: I wonder if Dr. Menzel would agree with that?

MENZEL: Intuitively no, I wouldn't but I would be inclined to believe Vinogradov's postulate, in which he suggests overlapping migratory chains in which one zooplankter feeds on another. I would like to believe that either the zooplankton at the depths are feeding on each other or that we are not measuring the particles on which they are feeding.

MORGAN: Would you say more about the possibility of species specific phenomena, such as polymer excretion, and the idea of adsorption of organic molecules on surfaces?

PARSONS: Some literature recently pointed out to me deals with various aspects of bacterial aggregation, polymers, etc. Two of the references to this literature are in the text of our paper although I didn't mention them. One of these refers to the addition of synthetic polymers to bacterial cultures and shows that if you add a very small amount of polymer, there will be no aggregation because there will be too little to join the active sites on two or more bacteria. If you put in just the right amount of polymer the bacteria will flocculate. If you put in too much polymer, however, individual sites on all bacteria will be saturated with polymer and no sites will remain for cross linking and aggregation. Thus it appears that one can simulate, at least in part, natural observations on bacterial flocculation. The suggestion is further made that certain bacteria have the ability to produce polymers and others do not. Once the flocculation of bacteria starts, other particles may become trapped in the aggregates as they are formed.

MORGAN: Do you feel there is any evidence for this in the systems which you looked at with the counter?

PARSONS: Oh yes, I think it is a natural situation. The question which we wanted to investigate was what is the basis of this observation, is it initiated by some nonbiological process (e.g., adsorption) or is it an active bacterial process?

ACKNOWLEDGMENTS

The authors are grateful to Dr. J. R. Vallentyne, Fisheries Research Board of Canada, Winnipeg, and to Dr. D. W. Menzel, Woods Hole Oceanographic Institution, who read and commented on the first draft of this manuscript.

REFERENCES

ADAMS, J. A., and J. H. STEELE. 1966. Shipboard experiments on the feeding of *Calanus finmarchicus* (Gunnerus) p. 19-35. *In* H. Barnes [ed.], Some contemporary studies in marine science. Allen and Unwin Ltd., London.

ALLEN, M. B. 1956. Excretion of organic compounds by *Chlamydomonas*. Arch. Mikrobiol., *24*: 163-168.

ANTIA, N. J., C. D. McALLISTER, T. R. PARSONS, K. STEPHENS, and J. D. H. STRICKLAND. 1963. Further measurements of primary production using a large-volume plastic sphere. Limnol. Oceanogr., *8*: 166-183.

BADER, R. G., D. W. HOOD, and J. B. SMITH. 1960. Recovery of dissolved organic matter in seawater and organic sorption by particulate material. Geochim. Cosmochim. Acta, *19*: 236-243.

BARBER, R. T. 1966. Interaction of bubbles and bacteria in the formation of organic aggregates in seawater. Nature, *211*: 257-258.

BAYLOR, E. R., and W. H. SUTCLIFFE, Jr. 1963. Dissolved organic matter in sea water as a source of particulate food. Limnol. Oceanogr., *8*: 369-371.

BUSCH, P. L., and W. STUMM. 1968. Chemical interactions in the aggregation of bacteria. Bioflocculation in waste treatment. Environ. Sci. Technol., *2*: 49-53.

CARLUCCI, A. F., and P. M. WILLIAMS. 1965. Concentration of bacteria from seawater by bubble scavenging. J. Cons., *30*: 28-33.

CHAVE, K. E. 1965. Carbonates: association with organic matter in surface seawater. Science, *148*: 1723-1724.

CONOVER, R. J. 1966a. Assimilation of organic matter by zooplankton. Limnol. Oceanogr., *11*: 338-345.

CONOVER, R. J. 1966b. Factors affecting the assimilation of organic matter by zooplankton and the question of superfluous feeding. Limnol. Oceanogr., *11*: 346-354.

CUSHING, D. H. 1964. The work of grazing in the sea, p. 207-225. *In* D. J. Crisp [ed.], Grazing in terrestrial and marine environments. Blackwells, Oxford.

DUURSMA, E. K. 1960. Dissolved organic carbon, nitrogen, and phosphorus in the sea. Ph.D. Thesis, J. B. Wolters, Groningen. 147 p.

DUURSMA, E. K. 1963. The production of dissolved organic matter in the sea, as related to the primary gross production of organic matter. Neth. J. Sea Res., 2: 85-94.

DUURSMA, E. K. 1965. The dissolved organic constituents of seawater, p. 433-475. *In* J. P. Riley and G. Skirrow [ed.], Chemical oceanography. Academic Press, New York.

EPPLEY, R. W., and P. R. SLOAN. 1965. Carbon balance experiments with marine phytoplankton. J. Fish. Res. Bd. Canada, 22: 1083-1097.

FOGG, G. E. 1952. The production of extracellular nitrogenous substances by a blue-green alga. Roy. Soc. (London), Proc., B. *139*: 372-397.

FOGG, G. E. 1962. Extracellular products, p. 475-489. *In* R. A. Lewin [ed.], Physiology and biochemistry of algae. Academic Press, New York.

FOGG, G. E. 1966. The extracellular products of algae. Oceanogr. Mar. Biol. Annu. Rev., 4: 195-212.

GAULD, D. J. 1951. The grazing rate of planktonic copepods. J. Mar. Biol. Ass. U.K., 29: 695-706.

HARVEY, H. W. 1937. Note on selective feeding by *Calanus*. J. Mar. Biol. Ass. U.K., 22: 97-100.

HELLEBUST, J. A. 1965. Excretion of some organic compounds by marine phytoplankton. Limnol. Oceanogr., 10: 192-206.

HERLINVEAUX, R. H. 1962. Oceanography of Saanich Inlet on Vancouver Island, British Columbia. J. Fish. Res. Bd. Canada, 19: 1-37.

HOBBIE, J. E., and R. T. WRIGHT. 1965. Competition between planktonic bacteria and algae for organic solutes. Mem. Ist Ital. Idrobiol., 18 Suppl: 175-185.

JANNASCH, H. W. 1967. Growth of marine bacteria in limiting concentrations of organic carbon in seawater. Limnol. Oceanogr., 12: 264-271.

JÖRGENSEN, C. B. 1966. Biology of suspension feeding. Pergamon, London. 357 p.

KOYAMA, T. 1962. Organic compounds in seawater. J. Oceanogr. Soc. Japan, 20th Anniv. Vol: 563-576.

KRAUSE, H. R. 1961. Einige Bemerkungen über den postmortalen Abbau von Süsswasser — Zooplankton unter laboratoriums — und Freiland Bedingungen. Arch. Hydrobiol., *57*: 539-543.

KRAUSE, H. R. 1962. Investigation of the decomposition of organic matter in natural waters. FAO Fish. Biol. Rep. No. 34. 19 p.

KRAUSE, H. R., L. MOCHEL, and M. STEGMANN. 1961. Organische Sauren als geloste Intermediarprodukte des postmortalen Abbaues von Süsswasser — Zooplankton. Naturwissenschaften, *48*: 434-435.

MARSHALL, S. M., and A. P. ORR. 1955. The biology of a marine copepod, *Calanus finmarchicus* (Gunnerus). Oliver and Boyd, Edinburgh. 188 p.

MARSHALL, S. M., and A. P. ORR. 1956. On the biology of *Calanus finmarchicus*. IX. Feeding and digestion in the young stages. J. Mar. Biol. Ass. U.K., *35*: 587-604.

MARSHALL, S. M., and A. P. ORR. 1958. On the biology of *Calanus finmarchicus*. X. Seasonal changes in oxygen consumption. J. Mar. Biol. Ass. U.K., *37*: 459-472.

MENZEL, D. W. 1966. Bubbling of sea water and the production of organic particles: a re-evaluation. Deep-Sea Res., *13*: 963-966.

MENZEL, D. W. 1967. Particulate organic carbon in the deep sea. Deep-Sea Res., *14*: 229-238.

MENZEL, D. W., and J. J. GOERING. 1966. The distribution of organic detritus in the ocean. Limnol. Oceanogr., *11*: 333-337.

MENZEL, D. W., and R. F. VACCARO. 1964. The measurement of dissolved organic and particulate carbon in sea water. Limnol. Oceanogr., *9*: 138-142.

NEWELL, R. 1965. The role of detritus in the nutrition of two marine deposit feeders, the prosobranch *Hydrobia ulvae* and the bivalve *Macoma balthica*. Zool. Soc. (London), Proc., *144*: 25-45.

NIELSEN, E. STEEMANN. 1965. On the determination of the activity in ^{14}C-ampoules for measuring primary production. Limnol. Oceanogr., *10*: R247-R252.

OLSON, J. S. 1963. Energy storage and the balance of producers and decomposers in ecological systems. Ecology, *44*: 322-331.

PARSONS, T. R. 1963. Suspended organic matter in sea water, p. 205-239. *In* M. Sears [ed.], Progress in oceanography, v. 1. Pergamon, Oxford and New York.

PARSONS, T. R., R. J. LeBRASSEUR, and J. D. FULTON. 1967. Some observations on the dependence of zooplankton grazing on the cell size and concentration of phytoplankton blooms. J. Oceanogr. Soc. Japan, *23*:11-18.

PARSONS, T. R., and J. D. H. STRICKLAND. 1962. On the production of particulate organic carbon by heterotrophic processes in sea water. Deep-Sea Res., *8*: 211-222.

PETIPA, T. S. 1966. Relationship between growth, energy metabolism, and ration in *Acartia clausi* Giesbr. Physiology of marine animals, p. 82-91. *In* Akad. Nauk SSSR, Oceanogr. Comm.

PÜTTER, A. 1909. Die Ernahrung der Wassertiere und der Stoffhaushalt der Gewasser. J. Fischer. Jena. 168 p.

RILEY, G. A. 1963. Organic aggregates in sea water and the dynamics of their formation and utilization. Limnol. Oceanogr., *8*: 372-381.

RILEY, G. A., D. VAN HEMERT, and P. J. WANGERSKY. 1965. Organic aggregates in surface and deep waters of the Sargasso Sea. Limnol. Oceanogr., *10*: 345-363.

SEKI, H. 1965a. Microbial studies on the decomposition of chitin in marine environment. IX. Rough estimation of chitin decomposition in the ocean. J. Oceanogr. Soc. Japan, *21*: 253-260.

SEKI, H. 1965b. Decomposition of chitin in marine sediments. J. Oceanogr. Soc. Japan, *21*: 261-268.

SEKI, H., J. SKELDING, and T. R. PARSONS. 1968. Observations on the decomposition of a marine sediment. Limnol. Oceanogr., *13*: 440-447.

SEKI, H., and N. TAGA. 1963. Microbiological studies on the decomposition of chitin in marine environment. I. Occurrence of chitinoclastic bacteria in a neritic region. J. Oceanogr. Soc. Japan, *19*: 101-108.

SHELDON, R. W., T. P. T. EVELYN, and T. R. PARSONS. 1967. On the occurrence and formation of small particles in sea water. Limnol. Oceanogr., *12*: 367-375.

SHELDON, R. W., and T. R. PARSONS. 1967a. A practical manual on the use of the Coulter Counter in marine science. Coulter Electronics Sales Co., Canada. 66 p.

SHELDON, R. W., and T. R. PARSONS. 1967b. A continuous size spectrum for particulate matter in the sea. J. Fish. Res. Bd. Canada, *24*: 909-915.

SIEBURTH, J. McN. 1965. Organic aggregation in sea water by alkaline precipitation of inorganic nuclei during the formation of ammonia by bacteria. J. Gen. Microbiol., *41*: XX.

SKOPINTSEV, B. A. 1966. Some aspects of the distribution and composition of organic matter in the waters of the ocean. Oceanology, *6*: 441-450. (Fish. Res. Bd. Canada Transl. No. 930).

SOCIETY OF AMERICAN BACTERIOLOGISTS. 1957. Manual of microbiological methods. McGraw — Hill, New York. 315 p.

STANLEY, S. O., and A. H. ROSE. 1967. On the clumping of *Corynebacterium xerosis* as affected by temperature. J. Gen. Microbiol., *48*: 9-23.

STEPHENS, G. C., and R. A. SCHINSKE. 1961. Uptake of amino acids by marine invertebrates. Limnol. Oceanogr., *6*: 175-181.

STEPHENS, K., R. W. SHELDON, and T. R. PARSONS. 1967. Seasonal variations in the availability of food for benthos in a coastal environment. Ecology, *48*: 852-855.

SUTCLIFFE, W. H., E. R. BAYLOR, and D. W. MENZEL. 1963. Sea surface chemistry and langmuir circulation. Deep-Sea Res., *10*: 233-243.

VALLENTYNE, J. R. 1957. The molecular nature of organic matter in lakes and oceans, with lesser reference to sewage and terrestrial soils. J. Fish. Res. Bd. Canada, *14*: 33-82.

VALLENTYNE, J. R. 1962. Solubility and the decomposition of organic matter in nature. Arch. Hydrobiol., *58*: 423-434.

VAN UDEN, N., and R. CASTELO-BRANCO. 1961. *Metschnikowiella zobellii* sp. nov. and *M. krissii* sp. nov., two yeasts from the Pacific Ocean pathogenic for *Daphnia magna*. J. Gen. Microbiol., *26*: 141-148.

WANGERSKY, P. J. 1965. The organic chemistry of sea water. Amer. Sci., *53*: 358-374.

WATT, W. D. 1966. Release of dissolved organic material from the cells of phytoplankton populations. Roy. Soc. (London) Proc., B. *164*: 521-551.

WEBB, K. L., and R. E. JOHANNES. 1967. Studies of the release of dissolved free amino acids by marine zooplankton. Limnol. Oceanogr., *12*: 376-382.

WILSON, D. P. 1955. The role of microorganisms in the settlement of *Ophelia bicornis savigny*. J. Mar. Biol. Ass. U.K., *34*: 531-543.

WINBERG, G. G. 1956. Rate of metabolism and food requirements of fishes. Nauchnye Trudy Belorusskovo Gosudarstvennovo Universiteta imeni V.I. Lenina, Minsk, 253 p. F. E. J. Fry and W. E. Ricker [ed.], Transl. Ser. No. 194, Fish. Res. Bd. Canada.

WRIGHT, R. T., and J. E. HOBBIE. 1966. Use of glucose and acetate by bacteria and algae in aquatic ecosystems. Ecology, *47*: 447-464.

ZOBELL, C. E. 1941. Studies on marine bacteria. I. The cultural requirements of heterotrophic aerobes. J. Mar. Res., *4*: 42-75.

SESSION I. DISSOLVED AND PARTICULATE ORGANIC MATTER DISTRIBUTION IN NATURAL WATERS AND SEDIMENTS.

Chairman: E.K. Duursma
International Laboratory of Marine
Radioactivity, IAEA
Musée Oceanographique
Monaco-Ville
Principality of Monaco

Research on dissolved and particulate organic matter in natural waters has had a pulsating development since the beginning of this century, mainly due to the irregular development of chemical techniques and the sporadic attention given to this type of research by marine and fresh water scientists. For long periods between 1910 and 1930, the dissolved organic matter was thought to be large and possibly a source of food. Between 1930 and 1960 it was supposed that these organic constituents occurred at constant concentrations at all depths in the sea, which implied they were very stable and not available as food.

Although the scant data were obtained using underdeveloped techniques based on erroneous assumptions these ideas were still prevalent in the literature in the late 1950's.

Rapid technical developments since 1960 have made it possible to do large series of elementary analyses of organic materials in natural waters and analyses of specific organic compounds. The result has been a break with the old ideas. The organic matters in natural waters are now seriously considered as compounds in relation to their environment, to the other properties of the fresh waters and oceans, and to life. Stable and unstable compounds have been determined as well as relations between particulate, dissolved and living material.

This first session of this symposium provides a view of very recent developments concerning the distribution of these compounds in quantities and environments.

DISTRIBUTION AND CYCLING OF
ORGANIC MATTER IN THE OCEANS

David W. Menzel and John H. Ryther
Woods Hole Oceanographic Institution
Woods Hole, Massachusetts 02543

ABSTRACT

The vertical distribution of particulate and dissolved organic carbon is nearly homogeneous below a depth of 200 to 300 m at all locations sampled, and they are present in concentrations of 3 to 10 μg C/liter and 0.35 to 0.70 mg C/liter, respectively. Above this depth concentrations are variable, with particulate matter directly proportional and dissolved carbon inversely proportional to the rate of primary production.

Simultaneous consideration of changes in oxygen and salinity in subsurface waters in the absence of variable quantities of organic matter indicates that both oxygen and carbon may be considered conservative properties. The entire biochemical cycle of organic matter including production, decomposition and solubilization appears to occur at depths probably not in excess of 200 to 300 m.

INTRODUCTION

A large body of data is now available on the rate of carbon fixation by photosynthetic organisms at the surface of the sea (reviewed by Ryther, 1963). This information, however, does little to clarify or quantify the influence of the associated processes of excretion, decomposition, solubilization, etc., on the concentration or recycling rates of organic matter in the oceans. Even less is known of the mechanisms and processes by which the concentration of dissolved and particulate matter in the deep sea is maintained, produced and distributed.

In particular, it has been found difficult to relate in time and space the distribution of non-living particulate and dissolved organic matter in the deep sea with events which take place in the upper, euphotic layers. While no one now seriously believes in an independent *in situ* origin of this deep-sea organic matter, it is becoming increasingly obvious that its biochemical cycling is not closely coupled with that of the plants and animals which produce and immediately consume organic matter in the familiar food cycle of the sea. In the following discussion we shall attempt to illustrate this fact with recent evidence concerning the distribution of both particulate and dissolved organic matter in the deep sea.

PARTICULATE ORGANIC CARBON

One of the earliest theories relating the influence of particles to the concentration of dissolved carbon and/or oxygen utilization was that settling rates are selectively altered at specific density surfaces which correspond to the density of the sinking matter (Seiwell, 1937; Miyaki and Saruhashi, 1956). Vertical perturbations in the concentration of light scattering particles (Jerlov, 1959) and particulate carbon (Dal Pont and Newell, 1963; Szekielda, 1967) have been related to the position of individual water masses within a given water column, or have otherwise been associated with water circulation (Hobson, 1967). This distributional pattern would require that entrained particles of neutral density are transported horizontally for great distances, or that density discontinuities at the interface of water masses favor their accumulation. Conversely, it has been shown that the concentration of particles is not variable, but rather is almost homogeneous with depth below the relatively shallow upper layers (Menzel and Goering, 1966; Menzel, 1967; Menzel and Ryther, 1968). This observation was first made by Riley et al. (1965), who noted however that seasonal variability in concentration may occur at a given location.

The relation between the concentration of particulate organic matter occurring at the surface and that in the underlying water was studied off the west coast of South America both within and outside an area of active upwelling (Menzel, 1967). The first aspect of this study was to follow the development and decline of a phytoplankton bloom in recently upwelled water, using drogues as tracers of water movement, and to measure simultaneously both the production rate and the resulting crop of organic matter. The particulate carbon values (Fig. 2) are those obtained by mathematical integration through the depths indicated. They show unequivocally that, in spite of an increase of nearly an order of magnitude in the surface water, little or no apparent increase in concentration was evident below 75 m.

Secondly, to rule out the possibility that downstream transport deposited these particles at a location remote from their source, or that they were artificially held in suspension by turbulence associated with upwelling, a course zigzagging into and away from the coast in the direction of the Peru Coastal Current was followed for approximately 2000 km north of the drogue station and west to the Galapagos Islands (Area G, Fig. 1). Fig. 3 is a running plot of that section, illustrating that no significant differences in particulate carbon occurred at any point below 100 m, and that in spite of greatly varying surface concentrations the depth of the 15 μg C isopleth was not altered by events occurring at the surface.

The vertical distribution of particulate carbon (PC) from widely separated locations in the Southeast Pacific and Atlantic oceans is not only uniform below a relatively shallow depth of 200 to 300 m but is remarkably uniform throughout all areas studied (Fig. 4, also Table 1). It appears that the maximum range of values is within the relatively narrow limits of 3 to 10 μg C/liter (although there has been a recent suggestion that slightly higher values may occur in close proximity to continental shelves). In view of this, it is highly unlikely that detectable seasonal variability occurs at depth at any given location. The latter was confirmed by a time series at a single location in the Sargasso Sea (Fig. 1, Area A) where the maximum deviation in PC below 300 m at four times of the year was 5 $\pm$ 3 μg C/liter. Surface

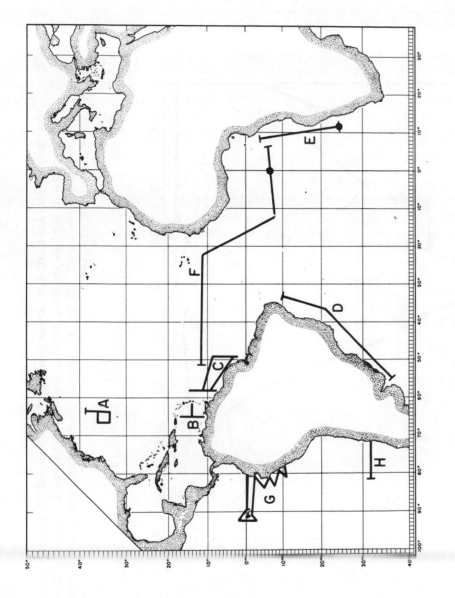

Fig. 1. Chart of the Atlantic and Pacific Oceans indicating sampling areas on which the present study is based.

Fig. 2. Integrated values for particulate carbon between 0 and 75 m and 75 and 150 m at a drogue station in the Peru upwelling. Stations were separated by two 6-hr intervals (73 to 75) and one 12-hr period (75 to 76) repeating in the same sequence for 5 days. (Reprinted from Menzel, 1967.)

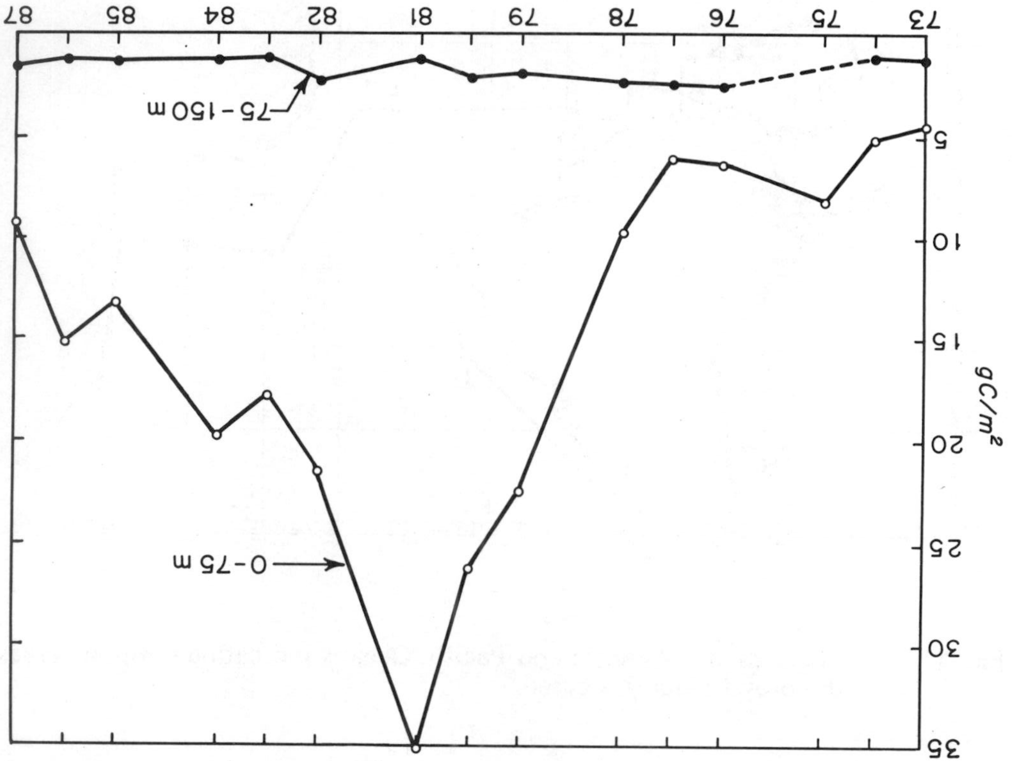

-34-

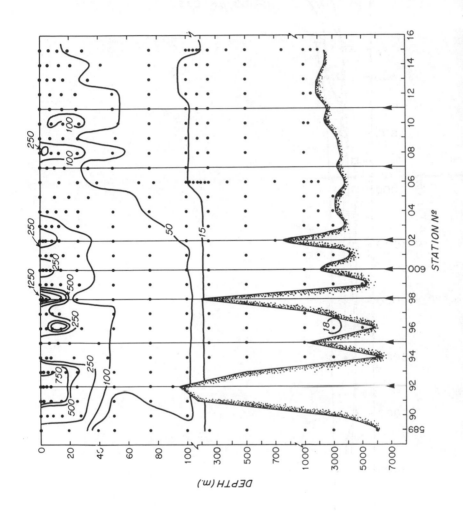

Fig. 3. Distribution of particulate carbon as a function of depth and distance (Area G, Fig. 1). Isopleths are in µg C/liter. (Reprinted from Menzel, 1967.)

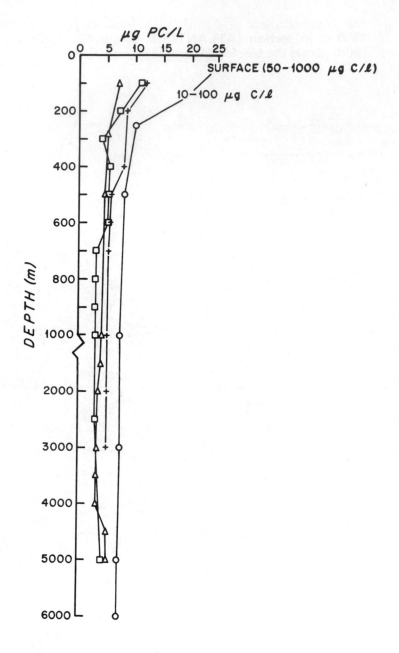

Fig. 4. The average vertical distribution of particulate carbon (μg C/liter) within Areas G (○), E (△), D (+) and A (□) indicated on Fig. 1.

Table 1. The concentration of particulate carbon at 700 and 1500 to 2000 m in section (ATLANTIS II Cruise 42, April and May, 1968) across the tropical Atlantic (Section F, Fig. 1).

Station no.	700 m (µg/liter)	1500-2000 m (µg/liter)
1175	-	4.4
1176	4.8	5.6
1179	1.5	4.6
1180	-	4.2
1181	8.0	6.7
1182	5.4	-
1183	6.1	4.0
1184	4.8	4.3
1185	7.6	2.6
1190	3.9	3.5
1192	5.0	6.2
1193	5.6	3.5
1194	5.3	5.4
1196	5.2	8.2
1197	-	6.1

values during the same periods ranged from 38 to 140 μg C/liter (Menzel and Ryther, 1968).

In summary, the concentration of particulate organic matter is, as expected, highly variable at the surface and is, in most instances, directly related to the level of organic production. The influence of variable surface concentrations is not, however, evident at any depth below 200 to 300 m, nor do concentrations vary spatially or seasonally.

Several possibilities exist either independently or together that may explain the above observations: (1) The amount present (3 to 10 μg C/liter) may represent the lower level of particulate matter that can be grazed by zooplankton. Direct measurements indicate that this threshold concentration is 40 to 75 μg C/liter (Parsons and LeBrasseur, in press), a value considerably higher than that encountered in deep water and very close to that at the surface in tropical oceans. (2) A major portion of the particulate matter at depth may be of such chemical nature that it is not utilizable by grazing organisms and is also refractory to heterotrophic decomposition. (3) Constant concentrations may be maintained by an equilibrium between utilization and adsorption of dissolved organic compounds onto the surfaces of otherwise relatively biologically inert particle nuclei (Riley et al., 1965), an argument that has been strengthened by the demonstration that adsorption of organic matter occurs onto calcium carbonate precipitates (Chave, 1965) and onto natural "detritus" (Khailov and Finenko, in press). (4) *In situ* production of particles (presumably bacteria) may occur and their concentration may be controlled by the amount of dissolved organic matter available for growth (Sheldon et al., 1967).

DISSOLVED ORGANIC CARBON

Dissolved organic compounds in the sea may originate from several sources or processes including excretion or extracellular loss by phytoplankton, excretion by animals, and bacterial decomposition or autolysis of dead organisms. River drainage and precipitation may also contribute dissolved organic matter from the land. Any or all of these sources may account for the relatively high and variable levels at the sea surface (0 to 300 m), as compared with the low and near-constant level at depth (see below).

In reference to the surface, Duursma (1963) has proposed that the level of dissolved organic matter may be used as an index of primary productivity by measuring its rate of accumulation. Quite the opposite was found, however, in the upwelling region off the coast of Peru (Barber, 1967) and in the Indian Ocean (Fig. 5), where the mean concentration of dissolved organic matter in the surface layers was inversely proportional to the size of the phytoplankton standing crop and to the level of primary organic production. Why this should be so is not clear. One possible explanation is that the adsorption, assimilation, and/or decomposition of dissolved organic matter may be facilitated or enhanced by such factors as actively-growing phytoplankton and bacterial populations, or the presence of a large amount of particulate matter in the water. Also, in this connection, Fogg et al.

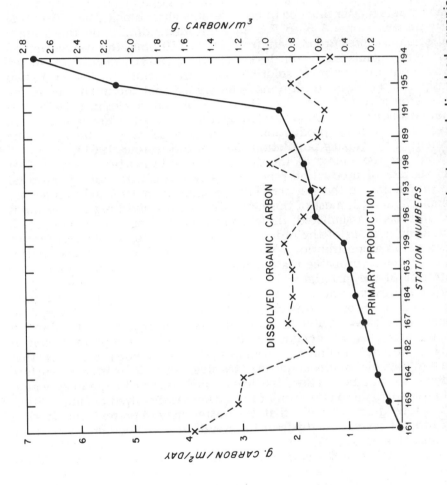

Fig. 5. The relation between primary production and dissolved organic carbon (DOC) in the Western Arabian Sea. Values are integrated through the euphotic layer (primary production) or to 100 m (DOC).

(1965) and Ryther et al. (in press) have shown that the percentage of photoassimilated carbon excreted as dissolved matter is inversely proportional to the absolute rate of photosynthesis. Thus, while the processes which lead to the formation of dissolved organic matter in the sea are recognized, the ecological conditions which regulate or control the rate of production and accumulation of this material are still not well understood.

Simple calculation shows that in a water column 5000 m deep, the dissolved organic matter must be of considerable chronological age. The total quantity present (some 1.5 to 7.5 kg C/m^2 depending upon the average concentration accepted) represents from 30 to 150 times the average annual production of organic matter in the sea (Ryther, 1963), even if 100% of the material produced entered solution and were not further degraded (obviously not the case). It has long been argued that the usual fate of the phytoplankton is to be eaten (e.g., Harvey et al., 1935; Cushing, 1958) and quantitative studies have demonstrated that under steady-state conditions in the open sea, primary production is just able to satisfy the metabolic requirement of the grazing population (Menzel and Ryther, 1961).

Whatever the source of the dissolved organic matter, it seems clear that (1) its rate of production represents a very small fraction of the total organic production in the sea, certainly no more than 10% and perhaps no more than 1%; and (2) most of this newly-formed dissolved organic carbon is rapidly adsorbed, assimilated or decomposed leaving an equally small fraction, again perhaps of the order of 1% or less, of biologically resistant or inert material as a contribution to the total pool of dissolved organic matter in the sea. It seems probable that, at least within large oceanic regions, the concentration of the material which makes up this "quasi-permanent" pool of dissolved organic matter is virtually constant from top to bottom. Superimposed upon this, within and slightly below the euphotic layer, is an additional and highly variable amount of dissolved organic matter directly related to processes of organic production and consumption which is short-lived. Recent preliminary evidence (Barber, 1968) indicates that bacteria are capable of decomposing dissolved organic matter in surface water down to, but not below, the level which occurs in the deep water, while they are unable to attack any of the deep-sea dissolved organic matter. It is therefore quite possible that the latter may represent the gradual accumulation of several hundreds of thousands of years, perhaps even of the ocean's entire history.

Recent studies of the concentration of dissolved organic matter in the ocean have demonstrated a degree of spatial and vertical homogeneity in concentration below the surface that is remarkable in view of the relatively large variation in other biologically associated parameters (Duursma, 1961; Skopintsev, 1960; Skopintsev and Timofeeva, 1962; Skopintsev et al., 1966; Menzel, 1967; Menzel and Ryther, 1968; Holm-Hansen et al., 1966; Barber, 1967; Ogura, 1967). Although uncertainty exists regarding absolute values, all the studies above, with the exception of Skopintsev and his co-workers, indicate concentrations ranging between 0.3 and 0.7 mg C/liter at all depths in excess of several hundred meters. Values reported by Skopintsev from the

Atlantic average some 2 to 3 times higher than the above, although the maximum variability recorded was less (± 30%). His data therefore do not alter the following arguments.

Composite, averaged vertical profiles showing the distribution of dissolved organic carbon (DOC) in the North and South Atlantic Ocean are shown in Fig. 6. While averaging of the type applied here, where as many as 13 stations are combined in one profile, will mask any real variations within a given area, differences noted at any given depth below ca. 300 m were generally within analytical precision (± 0.10 mg C/liter) and the data are, therefore, not consistent with any other type of presentation. It is apparent that, as in the case of particulate carbon, no significant vertical perturbations occur and that concentrations are nearly homogeneous below a depth of 300 to 500 m in any given profile. On the other hand, average differences of 0.35 to 0.70 mg C/liter do appear to occur regionally. If real, it is not clear how these differences arise. For example, the profiles (Fig. 6) for dissolved organic carbon (DOC) in the Sargasso Sea (Fig. 1, Area A), North Tropical Atlantic (Fig. 1, Area C) and Caribbean (Fig. 1, Area B) show that the average concentration above 2000 m in the Caribbean is lower than in either of the two other areas. Since the source of water above the sill depth in the Caribbean (1960 m) must be one of the areas indicated above, there is no obvious reason for the concentration of DOC above this depth to vary by the amount indicated.

It has been suggested (Duursma, 1961 and 1965; Menzel, 1964; Barber, 1967) that the concentration of DOC can be used to trace the movement of subsurface water. For example, regional variations of an order of magnitude (0.2 to 2.0 mg C/liter) were observed at specific density surfaces in the Indian Ocean. Simultaneous consideration of salinity led to the conclusion that here the concentration of organic matter is predictable from salinity and is quasiconservative in behavior (Menzel, 1964). How differences in subsurface concentrations of this magnitude can be produced and maintained in the Indian Ocean and not in the Atlantic is also obscure. If the assumption is correct that the deep-sea organic matter represents an accumulation of many thousands of years, and that it is contributed to imperceptibly by organic production at the sea surface, it may be that differences in subsurface concentrations in different parts of the world ocean, referred to above, reflect the frequency with which the deep water circulates and reaches the sea surface over long periods of time.

CYCLING OF ORGANIC MATTER

In contradiction to the conservative behavior of organic matter implied above, it has been postulated that continuing *in situ* decomposition occurs during the isentropic flow of subsurface water away from its source at the sea surface (Sverdrup, 1938; Redfield, 1942; Riley, 1951; Redfield et al., 1963; Pytkowicz, 1968). To test this hypothesis, dissolved organic carbon was examined along a section between 10°S and 35°S in the Southwest Atlantic (Fig. 1, Area D). Particular attention was paid to mixing and dilution of the Antarctic Intermediate Water (AIW) because (1) the AIW is

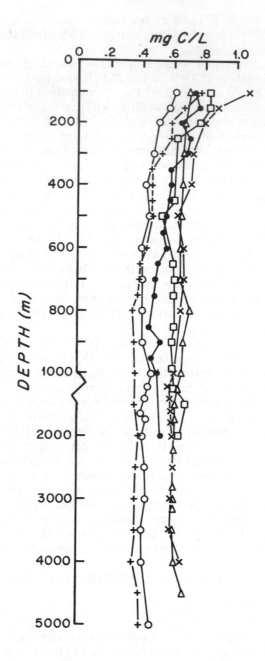

6.   The average vertical distribution of dissolved organic carbon (mg C/liter) within Areas A (△), B (○), C (x), D (+) indicated on Fig. 1, and at 7°S, 4°W (○) and 24°S, 12°E (□).

readily identified by its low salinity and (2) it is the water mass to which Redfield (1942) and Pytkowicz (1968) assign significant rates of *in situ* decomposition as determined by changes in phosphate and oxygen. The vertical profiles of DOC at the two terminal stations of the section are virtually identical at the core of the AIW (800 m), and the maximum deviation at intervening stations is ± 0.1 mg. The concentration of oxygen on the other hand differed markedly from a maximum of 6.32 at the southern end to a minimum of 3.67 at the northern end of the section (Fig. 7). This decrease in oxygen is equivalent to the oxidation of approximately 1.1 mg C/liter using an oxidative ratio of 2.6:1, O:C by atoms (Redfield et al., 1963). It is clear, therefore, that the observed changes in oxygen in the AIW along this transect cannot be attributed to the decomposition of dissolved organic carbon entrained within this water mass.

An alternate mechanism by which oxygen values may be modified, without accompanying changes in organic matter, is by the mixing of two water masses of equal carbon but unequal oxygen concentration. In the case in point, the highly-oxygenated, north-flowing Antarctic Intermediate Water is overlaid by south-flowing, low oxygen water (Fig. 8). By plotting salinity at the core of the AIW (salinity minimum) against measured oxygen, it may be seen (Fig. 9) that these bear a close relationship, indicating that oxygen concentration is dependent solely on mixing. The same phenomenon has been more recently observed by treating data in an identical manner from the opposite side of the Atlantic, between 10° and 28°S off the east coast of Africa (Fig. 1, Area E), although the slope of the two lines is significantly different (Fig. 9). The ocean-wide distribution of oxygen in the Atlantic clearly shows that the lowest values occur off the eastern coast of South Africa (reviewed by Richards, 1957; Bubnov, 1966). Therefore a relatively greater depletion of oxygen in the northward flowing AIW should be evident in the eastern basin, as is shown. An interesting feature is that, on extrapolation, these dilution curves appear to intercept at a salinity of ca. 34.26°/∘∘, and an oxygen level of 6.4 ml O_2 /liter. This value for oxygen may indicate a level which, when subtracted from that at saturation, is an index of the extent of oxidation that occurs immediately following the sinking of the water mass at its origin.

Conclusions that may be drawn from these data are (1) that water masses of the Atlantic once removed from their source all have essentially the same concentration of organic matter, (2) that dissolved organic matter is conservative in nature and is not decreased during horizontal transport at depth, and (3) that since oxygen may be predicted from salinity in easily identified water masses, little or no measurable influence is exerted on its concentration by particles decomposing during vertical and/or horizontal transport or by the respiration of organisms. Obviously these conclusions apply only to dominant controlling factors. It is not presumed that biological activity is absent at depth but rather that its influence is very small and is masked by water circulation. Also, while it is possible to postulate the above with respect to relatively deep water, there is no indication in these data as to the depth below which organic decomposition does not occur.

Obviously the production of the oxygen minimum must result from

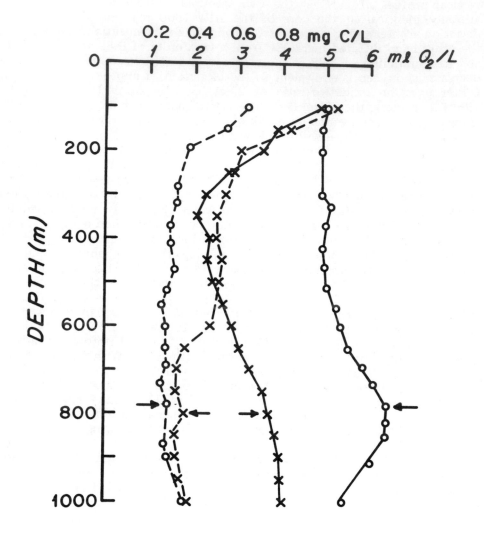

Fig. 7.   The vertical distribution of oxygen (solid lines) and dissolved organic carbon (dashed lines) at 10°S (x) and 35°S (○) along Section D, Figure 1. Arrows indicate the depth at which the core of the Antarctic Intermediate Water (salinity minimum) occurred.

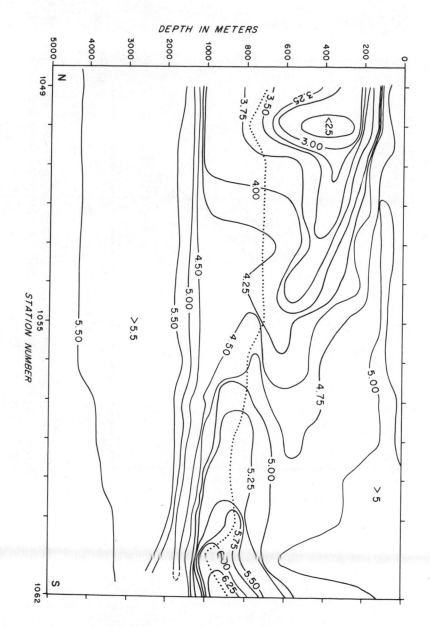

Fig. 8   The distribution of dissolved oxygen (ml/liter) in the Southwest Atlantic. Stations are separated by approximately 2° intervals along Section D, Fig. 1. The dashed line indicates the depth of the salinity minimum. (Reprinted from Menzel and Ryther, 1968.)

-45-

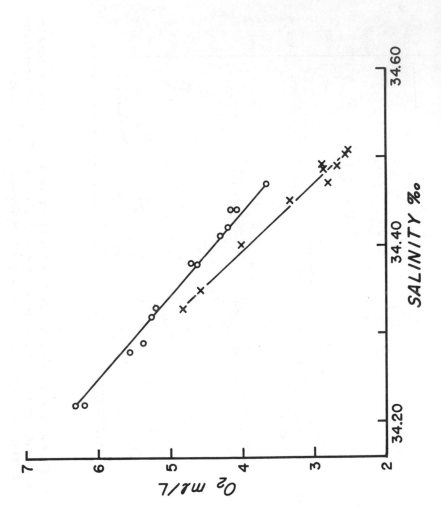

Fig. 9.   The relation between salinity (°/₀₀) and oxygen (ml/l) at the core of the Antarctic Intermediate Water (salinity minimum) along Section D, Fig. 1 (o) and Section E, Fig. 1 (x).

biochemical oxidation of organic matter at some stage in the history of a water mass. An insight into these problems may be gained from a consideration of salinity and oxygen off the west coast of South America at a latitude of approximately 32°S and extending some 2100 km offshore (Fig. 1, Area H). In this instance, the plot (Fig. 10) is at the midwater salinity maximum (200 to 400 m) where the lowering of salinity is presumably indicative of dilution of the Peru undercurrent (Wooster and Gilmartin, 1961). The relationship shown supports data from the Atlantic at a greater depth and, while no measurements of organic matter were made, indicates that oxygen is controlled by mixing even at the relatively shallow depths indicated above. An unexplainable feature is the interruption in the regression at approximately 0.75 ml O_2 /liter. This could have resulted from (1) a third unknown source of water interposed between the outer (high O_2) and inner (low O_2) stations, (2) a shift in oxygen demand due to the biological reduction of nitrate, or (3) imposition of an inshore depth (200 m) at which surface influence occurs.

It appears likely that the production of the oxygen minimum is restricted entirely to coastal areas of high production (see also Skopintsev, 1965; Bubnov, 1967) and that this occurs at some undetermined but shallow depth, probably not in excess of 200 to 300 m. Its absolute level and position is thereafter probably determined solely by mixing and diffusion. The association of high production areas with the oxygen minimum is clearly evident in both the Pacific (Reid, 1965) and Atlantic. A detailed example of the latter shows that the southern extension of low oxygen water along the coast of Africa is produced by localized coastal upwelling (Fig. 11) and that the erosion of this minimum occurs in the direction of the general surface circulation (Sverdrup, et al., 1942). A similar situation exists in the North Atlantic in the region of the Canaries Current (Bubnov, 1966 and 1967).

The behavior of oxygen, coupled with the spatial and vertical homogeneity of organic matter, suggests that the cycling of organic matter is almost entirely restricted to relatively shallow surface waters (see also Riley, 1951). No detectable cycling occurs in the deep sea and organic matter there may be considered stable and/or biochemically inert. This situation may exist either because the chemical nature of the compounds is such that they are refractory and thus resist bacterial decomposition (Menzel, 1964; Skopintsev, 1960; Williams, 1968; Barber, 1968), or because the concentration present is at a threshold level below which bacteria are not capable of growth (Jannasch,1967).

DISCUSSION

MALCOLM: Are there any analyses indicating qualitative differences in organic carbon with depth in the ocean?

MENZEL: What do you mean qualitative?

MALCOLM: The types of organic compounds.

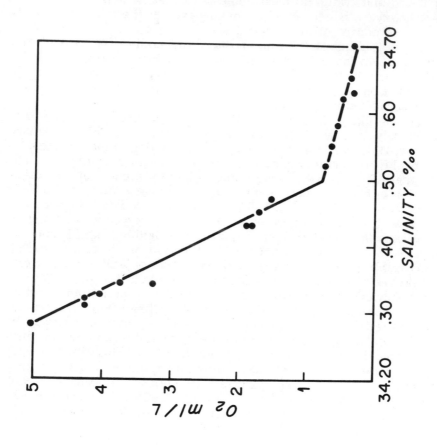

Fig. 10. The relation between salinity (°/oo) and oxygen (ml/l) at the midwater salinity maximum in a section along 32°S off the coast from Valpariso, Chile (Area H, Fig. 1).

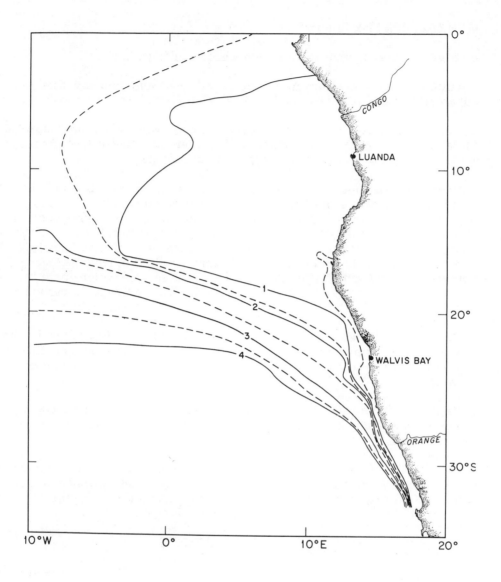

Fig. 11. The concentration of oxygen (ml/liter) in the oxygen minimum layer, at whatever depth it occurred, off the west coast of Africa.

MENZEL: Ask Max Blumer!

BLUMER: There is some difference in carbon/nitrogen ratio.

MALCOLM: This organic matter at depth — would you say that this is apparently completely devoid of anything that contains phosphorus?

MENZEL: Usually the carbon/nitrogen ratio is lower, which indicates that there is more nitrogen in the material than there is at the surface. As for the actual structure of it, I could not say. I am an ecologist.

DUURSMA: You mention production in relation to the dissolved organic carbon and indicate some disagreement among workers in this field. It might lead to a misunderstanding when you say there is disagreement. The production I considered in my earlier work was a total year budget in relation to production of dissolved organic carbon. If you have a high productivity then the increase of carbon and dissolved organic nitrogen does not occur at the same time. But if you are in an area where there is high production, it does not follow that a high dissolved organic carbon will occur.

MENZEL: What I am saying is that Barber (1967) found that water that had recently come from depth was very high in dissolved carbon, and that the carbon content decreased during the time the phytoplankton population was growing.

DUURSMA: In upwelling, time elapses before the bloom starts. The water comes up and then it takes some time before excretion and all the other products come.

MENZEL: Dr. Barber hypothesizes that a certain concentration of organic matter is necessary to complex certain toxic trace metals, that you get an accumulation of organic matter up to this point, and that once this toxicity is removed, the plants begin to grow and lower it again.

ACKNOWLEDGMENTS

Contribution No. 2212 from the Woods Hole Oceanographic Institution, Woods Hole, Massachusetts.

Supported in part by Atomic Energy Commission contract AT(30-1)-3862 Ref. NYO-3862-8, and Office of Naval Research contract Nonr CO 241.

REFERENCES

BARBER, R. T. 1967. The distribution of dissolved organic carbon in the Peru current system of the Pacific Ocean. Ph.D. Thesis, Stanford Univ., Palo Alto. 132 p.

BARBER, R. T. 1968. Dissolved organic carbon from deep waters resists microbial oxidation. Nature, *220*: 274-275.

BUBNOV, V. A. 1966. The distribution pattern of minimum oxygen concentrations in the Atlantic [In Russian]. Okeanologiya, Akad. Nauk SSSR, *6*: 240-250. Translated into English: Oceanology, *6*: 193-201.

BUBNOV, V. A. 1967. Some regularities in the formation of the oxygen minimum layer in the North Atlantic [In Russian, English abstract]. Okeanologiya, Akad. Nauk SSSR, 7: 997-1004.

CHAVE, K. E. 1965. Carbonates: association with organic matter in surface sea water. Science, *148*: 1723-1724.

CUSHING, D. H. 1958. The effect of grazing in reducing primary production: a review. Rapp. Cons. Explor. Mer, *144*: 149-154.

DAL PONT, G., and B. NEWELL. 1963. Suspended organic matter in the Tasman Sea. Aust. J. Mar. Freshwater Res., *14*: 155-165.

DUURSMA, E. K. 1961. Dissolved organic carbon, nitrogen and phosphorus in the sea. Nethl. J. Sea Res., *1*: 1-148.

DUURSMA, E. K. 1963. The production of dissolved organic matter in the sea, as related to the primary production of organic matter. Nethl. J. Sea Res., *2*: 85-94.

DUURSMA, E. K. 1965. The dissolved organic constituents of sea water, p. 433-475. *In* J. P. Riley and G. Skirrow [ed.], Chemical oceanography. Academic Press, London.

FOGG, G. E., C. NALAWAJKO, and W. D. WATT. 1965. Extracellular products of photosynthesis by phytoplankton. Mem. 1st. Ital. Idrobiol., *18* (Suppl.): 165-174.

HARVEY, H. W., L. H. N. COOPER, M. V. LEBOUR, and F. W. RUSSELL. 1935. Plankton production and its control. J. Mar. Biol. Ass. U. K., *20*: 407-442.

HOBSON, L. A. 1967. The seasonal and vertical distribution of suspended particulate matter in an area of the Northeast Pacific Ocean. Limnol. Oceanogr., *12*: 642-649.

HOLM-HANSEN, O., J. D. H. STRICKLAND, and P. M. WILLIAMS. 1966. A detailed analysis of biologically important substances in a profile off Southern California. Limnol. Oceanogr., *11*: 548-561.

JANNASCH, H. W. 1967. Growth of marine bacteria at limiting concentrations of organic carbon in seawater. Limnol. Oceanogr., *12*: 264-271.

JERLOV, N. G. 1959. Maxima in the vertical distribution of particles in the sea. Deep-Sea Res., *5*: 173-184.

KHAILOV, K. M., and Z. Z. FINENKO. In press. Organic macromolecular compounds dissolved in seawater and their inclusion into food chains. Proc. Symp. Marine food chains, Arhus, Denmark, 1968.

MENZEL, D. W. 1964. Distribution of dissolved organic carbon in the western Indian Ocean. Deep-Sea Res., *11*: 757-765.

MENZEL, D. W. 1967. Particulate organic carbon in the deep sea. Deep-Sea Res., *14*: 229-238.

MENZEL, D. W., and J. J. GOERING. 1966. The distribution of organic detritus in the ocean. Limnol. Oceanogr., *11*: 333-337.

MENZEL, D. W., and J. H. RYTHER. 1961. Zooplankton in the Sargasso Sea off Bermuda and its relation to organic production. J. Conseil, *26*: 250-258.

MENZEL, D. W., and J. H. RYTHER. 1968. Organic carbon and the oxygen minimum in the South Atlantic Ocean. Deep-Sea Res., *15*: 327-337.

MIYAKI Y., and K. SARUHASHI. 1956. On the vertical distribution of dissolved oxygen in the ocean. Deep-Sea Res., *3*: 242-247.

OGURA, N. 1967. Studies of the ultraviolet adsorbing materials in natural waters. Ph.D. Thesis, Tokyo Metropolitan Univ., Tokyo. 101 p.

PARSONS, T. R., and R. J. LEBRASSEUR. In press. The availability of food to different trophic levels in the marine food chain. Proc. Symp. Marine food chains, Arhus, Denmark, 1968.

PYTKOWICZ, R. M. 1968. Water masses and their propertities at 160°W in the southern ocean. J. Oceanogr. Soc. Japan, *24*: 21-31.

REDFIELD, A. C. 1942. The processes determining the concentration of oxygen, phosphate, and other organic derivatives within the depths of the Atlantic Ocean. Pap. Phys. Oceanogr. Meteor., *9*. 22 p.

REDFIELD, A. C., B. H. KETCHUM, and F. W. RICHARDS. 1963. The influence of organisms on the composition of seawater, p. 26-77. *In* M. N. Hill [ed.], The sea, v. 2. Interscience, New York.

REID, J. L. 1965. Intermediate waters of the Pacific Ocean. Johns Hopkins Press, Baltimore. 85 p.

RICHARDS, F. A. 1957. Oxygen in the ocean, p. 185-238. In J. Hedgepath [ed.], Treatise on marine ecology and paleoecology. Mem. Geol. Soc. Amer., 67.

RILEY, G. A. 1951. Oxygen, phosphate and nitrate in the Atlantic Ocean. Bingham Oceanogr. Coll., 13(1). 126 p.

RILEY, G. A., D. VAN HEMERT, and P. J. WANGERSKY. 1965. Organic aggregates in the surface and deep waters of the Sargasso Sea. Limnol. Oceanogr., 10: 354-363.

RYTHER, J. H. 1963. Geographic variations in productivity, p. 347-380. In M. N. Hill [ed.], The sea, v. 2. Interscience, New York.

RYTHER, J. H., D. W. MENZEL, E. M. HULBURT, C. J. LORENZEN, and N. CORWIN. In press. The production and utilization of organic matter in the Peru Coastal Current. ANTON BRUUN Reports, Southeastern Pacific Program.

SEIWELL, H. R. 1937. The minimum oxygen concentration in the western basin of the North Atlantic. Pap. Phys. Oceanogr. Meteor., 5(3). 24 p.

SHELDON, R. W., T. P. T. EVELYN, and T. R. PARSONS. 1967. On the occurrence and formation of small particles in sea water. Limnol. Oceanogr., 12: 367-375.

SKOPINTSEV, B. A. 1960. Organic matter in sea water [In Russian]. Trudy Morsk. Gidrofiz. Inst., Akad. Nauk SSSR, 19: 1-20.

SKOPINTSEV, B. A. 1965. Investigation of the water layer with oxygen minimum in the North Atlantic Ocean in the autumn of 1959 [In Russian]. Rez. Issled. Prog. Mezhd. Geofiz. Goda Mezhd. Geofiz. Komit, Presid. Akad. Nauk SSSR, 13: 108-114.

SKOPINTSEV, B. A., and S. N. TIMOFEEVA. 1962. Organic carbon content in the Baltic and North Sea, and in tropical and subtropical regions of the North Atlantic [In Russian]. Trudy Morsk. Gidrofiz. Inst., Akad. Nauk SSSR, 25: 110-117.

SKOPINTSEV, B. A., S. N. TIMOFEEVA, and O. A. VERSHININA. 1966. Organic carbon in the equatorial and southern Atlantic and in the Mediterranean [In Russian]. Okeanologiya, Akad. Nauk SSSR, 6: 251-260. Translated into English, Oceanology, 6: 201-210.

SVERDRUP, H. U. 1938. On the explanation of the oxygen minima and maxima in the oceans. J. Cons., *13*: 163-172.

SVERDRUP, H. U., M. JOHNSON, and R. FLEMING. 1942. The oceans. Prentice-Hall, New Jersey. 1087 p.

SZEKIELDA, K. H. 1967. Some remarks on the influence of hydrographic conditions on the concentration of particulate carbon in sea water, p. 314-322. *In* H. L. Golterman and R. S. Clymo [ed.], Chemical environment in the aquatic habitat. N. W. Noord-Hollandsche Uitgevers Maatschappij, Amsterdam.

WILLIAMS, P. M. 1968. Stable carbon isotopes in the dissolved organic matter in the sea. Nature, *219*: 152-153.

WOOSTER, W. S., and M. GILMARTIN. 1961. The Peru-Chile undercurrent. J. Mar. Res., *19*: 97-122.

LIPIDS OF MARINE WATERS

Lela M. Jeffrey
Department of Oceanography
Texas A & M University
College Station, Texas 77840

ABSTRACT

The concentration of chloroform extractable soluble organic compounds (lipids) in Gulf of Mexico waters ranges from 0.95 mg C/liter in shallow, highly productive Baffin Bay to 0.09 mg C/liter in subsurface waters of the western and southern Gulf. Chloroform extracts from these semitropical waters contain 10 to 20% of the total dissolved organic carbon. There is evidence that the lipids of Antarctic oceanic waters constitute 40 to 55% of the total dissolved organic carbon, and the lipid concentrations are double those in the Gulf of Mexico. This may be related to the higher productivity of the Antarctic and to the fact that Antarctic plankton contain much higher percentages of lipids than do Gulf of Mexico plankton.

δC^{13} values for oceanic Gulf of Mexico chloroform extracts of surface and subsurface samples range from -28.0 per mil in surface water to -25.1 per mil (relative to the Chicago PDB standard) at 2000 m. The water lipids apparently are less enriched in C^{13} than most of the other soluble organic carbon in sea water, but have approximately the same C^{13}/C^{12} ratio as do the lipids of the plankton.

The various compounds identified in lipid solvent extracts are reviewed for slicks, surface water, anoxic waters, and coastal and oceanic waters.

INTRODUCTION

Natterer (1892 to 1894) was one of the first investigators to report the presence of dissolved organic matter, including lipids, in sea water. He detected stearic and palmitic acids. Not until 1952 was the presence of fatty materials in sea water re-examined when Johnston (1955) and Wilson and Armstrong (1952, 1954) reported carotenoids and brownish waxy or fatty matter. At about the same time, Creach (1955) reported malic and citric acids in coastal waters.

In 1958, Jeffrey and Hood, evaluating methods for isolation of sea water soluble organic compounds, noted that liquid extraction of sea water with ethyl acetate removed a portion of the soluble organic compounds and that infrared patterns indicated the presence of fatty acids. Cryoscopic analysis indicated the average molecular weight of the mixture was about 400.

Slowey et al. (1959, 1962) and Williams (1961) reported for the waters of the Gulf of Mexico and the Pacific, respectively, that fatty acids ranging in chain length from 12 to 22 carbon atoms, including mono- and di-unsaturated species, were present in millipore-filtered sea water. Koyama and Thompson (1959) found acetic, lactic and glycollic acids in solution.

In 1960, Bentley discovered that certain components of a chloroform extract promoted the growth of *Avena* coleoptiles. They were considered auxins. One component had a concentration of 0.06 μg/liter and another 0.315 μg/liter. No other biological significance of the so-called soluble marine lipids has been reported. It is possible however that toxic lipids at certain times could be present in surface waters.

Jeffrey et al. (1963) pointed out that solvent extracts of sea water contain numerous compounds, most of which were not identified. They found free fatty acids, long-chain hydrocarbons, esters of fatty acids, sterols, and phosphorus- and nitrogen-containing compounds, some of which may be phospholipids.

Adams (1966) found sterols and phospholipids in petroleum ether and ethyl acetate extracts, respectively, of coastal and fjord waters. In the anoxic fjord water he discovered long-chain mercaptans which were not present in aerobic waters. In the deep anoxic water, there was a slight increase in organic carbon, increased amounts of hydrocarbon-like mercaptans with depth, and a decrease in the more polar lipids extracted by ethyl acetate.

Matthews and Smith (1968) identified cholesterol (10 to 17 μg/liter), B-sitosterol (135 μg/liter), and stigmasterol (10 to 17 μg/liter) in coastal Gulf of Mexico water. Their identification was based on infrared absorption and gas chromatography of the free sterols and their acetate and dimethylsilyl derivatives. The samples were filtered through diatomaceous earth, and they believed a portion of the sterols may have been extracted from the planktonic organisms suspended in the water. Autoxidation of cholesterol in sea water with aeration and light was demonstrated, so the free sterols may not exist as such very long after death of the organisms.

Hydrocarbons were reported in sea water by Jeffrey et al. (1963). Pristane was detected by Blumer et al. (1963, 1964); it has possibilities of being used as a tracer of water masses. Volatile hydrocarbons — methane, ethane, propane and butane — have been found at all depths in the ocean by Swinnerton and Linnenbom (1967). Garrett (1967) also found a variety of long-chain hydrocarbons in surface and near-surface sea waters.

Degens et al. (1964) have found a variety of phenolic compounds in sea water and sediments. At all depths they identified vanillic acid, p-OH-benzoic acid and syringic acid and estimated total concentrations of the three identified acids as 1 to 3 μg/liter.

Garrett (1967), in a study of surface and near-surface sea water at many locations under varying oceanographic conditions, has noted that certain chloroform extractable components, i.e., the less water-soluble, higher molecular weight alcohols and fatty acids, are the most surface-active and are more apt to be found at the surface. The more water-soluble, less surface-active compounds can be forced out of the surface by fatty materials. Garrett found some chloroform-soluble organic material in all areas sampled (0.2 to 1.0 mg/liter) whether the sea was biologically rich or sterile. The same classes of chloroform solubles occurred in all samples whether they were in a surface slick or not. However the slick samples contained less soluble molecules and had longer hydrocarbon chains than the subsurface water.

Table 1 summarizes investigations on lipid solvent extractable material in sea water.

SOLVENTS AND EXTRACTION PROCEDURES

Jeffrey and Hood (1958) noted that at pH 7 to 8.5 ethyl acetate, chloroform, and petroleum ether removed a small fraction of the soluble radioactive decomposition products of marine plants grown in sea water to which radiocarbon in the form of $NaHC^{14}O_3$ had been added. At a pH of 2 to 3, three extractions with ethyl acetate removed approximately 40% of the carbon-14 tagged organics, and extractions with chloroform and petroleum ether removed approximately 10% of the soluble organics. The aged tagged soluble organic material was not necessarily considered typical of marine soluble organic material, but results pointed to the need for further investigation of solvent extraction of natural sea water.

Table 2 shows that for one glass-fiber filtered coastal water sample, ethyl acetate extracts contained slightly more dissolved organic carbon than chloroform extracts. Petroleum ether extracted only one half as much lipid carbon as did chloroform or ethyl acetate. However, this extraction efficiency probably does not hold for all marine or fresh water. Adams (1966) reported that for river water, ethyl acetate extracted 0.85 mg/liter by weight and petroleum ether 0.77 mg/liter. He found for surface Lake Nitinat water that ethyl acetate removed 1.41 mg/liter and petroleum ether 0.20 mg/liter; for anoxic Lake Nitinat water, ethyl acetate removed 0.87 mg/liter and petroleum ether 0.22 mg/liter. In all cases ethyl acetate removed more dissolved organic material than did petroleum ether.

Petroleum ether extracts of marine water generally contain a higher percentage of carbon (Table 2) than do the chloroform or ethyl acetate extracts, indicating that the latter solvents extract more compounds with hydroxyl, amino, phosphate, and carboxylic acid functional groups than does petroleum ether. Petroleum ether extracts fairly efficiently hydrocarbons, sterols, fatty acids, triglycerides, i.e., the less polar lipids. Ethyl acetate does not extract sterols, but is reasonably efficient in extracting other lipids, including p-OH-benzoic, syringic and vanillic acids, phosphorus containing lipids, hydroxylated carboxylic acids, etc. (Jeffrey et al., 1963; Degens et al., 1964). Ethyl acetate has certain disadvantages: (1) acetic acid, which must be removed, may be formed by action of hydrochloric acid; (2) ethyl acetate dissolves more water and salt than chloroform or petroleum ether, increasing the difficulty of drying the extracts and sometimes causing false impressions of the concentration of extracted material unless carbon content is specifically determined; (3) ethyl acetate has a slightly higher solvent blank (0.26 mg/liter) than chloroform (0.22 mg/liter) or petroleum ether (0.14 mg/liter).

Chloroform, a less polar solvent than ethyl acetate but more polar than petroleum ether, is more convenient. It is heavier than sea water, it does not dissolve as much water and salt, and hydrochloric acid has no noticeable

Table 1. Summary of lipids found in sea water.

Compound	Method of extraction	Estimated concn (mg/liter)	Investigator
Stearic and palmitic acids	Extraction of dry salt	-	Natterer (1892, 1894)
Carotenoids and brown waxy matter	Adsorption on carbon and elution with acetone	2.5	Johnston (1955), Wilson and Armstrong (1952, 195
Acetic, formic, lactic and glycollic acids	Liquid-liquid extraction at pH 3 with ether or chloroform	>1.0	Koyma and Thompson (1959
Complex lipids (avg. MW 400)	Liquid-liquid extraction at 3 with ethyl acetate	-	Jeffrey and Hood (1958)
Fatty acids	Liquid-liquid extraction at pH 3 with ethyl acetate	0.1 to 0.8 (methyl esters)	Slowey et al. (1959, 196
Fatty acids	Liquid-liquid extraction with CCl_4 and $CHCl_3$	0.01 to 0.12	Williams (1961, 1965)
Plant hormones	Extraction with chloroform pH 5.0	-	Bentley (1960)
Hydrocarbons, glycerol esters of fatty acids, sterol esters, sterols, P- and N-containing compounds	Extraction with ethyl acetate or petroleum ether	0.4 to 8.0	Jeffrey et al. (1963), Jeffrey (1966)
p-OH benzoic, syringic and vanillic acids	Extraction of dried sea salt with ethyl acetate	1 to 3 μg/liter	Degens et al. (1964)
Malic acid	-	0.28	Creac'h (1955)
Citric acid	-	0.14	
Glycollic acid	-	0.1	Antia et al. (1963)
Cholesterol, stigma-sterol, β-sitosterol	Solvent extraction with hexane	not given	Matthews and Smith (1968)
Fatty alcohols, fatty acids, fatty esters, hydrocarbons	Co-precipitation of surface water slicks with ferric chloride and extraction with chloroform	0.2 to 1.0	Garrett (1967)
Mercaptans, P-containing lipids, sterols, etc.	Solvent extraction with ethyl acetate and petroleum ether	0.05 to 0.39 (coastal) 0.78 to 0.89 (river)	Adams (1966)
Pristane	Solvent extraction	traces	Blumer et al. (1963, 196
Methane, ethane, propane, butane	Flushing sea water with helium	10^{-4}ml/liter	Swinnerton and Linnenbon (1967)

Table 2. Comparative efficiency of solvents in removing dissolved organic carbon from coastal Gulf of Mexico water containing 1.30 mg C/liter.

Solvent	Lipid concentration (mg/liter)	Lipid concentration (mg C/liter)	%C	% of total DOC
Ethyl acetate	0.49	0.232	46.9	16.0
Chloroform	0.40	0.206	51.2	15.8
Petroleum ether	0.15	0.097	69.9	7.5

effect on it. Consequently, the lipid concentrations reported here are the result of chloroform extraction of 10 to 20 liters of glass-fiber filtered sea water adjusted to pH 2.0 with hydrochloric acid. The samples were extracted three times using a solvent:water ratio of 1:10. Garrett (1967) and Williams (1961, 1965) also used chloroform for extraction of sea water, although Garrett first co-precipitated the lipids with ferric hydroxide. For aerobic coastal and open ocean water, chloroform is almost as efficient as ethyl acetate and much more efficient than petroleum ether.

Quantitative determinations of the soluble solvent extractable organic carbon of sea water are not as accurate and reproducible as a chemist would like. The reasons are the dilute solution of organic compounds in sea water, trace contamination from samplers and extractors, the tendency of lipids in acid solution to stick to solid surfaces, differences in surface tension of the solvent and water, and other factors. However, precautions can be taken to improve extraction reproducibility. If quantitative results are desired, no polyethylene should be used in sampling, storing or extracting the water. All samplers, extractors and other ware should be chemically clean glass rinsed with the extracting solvent. The sea water should be extracted soon after collection. If a specific component is sought, a completely soluble tracer such as the internal standard of pentadecanoic acid used by Williams (1965) may be used. Finally, concentrations of lipid material should be expressed in terms of carbon concentration per liter instead of in terms of milligrams/liter because of possible salt, water or solvent inclusions.

DISTRIBUTION OF LIPIDS

Despite the difficulties of determining the true concentration of solvent extractable organic carbon in sea water, some representative values have been found for the concentration of chloroform extractable material in terms of weight (mg/liter) and carbon (mg C/liter) for northern Gulf of Mexico surface coastal waters and open ocean water at various depths. These are presented in Tables 3 and 4. The total dissolved organic carbon was also determined for the same water samples using a modified version of a method developed by Menzel and Vaccaro (1964), so that calculations could be made of the percentage recovery of the organic carbon by chloroform extraction. The carbon content of the chloroform extracts was determined in a combustion train designed by Craig (1953). The dried and weighed solvent extracts were combusted at 900 C, the water frozen out in a -100 C ethanol bath, the CO_2 frozen out in liquid nitrogen, the oxygen removed by vacuum, and the CO_2 melted and measured manometrically. Three to five milligrams of initial material were used for this determination.

As can be seen in Table 3, the chloroform extractable organic carbon concentration is directly proportional to the total dissolved organic carbon, which in turn is related to the depth of the water and the distance from land. Basically, of course, plankton production controls the concentration of dissolved organic carbon and thus the soluble lipid concentration. The lipid content of Gulf of Mexico plankton is 10 to 20% on the basis of total dry weight and the chloroform extractable soluble material is 10 to 20% of the total dissolved organic carbon.

Table 3. Organic carbon concentration and percentage of total dissolved organic carbon in chloroform extracts from Gulf of Mexico coastal water (summer).

Location	Water depth (fm)	Lipid concn (mg/liter)	Lipid DOC (mg C/liter)	Total DOC (mg C/liter)	% lipid DOC of total DOC
Baffin Bay, Texas	2	1.59	0.954	5.80	16.4
Channel, Port Aransas, Texas	6	0.72	-	-	-
28°56.8'N 89°12.1'W (South Pass, La.)	10	0.32	0.214	2.01	10.6
Southwest Pass, La.	10	0.59	0.407	2.35	17.3
28°05'N 91°49'W	20	0.40	0.206	1.30	15.8
27°54.2' 93°28.0'W	30	0.23	0.124	1.00	12.4
28°09.5' 98°07.6'W	100	0.17	0.107	0.81	13.3

Table 4. Organic carbon concentration and percentage of total dissolved organic carbon in chloroform extracts from central and western Gulf of Mexico water.

Location	Depth (m)	Lipid concn (mg/liter)	Lipid DOC (mg C/liter)	Total DOC (mg C/liter)	% lipid DOC of total DOC
25°41.7'N 92°33.3'W	10	0.31	0.16	0.81	19.9
	650	0.30	-	0.54	-
	2000	0.25	0.09	0.48	18.7
	3200	0.20	0.13	0.59	13.5
23°13'N 94°07'W	10	0.18	0.12	0.82	14.6
	650	0.20	0.11	0.53	20.7
	2000	0.15	-	0.48	-
	3200	0.18	0.12	0.57	21.0

In Table 4 it is seen that the central and western Gulf of Mexico water is considerably lower in chloroform extractable organic carbon than the coastal water and that lipid and total organic carbon concentrations below the surface layers are almost uniform. Degens et al. (1964) noted somewhat the same uniform distribution with depth of amino acids and sugars.

These values for the Gulf of Mexico compare reasonably well with those of Garrett (1967), who found concentrations by weight ranging from 0.2 to 2.0 mg/liter in surface and near surface waters in coastal, bay and offshore areas. Williams (1961, 1965) reported 0.01 to 0.12 mg/liter of fatty acids for oceanic Pacific water. Slowey et al. (1959, 1962) reported 0.1 to 0.8 mg/liter by weight of methyl esters of fatty acids in various Gulf of Mexico waters. Adams (1966) found in Pacific coastal water off Lake Nitinat, British Columbia, concentrations of 0.72 to 0.83 mg/liter at 10 m with higher values near the surface (1.62 mg/liter). Anoxic fjord water in Lake Nitinat had even higher concentrations of ethyl acetate and petroleum ether extractable material, 0.86 to 1.18 mg C/liter, with a total dissolved organic carbon concentration of 2.14 mg C/liter, representing a recovery of 40 to 62% of the total dissolved organic carbon. Organic carbon values for the coastal water were not given, but it appears that the concentrations of lipids in the coastal water near Lake Nitinat were greater than those reported here for the northern Gulf of Mexico coastal water. Adams' higher concentrations may be explained by his use of petroleum ether and ethyl acetate for extraction, the fact that the carbon content of the coastal sample extracts was not determined, and, also likely, the fact that colder waters may contain a higher percentage of lipid materials than warmer waters.

To support this last thesis, in a recent survey of marine organisms and water of the Antarctic Ocean, it was found that these cold oceanic waters contain 0.28 to 0.32 mg C/liter as lipid material, accounting for 40 to 55% of the total dissolved organic carbon. As indicated in Table 4, Gulf of Mexico oceanic lipid concentrations were about half those in the Antarctic, 0.12 to 0.16 mg C/liter, constituting 15 to 20% of the total dissolved organic carbon. Gulf of Mexico plankton samples contained 10 to 20% lipid on a dry weight basis, whereas Antarctic plankton contained 20 to 40% lipid by dry weight. Although the question should be further investigated, it presently appears that chloroform extractable organic matter concentrations in sea water may depend on the percentage lipid of the organisms in the water mass.

CHARACTERIZATION OF SOLVENT EXTRACTS OF SEA WATER

Various components of solvent extracts of sea water can be separated and characterized by thin layer chromatography, silicic acid column chromatography, gas chromatography or a combination of all three. For small samples representing extracts of 10 to 20 liters of sea water, thin layer chromatography is the most convenient method and gives important qualitative information. Thin layer silica gel plates spotted with a few micrograms of sample can be developed in 90:10:1 or 50:50:1 mixtures of petroleum ether, ethyl ether and acetic acid (Adams, 1966), or in a 19:1

toluene-ethyl acetate mixture (Jeffrey et al., 1963). To separate more polar components, a 14:5:1 solvent mixture of methanol, chloroform and 1N ammonium hydroxide can be used. Sprays can detect the separated organics. Concentrated sulfuric acid, dichromate, and 2,7-dichlorofluorescein will detect all organic spots. Specific sprays are: ninhydrin for amino groups, phosphomolybdate spray for phosphate groups, Liebermann-Burchard reagent for sterols, Dragendorff reagent for lecithins and ammoniacal cupric chloride for -SH groups in mercaptans and other such compounds. Thin layer chromatography has detected saturated aliphatic hydrocarbons, waxes, sterols, phospholipids, free fatty acids, esters of fatty acids and long-chain mercaptans in anoxic water (Jeffrey et al., 1963; Adams, 1966).

All these components are not present in every water sample, especially sterols, phospholipids and waxes. To confirm the presence of waxes, it is necessary to separate the waxes and hydrocarbons by means of silicic acid column chromatography and then to employ thin layer chromatography of this non-polar fraction in 19:1 toluene-ethyl acetate and then in cyclohexane. Waxes remain at the origin in cyclohexane and hydrocarbons travel with the solvent front. In toluene-ethyl acetate, both waxes and saturated hydrocarbons have an Rf value of 1.0.

Gas chromatography of the raw solvent extracts or of the methyl esters can also yield qualitative and near quantitative information on free fatty acids, fatty alcohol, and esterified fatty acid content (Garrett, 1967). Using this method Garrett found dodecyl alcohol in many surface sea water extracts, cetyl alcohol in a few, and various free and esterified fatty acids ranging in chain length from 11 to 22 carbon atoms, both saturated and unsaturated. Combining a lipid elution scheme (Hirsch and Ahrens, 1958; Nelson, 1962), thin layer chromatography of the fractions obtained and gas chromatography of derivatives of the various fractions, although time consuming, yields more quantitative information on classes of compounds and individual compounds of the solvent extracts than one technique alone.

Table 5 shows the results of fractionation of the chloroform extract of filtered Baffin Bay, Texas water and also of the particulate matter. This sample is unusual in that the suspended organic carbon concentration was almost double that of the dissolved organic material. Ordinarily in oceanic water the particulate organic carbon is one-tenth to one-twentieth that of the dissolved organic carbon. Baffin Bay is a very productive, shallow, warm and at times very saline bay. The particulate material was primarily a thick culture of green algae. Both soluble and particulate extracts were fractionated according to the combined procedures of Hirsch and Ahrens (1958) and Nelson (1962) in which 1%, 4% and 25% ethyl ether in petroleum ether; pure ethyl ether; acetone; 20% and 50% methanol in dichloromethane and pure methanol were used in sequence to elute the lipid classes according to their polarity from a silicic acid (Unisil, Clarkson Chemical Co.) column previously conditioned with ethyl ether and petroleum ether washings.

In comparing the percentage composition as well as the concentrations of the various fractions of the soluble and particulate extracts in Table 5, it is apparent that in the dissolved lipids, sterols (fraction V) and the

Table 5. Comparison of lipids in suspended material (heavy in green unicellular algae) and dissolved organics in Baffin Bay, Texas, water (19 liters filtered and extracted).

Fraction no.	Soluble lipids % of extract	concn (mg/liter)	Suspended lipids % of extract	concn (mg/liter)
I	7.2	0.11	0.4	0.15
II	12.0	0.18	2.6	0.07
III	2.0	0.03	1.5	0.06
IV	10.0	0.16	8.4	0.03
V	1.2	0.02	5.5	0.20
VI	1.9	0.03	3.2	0.12
VII	23.4	0.36	8.8	0.32
VIII	23.2	0.38	25.5	0.91
IX	15.4	0.24	42.1	1.41
X	2.8	0.04	2.0	0.07
TOTAL		1.55		3.54

I   – Paraffinic hydrocarbons and waxes
II – Unsaturated hydrocarbons
III – Sterol esters, tocopherols
IV – Triglycerides and free fatty acids
V   – Free sterols

VI   – Diglycerides
VII – Monoglycerides, Vitamin A
VIII – Pigments
IX   – Phospholipids (PE, PS, PC, PI)
X   – Sphingolipids

phospholipids (fraction IX) have a significantly lower percentage of total extract and concentration than the suspended material. However, for the combined hydrocarbon fractions (I and II) percentages and concentrations of the dissolved extract exceed those of the particulate extract. Apparently sterols and phospholipids do not exist very long in the dissolved state, whereas hydrocarbons are not consumed by bacteria very rapidly. It is possible that some of the hydrocarbons present originate in the oxidation of fatty acids or alcohols, although this has not been proven.

In fraction VII, the ethyl ether fraction containing monoglycerides, various forms of vitamin A, and hydroxylated acids, the percentage of soluble lipids is higher than in the particulate fraction VII. There are certainly other chemical differences, because the soluble lipids are decomposition products.

Percentages and concentrations of the various fractions of dissolved sea water lipids vary, but the pattern is the same. The concentrations of the various fractions are generally much lower than indicated in Table 5 for both dissolved and particulate lipids. In true oceanic water of low or moderate productivity the concentrations of the soluble lipids are at least one-tenth those indicated in Table 5. The concentrations of particulate lipids are ordinarily one-tenth to one-twentieth those of the dissolved lipids.

There are numerous unidentified components in all fractions, especially VII, VIII, IX and X of the soluble lipids. However, all the nitrogen and phosphorus in the sea water extract are found in fraction IX, which ordinarily contains the phospholipids. The other fractions contain C, H, O and in the case of fractions I and II, only C and H. Identification of more polar fractions (VII to X) of the soluble lipids is very difficult. From thin layer chromatography it is evident that many compounds are present in very low concentrations. Also, there are few available standards for use in the identification of decomposition products.

Each fraction of the sea water chloroform extracts eluted from silicic acid has been partially characterized by infrared absorption, gas and thin layer chromatography and colorimetric determinations (Jeffrey et al., 1963). Fractions III, IV, VI, VII, IX and X, upon transmethylation by the method of Stoffel et al. (1959) and gas chromatography of esters, indicate the presence of fatty acids in either free (fraction IV) or esterified form. Each fraction has a slightly different fatty acid spectrum, and each sea water sample examined in this manner is slightly different. The more polar lipid fractions (VII to X) tend to have more of the longer chain fatty acids (C20 to C22). Surface water extracts generally have more of the long-chain polyunsaturated fatty acids than do subsurface samples. Most often the predominant fatty acids in sea water are palmitic, stearic and oleic acids, but there are exceptions. Jeffrey et al. (1963) and Garrett (1967) report unidentified acids having a relatively high retention time on gas chromatographic columns. This is especially evident in fraction VII, which may contain hydroxylated acids. Odd-chain fatty acids are fairly common in sea water lipids, although they never constitute a major portion of the fatty acids (Jeffrey et al., 1963; Garrett, 1967). Garrett (1967), detected dodecyl and cetyl alcohols in the fatty acid chromatographs of surface water extracts.

The fatty acid composition of the suspended material or plankton samples and the dissolved lipids is not the same (Table 6). This is probably because the soluble fatty acid esters represent decomposition products of organisms existing much earlier as well as the occurrence of selective bacterial utilization, precipitation and adsorption.

Very little has been published regarding the identity of the various long-chain hydrocarbons in sea water, because of the lack of suitable standards for ordinary gas chromatographic or mass spectrometric identification. Contamination from various sources is also a deterrent to serious work on this fraction. Blumer et al. (1964) have identified pristane in marine plankton and sea water. Garrett (1967) reported a high molecular weight hydrocarbon (400) in an area of fish feeding and high biological productivity. Swinnerton and Linnenbom (1967) have identified and determined concentrations of the volatile hydrocarbons methane, ethane, propane, butane and others throughout the water column in the Gulf of Mexico and the Atlantic. In general, the concentrations tended to decrease with depth, but a maximum occurred in the samples taken from a depth of 30 to 50 m. Methane also was found in Lake Nitinat in oxygen depleted zones (Richards et al., 1965). Jeffrey et al. (1963) found 20 to 30 hydrocarbons by gas chromatography. From the retention times it appeared that decane, dodecane, tetradecane and octadecane were present. In subsequent work it has been found that even deep-sea samples contain aliphatic hydrocarbons, both saturated and unsaturated, in lesser amounts than does coastal water. Larger samples of subsurface oceanic water than previously extracted would be desirable to study the hydrocarbon fractions more thoroughly.

Sterols such as cholesterol, sitosterol and stigmasterol are present in areas of high productivity (Matthews and Smith, 1968). Jeffrey et al. (1963) detected them in nearshore samples by means of thin layer chromatography and colorimetric tests with the Liebermann-Burchard reagent. In many open ocean Gulf of Mexico samples, sterols are not detectable. Adams also found evidence of sterols in coastal and fjord waters.

Much more remains to be accomplished in identifying the components of lipid solvent extracts of filtered sea water, especially in the deep ocean. Nevertheless, it is apparent that aliphatic hydrocarbons, fatty acids in both free and esterified states, fatty alcohols and, in some surface waters, a small amount of sterols, phospholipids and phenolic acids occur. Hydrocarbonlike mercaptans have also been detected in anoxic waters.

STABLE CARBON ISOTOPE RATIOS OF SEA WATER LIPIDS

Some preliminary C^{13}/C^{12} ratios for chloroform extractable lipids and other forms of organic carbon occurring in the Gulf of Mexico are presented in Tables 7 and 8. The results are expressed as δC^{13} values relative to the Chicago PDB standard.

The solvent extracts of 10 to 20 liters of filtered sea water were quantitatively removed to combustion boats, air dried in a desiccator overnight and at 50 C for one hour, weighed and combusted at 900 C in a

Table 6. Comparison of the fatty acids in fraction IV of the lipids of Baffin Bay, Texas, suspended material and soluble organic lipids.

Fatty acid carbon no.	Baffin Bay algae (%)	Soluble lipid fatty acids (%)
14:0	4.84	3.94
14:1	3.80	1.75
14:2	0.18	0.70
15:0	0.39	0.79
15:1	0.72	-
16:0	30.15	11.82
16:1	6.51	2.63
16:2	0.47	2.16
16:3	0.43	-
17:0	0.41	2.10
18:0	2.48	5.52
18:1	8.84	5.17
18:2	3.24	4.47
18:2	0.58	4.38
18:3	6.47	9.19
18:4	4.41	19.16
19:0	-	2.89
20:1	0.80	11.38
20:2	trace	11.56
20:3	trace	-
20:4	0.45	-
20:5	3.58	-
22:1	0.53	-
22:4	2.10	-
22:5	4.43	-
22:5	3.13	-
22:6	5.37	-

Table 7. Stable carbon isotopic composition of chloroform extractable Yucatan Straits sea water organics related to the organic compounds eluted from charcoal.

$(C^{13}/C^{12}$ ratios relative to PDB_1 Belemnite Std.)

Depth (m)	Chloroform extractable fraction (per mil)	Chloroform extract from charcoal (per mil)	Average of all organic carbon eluted from charcoal (per mil)
30	-28.0	-24.0	-23.0
250	-25.6	-24.6	-23.5
≥000	-25.1	-22.3	-21.4
≥600	-	-21.4	-20.5

Table 8. Comparison of the carbon isotopic composition of the various forms of carbon at 250 m in the Yucatan Strait, Gulf of Mexico. (C^{13}/C^{12} ratios relative to PDB_1 Belemnite Std.)

Mixed plankton (per mil)	-17.4
Particulate organic carbon (per mil)	-23.3
Chloroform extractable fraction (per mil)	-25.6
Average of all organic eluted from charcoal (per mil)	-23.5

closed system similar to that described by Craig (1953). The purified carbon dioxide was analyzed in an isotope ratio mass spectrometer, using a secondary standard of lubricating oil with an assigned value of -29.40 per mil relative to the Chicago PDB standard.

The organic carbon contained in the chloroform extracts of Gulf of Mexico sea water (23°13'N, 94°07'W) had δC^{13} values ranging from -28.0 per mil at 30 meters to -25.1 per mil at 2000 meters. The δC^{13} values dropped very rapidly from -28.0 at 30 meters to -25.6 per mil at 250 meters. Apparently, the more hydrocarbon-like materials remain in the surface layers. It may be noted here that the percentage carbon of the extracts also decreased with increased depth. Many more stations must be sampled and measured before any firm conclusions are reached, but in this profile the liquid-liquid chloroform extracts were lighter than the chloroform extracts of activated charcoal over which 50 to 200 liters of sea water had been passed. This is probably because charcoal does not adsorb the aliphatic hydrocarbons and adsorbs more of the polar lipids than liquid-liquid extraction with chloroform removes from the water.

The dissolved organic carbon isolated by adsorption on charcoal represents only 65% of the dissolved organics originally present. Only 80 to 85% of the DOC was adsorbed and 80% removed by elution. The δC^{13} value relative to N.B.S. isotope reference material No. 20 that Calder and Parker (1968) reported was -20.6 per mil for Gulf of Mexico sea water containing 0.4 mg C/liter. Corrected to the PDB standard, their δC^{13} value for total dissolved organic carbon is -21.6 per mil, compared to the δC^{13} range of -23.5 to -20.5 for the material eluted from charcoal. Experiments are in progress to compare the values for charcoal adsorption and desorption of dissolved organic carbon and the method used by Calder and Parker (1968). Undoubtedly the stable carbon isotope ratios of the dissolved and particulate organic carbon in sea water will vary somewhat with location, depth and previous history of the water and the compounds present. Table 8 compares the δC^{13} values of chloroform extracts of sea water with those of other forms of organic carbon — the plankton carbon, particulate carbon and dissolved organic carbon eluted from charcoal. The lipids are obviously less enriched in C^{13} than the other fractions, as might be expected from the data so far presented.

Degens et al. (1968) have reported that chloroform extractable lipids of plankton in the Pacific had a mean δC^{13} of -29.8 per mil relative to the PDB_1 standard and the average value for the total plankton organic carbon was -19.3 per mil. The δC^{13} values for the Gulf of Mexico dissolved lipids are only slightly more enriched in C^{13} than the plankton lipids of the Pacific, but the subsurface dissolved lipids and other organic carbon become more enriched in C^{13} the longer they are exposed to bacterial action and chemical oxidation.

DISCUSSION

BELSER: In the Sephadex study you did with the organic extraction on sea water, did you try, for example, extracting with chloroform and following

mentioned that these compounds had been found in Galveston. I rather suspect that this was in areas of pollution. Occasionally I find it in bay water, but not in deep sea water.

BREZONIK: I wonder if you would define the quality of this dissolved organic carbon?

JEFFREY: As a working criterion, I would say that dissolved organic carbon is any organic matter that passes through a glass fiber filter with an average pore size about $0.3\,\mu$.

BREZONIK: This is under pressure or free filtration?

JEFFREY: I have been using both. Pressure I believe is the proper definition. I do not think there is a great deal of difference.

BREZONIK: How much pressure?

JEFFREY: About 30 psi.

HOLM-HANSEN: Did you say $0.3\,\mu$ on the glass fiber filters?

JEFFREY: Yes.

HOLM-HANSEN: Did you check this?

JEFFREY: Yes, with Gelman, the manufacturer; they claim $0.3\,\mu$. I would like to check it; it may not be correct.

MENZEL: That's for air filtration and not for water?

JEFFREY: No, these filters are for water. There is one kind for air and another for water.

DUURSMA: Are the quantities of lipids which you extract sufficient to analyze for trace metals which are bound to these lipids, by activation analysis?

JEFFREY: Yes, Slowey et al. (1967) did that once, and they found some copper.

SIEBURTH: What company makes 0.3 glass micron filters?

JEFFREY: Gelman. They are as good as Millipore. They are easy to work with because you can heat them to 500 C and get rid of any residual organic matter. In addition, they filter faster because they are thicker and have more surface area. Any of these values for filtering are arbitrary because after you have filtered some water, the size of particles passing the filters will change.

that with ethyl acetate? Did you extract any additional fractions in lower concentrations?

JEFFREY: I divided the water into three portions. The first was extracted with chloroform, the second with ethyl acetate, and the third with petroleum ether; each sample was extracted three times with fresh solvent. It might be a good idea to do this in sequence, say, extract with petroleum ether, then with chloroform and then with ethyl acetate, but this I did not do. I was simply comparing the efficiency of each of the solvents.

BELSER: My question really related to the quality of materials that you extracted with the solvents.

JEFFREY: Yes, ethyl acetate definitely extracts more polar type material, things that contain hydroxyl groups, amino groups, phosphate groups. I am not saying that it is a bad solvent, I just don't like to work with it. I did for many years, but it tends to dissolve salt and if you don't have time or enough sample to run carbon content, your concentrations may be misleading.

BLUMER: Are the values that you have given for a single one set batch extraction?

JEFFREY: No. I extracted each water sample three times with a fresh batch of solvent in a glass separatory funnel, which is rather primitive but reduces contamination since the glassware can be cleaned thoroughly.

CHRISTMAN: Could you add anything to the information regarding the isolation of vanillic and syringic acids? They are quite different from the other compounds which are related more to lipids.

JEFFREY: Degens et al. (1964) found these compounds when they extracted dry sea salt with ethyl acetate. I haven't personally identified these materials. I checked his results once and it looked like mine were about the same as his.

CHRISTMAN: What I was after was the near shore samples.

JEFFREY: No, these samples were taken from the open ocean — both surface and deep water.

ROSEN: I was interested in the sterols you found in Galveston Bay, the cholestrol and stigmasterol, because of the publication by Murtaugh and Bunch (1967). They used these as an indicator of fecal pollution and I suspect there must be some of that in Galveston Bay.

JEFFREY: Yes. I did not actually do that one. Matthews and Smith (1968) of the medical school in Galveston published those data and I simply

SIEBURTH: I find that they permit about 10% of the bacteria to pass, so the filtrate is not strictly dissolved organic matter.

JEFFREY: Well, I call that passing the filter soluble organic matter also. Some of the hydrocarbons which go through the filter may not be in true solution. But we have to accept something.

REFERENCES

ADAMS, D. D. 1966. Dissolved organic matter in Lake Nitinat, an anoxic fjord. M.S. Thesis, Univ. Washington. 46 p.

ANTIA, N. J., C. D. McALLISTER, T. R. PARSONS, K. STEPHENS, and J. D. H. STRICKLAND. 1963. Further measurements of primary production using a large volume plastic sphere. Limnol. Oceanogr. *8*: 166-183.

BENTLEY, J. A. 1960. Plant hormones in marine phytoplankton, zooplankton and sea water. J. Mar. Biol. Ass. U.K., *39*: 433-444.

BLUMER, M., M. M. MULLIN, and D. W. THOMAS. 1963. Pristane in zooplankton. Science, *140*: 974.

BLUMER, M., M. M. MULLIN, and D. W. THOMAS. 1964. Pristane in the marine environment. Helgoland. Wiss. Meeresunters., *10*: 187-201.

CALDER, J. A., and P. L. PARKER. 1968. Stable carbon isotope ratios as indices of petrochemical pollution of aquatic systems. Environ. Sci. Technol., *2*: 535-539.

CRAIG, H. 1953. The geochemistry of the stable carbon isotopes. Geochim. Cosmochim. Acta, *3*: 53-92.

CREAC'H, P. V. 1955. Sur la presence des acides citriques et maliques dans les eaux marines littorales. C. R. Acad. Sci., Paris, *240*: 2551-2553.

DEGENS, E. T., M. BEHRENDT, B. GOTTHARDT, and E. RAPPMANN. 1968. Metabolic fractionation of carbon isotopes in marine plankton — II: Data on samples collected off the coasts of Peru and Ecuador. Deep-Sea Res., *15*: 11-20.

DEGENS, E. T., J. H. REUTER, and K. N. F. SHAW. 1964. Biochemical compounds in offshore sediments and sea waters. Geochim. Cosmochim. Acta, *28*: 45-65.

GARRETT, W. D. 1967. The organic chemical composition of the ocean surface. Deep-Sea Res., *14*: 221-227.

HIRSCH, J., and E. H. AHRENS, Jr. 1958. Separation of complex lipid mixtures by the use of silicic acid chromatography. J. Biol. Chem., *233*: 311-320.

JEFFREY, L. M. 1966. Lipids in sea water. J. Amer. Oil Chem. Soc., *43*(4): 211-214.

JEFFREY, L. M., and D. W. HOOD. 1958. Organic matter in sea water; an evaluation of various methods for isolation. J. Mar. Res., *17*: 247-271.

JEFFREY, L. M., B. F. PASBY, B. STEVENSON, and D. W. HOOD. 1963. Lipids of ocean water. Advances in organic geochemistry. Proc. Int. Mtg., Milan, 1962.

JOHNSTON, R. 1955. Biologically active organic substances in the sea. J. Mar. Biol. Ass. U.K., *34*: 185-195.

KOYAMA, T., and T. G. THOMPSON. 1959. Organic acids in sea water, p. 925-926. *In* Preprints Int. Oceanogr. Congr.

MATTHEWS, W. S., and L. L. SMITH. 1968. Sterol metabolism. III. Sterols of marine waters. Lipids, *3*: 239-246.

MENZEL, D. W., and R. F. VACCARO. 1964. The measurement of dissolved organic and particulate carbon in sea water. Limnol. Oceanogr., *9*: 138-142.

NELSON, G. J. 1962. Studies on human serum lipoprotein phospholipids and phospholipid fatty composition by silicic acid chromatography. J. Lipid Res., *3*: 71-74.

NATTERER, K. 1892-94. Denkschr. Akad. Wiss. Wien, *59* 1st Reihe, 83; *60*, 2nd Reihe, 49; *61*, 3rd Reihe, 23.

RICHARDS, F. A., J. D. CLINE, W. W. BROENKOW, and L. P. ATKINSON. 1965. Some consequences of the decomposition of organic matter in Lake Nitinat, an anoxic fjord. Limnol. Oceanogr., *10*: (Suppl.) R185-R201.

SLOWEY, J. F., L. M. JEFFREY, and D. W. HOOD. 1959. Characterization of the ethyl acetate extractable organic material of sea water, p. 934-937. *In* Preprints Int. Oceanogr. Congr.

SLOWEY, J. F., L. M. JEFFREY, and D. W. HOOD. 1962. The fatty acid content of ocean water. Geochim. Cosmochim. Acta, *26*: 607-616.

STOFFEL, W., F. CHU, and E. H. AHRENS. 1959. Analysis of long chain fatty acids by gas-liquid chromatography: micro-method for preparation of methyl esters. Anal. Chem., *31*: 307-308.

SWINNERTON, J. W., and V. J. LINNENBOM. 1967. Gaseous hydrocarbons in sea water: determination. Science, *156*: 1119-1120.

WILLIAMS, P. M. 1961. Organic acids in Pacific Ocean waters. Nature, *189*: 219-220.

WILLIAMS, P. M. 1965. Fatty acids derived from lipids of marine origin. J. Fish. Res. Bd. Canada, *22*: 1107-1122.

WILSON, D. P., and F. A. J. ARMSTRONG. 1952. Further experiments on biological differences between natural sea waters. J. Mar. Biol. Ass. U.K., *31*: 335-349.

WILSON, D. P., and F. A. J. ARMSTRONG. 1954. Biological differences between sea waters. J. Mar. Biol. Ass. U.K., *33*: 347-360.

MOLECULAR NATURE OF NITROGENOUS COMPOUNDS IN SEA WATER AND RECENT MARINE SEDIMENTS

Egon T. Degens
Department of Chemistry
Woods Hole Oceanographic Institution
Woods Hole, Massachusetts 02543

ABSTRACT

Data and concepts on the molecular composition of nitrogenous organic matter in sea water and sediments are presented. Proteins and protein-derived metabolites, such as urea and amino acids, account for the bulk of the dissolved organic matter in the sea; the low C/N ratio with a mean of 2.5 to 3.0 supports this inference. These compounds, however, occur primarily in the combined rather than in the free state — e.g., in clathrate-type complexes. The particulate organic matter in surface waters is largely represented by living organisms and in deep waters by intact or partially degraded biogenic material.

Detritus and dissolved organic matter supplied to the sediments are used for *de novo* synthesis of proteins by microorganisms and burrowing animals. Polymerization may also be achieved via epitaxial growth on mineral surfaces. In oxidizing environments, nitrogenous compounds are diagenetically degraded rather rapidly unless they are protected by minerals such as organic clay derivatives or shell carbonates. In contrast, strongly reducing environments do favor the preservation of organic matter as a consequence of low biological activity. The latter circumstances may even lead to a redistribution and separation of distinct organic molecules via natural chromatography.

INTRODUCTION

The distribution of organic carbon and nitrogen in sea water is known in detail and certain trends are established. In general, the dissolved organic carbon decreases from a high of about 1 mg/liter in surface waters to values in the range of 0.4 to 0.6 mg/liter in waters below the 200 m mark (Duursma, 1961, 1965; Holm-Hansen et al., 1966; Menzel, 1967; Menzel and Ryther, 1968). Seasonal variations are only observed in surface waters. Skopintsev et al. (1966), using a different analytical method, obtain carbon concentrations three times as high.

Relative to the dissolved organic carbon, the particulate organic carbon content is lower by a factor of five to ten in surface waters and by a factor of fifty to one hundred in deep waters.

The C/N ratios of dissolved organic matter may fluctuate strongly in surface waters; they are particularly high in warm water environments with values as high as 20 to 30 (Duursma, 1961). At lower temperatures the C/N ratios are more in accordance with those observed in deep waters (C/N ~3). In contrast, the C/N ratio of planktonic material is in the order of 5 to 6

(Fleming, 1940; Holm-Hansen et al., 1966), and that of the particulate organic matter in the sea about 8 to 12 (Menzel and Ryther, 1968). The ratios for particulate organic matter actually represent upper limits because carbonate detritus is frequently present on filters combusted for organic carbon determinations.

In Recent marine sediments, the amount of organic matter falls in the range of 0.1 to 3% (Emery, 1960; Degens, 1967). A number of parameters control the variation in total yield — organic productivity, rate of deposition, mineral composition, activities of microorganisms and burrowing animals, and Eh/pH relationships. The C/N values are in the order of 8 to 12 and commonly increase with depth of burial. In ancient sediments the C/N values are most frequently around 20 to 30.

In comparison to the detailed knowledge of the carbon and nitrogen content of oceans and sediments, information on their molecular structure is limited. Only a small number of organic molecules which account for less than 10% of the total organic matter have so far been identified (Duursma, 1965; Degens, 1967). The present work is an attempt to understand the molecular nature of the nitrogenous fraction of the bulk organic matter. On the basis of C/N ratios, it seems that nitrogen-containing biochemicals represent a substantial portion of the total organic matter.

DATA PRESENTATION

Problem analysis

The amount of free amino acids, sugars, fatty acids and phenols in sea waters and sediments is small; they represent less than 10% of the total organic matter (Fig. 1). What is the molecular nature of the remaining 90%? As an approach to this problem we make the heuristic statement that:

(1) all organic matter in the ocean is biogenic, and that
(2) the bulk is principally derived from phytoplankton.

The possibility that terrigenous material may also add to the organic carbon pool in the sea should be ignored at this point.

Accordingly, the systematics of our data presentation is:

(1) plankton,
(2) particulate organic matter,
(3) dissolved organic matter, and
(4) sediments.

Plankton

The bulk of the nitrogen in organisms is tied up in the form of proteinaceous materials. Other biochemicals such as nucleic acids are quantitatively of minor significance as far as nitrogen balance estimates are concerned. Inasmuch as the identification of individual proteins and peptides is beset by too many analytical problems, the presentation will be limited to the amino acid spectrum of the total proteinaceous material.

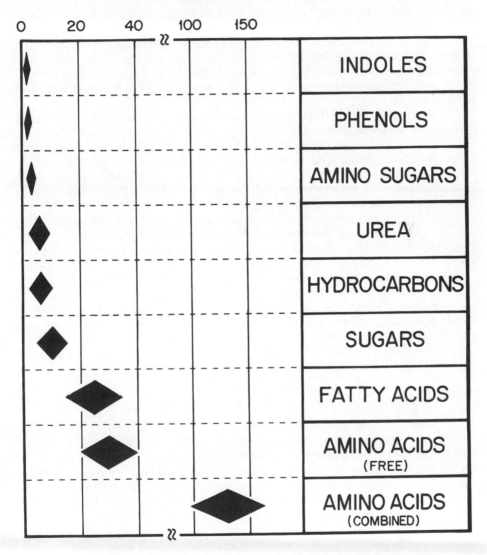

Fig. 1.   Distribution of free constituents in sea water. The individual samples have
            been grouped into systematic classes of compounds and have been plotted
            in the form of cumulative frequency diagrams to summarize the
            information in a comprehensive form. The diamond-shaped figures
            represent the 2 sigma range. The data are presented in μg C/liter to allow a
            direct comparison to the total dissolved organic matter which is generally
            reported in mg C/liter.

The amino acid content of plankton collected off the coast of Peru and Ecuador along the downstream course of the Humboldt Current is uniform (Table 1). This is noteworthy, because samples No. 2, 14 and 16 are predominantly phytoplankton (90%). In contrast, samples No. 4, 9 and 11 are predominantly zooplankton. The remainder of the samples represent mixtures of various amounts of phyto- and zooplankton. It is implied that except for total yield, which is higher for the zooplankton, there are no substantial changes occurring in the distribution of amino acids in the food chain phytoplankton-zooplankton. The abundance of acidic and basic amino acids is emphasized.

To study the effect of water temperature and of respiration in prolonged darkness, the neritic diatom, *Skeletonema costatum* (WHOI clone "Skel"), the estuarine clone "3H" of the diatom, *Cyclotella nana*, and the green flagellate, *Dunaliella tertiolecta* (clone "Dun") were grown in enriched sea water following a procedure outlined by Guillard and Ryther (1962). The cultures were subsequently left in darkness for up to 19 days (Table 2).

Two major trends become apparent:

(1) a gain in proteins with increasing water temperature, and

(2) a decrease in protein content with length of respiration.

The respiration effect implies that the organisms preferentially lose proteins when left in darkness. The *Dunaliella* values of Hellebust and Terborgh (1967), showing a respiration loss in carbon of 50 to 60% in 20 days, make it evident that at the initial stages of respiration (Table 2) proteins are lost more rapidly than carbohydrates or lipids (unpublished results). This metabolic characteristic influences the molecular pattern of dissolved organic matter in the sea since proteinaceous breakdown products are complex in nature (e.g., urea, amino acids, phenolic compounds, quinones, kindoles) and are constantly discharged into the sea water.

Particulate organic matter

Most of the particulate organic matter in surface waters is living plankton. The amino acid composition seems to support this inference (Table 3A), yet the presence of ornithine, citrulline, urea and some of the amino butyric acids suggests that degradation already has started. Values for urea range from not detectable to 5 μg/liter; α- and γ-amino butyric acids are present in trace amounts. The identification of urea is of special significance because urea is gradually decomposed upon acid hydrolysis. In turn, its presence even after 6N HCl hydrolysis for 22 hr must mean that before hydrolysis, larger quantities were present which must have been condensed in some fashion. This phenomenon would also account for the high yield in ammonia, since neither glutamine, asparagine, nor the hexosamines are abundant enough to explain this feature.

The depth relationships are of special significance. Aside from the decreasing trend in total yield, systematic changes in serine, glycine, alanine and the basic amino acids can be observed.

Table 2.   Dist

Species	Temp (°C)	Resp (days)	ASP	THR	SER	GLU	PRO	GLY	ALA	C
	8	0	143	56	71	133	59	130	131	
	8	6	153	53	68	140	42	118	115	
Skeletonema costatum ("Skel")	18	0	127	56	75	133	58	103	126	
	18	6	148	55	69	127	45	125	123	
	18	19	140	59	66	119	30	143	119	
	27.5	0	127	66	76	125	45	122	117	
Cyclotella nana ("3H")	20	0	129	60	60	110	50	117	121	
	30	0	121	61	72	129	23	126	117	
Dunaliella tertiolecta ("Dun")	20	0	124	55	67	134	45	129	134	
	20	5	109	56	60	111	48	103	136	
	20	12	107	55	59	110	46	108	136	
	20	19	101	60	58	107	50	111	95	

* at 10°C $\delta C^{13} = -18.8$

ibution of amino acids in plankton.
(in residues per 1000)

'S	VAL	MET	ILEU	LEU	TYR	PHE	LYS	HIS	ARG	TOTAL PROTEINS (% Dry Weight)	GLUCOSAMINE	δC^{13} (‰)
6	58	9	39	82	20	44	10	1	6	11.3	0.018	-21.0
4	61	10	39	66	19	47	24	4	27	8.0	0.006	
2	51	13	34	73	20	36	43	9	31	17.9	0.027	-18.9
4	60	14	37	79	17	40	27	10	9	15.2	0.015	
8	65	10	49	94	21	43	14	7	15	9.3	0.089	
3	64	19	45	88	20	45	21	8	10	22.4	0.033	-17.0
4	68	18	47	88	24	50	26	10	20	16.7	0.010	-17.0 *
8	65	17	49	97	14	51	24	4	13	18.8	0.016	-12.8
5	49	11	26	89	17	39	32	8	36	19.6	0.027	-16.2 **
6	46	17	25	102	13	38	62	11	55	6.0	0.025	-20.9
6	45	17	23	108	13	38	64	13	52	6.1	0.016	-21.8
6	45	28	26	86	14	28	63	33	87	6.3	0.009	-21.7

** after 1 day respiration δC^{13} = -18.8

Dissolved organic matter

a) Free: The distribution of free amino acids is surprisingly uniform throughout most of the water column (Table 3B and 3C); surface waters exhibit some spread. Most marked is the abundance of glycine, serine and ornithine. The virtual absence of arginine should be considered in conjunction with the high concentration of ornithine and urea; most of the samples have a urea content of 2 to 20 μg/liter. These three amino compounds plus aspartic acid and citrulline are biochemically connected via the so-called urea cycle. Glycine and serine are also related, and together with urea and ornithine, constitute two of the more prominent nitrogenous metabolic waste materials. Glucosamine is present in quantities of a few μg/liter.

b) Combined: Most amino acids in the dissolved organic matter occur in the form of higher molecular weight compounds with molecular weights between 400 and 10,000. Acid hydrolysis of filtered sea water which has passed through 0.4 μ filters releases amino acids in concentrations far above those reported for the free constituents (Table 3C). In some ways the amino acid spectrum bears a certain relationship to the particulate organic matter. In others it is more like the free amino acid pattern. However, the small amount of acidic amino acids represents a native feature. The high abundance of ammonia in connection with the presence of urea is a remarkable coincidence. The relationships in total yield between the particulate and dissolved organic matter are summarized in Fig. 2.

Sediments

a) Free: Amino acids dissolved in interstitial waters and those which can be extracted with water or ammonium acetate from the sediment material are generally termed "free". They occur in reasonable quantities in recent sediments. In oxidizing environments the amount and nature of the free amino acids appear to be closely related to the level of microbial activity. In sediments with a low level of microbial activity the amino acid concentration is in the order of 0.01 to 1 μg/g. Well populated sediments may contain up to 200 μg/g. In contrast, the free amino acid content is extremely high in reducing sediments, particularly if microorganisms are absent or the activites are low. Under such circumstances the amino acids separate along a vertical sediment profile (Fig. 3). This phenomenon can best be explained by natural chromatography along clay mineral surfaces in the course of diagenesis and compaction.

b) Combined: The amino acid distribution of representative cores from the Indian (Table 4A) and Atlantic (Table 4B) Oceans, indicates that the amino acid yield at various stations is within the same range, although the concentration of combustible organic matter may vary by a factor of 2 to 3. The amino acid content drops from a few hundred μg/g in the upper 2 m of burial to about 100 μg/g at depths greater than 5 m. In Pacific sediments from the Experimental Mohole (Rittenberg et al., 1963), the amount of amino acids decreases nearly exponentially from about 325 μg/g

Sample No.	APS	THR	SER	GLU	PRO	GLY	ALA	CYS	VAL	MET	ILE
											Particul
1	78	53	79	135	41	121	93	14	59	15	37
2	35	25	25	97	95	112	94	13	17	22	44
3	64	50	74	121	42	112	86	8	23	3	36
4	68	46	68	121	51	112	87	9	50	13	28
5	92	67	108	159	15	124	95	14	60	1	27
6	75	43	84	114	18	124	71	10	49	15	31
7	83	54	93	135	17	139	87	12	54	15	37
mean	78	48	76	126	40	121	88	11	45	12	34
											Total D
8	24	35	64	21	30	94	113	8	50	12	44
9	19	22	123	13	66	243	120	30	26	24	48
10	20	33	86	15	50	242	123	34	27	11	51
11	15	36	102	14	78	216	101	22	23	1	51
12	16	43	74	17	78	113	100	5	17	3	11
13	17	44	91	17	55	205	96	11	24	8	65
14	16	37	103	13	102	217	87	6	29	33	50
15	17	42	70	20	68	178	65	13	18	9	59
mean	18	39	89	16	66	189	100	16	27	13	47
											F
16	153	33	155	53	9	393	69	3	21		21
17	65	27	145	145	19	365	110	4	45		11
18	77	43	101	91	10	267	82	3	64		12
19	51	16	86	50	9	309	64	12	56		8
20	53	45	160	69	35	285	60	11	50		38
21	62	24	126	27	9	350	182	26	50		15
22	91	03	118	66	0	202	99	27	87		9
23	94	31	129	50	19	271	71	33	53		16
mean	81	32	127	69	15	329	91	15	53		16

	LEU	TYR	PHE	LYS	HIS	ARG	ORN	Total µg/liter
te Matter								
	69	25	29	71	17	60	2	179
	77	42	53	125	31	90	4	144
	69	34	37	84	32	95	33	198
	64	27	35	87	31	96	6	213
	60	7	15	64	23	62	5	172
	58	26	31	115	41	97	2	221
	74	26	38	75	12	45	4	178
	67	27	34	89	27	78	8	186
ssolved								
	67	26	32	89	137	54	108	401
	82	19	30	43	48	14	29	185
	86	20	32	77	11	49	30	187
	75	8	35	87	34	46	34	129
	72	28	47	110	55	100	111	240
	87	8	12	89	33	82	60	209
	58	3	13	57	53	54	67	197
	84	3	51	100	64	77	60	199
	76	14	31	81	54	60	62	218
ee								
	18	3	4	43	10		12	56
	11	3	4	6	10		30	72
	20	13	11	45	49		109	77
	8	3	4	122	10		191	50
	19	24	29	38	28		56	58
	17	14	15	58	10		14	38
	8	3	4	23	16		20	69
	12	9	9	85	41		83	66
	14	9	10	52	22		64	61

(after Siegel and Degens, 1966)

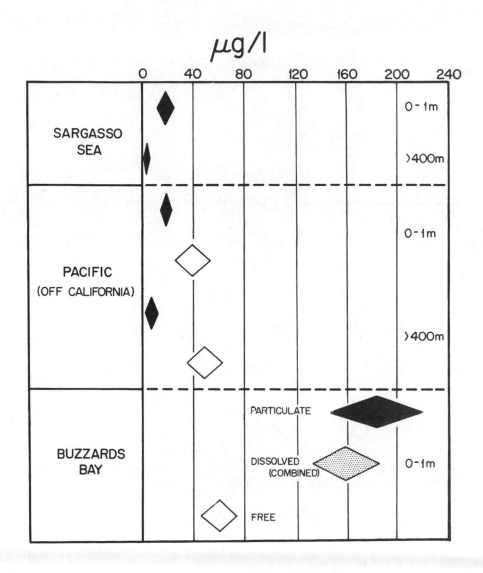

Fig. 2.   Distribution of free, combined and particulate amino acids in representative sea water samples. The diamond-shaped figures cover the 2 sigma range.

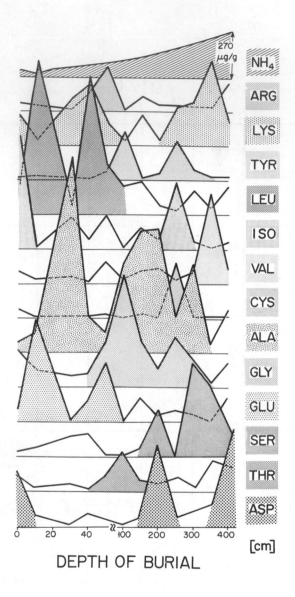

NH₄
ARG
LYS
TYR
LEU
ISO
VAL
CYS
ALA
GLY
GLU
SER
THR
ASP

270 µg/g

0   20   40   100   200   300   400

[cm]

DEPTH OF BURIAL

Fig. 3.   Separation of amino acids along a vertical sediment profile of Santa Barbara Basin sediments off the coast of California. Data are presented in residues per 1000. A zippeton pattern was used when the amount of amino acids exceeded 100 residues per 1000. On top of the figure the free ammonia content is shown; it gradually decreases from about 270 µg/g at a depth of 4 meters to about 50 µg/g at the sediment/sea water interface (Degens, 1967).

near the surface to 15 μg/g at 170 m depth. The section spans 25 million years of Earth's history.

The presence of hydroxyproline is of biochemical interest, since this amino acid is tied up in collagen-type proteins. The presence of β-alanine is a consequence of microbial utilization of aspartic acid in the early stages of diagenesis. Ornithine is principally derived from arginine with the simultaneous production of urea. Most of the urea has been destroyed during acid hydrolysis but fair amounts can still be recognized. Small quantities of α- and γ-aminobutyric acids can be recovered. They are principally derived from threonine and glutamic acid, respectively. Traces of allo-isoleucine and α-ϵ diaminopimelic acid are present in all samples investigated.

c) Shell material: Deep sea carbonate ooze contains large quantities of foraminiferal tests. These contain proteins which once served as templates for the epitaxial growth of the shell carbonates. Inasmuch as these proteins are intimately associated with the carbonate phase, they are protected from microbial degradation and survive the initial stages of diagenesis. There is little difference in the distribution of amino acids in samples taken from different time intervals over the last 8000 years (Table 5A). Eventually, however, these proteins hydrolyze and release their hydrolyzation products to the interstitial waters.

Contributions by shell proteins to the nitrogenous fraction of sediments can be substantial should organisms rich in mineralized tissues become part of the sediment deposit (Table 5B).

DISCUSSION

In surface waters, the bulk of the particulate organic matter is living plankton. Upon death of these organisms, most of the biochemical molecules are utilized again by organisms and consequently are recycled in a "continuous food chain" within the upper 200 m of the water column. The small fraction of organic debris that eventually escapes into deeper waters and gradually settles to the bottom of the sea still contains unaltered biochemical compounds. Condensation products from metabolic waste materials or decaying tripton are also incorporated in the deep sea particulate matter.

Tables 3A and 3B, and data on carbon content in deep waters (e.g., Menzel, 1967; Menzel and Ryther, 1968) indicate that more than 50% of the particulate organic matter is proteinaceous. Aside from intact peptides, so-called heteropolycondensates contain nitrogenous compounds. The molecular nature of heteropolycondensates is variable and is determined by the amount and type of the associated organic molecules. The abundance of aromatic compounds suggests that either depside or clathrate structures are involved. The latter arrangement is particularly favorable because mixtures of polar and neutral compounds can be accommodated within the same structural framework (Fig. 4). The abundance of oxygen functions (e.g., hydroxyl, carboxyl and carbonyl functions) is noteworthy. They enhance structural stabilization and promote the formation of metal ion coordination polyhedra (Degens and Matheja, 1967). The last phenomenon leads to a reorganization of the structural order (Fig. 5).

	Pelecypoda (51)	Gastropc (40)
		0. (
OH-Pro	–	(0-0.
Asp	136 (77-240)	114 (69-18.
Thr	28 (18-44)	46 (28-76
Ser	66 (43-102)	85 (58-12
Glu	50 (35-72)	87 (52-14:
Pro	52 (28-98)	61 (36-10:
Gly	271 (185-398)	153 (99-23
Ala	66 (43-101)	89 (52-15:
Cys	14 (6-33)	9 (4-23)
Val	33 (22-49)	48 (34-69)
Met	18 (8-39)	14 (6-31)
I-Leu	20 (13-31)	31 (20-46)
Leu	34 (26-44)	71 (51-10(
Tyr	11 (2-61)	11 (5-24)
Phe	30 (19-48)	24 (14-43
OH-Lys	0.03 (0-0.6)	0. (0-0.2
Lys	22 (13-38)	26 (17-41)
His	4 (1-14)	3 (1-16)
Arg	24 (6-96)	22 (9-52)
Total ** (µ/y)	3334	1415
Proteins ** Hexosamines	143.97	108.

* Geometric mean
** Arithmetic mean
Numbers in parentheses are 1 σ range

Amino acid distribution in shell materials*.
(in residues per 1000)

| | CaCO$_3$ | | | SiO$_2$ | |
	Cephalopoda (4)	Echinoidea (4)	Bryozoa (3)	Sponges (3)	Diatoms (1)
	–	1 (0-36)	0.1 (0-7)	–	–
	98 (75-128)	88 (78-98)	117 (110-136)	123 (109-142)	132
	34 (18-64)	48 (42-55)	59 (53-66)	47 (30-74)	82
	95 (62-146)	81 (77-86)	77 (60-98)	102 (58-173)	116
	65 (42-128)	109 (106-112)	102 (93-112)	83 (67-102)	109
	55 (15-205)	78 (66-92)	50 (36-67)	64 (49-85)	28
	153 (89-262)	171 (121-241)	148 (127-172)	134 (99-179)	115
	126 (74-216)	85 (79-91)	92 (89-95)	94 (79-112)	105
	7 (0-65)	1 (0.5-2)	13 (4-39)	5 (4-8)	15
	36 (20-64)	38 (31-45)	48 (38-60)	62 (55-69)	60
	8 (5-13)	21 (18-25)	16 (14-18)	8 (3-19)	26
	21 (17-26)	26 (21-32)	31 (25-39)	40 (27-59)	43
	44 (29-67)	58 (47-70)	59 (46-76)	70 (67-73)	91
	23 (15-75)	20 (16-25)	23 (21-25)	24 (16-35)	21
	30 (20-45)	25 (19-32)	28 (24-33)	24 (12-48)	32
	–	0.6 (0-11)	0.4 (0-8)	–	–
	20 (5-83)	45 (35-57)	49 (40-61)	40 (22-72)	5
	5 (0-35)	16 (13-20)	17 (10-30)	12 (7-23)	16
	23 (10-56)	69 (60-80)	50 (41-60)	30 (21-42)	2
	211 80	7813	43437	5852	90057
	1.37	33.36	21.23	10.98	0.53

(after Degens et al., 1967)

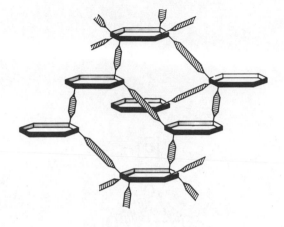

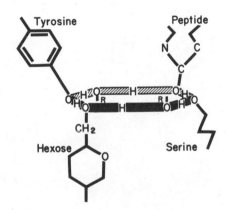

Fig. 4.   Structure of quinol (Fig. 4a). As a consequence of electron donator acceptor (EDA) interactions, polar OH-groups are combined with hexagonal ring structures. The structural organization in a hypothetical clathrate segment (Fig. 4b) illustrates the participation of OH-groups of sugars and amino acids, as well as the incorporation of peptides via the carbonyl group. The large interspace permits the incorporation of chain polymers and hydrophobic molecules. Metals may also be introduced into the structure (Degens and Matheja, 1967).

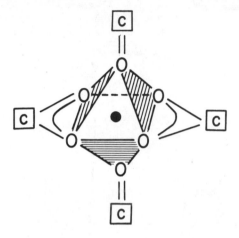

Fig. 5.   Metal ion coordination polyhedron. In this presentation, two carboxyl and
            two carbonyl groups are shown, resulting in an octahedral coordination for
            the central metal ion. An increase in the number of polyhedra introduces a
            structural reorganization of the biochemical molecules. Other oxygen
            functions may equally well participate in the coordination of metals and
            thus introduce an increase in the biocrystallographical order of the organic
            molecules involved (Degens and Matheja, 1967). Some of the transition
            elements in sea water may be part of such structures and represent one of
            the factors limiting the primary production in upwelling waters in certain
            parts of the oceans (Barber and Ryther, 1969).

Studies of the extracellular products released by planktonic organisms are a lively concern among biologists (e.g., Fogg, 1966; Hellebust, 1965; Webb and Johannes, 1967). Aside from glycollate, which is excreted by most photosynthesizing organisms, nitrogenous substances are the predominant metabolic waste materials. The release of intact peptides or amino acids still represents an unsolved problem (Wangersky, 1965). Experiments have shown (Stewart, 1963) that up to 45% of the nitrogen fixed by some organisms is excreted. In view of these figures and the low C/N ratio, nitrogenous compounds probably account for a substantial portion of the dissolved organic matter in the sea.

How these excretory products are stabilized in the sea is not yet completely understood, because of the complexity of the products and of the reactions involved. Much confusion has also been generated by the arbitrary separation of particulate and dissolved organic matter into distinct classes of compounds. Chemically speaking, such a classification does little to elucidate the molecular nature of the organic compounds in the sea. More than 90% of the so-called dissolved organic matter has a molecular weight (MW) greater than 400. The bulk of the organic compounds with MW>400 falls in the 3000 to 5000 MW-range as ascertained by molecular sieve techniques. Hydrolysis of this material releases substantial amounts of monomers, yet some high molecular weight products are intact after this treatment.

The generally low C/N ratio of dissolved organic matter, the presence of urea even after hydrolysis and the abundance of amino acids and aromatic compounds in connection with the high oxygen yields suggest that oxygen and nitrogen are involved in the structural stabilization of the high molecular weight fraction. Peptides do account for some of the materials. Urea's molecular structure (Lenné, 1954, Fig. 6) facilitates its reaction with aldehydes to produce long-chain polymers; alternatively its oxygen may be used for coordinative purposes.

The presence of urea represents a unique physiological phenomenon. This compound was long considered to be a metabolic product only of higher animals; the invertebrates were believed to excrete ammonia. Urea also occurs in plants (McKee, 1962). Arginase, which splits arginine into urea and ornithine, has been observed in marine algae (Smith and Young, 1955). Ornithine hereby acts catalytically in the synthesis of urea from added ammonia, and the abundance of arginine and aspartic acid (or asparagine) in marine plankton makes physiological sense. These molecules are both a convenient nitrogen storage reservoir and active metabolites.

Aside from arrangements involving peptides or urea condensates, oxygen may also be organized in the form of clathrates (Fig. 4). Thus phenols, quinones, amino acids, amines, sugars, fatty acids, alcohols and their respective polymers may coexist within the same polymer by virtue of their oxygen functions. Further molecular stabilization can be achieved by means of metal ion coordination polyhedra (Fig. 5).

Interactions of dissolved organic matter with inorganic detritus, in particular with clay minerals, leads to polymerization of organic matter by epitaxial growth (Degens and Matheja, 1967). Although these reactions may

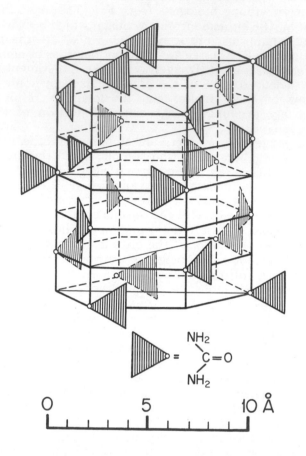

$$\boxed{\diagdown} = \begin{array}{c} NH_2 \\ | \\ C=O \\ | \\ NH_2 \end{array}$$

Fig. 6.   The unit cell of urea in adduct compounds is hexagonal and six urea molecules make up a unit cell (Schlenk, 1949; Smith, 1952; Lenné, 1954). Stability is achieved by hydrogen bonding between adjacent urea molecules and van der Waals forces between the individual urea molecules and between urea and the adduct compound located within the channel or tube formed by the urea molecules. Such a complex is structurally similar to clathrate compounds. The formation of cage structures in general requires strong interactions between neighboring extended groups of atoms or molecules of the same type resulting in large enough stable configurations for the inclusion of elements or molecules of different types. Urea adduct compounds resemble clathrates in that long-chain molecules force urea into configurations different from that of the normal tetragonal urea structure. The significance of oxygen in structural reorganizations of this type is apparent. Metal ions may even use this oxygen for coordinative purposes and thus increase the structural order of the participating molecules.

already proceed in the sea, they take place on a large scale only in the sediments. There, the metabolic waste materials generated by microorganisms and burrowing animals become an integral part of mineral structures — for example, organic clay derivatives (e.g., Weiss, in press) — or are adsorbed on mineral surfaces. Silicate surfaces are an effective polymerization agent for organic monomers and are also catalysts (Degens and Matheja, 1967). In consequence, metabolites can be condensed or chemically altered by means of organic-inorganic interactions in the sediment strata. Eventually, the heterogeneous condensation products formed in the initial stages of diagenesis are reduced either to aromatic condensates resembling graphite or to light paraffinic hydrocarbons — in particular, methane. Carbon dioxide, ammonia and water are simultaneously released. The ammonia subsequently substitute for cations in clay minerals or becomes adsorbed.

In the "Problem Analysis" it was stated that most of the organic matter in the sea is generated by phytoplankton δC^{13} analysis of the particulate organic matter in the sea supports this statement. The particulate matter in cold surface water has δC^{13} values of around -25 per mil (Sackett et al., 1965) while the particulate matter in tropical regions has values of around -15 per mil. This difference is related to photosynthetic processes (Deuser et al., 1968). The zooplankton inherit this isotope pattern. The δC^{13} content of organic matter in Recent marine sediments reflects the carbon isotope distribution in the local plankton population. In contrast, the dissolved organic matter is depleted in C^{13} by 5 to 10 per mil relative to the average plankton crop (Deuser, personal communication). There are several possible explanations for this phenomenon:

(1) lipid materials are the main constituents;
(2) terrigenous organic matter is the chief contributor;
(3) metabolic waste is isotopically light relative to its biochemical precursor.

The first suggestion can be dismissed. Organic solvent extractable compounds represent at most 5% of the total dissolved organic matter (Ed. Note: Jeffrey shows 8 to 16%, this volume); furthermore, the nitrogen content is too high. There is also little support for the second alternative. Seasonal fluctuations in total yield are a consequence of plankton bloom and are not related to continental runoff. The third suggestion appears to be the most likely one. It is known that the degradation of organic matter may introduce isotope fractionation. Abelson and Hoering (1961) have shown that the CO_2 resulting from decarboxylation of amino acids can be enriched by 20 per mil in C^{13} relative to the remainder of the molecule. In addition, internal variations among the amino acids cover a range of about 17 per mil. This mechanism may have caused the depletion in C^{13} in the dissolved organic matter. Controlled experiments with algal cultures are intended to test this supposition.

Indirect support for this inference can be obtained by following the carbon isotope distribution of organic matter in the course of diagenesis. Ancient marine sediments have a δC^{13} between -25 and -28 per mil (Fig. 7), whereas most Recent marine sediments have a δC^{13} in the range of -19 to

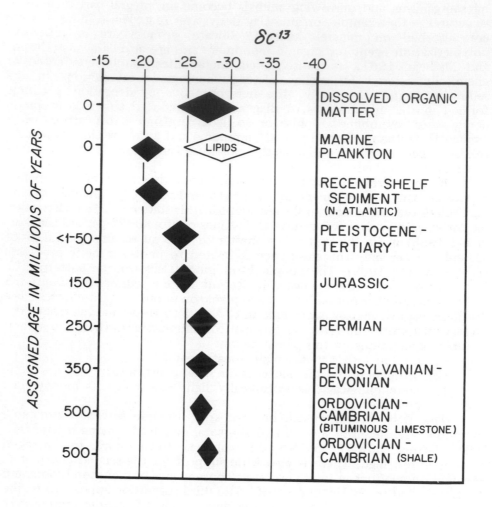

Fig. 7.   Stable carbon isotope distribution in plankton, sea water and marine sediments. The lipid fraction of plankton is generally depleted in C^{13} by 5 to 10 per mil relative to the total plankton sample. Similar depletions are observed for the dissolved organic matter relative to the particulate organic matter in the sea. Diagenetic processes also lower the C^{13} content of the organic matter to about the same extent. The diamond-shaped figures represent the 2 sigma range.

-21 per mil (Table 4). Thus, the isotope distribution of the organic matter in the sea follows the same trend as the organic matter in the sediment; the alteration products are several per mil lighter than the starting material. This relationship also proves that the particulate organic matter in the sea is the main contributor of the organic matter in the sediments. The dissolved organic matter, even though it is one to two orders of magnitude more abundant appears to be only a secondary carbon source for the sediments.

SUMMARY

The organic matter in the sea is largely composed of nitrogenous compounds. Aside from intact peptides and proteins, so-called "heteropolycondensates" are present. A clathrate-type molecular structure in which neutral and polar organic molecules coexist is suggested for these condensates. Free compounds, i.e., monomers, such as amino acids, fatty acids and sugars amount to less than 10 per cent of the total organic matter.

The bulk of the organic matter is metabolites derived from the plankton and microbes living in the sea. Terrigenous contributions to the organic matter in the oceans are negligible except within the immediate area of river discharge (estuarine environment).

Sediments derive their organic carbon principally from the particulate organic matter in the sea. Contributions from the dissolved organic matter are of secondary importance. In the course of diagenesis, nitrogenous organic matter is preferentially eliminated as ascertained by the gradual increase in C/N ratios with geologic time.

DISCUSSION

HOLM-HANSEN: In your introduction you mentioned that the nucleic acids compose an insignificant fraction of the particulate fraction. I assume you have some knowledge of their concentration. What is the concentration of DNA with depth in the ocean? What is the origin and form of bound ornithine?

DEGENS: Concerning the bases and the nucleic acids, I have developed a technique which allows the determination of bases and nucleic acids to 10^{-11} to 10^{-12} molar levels. If I analyze sea water using this technique, which is a combination of molecular sieve and ion exchange techniques, I can only find traces of constituents which may be related to the bases. These amount to not more than 1 to 5 μg/liter. When the material is hydrolyzed at the position where bases and nucleic acids would be located there are only small bumps barely above background. In view of the sensitivity of the technique, I question that nucleic acids are present in much greater concentrations. Amino acids, amines, peptides and proteins represent the bulk of the nitrogenous organic matter. Nucleic acids and the base constituents are unquestionably present, but as far as nitrogen balance calculations are concerned, they are insignificant. Now concerning the origin of ornithine, we have information that suggests that a certain plankton has ornithine in its protein. The only other case in which I know ornithine is built into some kind of protein is the green peel of the watermelon. I hardly think that watermelons are present in sufficient quantities in the ocean. However, urea and ornithine can be produced from a protein containing arginine, but the ornithine can still stay in the peptide or protein network without being released as a free constituent. Ornithine in the sea is present both in a combined and a free form. In summary, ornithine, serine and glycine are the three predominate free amino acids found.

HOLM-HANSEN: Who has shown ornithine bound in proteins of what organisms?

DEGENS: There is a paper by Smith and Young (1955). They have found ornithine in some plankton proteins.

HOLM-HANSEN: I'd like to comment that ornithine is known to be a bound constituent in some cyclic antibiotics of bacteria. I have also reported on the presence of bound ornithine in *Elexibacteria* and Blue-green algae. I do not think, however, that anyone has demonstrated the presence of ornithine as a constituent of protein in algae, although there are reports of ornithine as a constituent of algal peptides.

MORGAN: I find the urea structure very interesting. Do you consider the metal ion essential in these proposed structures of urea or is the urea playing a different role?

DEGENS: In the situation I suggested there are a number of possibilities for achieving structural stabilization. Structural stabilization can be achieved by hydrogen bonds or by interaction of organic molecules with metal ions. I only introduce another parameter — a metal ion bridge which may stabilize the structure. In the urea structure metal ions are not essential, but they may be involved.

JONES: Would you specify what metals you feel are particularly important in this structure?

DEGENS: Several metals. If sodium is connected either to the phosphate groups or to the oxygen of the sugar, the result is double stranded DNA. If, in addition, magnesium is involved, triple stranded DNA may develop. Similarly, a number of metal ions such as calcium can coordinate and perhaps even explain some of the features mentioned in my presentation — e.g., the transition from the dissolved to the particulate state. It would be a kind of interaction by metal ion coordination, which would result in a higher biocrystallographical order and increase in molecular weight.

NOAKES: I have a question about the connection between the organic material and the clay material. Are you saying the organic material is within the clay structure, say in the octahedral-tetrahedral layer?

DEGENS: Amino acids are first adsorbed onto the kaolinite protostructure. Subsequently, the product is split into peptides and kaolinites. Thus, peptides are generated from the amino acids via epitaxial growth on clay surfaces. The logic is very simple. The amino acids, being polar, do not polymerize in water because of the interference of the water. However, if the amino acids are in solid solution, there is no solvent interference. Therefore, polymerization can be achieved. This polymerization is thermodynamically favored, so it readily proceeds in a suitable solvent medium. Organic matter may also be essential to the formation of kaolinite. Without organic matter or some other protecting agent, kaolinite does not form. So the adsorption serves a dual purpose. Polymerization is initiated and kaolinite formation is achieved.

NOAKES: Is clay the template?

DEGENS: Yes. The clay serves the same function as the ribosomes in a biological system.

NEVÉ: Where is the energy?

DEGENS: Biochemists believe that if peptides are present, they eventually break down into amino acids. I contend in accord with data presented by Pauling and others (reviewed in Degens and Matheja, 1967) that the reverse process is thermodynamically favored if the relationship between bond energy and bond distance is taken into account, i.e., that when amino acids are present they tend to form peptides. One's conclusions are a function of the calculations done, of whether the Zwitterion or classic approach is taken. In any case, we did find peptides and proteins. We have observed that when clay minerals, urea, and succinic, formic or citric acid are present, amino acids form and immediately polymerize due to the catalytic action of the clay minerals.

NOAKES: Are these forming between the octahedral and tetrahedral layers?

DEGENS: In a six-member ring of silicates, for example, the location of the peptide along the clay surface has nothing to do with interlayer position. It is simply an arrangement along the surface of the clay.

MALCOLM: I have a question concerning the template mechanism of clay. Do you picture the exchange site on the clay as determining the type of polypeptide? For example, would you get a different protein with montmorillonite than with kaolinite or other clay minerals?

DEGENS: Yes you would. As I say, it is like a printing machine. The size and arrangement of the type determines the appearance of the final print.

MALCOLM: What would be the mechanism for preferential adsorption of a particular amino acid so that the linkage in the polypeptide would be correct?

DEGENS: The structure of the mineral would be the mechanism since no clay mineral is like any other. There are billions of different clay minerals even though we group them into distinct classes. They vary in size, chemistry and structure.

BREGER: I think the speaker used my name rather loosely in association with this paper and I would like to dissociate myself from it. Actually, I find myself in a most unenviable position because being the last speaker in the symposium and having some ideas on these things myself, to comment on your paper at this time would be an exercise in self-destruction. The only comment I will make at this time concerns the matter of urea in water and sediment. This is new to me. The solubility of urea is well known and I cannot understand where it is coming from. I think you recognize what I am about to say. Do you know what happened to your samples after you collected them?

DEGENS: Yes.

BREGER: Do you know who handled them and what they did with them?

DEGENS: I should mention that of course we have talked about amino acids in general. The most serious question asked in any work of this type is about contamination. There is not time to completely outline the precautions that were taken. I can only assure you we did take all the precautions possible in order to rule out contamination. What I want to emphasize is that the models I have presented tie in with the work of others, Dr. Duurmsa (1965), for example, with his C/N ratio, which is about 3, he says, in the dissolved organic matter. I should perhaps point out that plankton has a C/N ratio of 6. Something in the dissolved organic matter must account for these differences in nitrogen.

DUURSMA: Then my values were good?

DEGENS: Yes.

BREGER: I should like to suggest in the light of what has been said, that Nature is sophisticated and not malicious. I think that Nature has to be a little more simple. Perhaps some of these ideas are perceptive; I'd like to save my own ideas until the end.

DEGENS: What more simple organic compound can Nature break down everything into than urea?

GOLDBERG: I make the plea that, before we make general pronouncements about the marine environment, we recognize that the ocean is a very complex place. Already we have seen a very distinct difference between the coastal ocean and the deep sea. When dogma is presented that applies to both, I become confused. For example, Menzel (this volume) placed restraints upon the types of organic matter that may occur in the deep ocean and in the shallow coastal ocean. Yet one may have to invoke many factors to explain the differences in organic matter which exist in these two environments. The open ocean sediments are compositionally quite distinct from the coastal sediments. I would not accept without strong evidence that the organic matter in both of these sedimentary domains comes primarily from the particulate organic matter in sea water. I might make an interesting case for some of the organic matter in the coastal sediments coming along with the suspended load of rivers from terrestrial sources.

I want to comment upon Menzel's very exciting results concerning differences in concentration of the dissolved organic matter in adjacent profiles in the Atlantic Ocean. One possible explanation is airborne particles, falling to the water masses in different concentrations, adsorbing different amounts of organic matter as they fall to the bottom. Now, if the solid surfaces are always unsaturated with respect to organic matter, such a mechanism might explain this observation.

ACKNOWLEDGMENTS

The work was supported by National Aeronautics and Space Administration Project NSR-22-014-001 and by Petroleum Research Fund Project PRF-1943-A2, administered by the American Chemical Society.

Contribution No. 2172 from Woods Hole Oceanographic Institution.

REFERENCES

ABELSON, P. H., and T. C. HOERING. 1961. Carbon isotope fractionation in formation of amino acids by photosynthetic organisms. Proc. Nat. Acad. Sci., *47*: 623-632.

BARBER, R. T., and J. H. RYTHER. 1969. Organic chelators: factors affecting primary production in the Cromwell Current Upwelling. J. Exp. Mar. Biol. Ecol., *3*: 191-199.

CRAIG, H. 1957. Isotopic standards for carbon and oxygen and correction factors for mass-spectrometric analysis of carbon dioxide. Geochim. Cosmochim. Acta, *12*: 139-149.

DEGENS, E. T. 1967. Diagenesis of organic matter, p. 343-390. *In* G. Larsen and G. V. Chilingar [ed.], Diagenesis in sediments. Elsevier, Amsterdam-London-New York.

DEGENS, E. T. In press. Biogeochemistry of stable carbon isotopes. *In* G. Larsen and G. Eglinton and M. Murphy [ed.], Organic geochemistry: methods and results. Springer-Verlag, Inc., New York.

DEGENS, E. T., M. BEHRENDT, B. GOTTHARDT, and E. RAPPMANN. 1968. Metabolic fractionation of carbon isotopes in marine plankton. II. Data on samples collected off the coasts of Peru and Ecuador. Deep-Sea Res., *15*: 11-20.

DEGENS, E. T., and J. M. HUNT. 1968. Data on the distribution of stable isotopes and amino acids in Indian Ocean sediments. Woods Hole Oceanogr. Inst. Tech. Rep. Ref. No. 68-4. 49 p.

DEGENS, E. T., and J. MATHEJA. 1967. Molecular mechanisms on interactions between oxygen co-ordinated metal polyhedra and biochemical compounds. Woods Hole Oceanogr. Inst. Tech. Rep. Ref. No. 67-57. 312 p.

DEGENS, E. T., H. L. SAUNDERS, and R. R. HESSLER. Unpublished manuscript. Amino acid distribution in recent sediments of the Gay Head - Bermuda and Walvis Bay transects.

DEGENS, E. T., D. W. SPENCER, and R. H. PARKER. 1967. Paleobiochemistry of molluscan shell proteins. Comp. Biochem. Physiol., 20: 553-579.

DEUSER, W. G., E. T. DEGENS, and R. R. L. GUILLARD. 1968. Carbon isotope relationships between plankton and sea water. Geochim. Cosmochim. Acta, 32: 657-660.

DUURSMA, E. K. 1961. Dissolved organic carbon, nitrogen, and phosphorus in the sea. Nethl. J. Sea. Res., 1: 1-148.

DUURSMA, E. D. 1965. The dissolved organic constituents of sea water, p. 433-475. In J. P. Riley and G. Skirrow [ed.], Chemical oceanography. Academic Press, London.

EMERY, K. O. 1960. The sea off Southern California: A modern habitat of petroleum. Wiley, New York. 366 p.

FLEMING, R. H. 1940. The composition of plankton and units for reporting population and production. Proc. 6th Pacific Sci. Congr., Pacific Sci. Assoc., Vancouver, 1939, 3: 535-540.

FOGG, G. E. 1966. The extracellular products of algae. Oceanogr. Mar. Biol. Annu. Rev., 4: 195-212.

GUILLARD, R. R. L., and J. H. RYTHER. 1962. Studies of marine planktonic diatoms. I. Cyclotella nana Hustedt, and Detunola confervacea (Cleve) Gran. Can. J. Microbiol., 8: 229-239.

HELLEBUST, J. A. 1965. Excretion of some organic compounds by marine plytoplankton. Limnol. Oceanogr., 10: 192-206.

HELLEBUST, J. A., and J. TERBORGH. 1967. Effects of environmental conditions on the rate of photosynthesis and some photosynthetic enzymes in Dunaliella tertiolecta Butcher. Limnol. Oceanogr., 12: 559-567.

HOLM-HANSEN, O., J. D. H. STRICKLAND, and P. M. WILLIAMS. 1966. A detailed analysis of biologically important substances in a profile off southern California. Limnol. Oceanogr., *11*: 548-561.

LENNÉ, H. -U. 1954. Röntgenographische Strukturuntersuchungen hexagonaler Einschlussverbindungen des Thioharnstoffs. Acta Cryst., 7: 1-15.

McKEE, H. S. 1962. Nitrogen metabolism in plants. Clarendon Press, Oxford. 728 p.

MENZEL, D. W. 1967. Particulate organic carbon in the deep sea. Deep-Sea Res., *14*: 229-238.

MENZEL, D. W., and J. H. RYTHER. 1968. Organic carbon and the oxygen minimum in the South Atlantic Ocean. Deep-Sea Res., *15*: 327-337.

RITTENBERG, S. C., K. O. EMERY, J. HÜLSEMANN, E. T. DEGENS, R. C. FAY, J. H. REUTER, J. R. GRADY, S. H. RICHARDSON, and E. E. BRAY. 1963. Biogeochemistry of sediments in experimental mohole. J. Sed. Petr., *33*: 140-172.

SACKETT, W. M., W. R. ECKELMANN, M. L. BENDER, and A. W. H. BÉ. 1965. Temperature dependence of carbon isotope composition in marine plankton and sediments. Science *148*: 235-237.

SCHLENK, W., JR. 1949. Die Harnstoff-Addition der aliphatischen Verbindungen. Experientia, *5*: 204-220.

SIEGEL, A., and E. T. DEGENS. 1966. Concentration of dissolved amino acids from saline waters by ligand-exchange chromatography. Science, *151*: 1098-1101.

SKOPINTSEV, B. A., S. N. TIMOFEEVA, and O. A. VERSHININA. 1966. Organic carbon in the equatorial and southern Atlantic and in the Mediterranean [In Russian]. Okeanologiia, Akad. Nauk SSSR, *6*: 251-260. Translated into English, Oceanology, *6*: 201-210.

SMITH, A. E. 1952. The crystal structure of the urea-hydrocarbon complexes. Acta Cryst. *5*: 224-235.

SMITH, D. G., and E. G. YOUNG. 1955. The combined amino acids in several species of marine algae. J. Biol. Chem., *217*: 845-853.

STEWART, W. D. P. 1963. Liberation of extracellular nitrogen by two nitrogen-fixing blue-green algae. Nature, *200*: 1020-1021.

WANGERSKY, P. J. 1965. The organic chemistry of sea water. Amer. Sci., *53*: 358-374.

WEBB, K. L., and R. E. JOHANNES. 1967. Studies on the release of dissolved free amino acids by marine zooplankton. Limnol. Oceanogr., *12*: 376-382.

WEISS, A. In press. Organic derivatives of clay minerals, zeolites, and related minerals. *In* G. Eglinton and M. Murphy [ed.], Organic geochemistry: methods and results. Springer-Verlag, Inc., New York.

STABLE CARBON ISOTOPE RATIO VARIATIONS IN BIOLOGICAL SYSTEMS

P.L. Parker and J.A. Calder
The University of Texas
Marine Science Institute
Port Aransas, Texas 78373

INTRODUCTION

Chemical and physical isotope effects in the carbon cycle have provided geochemists with a powerful tool for gaining understanding of these natural processes. Isotope effects in the carbon cycle have produced carbon reservoirs with different and more or less characteristic C^{13}/C^{12} ratios. Fortunately many of these ratios persist for geologically long periods of time so that important insight into the ancient carbon cycle can be gained. For example, the slight C^{12} enrichment of organic matter associated with sediments from all geological periods, from Recent to Cambrian, is generally taken as evidence that the organic matter is derived from once living organisms. This same C^{12} enrichment in the reduced carbon associated with Precambrian sediments (Hoering, 1967) is evidence that this carbon too was once part of a living organism.

Isotope effects and the labeling of chemical reservoirs which they provide are useful in many fields of scientific investigation. Physical organic chemists have for many years used isotope effects to study reaction mechanisms. This paper points out some other areas of investigation where isotope effect studies might be useful and presents some preliminary results. Degens (in press) recently reviewed and compiled much of the carbon isotope data.

Two types of chemical isotope effects operate in natural carbon systems. The chemical basis of the equilibrium isotope effect is well understood (Urey, 1947). Isotope equilibrium constants may be calculated provided the necessary spectral data are available (Bigeleisen and Mayer, 1947; Bigeleisen, 1958). Perhaps the most important equilibrium isotope effect in the carbon cycle is:

$$C^{13}O_{2(g)} + HC^{12}O_3^-_{(aq)} = C^{12}O_{2(g)} + HC^{13}O_3^-_{(aq)}$$

The isotope equilibrium constant for this reaction has been measured by several workers (Deuser and Degens, 1967; Hoering, 1960; Vogel, 1961; Wendt, 1968). As a result of this isotope effect, atmospheric CO_2 is about 7 per mil enriched in C^{12} relative to the bicarbonate in sea water. In Fig. 1, $CO_{2(g)}$ is -7 and bicarbonate is near zero. The small amount of $CO_{2(g)}$ dissolved in sea water will remain at -7 per mil while it is in isotopic equilibrium with atmospheric CO_2. If sea water is isolated due to depth and the slowness of gas exchange at the air-sea interface and if biological processes draw on this small amount of $CO_{2(g)}$ (it is really $CO_{2(aq)}$ at -7) then it begins to reflect the more positive isotope ratio of the HCO_3^-.

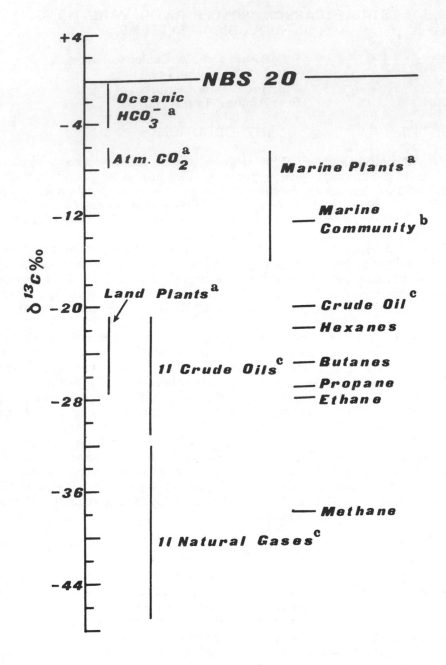

Fig. 1. δ C^{13} of some carbon reservoirs. a. Craig, 1953. b. Parker, 1964. c. Silverman, 1967.

Kinetic isotope effects in the biological carbon cycle are responsible for most of the isotope ratio variations observed in organic materials. Kinetic isotope effects, being mechanism dependent, are not as readily calculated as equilibrium isotope effects. Organic chemists have studied reaction mechanisms by comparing measured and calculated isotope effects (Bigeleisen and Wolfsberg, 1958).

Park and Epstein (1960) measured the kinetic isotope effect in the photosynthetic fixation of carbon in a cell-free system. This is perhaps the most important isotope effect in the carbon cycle. The reaction is:

$$RuDp + CO_2 + H_2O = 2PGA + 2H^+$$

where RuDp is ribulose 1:5 diphosphate and PGA is 3-phosphoglyceric acid. The fractionation factor was 1.017. Or in terms of δC^{13} the organic carbon is -17 with respect to the CO_2 from which it is derived. They also observed a 7 per mil isotope effect in the diffusion of CO_2 through leaf wall for higher plants giving an overall fractionation factor of 1.024. This value is of the right direction and magnitude to account for many of the observed δC^{13} values of natural plants. However, it is becoming clear that while this is the right approach there are more variations among plants than can be explained by a single isotope effect.

The overall results of the equilibrium and kinetic isotope effects in the various chemical reactions of carbon which constitute the carbon cycle in Nature are shown in Fig. 1. Natural carbon has been separated into a series of reservoirs each with a more or less characteristic isotope ratio. This figure is intended only to help us focus on problems, not to suggest that we understand the detailed distribution of the stable carbon isotopes in Nature.

Data in the field of isotope geochemistry are expressed in terms of δC^{13}, the per mil difference between the isotope ratio of the sample and a standard material:

$$\delta C^{13} = \frac{(C^{13}/C^{12})\text{ sample} - (C^{13}/C^{12})\text{ std.}}{(C^{13}/C^{12})\text{ std.}} \times 1000$$

Del-C^{13} is the quantity that most isotope ratio mass spectrometers yield. It can be related directly to the fractionation factor, α. In the case of a kinetic isotope effect:

$$\alpha = \frac{(C^{13}/C^{12})\text{ product}}{(C^{13}/C^{12})\text{ reactant}}$$

If we let the product be the sample and the reactant the standard then:

$$\alpha = 1 + \frac{\delta C^{13}\text{ sample}}{1000}$$

In this presentation National Bureau of Standards Isotope Reference Standard #20 is taken as zero. Since this material is a limestone, organic matter will have small negative δC^{13} values.

One must bear in mind that it is fractionation factors that characterize chemical reactions and hence biological processes. Thus an alga growing on inorganic carbon with δC^{13} of zero or -50 will show the same fractionation factor, but very different values of δC^{13}. Often one can safely assume that δC^{13} of inorganic carbon is close to zero and treat δC^{13} of the samples as a fractionation factor, but care must be taken.

δC^{13} OF INORGANIC CARBON RESERVOIRS

Del-C^{13} of atmospheric CO_2 has been shown to be almost constant with regard to time and location (Keeling, 1961). This is not the case for aquatic inorganic carbon (IOC), the total CO_2 that can be released by an excess of acid. Del-C^{13} of IOC is most constant for open marine waters and most variable for estuaries and bays. Variations in δC^{13} of IOC give some insight into the processes which give rise to the variations. The δC^{13} of the IOC must be known to provide data for calculation of the fractionation factors for the plants growing in a given environment.

Del-C^{13} of the IOC of several of the environments shown in Fig. 2 are as follows:

Gulf of Mexico	+ 0.5
Aransas Bay	- 0.8
San Antonio Bay, lower	- 1.0
San Antonio Bay, upper	- 4.8
Guadalupe River	- 7.5
Baffin Bay, fresh (1968)	- 6.7
Baffin Bay, hypersaline	+ 3.4

The largest variation was within the same body of water, Baffin Bay. In its normal hypersaline state ($65^{\circ}/_{\circ\circ}$) δC^{13}-IOC was +3.4. When a large amount of fresh water was introduced due to hurricane Beulah the δC^{13} fell to -6.7 and the salinity to around $3^{\circ}/_{\circ\circ}$. This change was due to the introduction of $CO_{2\,(aq)}$ with a δC^{13} of -7 per mil. The Bay has recovered very slowly. The organic matter produced during this period would be expected to be more negative with respect to δC^{13} than normal if all other factors were equal. Whether such shifts are recorded in the isotope ratio of organic matter in the sediment has not been established.

A similar shift in δC^{13}-IOC was seen in the Guadalupe River-San Antonio Bay system. The river water (δC^{13} of -7.5 per mil) influenced the upper Bay significantly and the lower Bay to some extent. The Bay retained a fairly uniform pH. The fact that the effect of the river $CO_{2\,(aq)}$ could be detected in the Bay suggests that transport through the Bay is faster than transfer of $CO_{2\,(g)}$ across the air-water interface. Rapid exchange across the interface, with isotopic equilibrium established, would produce a δC^{13}-IOC close to normal Gulf of Mexico water.

Del-C^{13} of the IOC associated with a productive biological community varied on a diurnal basis. The variation shown in Fig. 3A was 4 δC^{13} per mil. These measurements were made in a shallow marine bay in which *Thalassia* was the dominant producer. The flow of carbon isotopes in this system was complicated. Many species of plants and bacteria were

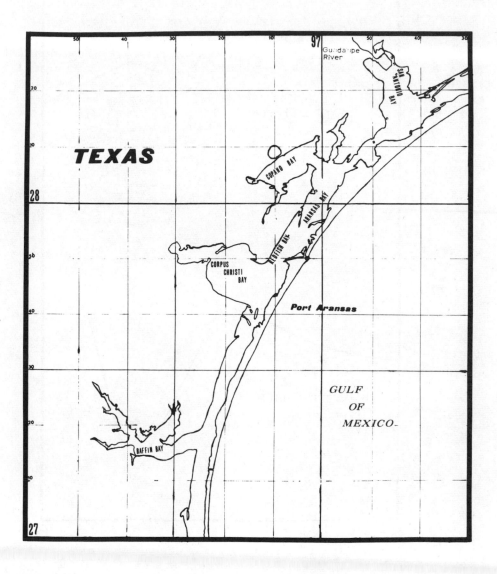

Fig. 2.   Map of sampling area.

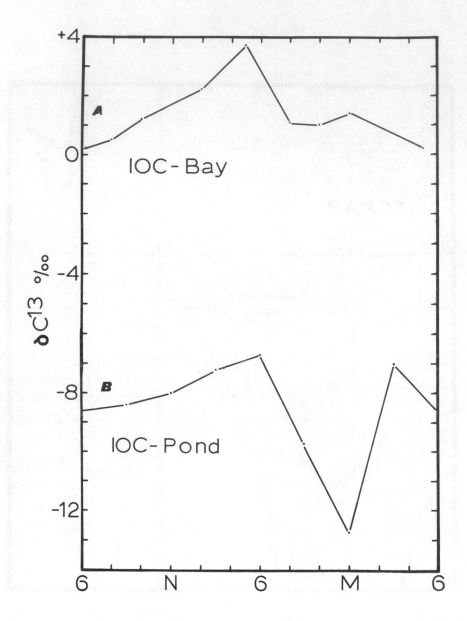

Fig. 3.   A. Diurnal variation of δ C^{13} of the IOC of a Redfish Bay *Thalassia* community.
B. Diurnal variation of δ C^{13} of the IOC of a concrete pond containing a *Thalassia* **community.**

present and many animals moved in and out of the sampling area. The water also circulated because of tidal influences. The variation may be related to a simple model. At sunup IOC with a negative δC^{13} was withdrawn due to the isotope effect in photosynthesis. This caused the δC^{13} value of the IOC remaining in solution to become more positive throughout the day. At sunset photosynthesis ceased while respiration continued. The more negative δC^{13} carbon was thus returned to the IOC pool. The sudden drop in δC^{13} at 5 P.M. suggests a rapid rate of change.

The fractionation factor for *Thalassia* was less than for most marine organisms (Table 1). Although this would tend to keep the diurnal variation small, the $4 \, \delta C^{13}$ per mil variation was significant especially when compared to the estimated errors of δC^{13} values for natural materials.

Fig. 3B shows the diurnal variation of δC^{13} in a *Thalassia* community in a concrete pond. The variation in this enclosed system was greater than in the natural one. The sharp change at 3:00 A.M. is inconsistent with the simple model already discussed. There was a similar but less pronounced break at 12:00 A.M. in Fig. 3A. The fact that δC^{13}-IOC varied on a time scale of a few hours makes it very difficult to assign fractionation factors for plants living in this very productive system. Less productive waters such as the open sea should show a very small but measurable variation.

Fig. 4 documents diurnal variations in δC^{13} and in the concentration of several carbon reservoirs — IOC, dissolved organic carbon and particulate organic carbon. For this experiment, 4 lb. of 10-10-5 commercial fertilizer were added to a fiber glass pond filled with 6700 liters of sea water. The duplicate control pond did not contain fertilizer. The pond was allowed to stand for five weeks and a heavy bloom of a small green alga developed. After five weeks, the IOC was sampled every hour for 24 hours. The particulate carbon (POC) and dissolved carbon (DOC) were sampled every 2 hours.

The concentration of IOC was much lower than in either normal sea water or the control pond, at times approaching zero (Fig. 4A). Del-C^{13} of the IOC showed the same diurnal variation as the natural *Thalassia* system (Fig. 4A). The values of δC^{13}-IOC were around -10, in contrast to the -0.2 value before the fertilizer was added. The reason for this shift is not clear. One explanation is that the bloom converted most of the IOC into organic matter during the early part of the bloom. The negative IOC after 5 weeks may then represent a reoxidation of a part of the organic matter.

Del-C^{13} of the DOC varied by 2.5 per mil during the 24 hour period, being slightly more negative at night. The concentration of DOC remained close to 7.5 mg/liter and that of the POC 2.5 mg/liter (Fig. 4C). Del-C^{13} of the POC varied by 2.3 per mil during the 24 hour period (Fig. 4B). Del-C^{13}-POC showed no clear day/night trend although if the 1:00 A.M. reading is neglected the day δC^{13} values were more negative than the night ones. This POC change would be consistent with an isotope effect in photosynthesis during the day being balanced by respiration at night.

The variations in pH and per cent oxygen saturation in the fertilized pond are given in Fig. 4D and 4E. The diurnal oxygen variation for the fertilized pond was three times that of the control pond. The pH and pH

Table 1.   Del-C^{13} of five marine grasses.

Sample	Whole plant	Total lipid	Fractionation*
Thalassia testudinum	– 9.2 – 8.4 – 7.8	–17.5 –14.8	-2.5 -5.4
Ruppia maritima	– 9.2 – 9.7	–13.	-3.0
Diplanthera wrightii	– 9.5 –10.3	–17. –15.4	-2.8 -7.9
Cymodocea manatorum	– 4.9 – 8.5	–12.0	-2.5 -7.7
Halophila sp.	–12.		-9.6

* The fractionation is taken as δ C^{13} of the plant minus δ C^{13} of the total inorganic carbon in the water.

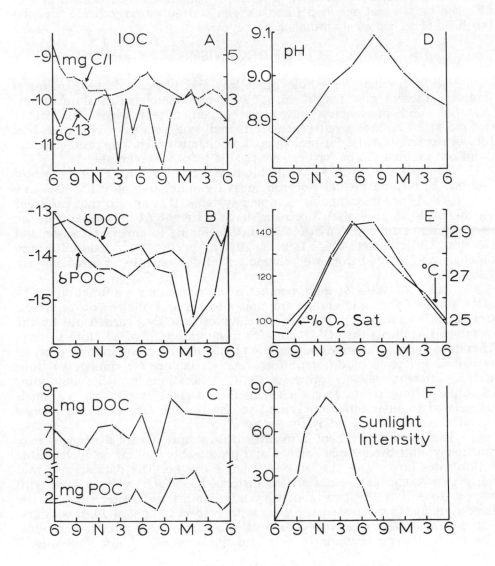

Fig. 4. Diurnal variations in a fertilized, planktonic pond community: the units of all carbon concentrations are mg C/liter.

range of the fertilized pond (8.85 to 9.1) is greater than that of the control pond (8.48 to 8.59). A relative measure of light intensity is shown in Fig. 4F. The large variations in pH and oxygen concentration indicate that the fertilized pond had an abnormal carbon cycle.

δC^{13} OF ORGANISMS

Del-C^{13} values for whole organisms and physiological or chemical fractions thereof give insight into biochemical and ecological processes. Biologists and biochemists have not concerned themselves with stable isotope ratios to the extent geochemists and geologists have. However, this tool has great potential for biology and biochemistry. Isotope ratio data can point out problems to be further investigated by other techniques.

The usefulness of δC^{13} in biology and biochemistry is presently limited. More fundamental research must be done to supply the base line data needed for understanding complex systems. It is known that different biochemicals from a given organism have different δC^{13} values but the reasons and patterns of variation are just beginning to emerge (Abelson and Hoering, 1961; Parker, 1964; Degens, 1968). Very few δC^{13} values for pure biochemicals isolated from well characterized photosynthetic organisms are known.

The δC^{13} value of each member of an ecosystem is a function of the δC^{13} value of the input carbon for that member and of the isotope effects (fractionation factors) in the various chemical reactions carried out by the member. For plants the δC^{13} value for input carbon is often close to zero. Therefore natural variations among the plants of a given community must be explained in terms of different fractionation factors for similar reactions and/or different reaction pathways. Del-C^{13} variations in plants may point to subtle differences in reaction mechanism. Del-C^{13} variations in animals are related to their food supply and to the isotope effects in the various chemical reactions induced by the animal.

The pond experiment illustrates how simple chemical changes may drastically alter the isotope balance and presumably the carbon cycle. Table 2 illustrates how stable the isotope balance can be. The data suggest that fairly drastic changes do not always disturb the carbon cycle, at least with respect to δC^{13}. The two laboratory microcosms were established at the same time and were treated the same with respect to light and temperature, but one was sealed in a large glass bottle for three years prior to sampling. The two organisms common to both had the same δC^{13} values even after 3 years.

The unusual δC^{13} values of the marine grasses in Table 1 are difficult to explain. Differences between the δC^{13} of the plants and the inorganic carbon in which they grew range between -2.5 and -9.6 δC^{13} per mil. These isotope data suggest something unusual about the mode of uptake and reduction of inorganic carbon in these plants. From a geochemical point of view sedimentary organic matter derived from these plants would certainly show a more positive δC^{13} than normal marine carbon. These plants are the dominant organism in many shallow bays along the Texas coast. When the

Table 2. Del-C^{13} of laboratory microcosms.

Sample		Del-C^{13}
System open to air		
Vallisneria sp.	grass	-20.2
Oedogonium sp.	algae	-21.4
Chara sp. (organic)	algae	-23.5
Chara sp. (inorganic)	algae	- 5.7
Sutroa sp.	worm	-20.7
System sealed for 3 years		
Vallisneria sp.	grass	-20.4
Oedogonium sp.	algae	-21.7
Planorbus sp. (organic)	snail	-18.4
Planorbus sp. (inorganic)	snail	- 6.7

plants die due to high salinity or low temperature the blades float. Blown to shore, they form deep deposits on the bay beaches.

Del-C^{13} of several marine animals collected from three environments are given in Table 3. The pond was an attempt to model a *Thalassia* grass flat in a concrete pond. The animals lived in the pond several weeks prior to sampling. The bay samples were collected in Redfish Bay (Fig. 2) in a large *Thalassia* grass flat. The Gulf samples were taken in a single trawl haul from the Gulf of Mexico just offshore from Port Aransas. Unfortunately, only once was the same species taken in all three environments. The data indicate that δC^{13} can vary with environment for a given species. This should be the case if the δC^{13} of the food source varies with environment. The Gulf samples were slightly more negative than the Bay and pond samples. Del-C^{13} values of the pond samples fell into a narrower range than the Bay or Gulf samples. This might be due to a more restricted diet in the pond. These limited results do not permit firm conclusions as to the flow of carbon in these complex food chains but they do suggest several lines of investigation. Perhaps they will prompt a few biologists to add stable isotope ratio variations to their list of tools.

We have found that pure cultures of algae grown under carefully controlled conditions have very similar δC^{13} values relative to their source CO_2. Three cultures of the blue-green alga *Agmenellum quadruplicatum* grown to approximately the same cell density had δC^{13} values of -29.3, -29.9 and -29.7. This is remarkable when one considers that the total cells contain many biochemicals some of which have different δC^{13} values. Individuals of the same species have the same δC^{13}, at least under ideal conditions. One wonders about the significance of variations in δC^{13} for individuals of the same species in natural populations. Table 4 represents a brief study of such variations based on samples collected at the same location and time. Del-C^{13} values for individual samples of the species *Laurencia* agree fairly well. The difference between the two species is probably real.

The range of δC^{13} values for the plant food available to the animals as shown in Table 4 was 12 per mil. The δC^{13} range for individuals of the same species was very small. These determinations were made on whole organisms. An analysis of chemical fractions such as total lipids or specific compounds such as fatty acids might further reduce the variations.

This is consistent with the concept of well established food chains operative at the atomic level. One would expect species with highly selective diets to show a narrower δC^{13} range than less selective feeders. It might be possible to trace specific compounds through the food chain by means of this natural isotopic tracer.

PRECURSOR - PRODUCT RELATIONSHIPS

Del-C^{13} values may serve as natural isotope labels in some biochemical and geochemical processes. If a precursor molecule with a large carbon skeleton is converted to a product with a similar carbon skeleton, the δC^{13} value of the product should reflect that of the precursor. We are now

Table 3. Del-C^{13} of marine organisms from three environments.

Sample	Pond	Bay	Gulf
Fish			
Lagodon rhomboides	-11.9	-13.1	-13.7
Mugil cephalus	-11.7	-11.	
Fundulus similis	-11.4	- 7.7	
Leiostomus xanthurus	-10.6	-13.4	
Menidia berylina	- 9.8		
Menticirrhus litoralis			-15.3
Galeichtthys felis			-15.8
Trichiurus lepturus			-17.9
Anchoa sp.			-17.5
Cyprinodon variegatus		- 9.3	
Baindiella chrysura		-11.2	
Polydactylus octonemus			-19.5
Invertebrates			
Calinectes sapidus	-10.1	-16.5	
Penaeus setiferus			17.0
Penaeus aztecus		-11.1	
Average	-10.9	-11.7	-16.8

Table 4.   Del-C^{13} individuals of same species.

Species	#1	#2	#3
Thalassia testudinum	-10.4	- 8.4	- 8.6
Laurencia poitei	-10.9	-10.7	-
Laurencia obtusa	-14.7	-13.2	-
Uca pugilator	-12.5	-13.3	-12.2
Leiostomas xanthuras	-12.8	-13.5	-13.0
Palemonetes vulgaris	-13.3	-13.8	
Penaeus aztecus (7)*	-15.6 ± 1.0		
Lagodon rhomboides (5)	-13.6 ± 1.5		
Mugil cephalus (7)	-11.5 ± 3.5		

The samples were all collected in a large grass flat of a bay at the same time.

* The number in ( ) indicates the number of individuals for which the standard deviation is given.

initiating studies to investigate the δC^{13} relationships of saturated fatty acids and saturated hydrocarbons in blue-green algae. Blue-greens are well suited for this work because the fatty acid and hydrocarbon patterns are very simple (Parker et al., 1967). The results of a preliminary run are:

	δC^{13}
Anacystis nidulans (whole cells)	0.0
total fatty acids (16 and 18 carbons)	-7.2
total hydrocarbons (95% n-C:17)	-5.6

The difference between δC^{13} values of the acids and the hydrocarbons, 1.6, is a little larger than we had hoped for. The mass spectrometry error is ± 0.2 δC^{13} per mil. Exact agreement in δC^{13} would be evidence of a product-precursor relationship. Until more is known about variations in δC^{13} values of other biochemicals isolated from organisms the meaning of less than perfect agreement will not be clear.

δC^{13} OF DISSOLVED AND PARTICULATE ORGANIC MATTER

Although many organisms including quite a few marine organisms have been surveyed with respect to δC^{13}, very little is known about the dissolved organic carbon (DOC) and particulate organic carbon (POC) in aquatic systems. In view of the magnitude of the DOC reservoir it is important to establish the range of δC^{13} values for several natural systems. We have observed changes in the amount and δC^{13} of the DOC and POC in a river-estuary system over a one-year period. Several other environments have been surveyed with respect to these same parameters.

Dissolved organic carbon in this work was that remaining in water passed through a glass filter pad (Gelman type A). Particulate organic carbon was that which was retained on the filter. The filter pads were combusted in a modified Leco radio-frequency furnace. The amount of evolved CO_2 was determined by manometry and set aside for the mass-spectrometric determination of δC^{13}. The DOC was converted to CO_2 by potassium persulfate oxidation in sealed 2-liter glass bulbs (Wilson, 1963). The CO_2 formed was distilled out of the sea water, collected by freezing with liquid nitrogen, determined by manometry and submitted to mass spectrometric analysis.

The results of a 1-year study at a collection station on the Guadalupe River are shown in Fig. 5. The amounts of DOC and POC were roughly equal. They varied over time in the same manner. Both ranged from 1 to 5 mg C/liter. The δC^{13} of the POC became more negative when the amount of POC increased. Del-C^{13} values for the POC ranged from -14 to -24. However, most of the time δC^{13}-POC was within one per mil of -17.

Del-C^{13} of the DOC became more negative when the concentration of DOC decreased, and more positive when the concentration increased. This may mean that the most refractory DOC, being the most negative, is enriched in lipid carbon. The DOC averaged 4 δC^{13} per mil more negative than the POC. This is also suggestive of the lipid-total cell relationship of living organisms. The causes of variations in DOC and POC concentrations are plankton blooms and changes in the amount of material derived from land runoff. The δC^{13} values have not been correlated with productivity or river flow.

DOC and POC from different environments have different δC^{13} values. Our samples from the Gulf of Mexico average -21.2 for DOC and -21.4 for the POC. P. M. Williams (1968) has recently reported that δC^{13} DOC values for 10 samples from offshore southern California range between -21.0 and -21.9 (vs. NBS 20). One suspects that the exact agreement for the Gulf of Mexico and the Pacific is chance. In contrast to open marine waters, rivers, bays and estuaries show a greater variation in δC^{13}. This is seen in the data from the Guadalupe River (Fig. 5). Samples from Baffin Bay, an arm of the Texas Laguna Madre, range as low as -23.1 in POC-δC^{13} and -23.8 DOC-δC^{13}

δC^{13} AS A QUANTITATIVE INDICATOR OF POLLUTION

The fact that characteristic stable carbon isotope ratios persist in natural carbon reservoirs led us to investigate the use of these ratios in recognizing various sources of organic chemical pollution of water. As noted in Fig. 1, δC^{13} of petroleum and natural gas is well separated from normal marine carbon. Thus the aquatic system consisting of a marine bay receiving effluents from oil refineries and petrochemical plants seemed to be an ideal case for detailed study. The Houston, Texas Ship Channel was selected as the study area. The results are shown in Table 5 (Calder and Parker, 1968).

There is little doubt that this system is rich in petrochemical carbon. The ratio of the amount of pollutant to normal carbon in the system is represented by the expression:

$$\frac{C_p}{C_n} = \frac{\delta n - \delta m}{\delta m - \delta p}$$

where C = concentration of carbon in mg per liter, $\delta = \delta C^{13}$, n refers to normal carbon, p to pollutant carbon, and m to the mixture of carbon in the system being studied. Although δn and δp values are somewhat uncertain, model calculations can be made for the Houston Ship Channel. A value of -20 for a normal marine bay, δn, is realistic. The average of all the DOC data for the Ship Channel, -30.5, is δm. If δp is taken as -35 then C_p/C_n is 2.3. This indicates there are two carbon atoms derived from petrochemical pollution for every natural one in this aquatic system. This approach gives no information about the chemical structure of the organic pollution or its toxic properties. It does provide insight into the carbon flux of complex systems based on a few relatively simple measurements. We are investigating pollution of marine bays by domestic sewage using this approach. Preliminary results also indicate that paper mill effluents flowing into rivers may be traced by means of δC^{13}, especially in the case of effluents rich in tall oil.

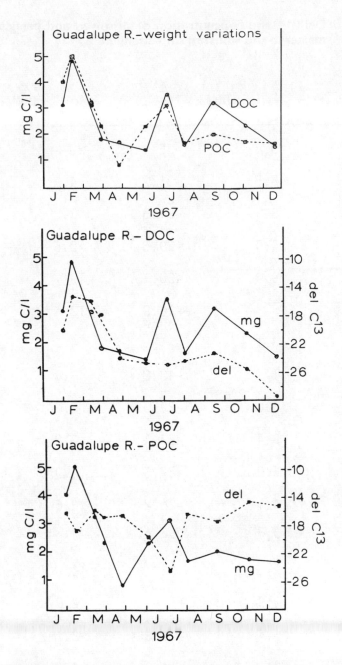

Fig. 5. Variations in carbon reservoirs at a collecting station on the Guadalupe River, Texas during 1967.

Table 5. Del-C^{13} and concentration of dissolved and particulate organic matter in the Houston ship channel.

Station	DOM mg C/liter	δ C^{13}	POM mg C/liter	δ C^{13}
1	5.8	-26	20	-19.8
2	5.6	-31.2	4.2	-21.3
3	3.9	-31.5	3.2	-24.2
4	4.0	-29.3	2.6	-23.1
5	9.0	-30.1	19	-26.3
6	26	-26.9	12	-24.4
7	3.1	-	4.0	-23.3
8	11	-48.8	8.8	-27.4
9	3.8	-29	2.4	-24.7
10	8.4	-27.1	3.8	-25.9
11	6.0	-27.5	2.9	-24
12	4.1	-28.2	3.6	-25.2
13	2.7	-28.2	4.0	-26
14	19	-32	16	-25.8
15	2.9	-	2.2	-23.0
16	1.4	-24.8	2.7	-23.3
17	2.1	-24.9	4.4	-21.1

SUMMARY

Stable isotope ratio variations may be useful in studying a variety of biochemical, biological and environmental problems. Our own efforts have been very rewarding. Only stable carbon isotope ratio variations have been discussed but other stable isotope pairs such as N^{15}/N^{14} and O^{18}/O^{16} are equally promising.

DISCUSSION

BELSER: You observed a much greater negative δC^{13} in lipids than in proteins in the living phytoplankters. Do you feel that that is due to a selective channelling of the isotopes during biosynthesis?

PARKER: Yes. We are working on that, trying to find at just what point the separation takes place. It appears that anything which has an acetate unit as a precursor is negative. We have done one experiment in which we isolated acetate and it is quite negative, like fatty acids. We are getting closer, but we are still not there.

BELSER: It is metabolically very interesting.

PARKER: You could draw a whole map if you knew enough about this phenomenon.

ACKNOWLEDGMENTS

Our work has been supported by National Science Foundation Grants GA-299 and GA-911.

Dr. B.J. Copeland and Dr. C. Van Baalen have helped with biological aspects of this study.

REFERENCES

ABELSON, P. H., and T. C. HOERING. 1961. Carbon isotope fractionation in formation of amino acids by photosynthetic organisms. Proc. Nat. Acad. Sci., *47*: 623-632.

BIGELEISEN, J. 1958. The significance of the product and sum rules to isotopic fractionation processes, p. 121-157. *In* J. Kisttemaker, J. Bigeleisen and A. O. C. Nier [ed.], Proc. Int. Symp. Isotope separation. Interscience, New York.

BIGELEISEN, J., and M. MAYER. 1947. Calculation of equilibrium constants for isotopic exchange reactions. J. Chem. Phys., *15*: 261.

BIGELEISEN, J., and M. WOLFSBERG. 1958. Theoretical and experimental aspects of isotope effects in chemical kinetics, p. 15-77. *In* I. Prigogine [ed.], Advances in chemical physics. Interscience, New York.

CALDER, J. A., and P. L. PARKER. 1968. Stable carbon isotope ratios as indices of petrochemical pollution of aquatic systems. Environ. Sci. Technol., 2: 535-539.

CRAIG, H. 1953. The geochemistry of the stable carbon isotopes. Geochim. Cosmochim. Acta, 3: 53-92.

DEGENS, E. T. In press. Biogeochemistry of stable carbon isotopes. In G. Eglinton and M. Murphy [ed.], Organic geochemistry: methods and results. Springer-Verlag, Inc., New York.

DEUSER, W. G., and E. T. DEGENS. 1967. Carbon isotope fractionation in the system $CO_{2\,(gas)}$ - $CO_{2\,(aq)}$ - $HCO_{3\,(aq)}^-$. Nature, 215: 1033-1035.

HOERING, T. C. 1960. The biogeochemistry of the stable isotopes of carbon. Carnegie Institution of Washington Year Book, 59: 158-165.

HOERING, T. C. 1967. The organic geochemistry of precambrian rocks, p. 87-111. In P.H. Abelson [ed.], Researches in geochemistry, v. 2. Wiley, New York.

KEELING, C. 1961. A mechanism for cyclic enrichment of carbon-12 by terrestrial plants. Geochim. Cosmochim. Acta, 24: 299-313.

PARK, R., and S. EPSTEIN. 1960. Carbon isotope fractionation during photosynthesis. Geochim. Cosmochim. Acta, 21: 110-126.

PARKER, P. L. 1964. The biogeochemistry of the stable isotope of carbon in a marine bay. Geochim. Cosmochim. Acta, 28: 1155-1164.

PARKER, P. L., C. VAN BAALEN, and L. MAURER. 1967. Fatty acids in eleven species of blue-green algae: geochemical significance. Science, 155: 707-708.

SILVERMAN, S. R. 1967. Carbon isotopic evidence for the role of lipids in petroleum formation. J. Amer. Oil Chem. Soc., 44: 691-695.

UREY, H. C. 1947. The thermodynamic properties of isotopic substances. J. Chem. Soc., 562-581.

VOGEL, J. C. 1961. Isotope separation factors of carbon in the equilibrium system CO_2 - HCO_3^- - $CO_3^=$. Comitato Nazionale per L'energia Nucleare, Summer course on nuclear geology, p. 216-221. Laboratorio Di Geolgia Nucleare, Pisa.

WENDT, I. 1968. Fractionation of carbon isotopes and its temperature dependence in the system CO_2 - gas - CO_2 in solution and HCO_3 - CO_2 in solution. Earth Planetary Sci. Letters, 4: 64-68.

WILLIAMS, P. M. 1968. Stable carbon isotopes in the dissolved organic matter of the sea. Nature, *219*: 152-153.

WILSON, R. F. 1963. Organic carbon levels in some aquatic ecosystems. Pub. Inst. Mar. Sci., Univ. Tex., *9*: 64-76.

DISSOLVED AND PARTICULATE CARBOHYDRATES

Nobuhiko Handa
Water Research Laboratory
Faculty of Science
Nagoya University
Chikusa-ku, Nagoya   JAPAN

ABSTRACT

Detailed profiles of dissolved carbohydrate and particulate organic carbon, organic nitrogen, carbohydrate and amino acid from sea water and from particulate samples from various depths at a station in Sagami Nada off Honsyu, Japan are presented. Dissolved carbohydrate is distributed uniformly from the surface to 1000 m. Values range from 0.24 to 0.37 mg/liter glucose. Results suggest that carbohydrate decomposes more rapidly than proteins and amino acids in the euphotic zone. The reverse is true in deep water, so C/N ratios for particulate matter increase with depth. Acid hydrolysis of the particulate matter yielded D-galactose, D-glucose, D-mannose, D-xylose and D-glucuronic acid. The monosaccharide composition of particulate matter changed with depth. Only the percentage of D-glucose in relation to the total particulate carbohydrate decreased with depth. Carbohydrates from particulate matter at 20 m were fractionated into water soluble and insoluble fractions. Analysis of these fractions indicates that the water soluble fraction consists of 1,3-glucan and related low molecular weight carbohydrates. These must polymerize between 50 and 300 m resulting in water insoluble carbohydrates resistant to biological attack. The relationship between biochemical changes in these carbohydrates with depth and the vertical distribution of particulate carbohydrates is discussed.

INTRODUCTION

The euphotic zone is the principal source of organic matter in the sea. Dissolved carbohydrate therefore must be derived from plankton there. Phytoplankton plays an important role in the production of dissolved carbohydrate in sea water. The concentration of dissolved carbohydrate was measured in the Gulf of Mexico, the South Atlantic Ocean and the Eastern Pacific Ocean by Wangersky (1952); Collier et al. (1953); Anderson and Gehringer (1958); Lewis and Rakestraw (1955); and Antia and Lee (1963). Recently, Handa (1900) found the concentration of dissolved carbohydrate in the Indian Ocean to be 0.19-0.66 mg/liter and in the Northwest Pacific Ocean to be 0.09-0.46 mg/liter. This carbohydrate was distributed homogeneously both horizontally and vertically in all of the areas studied.

Since particulate organic matter in deep water must come from overlying water the concentration of particulate matter would be expected to decrease with depth as particulate organic matter decomposes. The predation of zooplankton is also involved. Horizontal transport of water with varying concentrations of particulate organic matter would be expected to produce temporal concentration gradients.

Recent studies indicate that a rapid decrease in the concentration of particulate organic matter occurs between the surface and 300 m. The magnitude of the variation depends on the oceanic area being studied. Particulate organic matter is homogeneously distributed over time and space at depths greater than 300 m (Wangersky and Gordon, 1965; Riley et al., 1965; Menzel and Goering, 1966; Hobson, 1967; Menzel, 1967). Based on microscopic examination, Bogdanov (1965) reported that the organic content of particulate matter tends to decrease slowly from 100 m to the depths. Holm-Hansen et al. (1966) however found vertical variation in the amount of particulate carbon in waters between 50 and 1000 m off southern California, but no trends were apparent. A similar vertical and horizontal distribution of particulate carbohydrate was observed in Kuroshio and adjacent areas by Handa (1967a). In deep waters the carbohydrate concentration decreased to about one-third of that near the surface. Further, the concentration in deep water was homogeneous irrespective of the particulate carbohydrate concentration in the overlying waters.

The unexpected vertical distribution of the particulate organic carbon and carbohydrate was explained in terms of a theory of organic aggregate formation in sea water by Riley et al. (1965). Later, Menzel (1967) criticized this theory on the basis of two observations made in the tropical Atlantic and Pacific Oceans. First, there was no correlation between standing crop and the concentration of measurable particulate organic matter found in the deep ocean, and second, there was no decrease in dissolved organic carbon as depth increased. Menzel advanced an alternative mechanism for this distribution: the homogeneous distribution of particulate organic matter in deep water is caused by large-scale oceanic circulation of deep-ocean particulate matter resistant to biochemical degradation. He had observed that the carbon content of deep-ocean particulate matter did not change after exposure to natural sea water for as much as 90 days.

It is now realized that studies of the biochemical nature of the organic constituents of marine particulate matter are necessary for a better understanding of the vertical distribution of particulate carbohydrates and of the energy flow in marine organisms. In 1962, Parsons and Strickland first reported the monosaccharide and amino acid composition of deep water particulate matter. Unfortunately they did not determine the chemical nature of these materials. This information is necessary to an understanding of their significance as potential food for secondary producers.

This paper is mainly concerned with the carbohydrate composition of dissolved and particulate organic matter found in sea water. All samples of sea water and marine particulate material were taken from the Sagami Nada off Honsyu, Japan, during the Oct. 18-21, 1965, cruise of the Tansei Maru based at the Ocean Research Institute of Tokyo University.

MATERIALS AND METHODS

The water samples were collected in Nansen bottles, filtered through a Millipore filter (HA) and frozen. The dissolved carbohydrate concentration expressed in D-glucose equivalents, was determined using the phenol sulfuric acid method (Handa, 1966).

Particulate matter collected on 984-H ultra filters (H. Reeve Angel and Co.) from sea water at a station located at 35°00'N and 139°36'E frozen (-20 C) for later study. Particulate matter collected from five liters of sea water was analyzed for particulate carbohydrate, amino acids, organic carbon and organic nitrogen. One hundred liters of sea water were employed for the determination of monosaccharide composition. Phytoplankton analysis indicated that the particulate matter from surface and subsurface waters consists predominantly of diatoms, *Biddulphia* sp. and *Coscinodiscus* sp. The particulate carbohydrate analysis was made by means of the phenol sulfuric acid method (Handa, 1967a). The results were reported in terms of D-glucose equivalents to facilitate the determination of total carbohydrate. Particulate amino acids were determined using ninhydrin reagent (Yemm and Cocking, 1955) after hydrolysis of the particulate matter with 6N hydrochloric acid. This sample was standardized with the amino acid composition of a bulk protein of *Chlorella vulgaris* (Fowden, 1954). Particulate organic carbon and organic nitrogen were determined by measuring the carbon dioxide and nitrogen gas generated by dry combustion of the particulate matter using the Yanagimoto Scientific Instrument Manufacturing Co.'s CHN-Coder.

After hydrolysis of the particulate matter, the monosaccharides were separated by paper chromatography, and eluted from the filter paper with water. Then, the carbohydrate in an aliquot of the eluate was determined by the phenol sulfuric acid method (Handa, 1967b). The monosaccharides were identified by paper chromatography using ethyl acetate-pyridine-water (8:2:1 v/v) and n-butanol-pyridine-water (6:4:3 v/v) as chromatographic solvent systems. To isolate the carbohydrate in the particulate matter collected at 20 m the sample was treated first with 100 ml water at 100 C for an hour to extract the water soluble carbohydrate. The residue was separated from the extract by centrifugation and the carbohydrate was re-extracted from the residue repeatedly until the extracts became negative to the phenol sulfuric acid test. The combined extracts were evaporated, the dried material dissolved in 20 ml water, and after removal of the insoluble precipitate by filtration the filtrate was repeatedly evaporated. When the filtrate was free of water insoluble materials the carbohydrate was dissolved in 10 ml water. One volume of ethanol was added to the solution and the precipitate — the ethanol precipitated fraction — was collected by centrifugation, washed consecutively with aqueous ethanol (ethanol-water 1:1 v/v), absolute ethanol and ethyl ether and dried in a desiccator.

Two volumes of acetone were added to the supernatant. The precipitate — the ethanol-acetone precipitated fraction — was collected by centrifugation and washed consecutively with acetone and ether. The washed material was dried in a desiccator. The supernatant — the ethanol-acetone soluble fraction — was obtained after evaporation.

The residue from the above water extraction was shaken with 100 ml Schweizer's reagent containing 0.1 g sodium borohydride for three hours at room temperature to isolate polysaccharides. After filtration the filtrate was acidified with 4N hydrochloric acid to a pH of 1 and the resulting solution was dialyzed against 0.5N hydrochloric acid overnight. The precipitate formed during the dialysis was collected by centrifugation and washed consecutively with 0.5N hydrochloric acid, water, ethanol and ethyl ether. The resulting material was dried in a desiccator. The monosaccharide composition of these carbohydrate fractions was determined by paper chromatography as described before. Aspinall's colorimetric method was used for periodate oxidation of the carbohydrate (Aspinall, 1957). Several hundred micrograms of carbohydrate were dissolved in 0.5 ml water and 0.5 ml of 0.03M periodic acid was added. The resulting solution was allowed to stand in the dark to prevent the photodegradation of periodic acid. Periodically, the optical density of the reaction mixture was measured at 223 mμ and the molarity of the periodic acid was calculated. The consumption of periodic acid was then estimated in terms of the difference between the original and current molarities of periodic acid.

The degree of polymerization (D.P.) of carbohydrate was determined by the method reported by Unrau and Smith (1957). A few hundred micrograms of carbohydrate were dissolved in 1 ml water, 0.01 g sodium borohydride was added and the solution was allowed to stand at room temperature for 48 hours, while the reducing terminal monosaccharide residue was converted to sugar alcohol. After the addition of 0.2 ml of 10N sulfuric acid to destroy the excess sodium borohydride, 4 ml of 0.05M sodium periodate was added and the oxidation reaction proceeded in the dark. Periodically 1 ml of the reaction mixture was transferred to a small tube containing 4 ml saturated lead acetate to remove excess iodate and periodate ions. To this solution was introduced a dialysis tubing containing 1.5 ml water. The system was allowed to equilibrate overnight, then a formaldehyde determination was made on the solution in the dialysis tubing using the chromotropic acid method (Hay et al., 1965). D. P. of the polysaccharide was calculated from the amount of formaldehyde produced. This method was standardized with D-glucitol.

RESULTS

The concentration of dissolved carbohydrate ranged from 0.24 to 0.37 mg/liter and was uniform vertically (Fig. 1). These values are comparable to those obtained for the Indian and Northwest Pacific Oceans. A profile of the organic constituents of the particulate matter at various depths is important to a better understanding of the metabolism of particulate carbohydrate in the ocean as it sinks. The concentration of particulate organic carbon (POC) and nitrogen (PON) decreased with depth while the C/N ratio increased (Fig. 2). This indicates that the organic composition of the particulate matter varies vertically. The concentration of both particulate carbohydrate carbon (PCC) and particulate amino acid carbon (PAC) — assumed to be the main

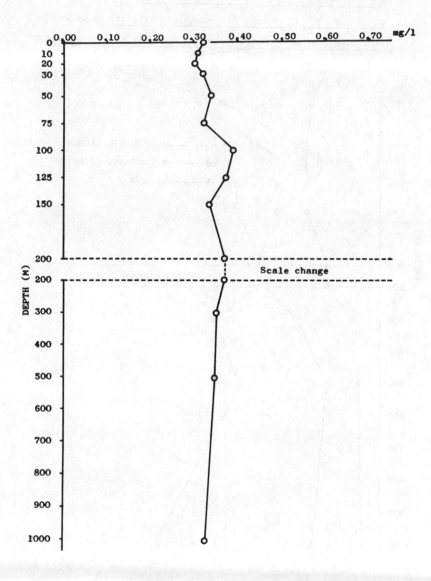

Fig. 1. Vertical distribution of dissolved carbohydrate.

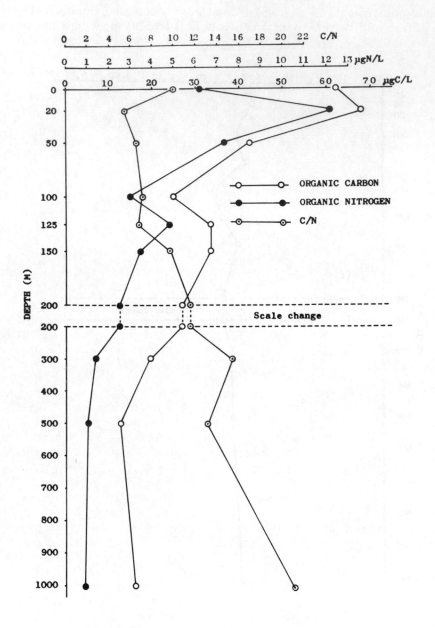

Fig. 2.   Vertical distribution of particulate organic carbon and nitrogen.

organic constituents in particulate matter — decreased rapidly between 20 and 125 m and became constant below 300 to 500 m, where the values of PCC and PAC were 1/4.9 and 1/7.8 respectively, of those at 20 m (Fig. 3). In addition, particulate amino acid nitrogen (PAN) accounted for more than 85% of total PON (Fig. 4).

Comparing the ratio of each organic constituent's carbon to POC illustrates the fact that particulate amino acids decay at a more rapid rate than particulate carbohydrates as depth increases. This accounts for the concurrent increase in the C/N ratio. Vertical profiles of the relative decay rates of organic constituents between 50 and 125 m differ from those of the underlying waters (Fig. 5). Between 50 and 125 m, PCC/POC decreased more rapidly as depth increased, and PAC/POC increased. This indicates that particulate carbohydrate carbon decomposes more readily than particulate amino acid carbon and the particulate matter is temporarily rich in protein. The fact that the ratio 1-(PCC+PAC)/POC did not vary significantly with depth indicates that some organic compounds are more susceptible to decomposition than the particulate amino acids, although the concentration of such compounds may be low. Contrary to this, only PAC/POC tended to decrease with depth while both PCC/POC and 1-(PCC+PAC)/POC increased. These data suggest that the particulate carbohydrate consists of at least two components, one susceptible and the other resistant to degradation.

The monosaccharide composition of the particulate matter was determined. All of the samples yielded D-galactose, D-glucose, D-mannose, D-xylose and D-glucuronic acid upon acid hydrolysis. The ratio of each monosaccharide to total particulate carbohydrate is shown in Fig. 6. Between 50 and 200 m the percentage of D-galactose, D-mannose and D-glucuronic acid increased with depth; that of D-glucose and D-xylose decreased. Below 200 m, the monosaccharide composition did not vary with depth.

Because the monosaccharides occur in living materials mainly as oligo- and polysaccharides, not as free sugars, the effort was made to isolate and characterize the carbohydrates comprising the particulate carbohydrate. The particulate matter from 20 m depth was treated with hot water to separate the carbohydrate into water soluble and water insoluble fractions. The water soluble fraction was further separated using ethanol and acetone (Table 1). The water soluble carbohydrate amounts to one-third of the total particulate carbohydrate. Acid hydrolysis of the three water soluble fractions yielded only D-glucose. Paper chromatographic analysis of the water soluble fraction indicated the presence of D-glucose and two oligosaccharides with much lower R_G values. Further characterization of this fraction has not yet been accomplished. Judging from its solubility in organic solvents, the carbohydrate in the ethanol acetone precipitated fraction must be D-glucan. The vertical decrease in per cent D-glucose must be the result of the high decay rate of the water soluble carbohydrates. Acid hydrolysis of the ethanol precipitated fraction yielded D-galactose, D-glucose, D-mannose and D-xylose. The water insoluble fraction yielded D-galactose, D-glucose, D-mannose, D-xylose and D-glucuronic acid in almost the same proportions as particulate matter from below 200 m (Table 2).

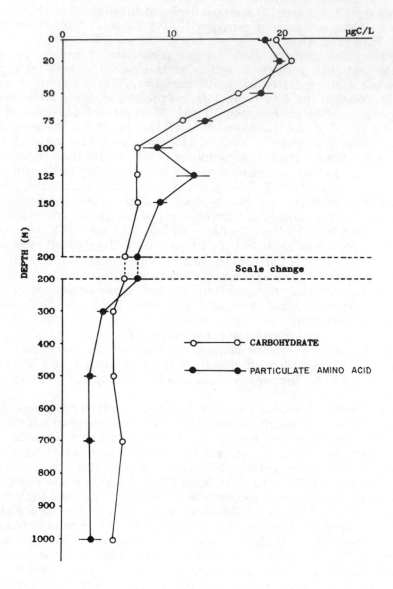

Fig. 3. Vertical distribution of particulate carbohydrate and particulate amino acid.

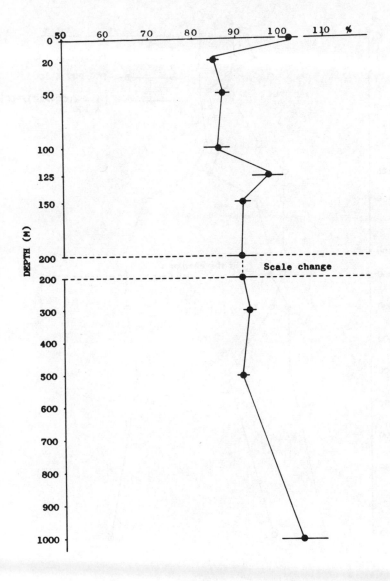

Fig. 4. Vertical distribution of the ratio of particulate amino acid nitrogen to total particulate organic nitrogen (%).

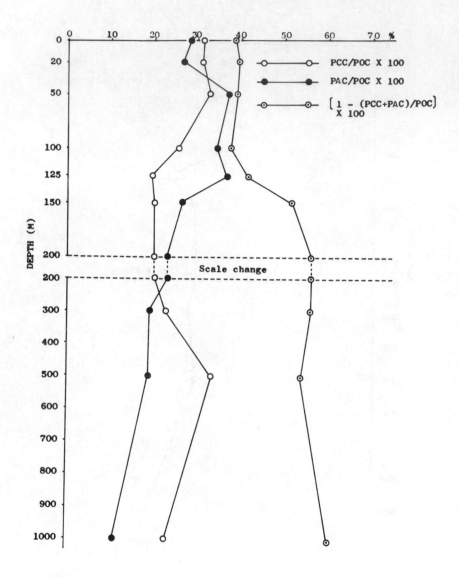

Fig. 5.   **Vertical distribution of the ratio of PCC, PAC and POC-(PCC + PAC) to (%).**

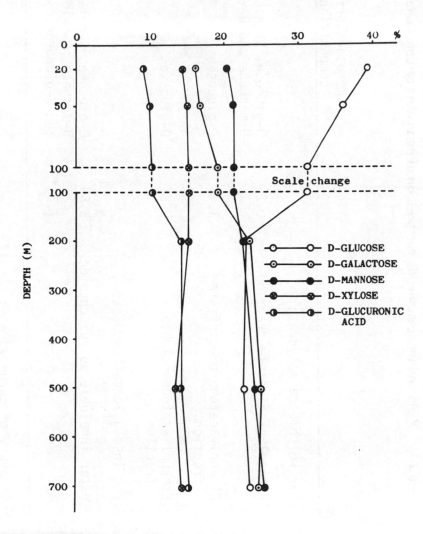

Fig. 6.   Vertical distribution of the ratio of each monosaccharide to total carbohydrate (%).

Table 1.   Yield and monosaccharide composition of particulate carbohydrate at 20 m.

	Yield (mg)	Monosaccharide composition
Water soluble carbohydrate		
Ethanol precipitate fraction	0.21	D-glucose, D-galactose, D-mannose and D-xylose
Ethanol-acetone precipitate fraction	1.41	D-glucose
Ethanol-acetone soluble fraction	0.57	D-glucose
Water insoluble carbohydrate		
Water insoluble polysaccharide	5.59	D-glucose, D-galactose, D-mannose, D-xylose and D-glucuronic acid
	7.78*	

* Recovery of carbohydrate: 95.1%

Table 2. Monasaccharide composition of the water insoluble polysaccharide at 20 m and of the particulate matter at 500 and 700 m.

	D-galactose (%)	D-glucose (%)	D-mannose (%)	D-xylose (%)	D-glucuronic acid (%)
Water insoluble polysaccharide	26.2	21.2	25.5	14.4	12.5
Particulate at 500 m	25.0	23.3	24.2	13.0	14.5
Particulate at 700 m	24.5	23.4	24.2	13.0	15.1

Structural investigations focused on the D-glucan isolated from the ethanol-acetone precipitated fraction and the polysaccharide from the water insoluble fraction, the main components of these fractions. The carbohydrate was first subjected to periodate oxidation to determine the linkage type (Fig. 7). A synthetic sample of cellobiose was oxidized simultaneously with sodium periodate as a control. The consumption of periodate by all three samples became constant after two or three days. Prolonged reaction, however, led to consumption of more periodate due to overoxidation. Cellobiose theoretically consumes 2M periodate in non-reducing terminal glucose residues and 3M periodate in reducing terminal glucose residues during oxidation. One would expect a similar uptake of periodate by the D-glucan. In these experiments, 2.48M periodate per anhydrous glucose unit were consumed by cellobiose, 0.02M by the D-glucan fraction and 0.87M by the water insoluble polysaccharide. The very low periodate uptake per anhydrous glucose unit of D-glucan indicates that almost no uptake occurs on glucose residues except at the terminal ends. Since the other glucose residues in the molecule do not contain viciniac diols this carbohydrate must be a 1,3-glucan in which another glucosyl residue takes the place of the hydroxyl group at the C-3 position. Each monosaccharide in the water insoluble carbohydrate consumed about one mole of periodate per anhydrous monosaccharide unit so each must average one viciniac diol. This indicates that this carbohydrate is a 1,2- or 1,4-polysaccharide with monosaccharide linkages at the C-2 or C-4 position of the monosaccharide residue. Although the periodate oxidation data suggest that this carbohydrate is an equal mixture of 1,3- and 1,6-polysaccharides this is unlikely because the only known 1,6-polysaccharide in plant materials occurs in the pustulan of lichens.

The degree of polymerization (D.P.) of these polysaccharides was determined by the periodate oxidation method. The polysaccharides were first reduced with sodium borohydride to polysaccharide alcohols in which the terminal monosaccharide is converted to the corresponding sugar alcohol. The resulting polysaccharide alcohol was oxidized with sodium periodate to produce oxopolysaccharides and one or two moles of formaldehyde per mole of polysaccharide, depending on the linkage type. If the polysaccharide residue attaches at the C-2 or C-6 position of the sugar alcohol only one mole of formaldehyde is produced from each polysaccharide alcohol. If the polysaccharide residue is attached at C-3 or C-4, two moles of formaldehyde are produced. The 1,3-glucan and water insoluble polysaccharide fractions yielded two moles of formaldehyde per mole of polysaccharide alcohol (Table 3). (The D.P. calculated on the basis of 1,2-polysaccharide is in parentheses.)

DISCUSSION

Judging from the distribution of particulate and dissolved carbohydrates in the Kuroshio and adjacent areas (Handa, 1967a), the concentration of particulate carbohydrates is high where the plankton production is high, while the concentration of dissolved carbohydrate is

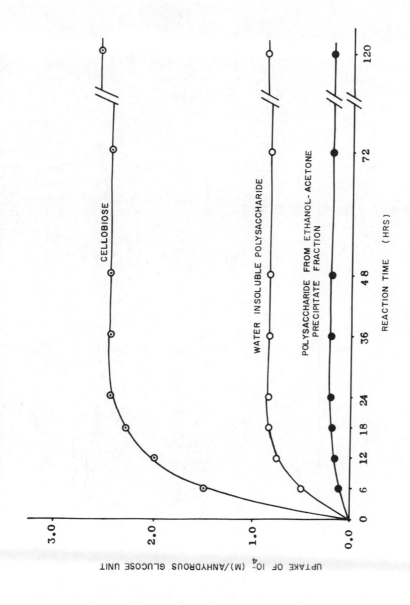

Fig. 7. Result of periodate oxidation of polysaccharides from the particulate matter at 20 m.

Table 3. D.P. and periodate uptake of polysaccharides from particulate matter at 20 m.

	D.P.	Uptake of IO_4^-(M) per anhydrous glucose unit
D-glucan	28.2	0.20
Water insoluble polysaccharide	57.0 (114.0)	0.87

independent of the rate of plankton production. As might be expected the concentration of the dissolved carbohydrate is much higher than the concentration of the particulate carbohydrate. The relative abundance of dissolved and particulate carbohydrate in these samples is very similar to that observed in the Kuroshio area. This suggests that dissolved carbohydrate is resistant to further decay reactions. The homogeneous vertical distribution of the dissolved carbohydrate can be explained in terms of the supply/decay balance of this carbohydrate. The higher water temperature and the enrichment of substrates through the decomposition of microflora favor the growth of flora in the surface and the subsurface layers. Therefore, supply and decay rates of the dissolved carbohydrates are higher in these layers and the balance of these two processes determines the equilibrium concentration of the dissolved carbohydrate.

At deeper levels the situation is different. The lower temperature and the low density of marine bacterial populations in deep waters limit the decay rate of dissolved carbohydrates. The supply rate of dissolved carbohydrate must also be low because supply and decay rates of dissolved carbohydrate balance even in deep waters.

In 1962 Parsons and Strickland reported that oceanic detritus from the northeastern Pacific Ocean is unexpectedly protein rich and that carbohydrate is only a minor component of the detritus. McAllister et al. (1960) had speculated that such detritus originated from some fragment of zooplankton. They assumed the carbohydrate in the detritus to be largely long cellulose fibers of terrestrial origin.

Particulate matter examined in this study has a very different organic composition from the detritus reported by the above authors. Its C/N value increases with depth just as the C/N ratio increases as biological degradation of living organisms proceeds. This suggests that deep water particulate matter originates from the plankton living in the surface and the subsurface waters. The monosaccharide composition of particulate matter from various depths also supports the hypothesis that phytoplankton, not terrestrial materials such as cellulose, are the principal source of deep water particulate matter. All samples contained D-glucuronic acid, a typical component of algal polysaccharides.

Both 1,3-glucan and β-polysaccharide are abundant in the plant kingdom. β-1,3-glucans such as laminarin and paramylon have been isolated from a wide variety of brown algae and *Euglena* sp. They serve as carbohydrate storage depots. Recently, chrysolaminarin, a water soluble laminarin polysaccharide, has been found in *Phaeodatylum tricornutum* (Ford and Percival, 1965) and in a few other species of *Bacillariophyceae*. The D.P. of the 1,3-glucan obtained here strongly resembles that of laminarin (D.P. 20 to 28) (Ann et al., 1965; Fleming, et al., 1966; Handa and Nisizawa, 1961) and chrysolaminarin (D.P. 21) (Beattie et al., 1961). Considering the phytoplankton composition of the particulate matter found at 20 m in this experiment, it is likely that the 1,3-glucan is a laminarin type storage polysaccharide. These storage substances are biologically unstable. Most species of *Phaeophyceae* show daily and seasonal variations in laminarin content. Rapid decreases in laminarin were also observed just after spore formation in *Eisenia byclis* and *Ecklonia cava* (Nisizawa, 1938). These facts suggest that 1,3-glucan will decay before the structural polysaccharides do. The rapid decrease in D-glucose within 100 m indicates that 1,3-glucan decays very quickly as the particulate matter sinks into water layers where light conditions do not favor phytoplankton photosynthesis. Such decay is assumed to be mainly due to algal respiration. Low molecular weight carbohydrates containing D-glucose are probably metabolized in similar processes. D-mannitol and low molecular weight carbohydrates from *Phaeophyceae* are good metabolites for respiration and photosynthesis (Bidwell and Ghosh, 1962).

Lewin et al. (1958) reported that *Phaeodactyum tricornutum* mucilage, which is extractable with hot water, consists of xylose, mannose, fucose and galactose. The polysaccharide in the ethanol precipitated fraction is presumably an analogous carbohydrate although some differences in monosaccharide composition were found. However our information is limited with regard to the metabolism of this polysaccharide as the particulate matter sinks.

The case of the water insoluble polysaccharides is very different from that of the water soluble carbohydrates. Cellulose, mannan and xylan, typical algal cell wall polysaccharides, are homopolysaccharides consisting of D-glucose, D-mannose and D-xylose. In addition, some heteropolysaccharides such as the xylan found in siphonousceous green algae — 90% D-xylose and 10% D-glucose (Iriki et al., 1960; Mackie and Percival, 1959) — and the glucuronomannan in *Bacillariophyceae* (Ford and Percival, 1965) have been reported as cell wall constituents. More complex polysaccharides have never been found in the cell wall. These data suggest that the water insoluble carbohydrate fraction, which contains several monosaccharides, must be a mixture of polysaccharides. As stated before, periodate oxidation data indicate the water insoluble carbohydrate consists of a polysaccharide with 1,2- or 1,4-linkages. The abundance of 1,4-polysaccharides in the cell walls of plants makes it likely that water insoluble polysaccharides from the marine environment are 1,4-polysaccharides. The D. P. of several algal cell wall polysaccharides has been determined. Cellulose from some *Phaeophyceae* species consists of about 160 D-glucose residues (Percival and Ross, 1949). Xylan with a D.P. of 40 to 50 has been isolated from *Rhodophyceae* (Percival and Chanda, 1950; Barry et al., 1950). Algal mannan of a similar molecular weight has also been isolated (Love and Percival, 1964). When a mixture of polysaccharides is exposed to biological attack, their resulting monosaccharide composition varies due to differences in biological susceptibility among the polysaccharides. These differences are a function of chemical characteristics such as monosaccharide composition and linkage type. The lack of variation in the monosaccharide composition of water insoluble carbohydrates over a range of depths indicates that the water insoluble polysaccharides are highly resistant to biological attack. For this reason, water insoluble polysaccharides are the main component of the deep water particulate fraction. Similar results were obtained for samples from various depths of Sagami Nada on April 18 to 21, 1966 (Handa, 1967b). These water insoluble carbohydrates consisted of D-glucose and D-mannose and had similar D.P.'s. This indicates that such polysaccharides remain intact as they sink to 1000 m. Extensive studies of microbiological degradation and utilization of cellulose, xylan, mannan and other cell wall polysaccharides make it difficult to assume that these water insoluble carbohydrates are permanently free from microbiological attack, however. The influence of the biochemical properties of these carbohydrates on vertical changes in particulate carbohydrate concentration will be briefly discussed here. The decrease in the particulate carbohydrate concentration from 20 m (21.1 μg C/liter) to 300 m (4.3 μg C/liter) is 16.8 μg C/liter. If all the water soluble carbohydrate (6.1 μg C/liter) is degraded as the particulate matter sinks to 300 m then 10.7 μg C/liter (64%) of the water insoluble carbohydrate must also be removed during the descent. However, as noted above, it is unlikely that the monosaccharide composition of the water insoluble carbohydrate remains constant between 20 m and 300 m.

On the other hand the predation of phytoplankton by zooplankton is also an important influence on the vertical distribution of particulate carbohydrate. Since zooplankton eat the whole cell they would not have a differential effect on the monosaccharide composition of water insoluble polysaccharides regardless of the depth at which the particulate matter is collected. Estimates of this predation will be of great value in interpreting the rapid decrease in particulate carbohydrate concentration in subsurface waters.

The concentration of particulate carbohydrates at a given depth is reciprocally related to the sinking rate of the particulate matter provided the particulate carbohydrate is free from biological attack. The sinking rate of living marine unicellular algae ranges from 0.03 to 20 m/day (Smayda and Boleyn, 1965, 1966a, 1966b). Recently, Eppley et al. (1967) demonstrated that the sinking rate is reciprocally related to the growth rate of cultured algae and that the sinking rate of senescent cells is several times higher than that of growing cells. In oceanic water as a living phytoplankton cell produced in the surface and the subsurface waters sinks gradually it becomes a senescent cell and then dies as its storage carbohydrate is consumed. The faster sinking rate of senescent and dead cells results in a vertical decrease in the phytoplankton concentration especially in waters between 20 and 300 m. It also leads to a vertical decrease in the particulate carbohydrate concentration in the same water layers. The vertical decrease in the particulate carbohydrate concentration in subsurface waters is a result of several factors: the high decay rate of 1,3-glucan and other water soluble carbohydrates from the particulate matter; the predation of phytoplankton by zooplankton and the higher sinking rate of senescent and dead phytoplankton cells. However, it is premature to discuss the relative importance of these factors because of a lack of data obtained in the natural environment. The refractory properties of the water insoluble carbohydrates which reach the depths are probably a major factor in the homogeneous distribution of particulate carbohydrates over time, space and depth in the ocean.

SUMMARY

1) The concentration of dissolved carbohydrate was determined in sea water samples collected from Sagami Nada. The range was 0.24 to 0.37 mg/liter. The vertical distribution was uniform from the surface to 1000 m at several locations.

2) The organic carbon, organic nitrogen, carbohydrate and amino acid content of particulate matter from various depths were determined. The concentration of these decreased with depth, most rapidly between 50 and 200 m.

3) All samples yielded D-galactose, D-glucose, D-mannose, D-xylose and D-glucuronic acid upon acid hydrolysis. The monosaccharide composition of the particulate matter changed with depth. D-glucose decreased preferentially with depth to 100 m but samples from below 200 m had a constant monosaccharide composition.

4) Storage and structural polysaccharides were isolated from particulate matter at 20 m. Analysis of their monosaccharide composition, linkage type and D.P. indicates that they are laminarin and 1,4-polysaccharides respectively. Because the monosaccharide composition of structural polysaccharides closely resembles that of deep water particulate matter it was concluded that, unlike storage polysaccharides, structural polysaccharides are not susceptible to biological attack and become the main carbohydrate component of deep water particulate matter.

5) On the basis of the biological susceptibilities of these storage and structural polysaccharides, vertical variations in particulate carbohydrate concentration were discussed.

DISCUSSION

PARSONS: In your Table 1 you only reported finding certain monosaccharides. I would have expected you to find some others such as fucose, arabinose and ribose. Did you not find these or is it simply that you didn't estimate them?

HANDA: I have done several experiments regarding determination of the monosaccharide composition of the particulate matter. In one case, I got a monosaccharide composition of the particulate matter different from this one. This sample from the eastern Pacific consists of glucose, mannose, fructose, xylose and fucose. I think the monosaccharide composition of particulate matter varies from sample to sample, from particulate to particulate.

BREGER: I would like to know if you fractionated the water insoluble carbohydrate and monitored with hydrolysis to make sure that these materials are truly carbohydrate.

HANDA: For this preparation I used the phenol sulfuric acid method; I also used the anthrone method.

BREGER: But you did not hydrolyze them to see what the individual monosaccharides were?

HANDA: Hydrolysis is not needed, because this method uses concentrated sulfuric acid through which hydrolysis occurs.

SIEBURTH: Do you feel that you are missing some of the carbohydrates with the phenol sulfuric method? For instance, the mannitol is not detected, and mannitol is the principal low molecular weight carbohydrate in many seaweeds.

HANDA: Yes, I think I miss the mannitol.

SIEBURTH: Do you think there is a better method than the phenol sulphuric acid method?

HANDA: To determine mannitol, I think it is better to use the periodate oxidation method and determine the formaldehyde.

SIEBURTH: How do you explain the refractory nature of this insoluble fraction? Why do you think it is so refractory in the deeper waters?

HANDA: This polysaccharide occurs in sea water from the surface to deep water.

SIEBURTH: Yes, but why should it be refractory?

HANDA: It is very difficult for microorganisms to attack this or any other water insoluble polysaccharide. I do not think this water insoluble polysaccharide is stable permanently in the ocean because there are many polysaccharide-splitting enzymes in microbiological organisms. I think even this comparatively refractory polysaccharide can eventually be hydrolyzed by microorganisms.

REFERENCES

ANDERSON, W. W., and J. W. GEHRINGER. 1958. Physical oceanographic biological and chemical data. South Atlantic Coast of the United States. M/V THEODORE N. GILL Cruise 6 and 8. Spec. Sci. Rep. — Fisheries. No. 265: 1-99; 303: 1-227.

ANN, W. D., E. L. HIRST, and D. J. MANNERS. 1965. The constitution of laminarin. V. The location of 1,6-glucosidic linkages. J. Chem. Soc., 885-893.

ANTIA, A. L., and C. T. LEE. 1963. Studies on the determination and differential analysis of dissolved carbohydrate in sea water. Fish. Res. Bd. Canada. (Manuscript Rep. Ser. 168).

ASPINALL, G. O. 1957. Simplified periodate oxidation. Chem. Ind., 1216.

BARRY, V. C., D. T. DILLON, B. HAWKINS, and P. O'COLLA. 1950. The xylan of *Rhodymenia palmata*. Nature, *166*: 788.

BEATTIE, A., E. L. HIRST, and E. PERCIVAL. 1961. Studies on the metabolism of the Chrysophyceae. Comparative structural investigations on leucosin (Chrysolaminarin) separated from diatoms and laminarin from the brown algae. Biochem. J., *79*: 531-537.

BIDWELL, R. G. S., and N. R. GHOSH. 1962. Photosynthesis and metabolism in marine algae. IV. The fate of C^{14}-mannitol in *Fucus vesiculosus*. Can. J. Bot., *40*: 803-811.

BOGDANOV, Y. A. 1965. Suspended organic matter in the Pacific. Okeanologiya, *5*: 77-85.

COLLIER, A., S. M. RAY, A. M. MAGNITZKY, and J. O. BILL. 1953. Effect of dissolved organic substances on oysters. U.S. Dept. Int., Fish. Wild. Fish. Bull., *84*: 167-185.

EPPLEY, R. W., R. W. HOLMES, and J. D. H. STRICKLAND. 1967. Sinking rates of marine phytoplankton measured with a fluorometer. J. Exp. Mar. Biol. Ecol., *1*: 191-208.

FLEMING, M., E. L. HIRST, and D. J. MANNERS. 1966. The constitution of laminarin. VI. The fine structure of soluble laminarin, p. 255-260. *In* E. G. Young and J. L. McLachlan [ed.], Proc. Fifth Int. Seaweed Symp., Halifax, Canada.

FORD, C. W., and E. PERCIVAL. 1965. The carbohydrate of *Phaeodactylum tricornutum*. I. Preliminary examination of the organism, and characterization of low molecular weight material and of a glucan. J. Chem. Soc., 7035-7042.

FOWDEN, L. 1954. A comparison of the composition of some algal protein. Ann. Bot. *18*: 257-266.

HANDA, N. 1966. Distribution of dissolved carbohydrate in the Indian Ocean. J. Oceanogr. Soc. Japan, *22*(2): 16-22.

HANDA, N. 1967a. The distribution of the dissolved and the particulate carbohydrates in the Kuroshio and its adjacent areas. J. Oceanogr. Soc. Japan, *23*(3): 1-9.

HANDA, N. 1967b. Identification of carbohydrates in marine particulate matters and their vertical distribution. Rec. Oceanogr. Works Japan, *9*(1): 65-73.

HANDA, N., and K. NISIZAWA. 1961. Structural investigation of a laminarin isolated from *Eisenia bicyclis*. Nature, *192*: 1078-1079.

HAY, G. W., B. A. LEWIS, and F. SMITH. 1965. Determination of the average length of polysaccharides by periodate oxidation, reduction and analysis of the derived polyalcohol, p. 377-380. *In* R. L. Whistler [ed.], Methods in carbohydrate chemistry. Academic Press, New York.

HOBSON, L. A. 1967. The seasonal and vertical distribution of suspended particulate matter in an area of the northeast Pacific Ocean. Limnol. Oceanogr., *12*(4): 642-649.

HOLM-HANSEN, O., J. D. H. STRICKLAND, and P. M. WILLIAMS. 1966. A detailed analysis of biologically important substances in a profile off Southern California. Limnol. Oceanogr., *11*: 548-561.

IRIKI, Y., T. SUZUKI, T. MIWA, and K. NISIZAWA. 1960. Xylan from siphonaceous green algae. Nature, *187*: 82.

LEWIN, J. C., R. A. LEWIN, and D. E. PHILPOTT. 1958. Observation of *Phaeodactylum tricornutum*. J. Gen. Microbiol., *18*: 418-426.

LEWIS, G. J., and N. W. RAKESTRAW. 1955. Carbohydrate in sea water. J. Mar. Res., *14*: 253-258.

LOVE, J., and E. PERCIVAL. 1964. The polysaccharides of the green seaweed *Codium fragile*. III. A β-1,4-linked mannan. J. Chem. Soc., 3345-3351.

MACKIE, I. M., and E. PERCIVAL. 1959. The constitution of xylan from the green seaweed *Caulerpa filiformis*. J. Chem. Soc., 1151-1156.

McALLISTER, C. D., T. R. PARSONS, and J. D. H. STRICKLAND. 1960. Primary productivity and fertility at Station "P" in the North East Pacific Ocean. J. Cons., *25*: 240-259.

MENZEL, D. W. 1967. Particulate organic carbon in the deep sea. Deep-Sea Res., *14*: 229-238.

MENZEL, D. W., and J. J. GOERING. 1966. The distribution of organic detritus in the ocean. Limnol. Oceanogr., *11*: 333-337.

NISIZAWA, K. 1938. Physiological studies on laminarin and mannitol of brown algae. I. Diurnal variation of their content in *Eisenia bicyclis*. Sci. Rep. Tokyo Bunrika Daigaku Sect., *B3*: 289-301.

PARSONS, T. R., and J. D. H. STRICKLAND. 1962. Ocean detritus. Science, *136*: 313-314.

PERCIVAL, E. G. V., and S. K. CHANDA. 1950. The xylan of *Rhodymenia palmata*. Nature, *166*: 787.

PERCIVAL, E. G. V., and A. G. ROSS. 1949. Marine algal cellulose. J. Chem. Soc., 3041-3043.

RILEY, G. A., D. VAN HEMERT, and P. J. WANGERSKY. 1965. Organic aggregates in surface and deep waters of the Sargasso Sea. Limnol. Oceanogr., *10*: 354-364.

SMAYDA, T. J., and B. J. BOLEYN. 1965. Experimental observations on the flotation of marine diatoms. I. *Thalassiosira cf. nana, Thalassiosira rotula*, and *Nitzschia seriata*. Limnol. Oceanogr., *10*: 499-509.

SMAYDA, T. J., and B. J. BOLEYN. 1966a. Experimental observations on the flotation of marine diatoms. II. *Skeletonema costatum* and *Rhizosolenia setigera*. Limnol. Oceanogr., *11*: 18-34.

SMAYDA, T. J., and B. J. BOLEYN. 1966b. Experimental observations on the flotation of marine diatoms. III. *Bacteristrum hyalinum* and *Chaetoceros lauderi*. Limnol. Oceanogr., *11*: 35-43.

UNRAU, A. M., and F. SMITH. 1957. A chemical method for the determination of the molecular weight of certain polysaccharides. Chem. Ind. (London): 330-331.

WANGERSKY, P. J. 1952. Isolation of ascorbic acid and rhamnoside from sea water. Science, *115*: 685.

WANGERSKY, P. J., and D. C. GORDON, Jr. 1965. Particulate carbonate, organic carbon, and Mn^{2+} in the open ocean. Limnol. Oceanogr., *10*: 544-550.

YEMM, E. W., and E. C. COCKING. 1955. Determination of amino acids with ninhydrin. Analyst, *80*: 209-213.

DISSOLVED ORGANIC COMPOUNDS IN SEA WATER: SATURATED AND OLEFINIC HYDROCARBONS AND SINGLY BRANCHED FATTY ACIDS

M. Blumer
Woods Hole Oceanographic Institution
Woods Hole, Massachusetts 02543

ABSTRACT

Organic compounds are introduced into the sea from many sources. Each source contributes a characteristic pattern of compounds differing in relative concentrations, molecular weight and type distributions. From a quantitative analysis of the organic compounds in sea water it is possible to estimate the relative environmental contributions to different water masses.

This paper discusses the analytical program in progress at Woods Hole. It documents the methods presently used and describes the compounds which have been isolated. Their potential use as tracers for the study of marine processes is explained.

INTRODUCTION

Organic compounds are introduced into the sea from many and varied sources. The largest fraction probably derives from organisms, especially the marine phyto- and zooplankton. Other contributions come from the atmosphere, marine sediments and terrestrial sources via rivers and tidal inlets. Marine pollution plays an ever increasing role, introducing into the sea both originally biogenic compounds which have been recycled through other environments, and compounds foreign to marine organisms. In addition, many marine compounds may be secondary condensation and reaction products of organic chemicals present in the sea.

On a gross scale, the organic chemistry of the sea appears monotonous. Thus, Menzel and Ryther (1970) find little variation in the total dissolved organic carbon content of water below the thermocline. A similar, if lesser, monotony may be found in other bulk properties, like C, O, H isotope or thermal pyrolysis patterns (Lysyj, 1970) of chemically unresolved isolates.

This monotony of composition is not encountered on a molecular level in the sources of marine organic compounds. The body chemistry, even of closely related organisms, exhibits amazing variety and specificity (Blumer et al., 1964). Plankton samples from different geographical, chemical and temperature regimes show pronounced differences in their chemistry, often for the same species.

Pollution products are variable and often differ structurally from natural compounds. Thus, aromatic systems, especially highly substituted ones, are much more abundant in crude oil and its products than in plants and animals. Bacterial alteration of the organic matter in sediments produces an imprint easily distinguishable from that of planktonic organisms characteristic of sea water.

Such chemical differences in the sources of marine organic matter must be reflected in the molecular type and size distribution of the dissolved organic matter in the sea. The molecular nature of the dissolved organic matter should show great variability, even if compensation on a bulk level leads to a relatively featureless picture.

This expected variability in the molecular nature of marine organic matter should be of great diagnostic value in the study of marine processes. It may provide specific tags, originating in small regions, which remain recognizable in specific water masses for long time periods. The introduction of such tags may occur continuously or it may be tied to specific circumstances or events, e.g., an oil spill, a plankton bloom or a change in water temperature.

We have embarked on a study of the dissolved organic compounds in the sea. Our long-term goal is to understand from what sources and in what manner organic compounds are introduced into the sea, how they vary in amount and structure, what their long-term fate is and how we can use this knowledge to better understand the marine environment as a whole. A related, but neglected, area to which we plan to devote much attention concerns the interaction of dissolved organic compounds with marine organisms. There is good evidence that many life processes of marine organisms are stimulated by extremely small amounts of dissolved organic compounds and that such chemotactic processes play a very important ecological role (Whittle and Blumer, 1970).

This paper summarizes our work in this field, documents the methods used, and discusses the significance and potential application of the measurements already made. Our work to date has concerned the identification and determination of organic compounds in the pentane soluble fraction of local near-shore surface waters. Later this will be expanded to other waters and to different fractions of the dissolved organic matter. We will first establish the presence of a large number of compounds and then attempt to find the simplest technique for their analytical determination. Thus, the initial isolation may involve numerous, though not necessarily quantitative, steps and sophisticated analytical tools like infrared, nmr and mass spectrometry. Eventually we hope to develop an analytical procedure involving a minimum number of steps through which the presence of a specific compound can be reestablished and its concentration can be accurately measured. This procedure should be simple and rapid enough to permit monitoring of organic chemicals at sea and with fast response time.

PROCEDURE

Clean extracted filter paper is used for the filtration of the sea water samples (Table 1). While not as retentive as membrane filters, paper permits gravity filtration and eliminates the rupturing of cells upon impact. Duplicate analyses comparing paper filtration to consecutive filtration through paper and clean Millipore filters, show that all compounds reported

Table 1.   Analytical procedure.

Filtration   (paper)
Acidification   (pH 2)

Extraction   (pentane)
Chromatography   (Silica gel + 5% H₂O)

Fraction 1	Saturated hydrocarbons	Analysis by GC (Apiezon L, FFAP), MS
Fraction 2	Olefinic and aromatic	Analysis by GC and MS, hydrogenation
Fraction 3	Polar materials	Conversion to methyl esters, isolation of unsaponifiables
		Analysis by GC, GC-MS, hydrogenation, urea separation
		TLC of unsaponifiables

here were present in a dispersion which passes through 0.45 μ filters. Thus, paper filtration appears to be sufficient for qualitative identification of dissolved compounds; for quantitative analysis gravity filtration followed by membrane filtration is preferred.

Extraction is performed at pH 2. At higher pH, free acids are partly ionized and incompletely extracted; at lower pH, extracts increase with time, either through hydrolysis of nonextractable polymers or through the destruction of cells or cell fragments which have passed through the filters.

Pentane was chosen as the solvent because of its high volatility and relative ease of purification. Commercial pentane contains olefins which may polymerize and in time form higher boiling products that interfere with the analysis. If stored at 0°C in the dark, the purified solvent is stable for at least a week; an alternative method, to stabilize pentane for a longer time, is to hydrogenate the solvent exhaustively or to remove the olefins chemically or by adsorption. In both cases the pentane must be redistilled after the treatment.

Chromatography is carried out on silica gel because it is capable of a much better resolution between saturated and olefinic hydrocarbons than is alumina. The adsorbent should be partially deactivated to reduce the danger of catalytic reactions such as the dehydration of phytol to phytadienes.

A simple chromatographic procedure concentrates individual compounds in one eluate fraction. Individual compounds are then identified by means of their column and gas chromatographic behavior. Whenever possible, chemical and spectral confirmation is sought.

METHODS AND MATERIALS

Handling of equipment

Great care is used to avoid contamination of samples. New equipment is washed with hot detergent, hot water, cold water, distilled acetone, pentane and redistilled pentane. After this the same equipment is reused and washing is restricted to the last-named solvents. Accidental contamination has been observed from dust, dirty laboratory air (Blumer, 1965), plastic ware, fingerprints and the contact of glassware with plastic-coated laboratory clamps. (The vinyl coating on Fisher, Castaloy versatile clamps contains sizable amounts of dioctyladipate).

Sampling, filtration and extraction

Surface sea water samples are collected in glass or stainless steel beakers and transferred to glass bottles or 5-gallon glass carboys. The samples are immediately filtered through Whatman #54 filter paper which has been Soxhlet extracted with benzene-methanol azeotrope.

For qualitative analysis, the filtered sea water sample is extracted in a 5-gallon carboy by agitation with a Model E-1 Vibromixer (Chemapec Inc., Hoboken, N. J.) with a 45 mm o.d. glass stirrer, conical holes tapered downward. The sea water is first acidified to pH 2 (approximately 1.25 ml conc. HCl/liter), then 500 ml pentane is added per 20 liters of water. After a 10-minute agitation, the two phases are permitted to separate, the aqueous phase is siphoned off and the pentane is separated from the remaining water in a 1-liter separatory funnel. The pentane layer is dried with a small amount of extracted sodium sulfate and the solvent is removed in a rotary evaporator at 0 to 10°C.

Quantitative extractions are performed in a separatory funnel with 200 ml pentane/2 liters of water. Five consecutive extractions are required. Four extracts are combined and the last one is worked up separately to check the efficiency of the extraction.

Solvents and reagents

All solvents are pure grade or equivalent and are redistilled from 3-liter flasks through a fractionating column (2.2 cm o.d., 60 cm long, packed with Raschig rings). Foreruns and bottoms are discarded. The distillates are stored in brown glass bottles in the dark.

Pentane is distilled a second time through a longer column (2.2 cm o.d., 130 cm long, packed with Berl saddles). This solvent is stored in the dark near 0°C. Blank checks are carried out by evaporating 150 ml pentane to about 1 ml, transferring this to a small evaporating flask, evaporating almost to dryness, and taking up the residue in 0.05 ml pentane. This is then evaporated on the outside surface of an etched 3 x 60 mm glass tube. Immediately after evaporation of the pentane the tube is inserted into the injection port of the gas chromatograph. The port is rapidly closed with septum and injector nut and the chromatograph is programmed at 8°C/min. This provides a more satisfactory sample introduction than solvent injection. The absence of a large peak reveals trace impurities in the early part of the chromatogram.

After two or three distillations high boiling impurities break through the distillation column which is then cleaned by the distillation of 1 liter of water followed by washing with redistilled acetone and air drying of the column. A two-zone, 3-liter heating mantle prevents overheating of the walls of the flask; the solvent level is not permitted to drop below 2/5 of the height of the flask.

Silica gel (Grade 922, through 200 mesh, Davison Chemical Co., Baltimore) is Soxhlet extracted by benzene-methanol azeotrope. Next, it is vacuum dried, reactivated at 150°C and deactivated with 5% water (v/v).

Anhydrous, granular sodium sulfate is Soxhlet extracted with the same solvent and vacuum dried before use.

Methanol-BF_3 is freshly prepared from redistilled methanol and BF_3 gas.

Saturated sodium chloride solution is prepared from ignited or Soxhlet extracted reagent grade sodium chloride.

Methyl esters are prepared by a technique scaled down from that described by Metcalfe et al. (1966): the lipids are transferred to a 10-ml vial with a Teflon-lined screw cap. They are dissolved in 0.05 ml benzene and 0.4 ml of 0.5N KOH in absolute methanol is added. The vial is capped and heated to 50°C for 5 minutes with frequent agitation. Next, 0.5 ml saturated BF_3 in absolute methanol is added, the vial is capped again, and it is heated for another 5 minutes to 50°C. The mixture is cooled and 1 ml saturated aqueous sodium chloride and 3 ml pentane are added. The esters are extracted by shaking and recovered by withdrawal and evaporation of the upper layer. The extraction is repeated twice.

Hydrogenation

Redistilled isooctane is chromatographed through a dry packed bed of activated silica gel to remove traces of inhibitors. The initial 0.3 bed volumes of eluate are discarded. The next 0.5 bed volumes are collected and used for the hydrogenation. Platinum oxide (1 mg) is added to 1 ml of the purified solvent in a magnetically stirred 10-ml flask. The catalyst is reduced under hydrogen at room temperature; with clean solvent, complete reduction should occur in less than one minute. Platinum and solvent are then transferred by pipette to a 10-ml roundbottom flask containing the sample and a magnetic stirrer.

The flask is immediately evacuated and backfilled with hydrogen and flushing is repeated three times. The catalyst must not be allowed to dry during the initial transfer or in sample recovery because self-ignition may occur. Hydrogenation proceeds to completion within one hour at atmospheric pressure and 40 to 50°C. The sample is separated from the catalyst by withdrawing the solution through clean cotton; flask and catalyst are washed in the same manner.

Column chromatography

A 1-ml column (3 mm i.d. x 220 mm) packed with 1 ml silica gel containing 5% water is used for all separations. Several ml pentane are forced through the dry packed column to displace the air and the sample is added from a microsyringe in the smallest volume of pentane.

For the initial fractionation (Table 1) the following fractions are collected: 1.5 ml pentane (saturated hydrocarbon fraction), 6 ml pentane (olefins and aromatics) and 4 ml of 1:1 benzene-methanol (polar compounds).

An alternate procedure is used to isolate methyl esters from a methylation mixture: the first eluate consisting of 3 ml pentane is discarded and the esters are eluted by 4 ml pentane with 40% benzene.

Urea separations

The sample contained in a 5-ml evaporating tube (13 x 60 mm, test tube bottom, attached to 24/40 female standard taper joint) is dissolved in 0.2 ml pentane. To this are added 0.05 ml acetone and 0.05 ml urea solution in methanol (10% by weight). The solution is dried on a rotary evaporator with the tube in near-horizontal position. The nonadducted, soluble fraction is recovered by washing and filtration through a pad of clean cotton. The adduct may be split by hot water and recovered by pentane extraction.

Gas chromatography

The equipment consists of Model 1200 Varian gas chromatographs with linear temperature programmer and 1 mv recorders with automatic attenuators. The columns are stainless steel (3.6 mm x 3.2 mm o.d. x 0.07 mm i.d.) packed with 0.8% acid-washed, siliconized, Apiezon L on 80/100 mesh Chromosorb G, and 12.5% FFAP (Varian-Aerograph) on the same substrate. The columns are operated at optimum flow rates (about 10 ml N_w/min) and programmed from 60 to 300°C at 4°/min (Apiezon) or from 125 to 260°C at 2°/min (FFAP).

RESULTS

Saturated hydrocarbons

Straight chain hydrocarbons from C_{14} to C_{33} have been identified. Lower and higher molecular weight paraffins may be present but undetected due to volatilization or due to retention in the gas chromatograph. The paraffin concentration increases gradually and reaches a maximum at C_{25} to C_{28}. No systematic odd carbon predominance is observed; however, normal heptadecane is more abundant than either adjacent normal paraffin.

The molecular weight distribution pattern resembles that of marine algae (Clark and Blumer, 1967) and is dissimilar from that of recent marine sediments with their pronounced odd carbon predominance. This suggests that the paraffins in sea water are plankton rather than sediment-derived, even in shallow water, near-shore samples.

Branched paraffins are represented by at least 5 homologous series, eluting between the straight chain members and one to two orders of magnitude lower in concentration. Retention indices suggest 3- and 4-methyl, and possibly 2-methyl homologues. The remaining peaks may indicate dialkyl or possibly cycloalkylparaffins. Further confirmation by trapping, rechromatography and mass spectrometry is necessary but difficult because of the very small quantities present. Relative to straight chain compounds, branched alkanes are much less abundant in most organisms than in crude oil and therefore may provide suitable sensitive markers for oil pollution in sea water.

The **isoprenoid hydrocarbons** are represented by pristane (C_{19}) and phytane (C_{20}). Both are characterized by their retention indices, 1682 and 1790 on Apiezon and 1600 and 1760 on FFAP. Pristane's index value exceeds that of normal heptadecane; phytane is present just below the level of octadecane. Pristane occurs in marine algae (Clark and Blumer, 1967) and in zooplankton (Blumer et al., 1964). Phytane occurs in some organisms (Try, 1967) but is not as common as pristane, especially in the marine environment. Concerted efforts to identify it in marine algae (Clark and Blumer, 1967), in zooplankton, in the liver of basking shark (Blumer, 1967), and in recent marine sediments (Blumer and Snyder, 1965) have not been successful. Gelpi and Oro (1968) also reported the absence of phytane in basking shark liver oil; in contrast to our findings, they isolated phytane from commercial pristane which had been distilled from basking shark liver oil. We have obtained a sample of commercial pristane from the same source as did Gelpi and Oro (Robuoy, Robeco Chemicals, Inc., New York). Combined silica gel and gas chromatography detected no phytane; the detection limit was 1 part in 20,000 parts pristane. Phytadienes occurred at about 1% of the pristane concentration. It is plausible that the phytane Gelpi and Oro isolated at 1% of the pristane concentration is an artifact formed by saturation of the phytadienes during the distillation of the crude liver oil or during their redistillation of the pristane in a spinning band still. Thus, the source of phytane in our water samples remains obscure. It may be derived from plants or animals which have not yet been analyzed or from the rather abundant phytanic acid. Phytadienes are not sufficiently abundant to be precursors of the dissolved phytane.

Isoprenoid hydrocarbons, common constituents of crude oil where pristane and phytane are accompanied both by a higher and several lower homologues, should serve as sensitive markers for marine pollution by crude oil and certain oil products. The absence of higher and lower homologues of pristane and phytane in our water samples suggests that the hydrocarbons have been derived predominately from plankton rather than from pollution.

Olefinic hydrocarbons

The gas chromatograms of the second eluate fractions from silica gel are dominated by two large peaks. Hydrogenation shifts the retention indices of both compounds. Squalene (Ret. Ind. 2737, after hydrogenation to squalane 2620, both on Apiezon) boils at a higher temperature than the major compound, which can be hydrogenated to normal heneicosane. The low retention index (2020 on Apiezon) suggests a polyunsaturated derivative of heneicosane. A C_{21} hexaene with an identical retention index and similar chromatographic and chemical characteristics has previously been isolated from *Rhincalanus nasutus* (Blumer, Mullin and Thomas, unpublished) but the double bond positions have not yet been established. Numerous additional minor and partly unresolved compounds occur in this fraction. Their retention indices are unaffected by hydrogenation with Adam's catalyst which suggests they are aromatic rather than olefinic hydrocarbons. No evidence has been obtained for the presence of those phytol-derived C_{19} and C_{20} olefins which are common constituents of zooplankton and larger marine organisms.

The presence of squalene is not surprising. It occurs in most organisms, although only higher organisms appear able to accumulate large amounts of this hydrocarbon. Thus, copepod lipids contain 0.1% squalene while lipids in basking shark livers may contain more than 20% squalene. The squalene in our water samples cannot be tied to a specific source; however, it is definitely a product of living organisms and it is found neither in ancient sediments nor in pollution. The C_{21} hexaene in *Rhincalanus* may be derived by that organism from docosahexenoic acid through decarboxylation. Changes in the unsaturation of copepod lipids have been observed with changes in water temperature (Farkas and Herodek, 1964). In concurrence with this, the C_{21} hexaene was more abundant in plankton sampled in winter than in summer. Additional work on this topic is in progress. This hydrocarbon and the corresponding unsaturated acid may be useful as seasonally and temperature dependent tags of sea water.

Further investigation of the aromatic hydrocarbons in sea water is necessary and promising. Because of their abundance in crude oil and crude oil distillates, aromatics should be sensitive markers of marine pollution.

Fatty acids

Straight chain saturated and unsaturated acids have previously been characterized (Jeffrey, 1970; Williams, 1965). Our chromatograms of the fatty acid methyl esters suggested the presence of singly branched acids, though their peaks were partly obscured by those of the olefinic straight chain esters. Hydrogenation simplified the chromatograms and the measurement of the retention indices (Cooper and Blumer, 1968) and mass spectra confirmed the presence of iso- and anteisoacids in the C_{12} to C_{19} range (Table 2).

Iso- and anteisoacids are common minor constituents of bacteria (Kates, 1964; Kaneda, 1967), the lipids of marine plankton and larger organisms (Ackman and Sipos, 1965) and marine sediments (Leo and Parker, 1966; Cooper and Blumer, 1968). In bacteria, Kaneda found the C_{15} and C_{17} anteisoacids to predominate over all other branched acids. The same acids predominate in our sea water samples. The branched acids in marine sediments are thought to be bacterially derived. The smaller amounts in marine lipids are believed to derive from zooplankton and to be transferred through the food chain. The concentration of branched acids relative to straight-chain acids in sea water is greater than in sediments and less than in marine lipids. This suggests at least partial bacterial derivation of the marine iso- and anteisoacids.

Saturated and unsaturated normal, iso- and anteisoacids account for close to 97% of the total fatty acids in the water samples. Numerous minor peaks suggest the presence of other acids than those found in typical plankton lipids; sufficient amounts for mass spectral characterization have yet to be isolated.

No evidence has been found for the presence of those C_{16}, C_{19} and C_{20} isoprenoid acids common to most marine organisms and sediments. If present, they occur at concentrations below those at which they are found in zooplankton.

CONCLUSIONS

The characteristic relative concentrations and molecular weight distribution patterns within each group of dissolved organic compounds permit one to tie them to specific sources. In contrast to the diffuse picture

Table 2. Normal, iso- and anteisoacids in a coastal water sample, Buzzard's Bay, Mass., Aug. 24, 1968. Values represent combined saturated and unsaturated acids as methyl esters. Total esters: 19.7 μg/liter.
(Concn in μg/liter)

Carbon number	Normal (sat. and unsat.)	Iso	Anteiso
11	0.058		
12	0.84	0.0078	0.0056
13	0.089	0.0088	0.027
14	1.76	0.042	
15	0.79	0.10	0.27
16	7.28	0.069	
17	0.52	0.012	0.19
18	6.23	0.012	
19	0.077	<0.02	0.067
20	0.52		
22	0.15		

$\dfrac{\text{Iso}}{\text{Anteiso}}$ sea water 0.49   sediments 1.6-2   marine fats 4-8

$\dfrac{\text{Normals}}{\text{Iso + Anteiso}}$ sea water 22   sediments 3-7   marine fats 50-100

derived from bulk measurements such as that of the total dissolved organic content, the analysis of the molecular composition of sea water promises to become a sensitive tool for the study of marine processes. Even at the present qualitative stage of our investigation, every class of compounds is so closely associated with a specific source, and will be so severely altered in its relative composition by contributions from other sources, that the usefulness of organic compounds as marine environmental tracers is readily apparent (Table 3). As other types of compounds are isolated other environmental markers should become available. As we progress to quantitative measurements, these markers should more sharply define relative environmental contributions to different water masses.

DISCUSSION

BELSER: Don't you find the failure to find the C_{16}, C_{19} and C_{20} isoprenoids of animal origin somewhat at odds with the presence of squalene? It looks as if there is a contribution from animals but the isoprenoid data suggest that this is not true. Would you care to speculate on the possibility that the isoprenoids are selectively degraded?

BLUMER: Yes, this is a possibility. On the other hand, I think they may well be there in concentrations that are covered up by those other acids which have been detected so far. Further separation will be required to find them.

MALCOLM: What percentage of the total dissolved organic fraction does the lipid represent?

BLUMER: I cannot yet give you a very good figure, because we have not gone very far into quantitative determination. As I said, the range of carbon in a single extraction was 12 to 55 μg/liter. Double that figure and you may have a reasonable value. The fatty acids are running around 20 μg/liter, a fairly large fraction of the total — certainly far larger than the hydrocarbons.

SVERGA: Can you say anything about the aromatic fraction? You mentioned only that they looked very promising.

BLUMER: No, we have not identified any specific compounds.

BREGER: I think it should be pointed out that there is no known direct mechanism for the bacterial decarboxylation of the fatty acids, to the best of my knowledge. If there is any conversion from the fatty acids to hydrocarbons, we will have to take another look at this, and see exactly where it does go. Also, you found that most of the fatty acids are odd-numbered; if you reduced these they would yield even-numbered hydrocarbons.

Table 3. Potential uses of dissolved organic compounds as environmental markers.

Compound type	Useful as markers for
Normal paraffins	Contribution by algae/sediment/pollution
Branched paraffins	Contribution by organisms/pollution
Isoprenoid hydrocarbons	Contribution by plankton/pollution
Olefinic hydrocarbons	Contribution by organisms/pollution; potential temperature and time markers
Polyunsaturated acids	Potential temperature and time markers
Singly branched acids	Contribution by bacteria/plankton
Isoprenoid acids	Contribution by zooplankton

BLUMER: Fatty acids are even-numbered and would yield odd-numbered hydrocarbons.

BREGER: Did odd-numbered hydrocarbons predominate in one case, or was it even-numbered hydrocarbons?

BLUMER: In the case of acids, even-numbered predominate. With regard to the decarboxylation, we have fed *Calanus* C^{14}-labeled phytol. This is converted to phytanic acid, and the label turns up in pristane. Decarboxylation takes place, but we do not know whether the *Calanus* or the intestinal bacterial flora accomplish it.

PARKER: What alcohols have you found?

BLUMER: We have evidence of sterols — and possibly phytol.

PARKER: We have been looking at alcohols in sediments and are really surprised at their abundance, in particular, the dihydrophytols. Even more puzzling is the general GLC pattern of these compounds, which looks much like the GLC pattern of fatty acids in terms of the carbon skeleton. Apparently there is either some kind of joint source or interconversion. This does not fit in with any organic chemistry I know which would explain the interchange between these compounds. We have not looked at water and have no plans to look at water, and I would be interested in knowing if you could find these in water. It is very abundant in recent sediments.

BREGER: In a recent paper, John Smith, CSIRO, reports finding exactly what Dr. Parker says — that the alcohols in certain extractions are very similar to fatty acids. He seems to feel that they are both derived from esters.

DUURSMA: What percentage saturation can you expect for hydrocarbons in sea water?

BLUMER: We do not know yet, whether the hydrocarbon concentration is solubility-limited; certainly not at the low end.

ACKNOWLEDGMENTS

Contribution No. 2124 from the Woods Hole Oceanographic Institution.

This research was supported by ONR (N0014-66-contract CO-241), by NSF (GA-539 and GA-1625) and by API (85A).

Miss C. McLaurin helped in the identification of the branched fatty acids.

REFERENCES

ACKMAN, R. G., and J. C. SIPOS. 1965. Isolation of the saturated fatty acids of some marine lipids with particular reference to normal odd-numbered fatty acids and branched chain acids. Comp. Biochem. Physiol., *15*: 445-456.

BLUMER, M. 1965. Contamination of a laboratory building by air filters. Contamination Control, *4*: 13-14, Sept.

BLUMER, M. 1967. Hydrocarbons in digestive tract and liver of a basking shark. Science, *156*: 390-391.

BLUMER, M., M. M. MULLIN, and D. W. THOMAS. 1964. Pristane in the marine environment. Helgoländ. Wiss. Meeresunters., *10*: 187-201.

BLUMER, M., and W. D. SNYDER. 1965. Isoprenoid hydrocarbons in recent sediments: presence of pristane and probable absence of phytane. Science, *150*: 1588-1589.

CLARK, R. C., Jr., and M. BLUMER. 1967. Distribution of n-paraffins in marine organisms and sediment. Limnol. Oceanogr., *12*: 79-87.

COOPER, W. J., and M. BLUMER. 1968. Linear, *iso* and *anteiso* fatty acids in recent sediments of the North Atlantic. Deep-Sea Res., *15*: 535-540.

FARKAS, T., and S. HERODEK. 1964. The effect of environmental temperature on the fatty acid composition of Crustacean plankton. J. Lipid Res., *5*: 369-373.

GELPI, E., and J. ORO. 1968. Gas chromatographic-mass spectrometric analysis of isoprenoid hydrocarbons and fatty acids in shark liver products. J. Amer. Oil Chem. Soc., *45*: 144-147.

JEFFREY, L. M. 1970. Lipids of marine waters. *In* D. W. Hood [ed.], Proc. Symp. Organic matter in natural waters. Inst. Mar. Sci. Occa. Pub. No. 1, Univ. Alaska, this volume.

KANEDA, TOSHI. 1967. Fatty acids in the genus *Bacillus*. I. Iso- and anteiso fatty acids as characteristic constituents of lipids in 10 species. J. Bact., *93*: 894-903.

KATES, M. 1964. Bacterial lipids, p. 17-90. *In* R. Paoletti and D. Kritchevsky [ed.], Advances in lipid research, v. 2. Academic Press, New York.

LEO, RICHARD F., and P. L. PARKER. 1966. Branched chain fatty acids in sediments. Science, *152*: 649-650.

LYSYJ, I. 1970. Instrumental techniques for the identification of pollutants. *In* D. W. Hood [ed.], Proc. Symp. Organic matter in natural waters. Inst. Mar. Sci. Occa. Pub. No. 1, Univ. Alaska, this volume.

MENZEL, D. W., and J. H. RYTHER. 1970. Distribution and cycling of organic matter in the oceans. *In* D. W. Hood [ed.], Proc. Symp. Organic matter in natural waters. Inst. Mar. Sci. Occa. Pub. No. 1, Univ. Alaska, this volume.

METCALFE, L. D., A. A. SCHMITZ, and J. R. PELKA. 1966. Rapid preparation of fatty acid esters from lipids for gas-chromatographic analysis. Anal. Chem. *38*(3): 514-515.

TRY, K. 1967. Presence of the hydrocarbons pristane and phytane in human adipose tissue and the occurrence of normal amounts in patients with Refsum's disease. Scand. J. Clin. Lab. Invest., *19*: 385.

WHITTLE, K. J., and M. BLUMER. 1970. Interactions between organisms and dissolved organic substances in the sea. Chemical attraction of the starfish *Asterias vulgaris* to oysters. *In* D. W. Hood [ed.], Proc. Symp. Organic matter in natural waters. Inst. Mar. Sci. Occa. Pub. No. 1, Univ. Alaska, this volume.

WILLIAMS, P. M. 1965. Fatty acids derived from lipids of marine origin. J. Fish. Res. Bd. Canada, *22*: 1107-1122.

VOLATILE ORGANIC MATERIALS IN SEA WATER

James F. Corwin
Antioch College
Yellow Springs, Ohio   45387

ABSTRACT

A review of the literature concerning the presence of dissolved organic materials in the ocean is coupled with a discussion of the development of methods to assay the organic content. Attention is called to procedures that eliminate or destroy the volatile material. Methods for determining the volatile organic content of sea water are reviewed and a new method for determination of low molecular weight oxygen containing organic compounds is reported along with results obtained for sea water. Suggested future work could result in a complete method for volatile organics.

INTRODUCTION

Our approach to the separation, detection and identification of volatile organic materials in the sea water consisted of dispersing an inert gas stream through a water sample. The gas containing the volatile organics then went either directly to a gas chromatograph or to a series of two traps, one of which contained carbon disulfide, while the other was a cold trap. Samples collected in both traps were then injected into the gas chromatograph. While these studies (Corwin, 1960; Alexander and Corcoran, 1961) demonstrated the feasibility of lifting volatile organic substances directly from sea water with an inert gas, the method in practice had several disadvantages. The samples required lengthy preparation time during which contamination or alterations in constituents could take place. The carbon disulfide, while inert to the ionization detector, becomes self-contaminated on standing and slowly decomposes in the presence of water vapor in the gas stream. When intermediate solution or adsorption is not used the resulting gas chromatogram of the organic materials does not have sharp peaks.

Swinnerton et al., determined the fixed gases CO, CH_4, N_2, O_2 and CO_2 (1962) and Ar (1964) using a modified direct dispersion gas collection method. Hydrocarbons containing C_1 to C_5 were separated and measured using the dispersion method plus the adsorption of low molecular weight hydrocarbons on activated carbon at liquid N_2 temperatures (Swinnerton and Linnenbom, 1967). Subsequent reheating of the activated carbon drove the adsorbed material into a sensitive gas chromatograph. Three ocean areas and one estuary were examined. Samples came from the Gulf of Mexico (28°59'N, 88°11'W), the North Atlantic (52°35'N, 20°9'W), the Bahamas and Chesapeake Bay bottom water. Methane, ethylene, ethane, propane, propylene, isobutane, butene, n-butane, isopentane and n-pentane were identified. A recalculation of the results in terms of ml/liter of hydrocarbons shows that as much as 0.300 ppm of volatile hydrocarbons can be present in sea water. Previous work had involved only methane determinations in fresh water lakes and marshes (Hutchinson, 1957), and in Lake Nitinat (Richards et at., 1965).

A modification of the head-space method developed by Bassette et al., (1962, 1964) and used by Kepner et al. (1964) to determine low molecular weight soluble organic components in water solutions has been used by this author for sea water analysis. Systematic methods for the detection and measurement of low molecular weight aldehydes, ketones and esters are reported here. The method could also be used for hydrocarbons, but was not because a method was already available for these. Three areas have been examined. One station in the Florida Straits collected in February, 1968, one station in the Eastern Mediterranean (August, 1965) and three stations in the Amazon Estuary (February, 1965).

Graduated 1200 ml glass intravenous bottles fitted with a silicone stopper and a plastic screw cap were used (Corcoran et al., 1967). The sample bottles were prepared by introducing 350 g of anhydrous Na_2SO_4, C.P., into the bottle and heating the combination to 250 C for five hours. After cooling the laboratory atmosphere was displaced by oil free nitrogen until the free space was free of traces of organic compounds. The method used for final analysis was used to prove the absence of organic compounds in the sample bottles. A control bottle treated in the same manner was prepared and 600 ml of triple distilled water prepared by Walter Drost-Hansen and his associates, Institute of Marine Sciences, Miami, Florida, was added. The control bottle was left open to the ship atmosphere while the sample bottles were charged with 600 ml of sea water each from 1200 ml Niskin Sample equipment. The sample was taken following three salinity samples of 100 ml each.

The analysis was performed by withdrawing 0.1 ml of gas from the head space with a gas tight syringe, and injecting it into a Beckman G. C. 5 gas chromatograph set for a sensitivity of 5×10^{-12} amp full scale deflection. The instrument was equipped with a dual path hydrogen flame detector. Matched ten foot, 1/8', stainless steel columns charged with Carbowax 20 M, 10% on acid washed Chromasorb W, 60/80 mesh were used. These columns were prepared by the Beckman Instrument Company. Temperatures were: oven 95 C, injection port 125 C and detector 125 C. Helium carrier gas 30 ml/min, H_2 15 ml/min and air 300 ml/min, completed the analytical conditions.

The gas chromatographic peaks were identified by retention times of standard mixtures of low molecular weight aldehydes, ketones, alcohols, esters, acids, amines and hydrocarbons. These standards, prepared by adding 400 to 410 μg/liter of pure Eastman reagents (A.C.S. specifications) to triple pure water, were treated in the same manner as the sea water samples. The acids and amines refused to salt out at these concentrations. The hydrocarbons had almost zero retention times. Methyl alcohol, formaldehyde and ethyl alcohol were not detectable at these concentrations either. The relative peak areas of the standards and sea water samples determined by triangulation were used to calculate concentrations. The standard samples were diluted to concentrations similar to those in sea water to make sure the process was feasible. Fig. 1 contains sample chromatograms showing comparative values of a standard sample and a typical station sample.

Table 1 summarizes the data from one oceanographic cast in the Florida Straits on February 27, 1968. Table 2 summarizes a deeper cast made in the Eastern Mediterranean during August 1965, and Table 3, the Amazon data. Although there is no assurance that the older samples have retained their properties, one would not expect much bacterial or plankton activity in a solution saturated with Na_2SO_4.

The profiles representing Tables 1 and 2 are found in Fig. 2 and Fig. 3. One interesting difference is the absence of butyraldehyde in the Mediterranean sample. Very small peaks on the chromatogram of all samples have not been identified.

In 1960 Armstrong and Boalch described a UV absorption method for examination of volatile organic constituents in an algal culture medium and sea water. Vacuum distillates of the water were concentrated by collection in a trap using ice as a coolant. They estimated that 250 ml collected from a 2.5 liter sample contain about 50 per cent of the volatile organic material present. This sample showed an absorption peak at 200 to 250 mμ. They further estimated that 10 mg/liter was necessary to give this type of absorption. Absorption at this wavelength could be accounted for by formic, acetic, propionic, hydroxyacetic or boric acids; formaldehyde or acetaldehyde; dimethylketone or methylethylketone; or, ammonia, ethylamine, dimethylamine, trimethylamine or propylamine. Acetone and 2-butanone found in this work were suggested as possible constituents of sea water on the basis of qualitative ultraviolet absorption measurements of sea water concentrates from the English Channel, $50°52'N$, $4°22'W$. Butyraldehyde was not suggested.

The other constituents suggested by Armstrong, low molecular weight acids and amines, are not susceptible to the method of analysis used in this report. The total carbon determinations reported in the same publication for samples ranging from 20 to 50 μg/liter suggest that the analyses do not account for the total amount. For a complete analysis, methods for determination of the low molecular weight acids and amines are needed.

The oceanographic data collected simultaneously with the samples (Tables 1 and 2) do not explain either the organic content or the distribution. Analysis of the Amazon samples showed an unexpectedly small amount of organic material. Plankton counts made by Harding Owre (personal communication) on samples collected from almost the same stations showed a complete absence of the usual plankton population. Larval hermit crabs were found in abundance. The collection and analysis of samples in conjunction with plankton tows and other biological assays may offer explanations.

SUMMARY

It is becoming possible to provide a complete picture of the organic content of the ocean. It is now possible to determine some low molecular

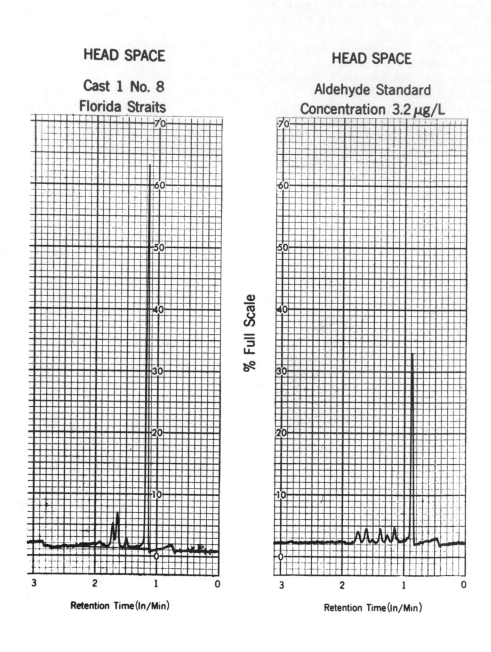

Fig. 1.   Sample chromatograms.

Table 1.   Florida Straits samples (25° 41'N, 79° 42'W), February, 1968.
(Concn in mg/liter)

Sample no.	Acetone	Butyraldehyde	2-Butanone	Depth (m)	Temp (°C)	Salinity (°/oo)
1	0.020	0.022	0.016	0	25.10	35.863
2	0.021	none	none	24	25.18	35.875
3	0.052	0.020	none	47	25.15	35.880
4	trace*	trace	trace	71	25.11	35.896
5	0.016	0.024	0.008	91	25.14	36.243
6	0.020	0.024	none	118	24.00	36.662
7	0.023	trace	trace	141	22.66	36.743
8	0.020	0.048	0.022	165	21.54	36.737
9	0.027	0.018	0.007	238	17.21	36.347
10	0.020	trace	0.017	373	11.62	35.465
11	0.014	0.013	trace	518	8.80	35.036

*trace represents <0.005 mg/liter

**Table 2. Eastern Mediterranean (33°00′N, 32°58′E), August, 1965.
(Concn in mg/liter)**

Sample no.	Acetone	Butyraldehyde	2-Butanone	Depth (m)	Temp (°C)	Salinity (°/₀₀)
1	0.028		0.007	0	26.83	39.375
2	0.030		0.005	10	26.83	39.382
3	0.034	None found	0.005	20	26.85	39.379
4	0.018		0.007	30	21.78	39.888
5	0.037		0.005	50	18.81	39.814
6	0.024		0.005	100	16.79	38.851
7	0.053		trace*	150	16.55	38.992
8	0.041		trace	200	16.11	39.007
9	0.028		0.007	250	15.62	38.987
10	0.034		0.007	300	15.00	38.944
11	0.028		0.005	400	14.42	38.859
12	0.034		0.006	500	14.01	38.789
13	0.030		0.008	600	13.88	38.758
14	0.032		0.006	800	13.69	38.711
15	0.047		0.006	1001	13.60	38.688
16	0.028		trace	1200	13.60	38.682

*trace represents <0.005 mg/liter

Table 3. Amazon estuary (H-6 01°42'N, 49°44'W), (H-8 02°02'N, 49°06'W), (H-10 04°00'N, 48°10'W), February, 1965. (Concn in mg/liter)

Station	Depth	Acetone	2-Butanone	Salinity
H-6	Surface	0.029	0.005	22.80
H-6	Bottom	0.018	0.007	22.62
H-8	Surface	0.033	trace*	33.70
H-8	Bottom	0.014	trace	35.30
H-10	Surface	0.046	trace	35.85
H-10	Bottom	0.018	trace	34.83
H-10	Core	0.015	0.005	-

*trace represents <0.005 mg/liter

-175-

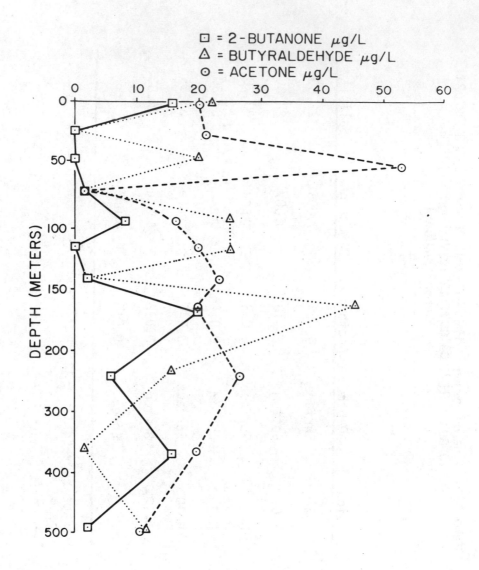

Fig. 2.   Florida Straits.

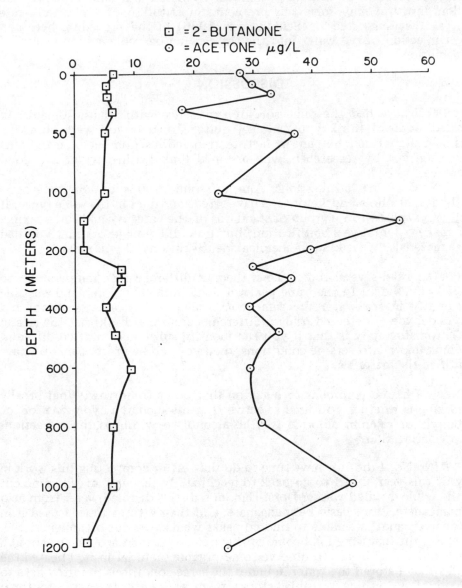

Fig. 3.   Eastern Mediterranean.

weight hydrocarbons, aldehydes other than formaldehyde, ketones and esters — by direct methods. Alcohols, acids and amines remain a problem. Further refinement of freezing techniques by Baker and Malo (1967) at the Mellon Institute may solve this problem. Substitution of a new substrate such as that suggested by Schlunegger (1966) in the procedure here and direct injection of sea water into the gas chromatographic column may lead to a solution.

DISCUSSION

ROSEN: I have had the same sort of experience with volatile organics in distilled water. I think you can feel quite sure that you were observing organic material and not an artifact. A tremendous number of man-hours have been lost by researchers who assumed that distilled water is a good reference.

Now I have a question. Your different groups of components — aldehydes, alcohols and ketones — have retention times in the same range. It is all very well to run a group of standards of one category and run a sample and make a tentative identification, but how did you know that you had these materials? What kind of chemical identification did you make?

CORWIN: I did several things. I ran them at different oven temperatures to see if I could identify the same peaks. I used an Se-30 column and was able to identify in sea water the same compounds — acetone, 2-butanol and butyraldehyde — detected using a different column. I think that the rule in gas chromatography is that if you can identify substances on two different columns under two sets of conditions, then you can be pretty sure you have identified the materials.

ROSEN: I have a comment to make on that point tomorrow. What I really am asking is whether you used selective reagents such as a hydrazine for the carbonyls or calcium chloride for the alcohol to withhold these fractions from volatilization?

CORWIN: No, I did not have time to do that. After completing this work in May of this year, I had to go back to teaching. By the way, may I comment on the triple-distilled water? Dorst-Hansen redistills distilled water from acid permanganate, from basic permanganate, and then a third time. I used it in my analysis and I was able to find no peaks whatsoever for organic material. However, the first time I got some of this water I let it sit around for about a week, and then I began to observe some organic material in it. I heated the bottles that I stored the water in under the same conditions reported here to get rid of everything possible, stored them and kept them up to three months with no problems. But material seems to be adsorbed even on the surface of the bottle.

DUURSMA: Organic contamination of distilled water was also a problem in the carbon determinations I did in 1959 (Duursma, 1961). Essentially the same treatment you used for oxidation still gave high blanks in the distilled water.

ACKNOWLEDGMENTS

The purchase and building of equipment for this project was made possible by the Kettering Foundation, Dayton, Ohio in 1959. From 1962 to 1964, research support was provided by the National Science Foundation.

REFERENCES

ALEXANDER, J., and E. CORCORAN. 1961. A further report on the separation of dissolved organic material from sea water. Personal communication.

ARMSTRONG, F. A. J., and G. T. BOALCH. 1960. Volatile organic matter in algal culture media and sea water. Nature, *185*: 761-762.

BAKER, R. A., and B. A. MALO. 1967. Water quality characterization — trace organics. Proc. Am. Soc. Civil. Eng., *SA6*: 41-54.

BASSETTE, R., S. OZERIS, and C. H. WHITNAH. 1962. Gas chromatographic analysis of head space gas of dilue aqueous solution. Anal. Chem., *34*: 1540-1543.

CORCORAN, E. F., J. F. CORWIN, and D. B. SEBA. 1967. Gas chromatographic analysis of chlorodane by head gas. J. Amer. Water Works Ass., *59*: 752.

CORWIN, J. F. 1960. The separation of dissolved organic materials from sea water. Report to the Charles Kettering Foundation. (Unpublished.)

HUTCHINSON, G. E. 1957. A treatise on limnology, v. 1, Wiley, New York, 1087 p.

KEPNER, R. E., H. MAARSE, and J. STRATING. 1964. Gas chromatographic head space techniques for the quantitative determination of volatile components in multicomponent aqueous solutions. Anal. Chem., *36*: 77-82.

RICHARDS, F. A., J. D. CLINE, W. W. BROENKOW, and L. P. ATKINSON. 1965. Some consequences of the decompostion of organic matter in Lake Nitinat, an anoxic fjord. Limnol. Oceanogr., *10*: R185-201.

SCHLUNEGGER, U. P. 1966. Gas chromatographic separation of aliphatic oxygen-containing compounds dissolved in water. J. Chromatogr., *22*: 229-233.

SWINNERTON, J. W., V. J. LINNENBOM, and C. H. CHEEK. 1962. Determination of dissolved gases in aqueous solutions by gas chromatography. Anal. Chem., *34*: 483-485.

SWINNERTON, J. W., V. J. LINNENBOM, and C. H. CHEEK. 1964. Determination of argon and oxygen by gas chromatography. Anal. Chem., *36*: 1669-1671.

SWINNERTON, J. W., and V. J. LINNENBOM. 1967. Gaseous hydrocarbons in sea water: determination. Science, *156*: 1119-1120.

SWINNERTON, J. W., and V. J. LINNENBOM. 1967. Determination of C_1 to C_4 hydrocarbons in sea water by gas chromatography. J. Gas Chromatogr., *5*: 570-573.

CHEMICAL STRUCTURES OF COLOR PRODUCING ORGANIC SUBSTANCES IN WATER

R. F. Christman
Dept. of Civil Engineering
University of Washington
Seattle, Wash. 98105

INTRODUCTION

The general physical and gross chemical properties of the natural product organic material responsible for the yellow color of fresh water have been well documented (Shapiro, 1957; Christman and Ghassemi, 1966). These materials are often referred to as "fulvic acids", which implies their complex, polyphenolic nature and their relation to soil or sedimentary organic matter. Estimates of the molecular weights of these acids have varied from 180 to 10,000 (Shapiro, 1964 and 1966; Gjessing, 1965). An extensive association with iron appears to be a general property.

So little is known regarding the chemical structure of these macromolecules that it is not possible to judge the degree of similarity among colored fresh waters of different geographic origin. Certainly variation does exist. It has recently been noted that different waters of equal color value (100 color units on the chloroplatinate scale) contain anywhere from 10 to 30 mg C/liter (Christman and Ghassemi, 1966).

Knowledge of the chemical structures of lignitic and soil humic substances has been substantially advanced within the last decade as a result of degradative studies of these complex natural products (Sarkanen, 1963; Christman and Oglesby, 1968). Although the macromolecular structure of these materials remains speculative, their phenolic nature is well established. Our recent research efforts have focused on the development of mild degradative techniques for color-producing substances isolated from natural waters so that the relation of color to environmental soil and vegetative conditions as well as the significance of these organics to the aqueous biologic community may be better understood.

METHODS

Sample concentration

Colored waters used in this study were obtained from a low-color stream in the Sultan River valley near Sultan, Washington, and a high-color lake (Lake Thomas) near Snohomish, Washington. Samples were collected in five-gallon polyethylene drums and subjected only to rough filtration prior to vacuum concentration at temperatures not exceeding 50 C. After approximately twenty-fold concentration the color samples were dialyzed against constant changes of fresh water for 48 hours.

The concentrated and dialyzed water samples were next frozen and the remainder of the water was sublimed in a high capacity lyophilizer unit assembled in our laboratory. The lyophilizer apparatus consists of two stainless steel cylinder halves. The top half (2″ x 25″) has 48 attachment ports welded onto the cylinder. The bottom half (3″ x 10″) is a water trap designed so that the air travels down through the center to the bottom of the cylinder, then up along the outside wall to an exit port connected to a vacuum pump. A Dewar flask containing dry ice in acetone (-70 C) is placed around the outside of the lower cylinder to provide a coolant for the water trap. The sample is placed in a thick-walled vacuum filter flask which is then capped with a rubber stopper and joined to one of the attachment ports with vacuum tubing. All joints are sealed with a suitable high-vacuum grease. The system is then evacuated.

Up to four flasks have been operated at the same time. The system is able to remove approximately 8 ml H_2O/flask/hr. Limiting the number of flasks does not affect the rate of sublimation, so the most rapid removal is attained by using several one-liter flasks simultaneously.

The solid residue (color solids) obtained in this manner is virtually ash-free and is completely and easily redissolved in water. Gel filtration samples were subjected only to vacuum concentration prior to elution on the Sephadex columns.

Degradation

Oxidative degradation was performed in a stainless steel oxidation bomb. Reactants and weight ratios employed were: 250 mg color solids, 250 mg $CuSO_4$, 1.5 g NaOH and 10 ml water. After reagent addition, the bomb and its contents were purged with nitrogen for 15 minutes. For good degradation it is essential to deoxygenate the bomb prior to heating. The bomb was then sealed and shaken in an oven at 180 C for 3.0 hours. After cooling the pH was adjusted to 1.0 with H_2SO_4 and the aqueous phase exhaustively extracted with ethyl ether.

Reductive degradation was performed under total reflux at atmospheric pressure. Color solids, 250 mg or less, were dissolved in 100 ml of 10% NaOH containing 50 g 3% sodium amalgam (3% sodium in mercury). The system was boiled under reflux for at least three hours. During the reductions the color of the aqueous phase invariably changed from a rich brown-black to a grey-green color. After cooling, the aqueous portion was decanted from the remaining free mercury, acidified and extracted with ether.

To ensure reproducible results with either the oxidative or reductive procedures it is essential that the organic extractions be performed immediately and that the residue after solvent evaporation be stored until dry in a nitrogen-filled dessicator. The phenolic degradation products found by these procedures are apparently subject to rapid oxidation and perhaps re-polymerization in the presence of oxygen.

The total ether extractable yields from the degradation procedures are appreciable (30 to 40%) and are slightly better for the reductive than for the oxidative technique.

Chromatographic separation

Adequate resolution of the degradation mixture can be obtained on thin layers of Silica Gel G with various solvent systems and detection sprays described by Christman and Ghassemi (1966).

More satisfactory results can be obtained by converting the degradation products to trimethylsilyl ethers and esters and resolving the mixtures gas chromatographically. The thoroughly dried residue from the solvent extraction was mixed with 2.0 ml of BSA [N,O-bis-(trimethylsilyl)acetamide] obtained from Pierce Chemical Company, Rockford, Illinois. Fifteen minutes were allowed for completion of the silylation reaction before the entire volume, now exhibiting a rich yellow color, was placed in a vial and covered with a serum cap prior to injection into the gas chromatograph.

The gas chromatograph was a Hewlett-Packard Series 700 dual column instrument equipped with hydrogen flame detection. The stationary phase was silicone gum SE-30 on acid-washed Chromasorb W, packed in 1/8 inch stainless steel columns three feet long. Injection block and detector temperatures were maintained at 235 C. Column temperature normally was 140 C, although for work exclusively with flavinoid or polyhydroxy aromatic acids temperatures of 220 C are preferable.

Size distribution and iron association

Effluents from the gel filtration columns were monitored for carbon, absorbance at 350 mμ, fluorescence emission at 490 mμ and total iron. All samples were excluded from G-10 and included on G-75 Sephadex, although there was some evidence of adsorption of the color in the latter case and on G-25 columns. Six different colored waters gave similar elution profiles (Fig. 1). Although there are two distinct patterns the molecular weights relative to dextrans are apparently slightly less than 10,000 with a small fraction in excess of 50,000. Increasing the pH tends to increase and broaden the size spectrum (Fig. 2). Iron was associated with all size fractions of color, although in the pH range 7 to 8 iron apparently is less strongly bound and appears in the effluent beyond the inclusion volume limit. At all other pH values the carbon, absorbance and iron values coincided. A strong chelating agent was not able to remove all the iron from the color macromolecules and was least efficient in stripping iron from the largest size fractions (Fig. 3).

Degradation

Evaluation of mixtures produced during degradation requires familiarity with the response of the trimethylsilyl derivatives of known structures in the chromatographic system. Model compounds representing the types of aromatic substitution patterns likely to be found in water that has contacted soil and vegetation are rapidly and reasonably well separated by this technique (Tables 1 and 2).

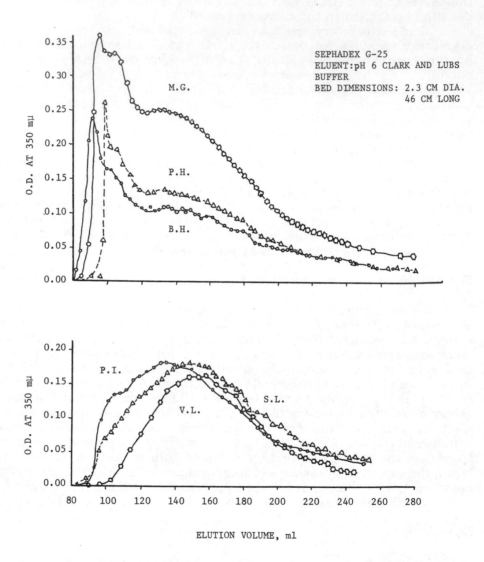

Fig. 1. Elution profiles for six different colored waters.

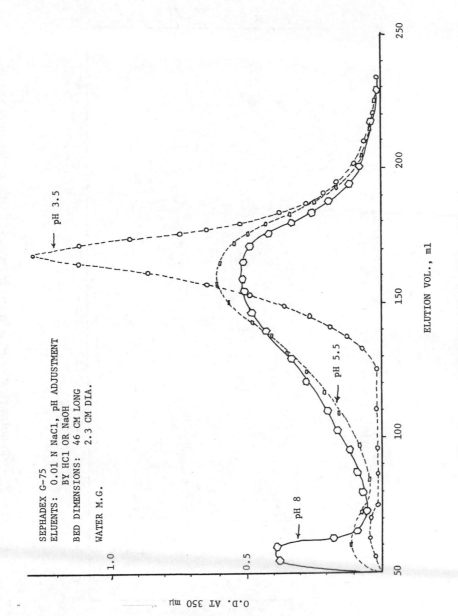

SEPHADEX G-75
ELUENTS: 0.01 N NaCl, pH ADJUSTMENT
BY HCl OR NaOH
BED DIMENSIONS: 46 CM LONG
2.3 CM DIA.

WATER M.G.

pH 3.5

pH 5.5

pH 8

O.D. AT 350 mµ

ELUTION VOL., ml

Fig. 2.   Effect of pH on molecular size.

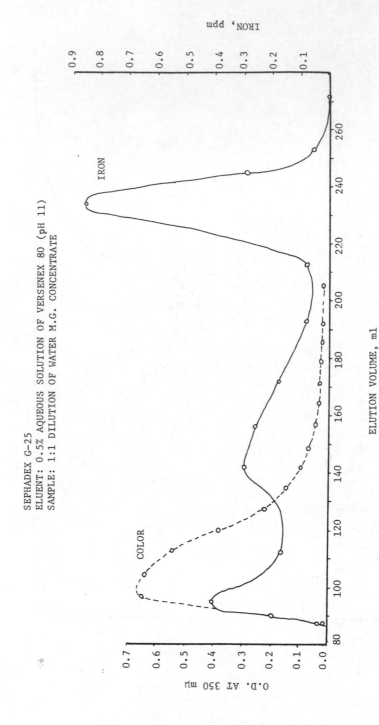

SEPHADEX G-25
ELUENT: 0.5% AQUEOUS SOLUTION OF VERSENEX 80 (pH 11)
SAMPLE: 1:1 DILUTION OF WATER M.G. CONCENTRATE

Fig. 3.   Iron-color relationship in the presence of strong chelating agents.

Table 1. Relative retention times of TMS derivatives of selected phenols.

Model compound	Relative retention (R_{cresol})
Phenols	
phenol	-*
catechol	2.1
resorcinol	2.5
phloroglucinol	8.7
o-methoxyphenol	1.4
p-methoxyphenol	1.7
p-methylphenol	1.0
orcinol	3.6
2-methylresorcinol	4.1
vanillin	4.8
acetovanillone	6.1

*appears under solvent window

Table 2. Relative retention times of TMS derivatives of selected phenolic and methoxylated acids.

Model compound	Relative retention (R_{cresol})
benzoic acid	1.5
p-methylbenzoic acid	2.2
p-methoxybenzoic acid	4.3
m-methoxybenzoic acid	3.5
hydrocinnamic acid	2.9
3,4-dimethoxyhydrocinnamic acid	-*
o-hydroxybenzoic acid	4.1
m-hydroxybenzoic acid	5.2
p-hydroxybenzoic acid	6.8
2,3-DHBA**	15.0
2,4-DHBA	13.6
2,5-DHBA	12.0
3,4-DHBA	20.5
3,5-DHBA	8.2
2,4,6-THBA	-*

*does not appear

** dihydroxybenzoic acid

Emergence from the column in order of increasing retention times is as follows:

phenol < methylphenol < benzoic acid < methoxylphenol
< dihydroxyphenol ≅ methyl acid < methoxyl acid
< monohydroxy acid < polyhydroxy acid

Structures apparently present in degraded mixtures of color solids are shown in Table 3. These identifications should be regarded as tentative since matching retention times have been obtained on one column only, although agreement is good at different temperatures. For the CuO oxidation, many of the same components have been detected using TLC. Benzoic acid, cresol, guaiacol and p-hydroxybenzoic acid, however, were not detected.

In interpreting these results knowledge of the effects of each degradation technique on known structures is important. Alkaline CuO oxidation is capable of breaking alkyl C-C linkages when the aromatic ring is sufficiently activated (Fig. 4). Thus protocatechuic acid is partially decarboxylated, forming catechol, and 2,4-DHBA similarly forms resorcinol. In the absence of ring activation (ortho or para location of hydroxyl) no cleavage or decarboxylation occurs. Sodium amalgam reduction, however, is not capable of alkyl C-C cleavage; hydrogen evolution serves only to deoxygenate the aqueous phase during alkaline hydrolysis. In addition no reduction of model compound carboxylic acids was observed. Both techniques should result in extensive hydrolysis of ester and ether linkages due to the strongly alkaline environment and the elevated temperatures.

For alkaline CuO oxidation it is apparent that:

a. Aromatic rings survive the oxidation in all cases. Therefore, it seems likely that no aromatic structures in the parent color molecule are destroyed during oxidation.

b. Alkyl side chains are cleaved to one carbon acid functions only when the aromatic ring is activated by the appropriate hydroxylation pattern. The absence of alkyl side chains containing two or more carbon atoms in the identified color oxidation products thus indicates that unsubstituted aromatic rings are a relatively unimportant structural feature of the parent molecule. However, the absence of appreciable alkyl substituents among the aromatic oxidation products does not preclude their existence in the parent molecule. It is quite probable that the aromatic nuclei are linked in natural color through extensive side chain networks. As long as all of the rings are activated these chains would be cleaved and reduced to one carbon acid functions during oxidation.

c. The loss of the carboxylic acid group depends on ring activation. It seems justifiable, therefore, to consider 2,4- and 2,6-dihydroxybenzoic acids as intermediate oxidation products of color converted to resorcinol during oxidation. Similarly protocatechuic acid produces catechol during oxidaton. The possibility that catechol and resorcinol actually exist in the parent molecule in ester or weak ether linkages is negated by the fact that acid hydrolysis of unoxidized color solids failed to produce these phenols.

d. Since no aromatic polycarboxylic acids were found in the oxidation mixtures, aromatic rings in the parent molecule containing a

Table 3. Components of oxidative and reductive degradation mixtures of color solids.

Compound	Alkaline CuO oxidation	Na-amalgam reduction
catechol	+	+
resorcinol	+	-
p-methylphenol	+	++*
o-methoxylphenol	+	++
benzoic acid	+	++
3,4-dihydroxybenzoic acid	+	-
3,5-dihydroxybenzoic acid	+	-
vanillin	+	+
vanillic acid	+	-
syringic acid	+	-
p-hydroxybenzoic acid	+	+

*++ indicates greater concentration

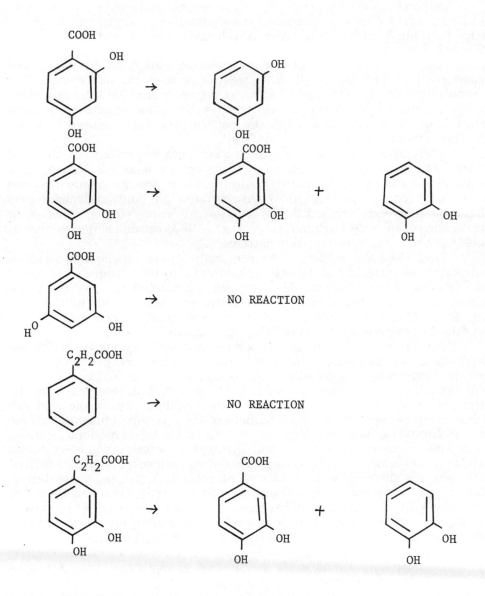

Fig. 4.   **Effect of CuO oxidation on known structures.**

substituent carboxyl group are probably bound in the macromolecule through ether linkages. In addition, the absence of polybasic acids in the oxidation mixtures indicates that there is only one alkyl-aryl carbon-carbon linkage per ring in the original molecule.

In light of these mechanisms it is attractive to regard the aromatic acids in Table 3, with the exception of p-hydroxybenzoic and benzoic acids, as more basic structural elements, core structures of the macromolecule, which can be found by means of extensive alkylation of the unoxidized material (Fig. 5). Under reductive treatment they do not appear. The phenols and simple acids must be found primarily through ester and ether linkages liberated by extensive base hydrolysis. In the reductive procedure when the absence of oxygen is more certain they are produced in much greater concentrations.

It is interesting that the substitution patterns present in the acid "core" are not exclusively derivable from lignitic material. Native lignin contains no meta-oriented hydroxylation patterns and apparently contains exclusively syringyl, guaiacyl, or p-hydroxy aromatic moities, depending on the type of wood. The extractive fraction of woody tissue, other plant substances of microbial action (Martin et al., 1967) provide ample sources of such meta-oriented hydroxylation patterns.

That the color molecule is structurally similar to those in aqueous extractives of wood and in soil organic matter is apparent from the similarity of their oxidation products. All compounds identified in color oxidation mixtures were also found in wood extractive samples oxidized by the same procedure. These compounds, with the exception of syringic acid are also produced during the oxidation of soil organic matter.

The presence of m-dihydroxyphenols and acids among the oxidation products is understandable when one considers a structural pattern found in certain extractives. Quercetin, for example, upon oxidation yields phloroglucinol, 3,4-dihydroxybenzoic acid and catechol, resulting from the cleavage of the pyran ring. Similarly, the 3,5-dihydroxybenzoic acid can conceivably come from the oxidation of certain stilbenes. These m-dihydroxy configurations bear no relation to the lignin monomeric units. Even the discovery of guaiacyl and syringyl structures in the oxidation products of color is not sufficient reason to suspect that lignin-derived materials are involved in the structure of color to any appreciable degree. Tannins and some other extractives contain these lignin-type structures; the oxidation of bark extract confirms this. Although this point must be further investigated, it has been definitely established that lignin is not the sole precursor of color in water. In addition the aqueous phase left after ether extraction of the degraded samples has given in all cases an intense positive ninhydrin reaction. Amino acids are present in significant concentrations although their structures have not been determined.

This technique appears to offer a significant research tool for relating the nature of aqueous organic material to environmental conditions. At the time of this writing many questions remain unanswered. The components in Table 3 were observable in all waters studied. This is not to imply that qualitative variations do not exist among different waters, merely that those

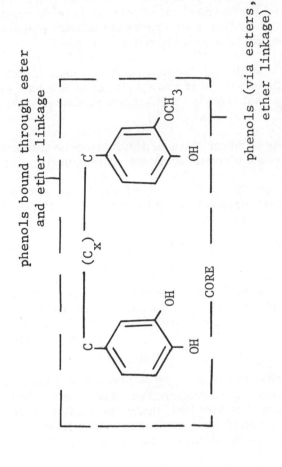

phenols bound through ester and ether linkage

phenols (via esters, ether linkage)

Fig. 5. Symbolic description of unoxidized macromolecule.

compounds tentatively identified have been found in all waters. Several well defined chromotographic peaks have not been identified. These occur in all samples at R_{cresol} values of 0.68 and 0.87 and are apparently simple structures. No attempt has been made to quantify these results.

DISCUSSION

BARSDATE: I understand that your molecular weight spectrum ended rather abruptly at something on the order of 50,000. Is this correct? Is there anything in the pretreatment that is applied to the samples that would cause it to do this? In other words, have you filtered the samples?

CHRISTMAN: We have subjected them to only a rough filtration; i.e., I made attempts to get the leaves and the wood chips out. We have exercised a modicum of caution in that regard. I think I would answer your question, "No".

MALCOLM: What is the titration curve of the hydrogen-saturated material you obtained from the crude-colored substances after concentration?

CHRISTMAN: I have not titrated them. Some titrations were done on the unoxidized and unreduced materials in the early phases of the work. In fact, Shapiro had reported some of these.

MALCOLM: My question concerned the native materials, unoxidized or unreduced.

CHRISTMAN: These materials in the aqueous titrations show a very poorly defined equivalence point. Non-aqueous titrations, which I had done before this degradation work, show a much stronger break, but only one break. They apparently are mono-acidic, at least if there was not some leveling effect exerted by my solvents.

MALCOLM: I know that partially hydrogen-saturated exudates may be washed from various canopies during rainfall. With these I had the same problem of concentration that you had, using the same techniques. When these materials were completely hydrogen-saturated by resin exchange they were very acidic so I was curious about the acidity of your materials.

CHRISTMAN: This was one of the first things known about them. They are apparently acid in nature. A pronounced carboxylic acidity has been read into some of the unoxidized IR spectra. I simply have not chosen to go along with that because, frankly, the IR spectrum looked like somebody sat on it while it was being determined. The only thing I can say about the acidity is that it is observable in the raw state. And in the non-aqueous titrations I have done in ethanolamine there is apparently a mono-acid function; i.e., I observed just one break in my titration curves. I have not gathered any more of that type of data. It was suggested to me by some of the people at the conference considering the nature of the functional groups on the rings that I have found, that some of them must have come from oxygenated side chains. Whether the side chains in the unoxidized materials contain oxygen I have not speculated on. My techniques obviously rake off the side chains. I have not tried to build any interpretation into the analysis. The carboxyl groups must be there but how would you account for the vanillin or the aldehydic substances on the ring I ended up with?

ZUBOVIC: Did you do any equivalent weight study on this?

CHRISTMAN: I only did the non-aqueous titrations.

ZUBOVIC: Was there indigenous iron?

CHRISTMAN: The ash content would be less than 5% for the cleaned up material.

ZUBOVIC: You did not do any analyses of the ash?

CHRISTMAN: No, I have not done any analyses of the ash yet. In fact, for the most recent samples, I do not even have a nitrogen analysis, but I would be surprised if it were higher than 2%. This is the largest I've seen. Some work has indicated that this material is the same as substances which appear in active microbial solutions. In J. P. Martin's work at Riverside, organisms that I do not understand were used (Martin, 1967). These are soil fungi of some description which, when fed glucose and asparagine for two to three weeks, excrete ten or eleven phenols of the methyldihydroxy phenolic type, orsonillic acid, methylpyrogallol, etc., nearly a dozen compounds. These phenols build up in concentration as the organisms grow. Amino acids begin to appear after about three weeks, then, the phenols and amino acids begin to disappear. A yellow color begins to appear in the solution, as well as what he calls humic acid, a substance which is precipitated by acid. I have not gone into that today. He was able to isolate this humic substance from the water, hydrolyze it, subject it to alkaline hydrolysis, and regenerate the phenols and amino acids. In so doing he found more carboxylic acid acidity than was originally present. It is as if after incorporation into the polymer, there was some microbial introduction of acidity.

BREZONIK: Apparently the iron is not an essential component of the color. A sample I picked up this summer in a swamp near Gainesville had about a thousand ppm of color and the iron content was about 1/10 ppm; in typical colored lakes around the area with color of 100 or 200 ppm, one finds 1/2 to 1 ppm iron.

CHRISTMAN: I have found no correlation between iron and color values in natural water samples.

BREZONIK: Russ Plum, one of Fred Lee's students, has done considerable Sephadex elution work on color, and he told me there is apparently a change in the elution pattern with concentration.

CHRISTMAN: I have talked with Russ Plum and I have seen his data. I cannot say that I have made the same observation, if that is your question.

DUURSMA: In relation to the iron you have mentioned, have you also investigated combinations with other metals? With copper, zinc or cobalt?

CHRISTMAN: No, I have not looked for cobalt, copper or zinc in the material.

DUURSMA: You have looked preferentially for iron?

CHRISTMAN: Yes, of course, as I said at the outset, one of the reasons I began this work was our concern about the removal of humic substances from water. This leads to the area of stability constant determination, and one is faced, as Dr. Morgan is faced right now, with studying the stability constants of something of which you don't know the structure. In connection with doing this, we have been trying to determine the classical precipitation curves of this color with, say, aluminum or iron sulphates. If the sample is sufficiently alkaline the addition of aluminum or iron removes the color over a narrow pH range of, say 4.5 to 5.5, sometimes up to 6.0. But in the presence of calcium, manganese, cobalt, zinc and several other such elements, the removal curve is extended to the basic side of the pH. Whether this is associated solely with basic precipitation of the hydrous oxides of these metals, I do not know. I do know that a little calcium does, for instance, widen the pH range of the removed curve, so these materials do interact with it. One other thing: the materials are extremely fluorescent in the natural state, and their excitation peaks are generally in the vicinity of 300 mμ. Their major fluorescent emission is centered around 490 mμ. The fluorescent spectra of some of the flavonoid compounds vary all over the map. Adding a trace of iron to the same flavonoids shifts their fluorescent spectra down to match the natural color of water centering around 490 or 500 mμ.

BREGER: I would like to suggest that you try to compare the results of this degradation to that of lignin. Lignin could be the progenator of such substances, however, I would expect it to decompose early in chemical transformations leading to the compounds you are considering. Rather, I would suggest that this degradation might be much more similar to that of the humic acids in soil or low rank coals which, under the same conditions, provide the same general spectrum of types of compounds, including vanollin, vanillic acids and the whole gamut of type compounds that you refer to here. I am also concerned about the iron. Is there proof that the iron is directly associated with these materials, or that it is even present? We have spent a lot of time trying to get iron into these compounds and it doesn't go very readily. Soil scientists have shown that humic substances analyzed from a physical-chemical point of view behave identically in the presence and absence of iron. I think there is an old term fallacy that perhaps the color in these groups is associated with an iron complex, whereas iron may not even be present. The presence of iron has to be shown without any question at all.

CHRISTMAN: I agree with what you have said, and I do not mean to present these materials as either humic acids or as lignins. I think it is reasonably clear that they are different. I have never seen a sample of the water, however, that did not yield appreciable iron when analyzed.

BREGER: But it may be present but not associated. As a matter of fact, if you try to put the iron in, the pH relationship is such that the iron probably hydrolyzes before it can react.

CHRISTMAN: The only evidence I can offer on that point, Dr. Breger, is that we get small iron association at the head end of our Sephadex effluent, and iron is adsorbed on the Sephadex, and there is no other way that this iron could get through my Sephadex column and appear at the same spot as the color and carbon effluents appear unless it is associated with color.

BREGER: Do you analyze this for iron?

CHRISTMAN: Oh, yes.

DUURSMA: One question more about fluorescence. Have you found, as the color suggests, that the fluorescence indicates the degree of condensation in the water? Does it show that it is less polymerized than in soil? If so, this means that you have not built up a very complex compound and that in water there tends to be a maximum size. Have you confirmed this?

CHRISTMAN: No, other than the fact that there is a remarkable uniformity in the fluorescence behavior of waters from many sources. I have not studied the fluorescence of soil or of extracts of soils. Simple extracts I have made of soil sometimes exhibit different fluorescence spectra.

DUURSMA: I saw a Russian paper in which the origin of sea water was traced to the North Sea, the Rhine, the Thames and other rivers on the basis of slight differences in fluorescence.

COHEN: With regard to fluorescence, we found that in Alaskan waters when we tried to correlate fluorescence with color by means of removal studies, color concentration dropped from about 80 to about 5 color units but 80% of the fluorescence remained.

CHRISTMAN: It's so sensitive, in fact, that to get Sephadex profiles of natural water without concentrating it one need only monitor the fluorescence in the effluent. The profiles are the same as would be obtained monitoring carbon on concentrates.

REFERENCES

CHRISTMAN, R. F., and M. GHASSEMI. 1966. Chemical nature of organic color in water. Amer. Water Works Ass., *58*: 723-741.

CHRISTMAN, R. F., and R. T. OGLESBY. In press. Chapter 18. The microbiological degredation of lignin and the formation of humus. *In* K. V. Sarkanen and C. H. Ludwig [ed.], Lignins, chemistry and utilization. Interscience, New York.

GJESSING, E. T. 1965. Use of sephadex gel for the estimation of molecular weight of humic substances in natural water. Nature, *208*: 1091-1092.

MARTIN, J. P., S. J. RICHARDS, and K. HAIDER. 1967. Properties and decomposition and binding action in soil of humic acid synthesized by *Epicoccum nigrum*. Soil Sci. Amer., Proc., *31*: 657-662.

SARKANEN, K. V. 1963. Chapter 10. Wood lignins, p. 249-311. *In* B. L. Browning [ed.], The chemistry of wood. Wiley, New York.

SHAPIRO, J. 1957. Chemical and biological studies on the yellow organic acids of lake water. Limnol. Oceanogr., *2*: 161-179.

SHAPIRO, J. 1964. Effect of yellow organic acids on iron and other metals in water. Amer. Water Works Ass., *56*: 1062-1082.

SHAPIRO, J. 1966. Yellow organic acids of lake water: differences in their composition and behavior. Paper presented at Symp. Hung. Hydro. Soc. Budapest-Tihany. Sept. 25-28, 1966.

GENERAL DISCUSSION AFTER SESSION I

HOLM-HANSEN: Dr. Menzel, I wonder if you would repeat and elaborate on two points. The first is your statement that the particulate matter contains no phosphorus. The second is your statement about changes in the C/N ratio with depth. Would you correlate that with the presentations of Drs. Handa and Degens (this volume)?

MENZEL: That is a misunderstanding; I was referring to the dissolved and not the particulate material. I have not done enough with the C/N ratio in particulate matter to know anything about it. As a matter of fact, when you get samples that we consider very clean for nitrogen and for carbon, unless you filter tremendous quantities of water, you do not get enough nitrogen for an accurate determination. In other words, if you have 3 or 4 μg C/liter and nitrogen is at a normal ratio of 6:1, you have to concentrate large volumes. Now the precision of the nitrogen measurements is roughly 1 μg ± 1 μg, so if you filter 6 liters, you have a 50% error.

HOLM-HANSEN: Which nitrogen procedure is this?

MENZEL: This is on a Perkin-Elmer automatic CHN analyzer.

HOLM-HANSEN: You can do better by using the hydrindantin-ninhydrin colorimetric procedure, which enables you to measure as little as 0.1 μg of nitrogen per sample. This means that you can get by with only 1 liter of deep water.

MENZEL: I have not done that. I would say that if you take all the numbers that you obtain and average all these numbers across the ocean, then the nitrogen content of the particulate matter decreases with depth, it does not go up. It is about 10:1. That is about what you get, isn't it?

HOLM-HANSEN: Yes.

DUURSMA: There was a problem involved in this particulate matter, also, in that there was a constant value all over the deep ocean. Dr. Goldberg (this volume) said that it might be from adsorption of organic matter on air dust. Is it also possible that these particles are so small that normal water turbulence can maintain them in steady state suspension? If so, one should know something about the particulate size, the falling rate and the turbulence of the water. Is this known?

MENZEL: I do not know. It is a good possibility.

DEGENS: An alternative possibility is related to the molecular weight and the size of the organic matter. I have found particles and compounds in this so called "dissolved organic matter" with molecular weights exceeding

10,000. Since we make the arbitrary separation between dissolved and particulate organic matter at the 0.4 μ level, it is conceivable that these high molecular weight compounds behave mechanically like the particulate organic matter, and thus increase in certain profiles or decrease in certain profiles, causing the variations in distribution observed among hydroprofiles. Actually, then, this would be a semi- or sub-particulate material which settles to the bottom of the sea like particulate organic matter. If the difference can be thus explained, we do not have to rely on turbulence or on the contribution from air dust.

DUURSMA: Have you any figures regarding these possibilities, Dr. Goldberg?

GOLDBERG: Yes, I cannot give them to you offhand, but they are calculable on the basis of the measured standing crops of the dust in the air and Stokes' law of settling velocities. Most people studying the fate of dust particles in the ocean believe they do not fall particle by particle, but most probably are accumulated into larger masses by organisms in the surface waters.

PRAKASH: I want to comment on Dr. Christman's reference to fluorescence. We have been measuring fluorescence in yellow waters and find that fluorescence is related partially to the proportion of humic and fulvic acids in the sample. Fulvic acid fluoresces more than the low molecular weight humic acids and the high molecular weight humic acids do not fluoresce at all.

SESSION II. BIOLOGICAL PRODUCTION AND UTILIZATION OF ORGANIC MATTER IN NATURAL WATERS

Chairman: M.B. Allen
Department of Biological Sciences
University of Alaska
College, Alaska 99701

The importance of both the production and utilization of organic matter in natural waters is evidenced by the profound effect of organic micronutrients such as vitamins produced by aquatic microorganisms on the growth of other microorganisms and the contributions of extracellular organic products of photosynthetic organisms to heterotrophic growth of various microbes.

The influence of dissolved organic compounds on higher animals may be less certain (although the effect of algal toxins should not be forgotten), but particulate organic matter is certainly important to the feeding of many invertebrates.

The role of organic matter is of special interest to us here in the North, where large standing stocks of phytoplankton and benthic plants are maintained despite the fact that these organisms live much of the year in near or complete darkness. Heterotrophic metabolism of these organisms is the most likely explanation of this phenomenon.

PRODUCTION AND TRANSFORMATION OF EXTRACELLULAR ORGANIC MATTER FROM LITTORAL MARINE ALGAE: A RESUME.

John McN. Sieburth and Arne Jensen
Narragansett Marine Laboratory
University of Rhode Island
Kingston, Rhode Island 02881

Norwegian Institute of Seaweed Research
N.T.H.
Trondheim, Norway

ABSTRACT

Published and unpublished observations on *Fucus vesiculosus* summarize our studies of the general nature of extracellular organic matter production by phaeophytes and the fate of this material in sea water. When precautions were taken to minimize bacterial activity, exudation during photosynthesis averaged 42 mg C/100 g dry weight of algae/hr. Exudation also occurred as a result of desiccation and rain during emersion. Total exudation accounts for some 40% of the net carbon fixed. A small but visible yellow fraction appears to be formed as a result of polyphenol condensation with carbohydrate and proteinaceous material. This humic material (Gelbstoff) slowly builds in size until it precipitates as organic aggregates. In littoral marine waters, the algae, dominated by the brown seaweeds, may be a major source of primary production via the transformation of extracellular organic matter to bacterial biomass and chemically produced organic aggregates.

INTRODUCTION

Primary productivity in the sea has been classically thought of in terms of the productivity and standing crops of phytoplankton which are grazed directly. Interest in the dissolved organic constituents of sea water has been largely of an analytical nature (Vallentyne, 1957) or due to their growth-enhancing and growth-inhibiting properties (Lucas, 1961; Nigrelli, 1958). Appreciable excretion rates of the unicellular algae (Hellebust, 1965; Fogg, 1966) have focused attention on the phytoplankton as the primary source of dissolved organic matter in natural waters. The benthic seaweeds, whose standing crops are a hundred times as great as those of phytoplankton in littoral waters (Blinks, 1955), have largely been ignored (Strickland, 1965). In regard to biomass the brown algae (*Phaeophyta*) are the dominant group in polar, subpolar and many temperate waters. The ability of these rockweeds and kelps to produce extracellular organic matter has been studied only with regard to their ability to produce yellow substances (Khailov, 1963; Craigie and McLachlan, 1964) which may contribute to the Gelbstoff of sea water noted by Kalle (1937, 1966). Our data on *Fucus vesiculosus* illustrate the emerging picture of the production of extracellular organic matter by phaeophytes and its transformation in sea water as part of the food chain (Sieburth, 1969; Sieburth and Jensen, 1968, 1969). Organic carbon was determined in acidified CO_2 degassed samples (nitrogen sparging) by the combustion of 20 to 50 μliter portions to form CO_2 which was measured in an infrared analyzer.

EXUDATION DURING IMMERSION

In stagnant raw sea water with its natural microflora, extracellular seaweed substances may be consumed rapidly except for a small but visible yellow fraction which is more refractory to attack. Fig. 1 shows the effect of water exchange rate on the apparent exudation of extracellular organic matter from *Fucus vesiculosus*. The plants were wired onto a frame attached to the shaft of a low speed motor and rotated in a water-jacketed open separatory funnel in natural sunlight while either raw or 0.45 μ membrane-filtered sea water flowed from a reservoir to maintain a constant volume. The flow rate was controlled by the gauge of the hypodermic needle inserted in the effluent tube. Increasing the flow rate up to the point where the samples became too dilute for analysis increased the apparent rate of exudation. The difference in exudation between filtered and raw sea water at low and moderate dilution rates indicates that the epiphytic microflora as well as the planktonic bacterial flora in the raw sea water utilize the extracellular algal substances at an appreciable rate.

Average exudation values obtained during spring for photosynthesizing plants at normal salinities, temperatures and solar radiation were 44.6, 41.6, 37.8 and 31.3 mg C/100 g/hr for *Laminaria digitata*, *Fucus vesiculosus*, *Laminaria agardhii* and *Ascophyllum nodosum* respectively.

Physical factors which affect the rate of exudation from *Fucus vesiculosus* are shown in Fig. 2. As salinity and solar radiation decrease, the rate of exudation decreases in a linear manner. Unlike *Fucus vesiculosus*, which did not exude during respiration, *Laminaria agardhii* and *Laminaria digitata* were quite leaky in the dark, the rate being some 60% of that during photosynthesis. Increasing the temperature, which up to a point speeds up the rate of photosynthesis, had the opposite effect on exudation by *Fucus vesiculosus* and *Ascophyllum nodosum*. This is probably an artifact of the increased rate of metabolism in the epiphytic microflora as temperature increases.

EXUDATION RESULTING FROM EMERSION

Intertidal seaweeds such as *Fucus vesiculosus* are out of water approximately half the time. The most obvious effect is desiccation; as much as 90% of the water content may be lost during a tidal exposure (Kanwisher, 1957). The correlation of moisture loss with exudation of organic carbon after reimmersion in sea water for 10 minutes (Fig. 3) shows the extreme case of fronds on the surface of the clumps hanging down from the rocks

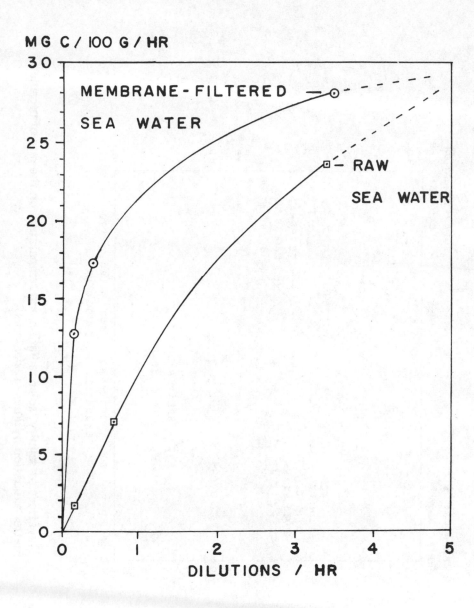

Fig. 1. The effect of the flow-rate of membrane-filtered sea water (effect of epiphytic bacterial flora) and raw sea water (effect of planktonic and epiphytic floras) on the apparent rate of exudation from *Fucus vesiculosus* (19 to 20 C, 30.84 °/oo S, and 24 to 35 anglies/hr solar radiation).

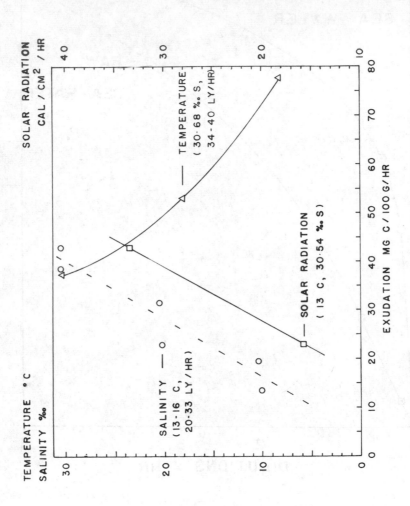

Fig. 2.   The effect of salinity, solar radiation and temperature on the rate of organic matter exudation by *Fucus vesiculosus*.

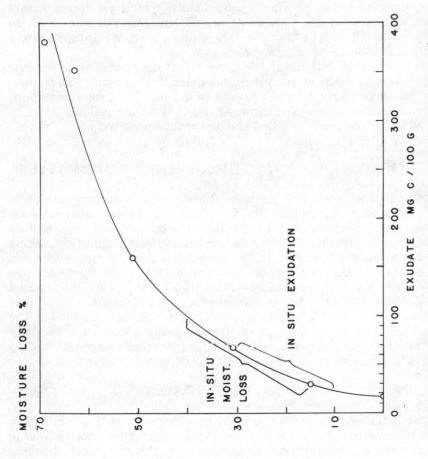

Fig. 3. Correlation of moisture loss with loss of organic matter upon reimmersion of surface fronds of *Fucus vesiculosus*. The range of values for cross-section of naturally exposed algae shows *in situ* changes.

which protect the underlying fronds and conserve their moisture. Moisture loss and exudation observed in cross-sections of clumps of *Fucus vesiculosus* left *in situ* on the rocks is indicated in Fig. 3. An average exudation value was 39 mg C/100 g.

The effect of rain on the release of extracellular organic matter from a number of intertidal species is shown in Fig. 4. Considering that this was a light shower of short duration, the amount of exudation was appreciable. This was particularly true of *Fucus vesiculosus*, which yielded a highly yellow-orange exudate at the rate of 46 mg C/100 g/mm of rain. With an average spring rainfall of 2.08 mm/day this would amount to approximately 46 mg C/100 g for the 12-hour exposure day.

Freezing at -15 C had about the same effect on exudation as holding at 5 C for the same period before reimmersion in sea water. Therefore, winter temperatures encountered in Rhode Island and the Trondheimsfjord would have little effect upon exudation. At -30 C, however, cellular integrity was affected and a loss equal to 3% of the dry weight occurred upon thawing in sea water.

ESTIMATE OF CONTRIBUTION TO DISSOLVED ORGANIC MATTER

A daily balance sheet for photosynthesis, respiration and exudation for *Fucus vesiculosus* in spring is shown in Table 1. These plants are only immersed for approximately half of the illuminated day and total carbon fixed approximates 1100 mg C/100 g during this period. Respiration, taking into account reduced metabolism in the desiccated state, amounts to some 280 mg C/100 g, so that net carbon fixation is 820 mg C/100 g. Average exudation values for illuminated immersion (250 mg C/100 g), exposed desiccation (40 mg C/100 g) and rainwater extraction (50 mg C/100 g) total some 340 mg C/100 g during a 24-hour period. This suggests that 30% of the total carbon and 40% of the net carbon fixed is exuded into sea water daily by this plant. *Laminaria* species, which are not normally exposed but do exude during respiration, appear to have similar exudation values.

COMPOSITION OF EXUDATES

Extracellular organic matter exuded by seaweeds must be soluble in sea water at a pH of 7.5 to 8.5. This eliminates many water-insoluble constituents such as lipids, pigments and most of the structural elements such as cellulose, polysaccharides and proteins (Mautner, 1954). Among the most obvious of the water-soluble group are the polyphenols in the physodes of the cortical cells which can make up 10% of the dry matter. Although the individual polyphenols present vary from species to species, their properties and activities are similar.

The largest fraction of the exudates appears to be carbohydrates. Undoubtedly some of this is due to ascophyllan, laminarin and especially fucoidan. However, the major product of photosynthesis and the major substrate for respiration in *Fucus vesiculosus* is the major low-molecular carbohydrate, D-mannitol (Bidwell, 1967). Other low-molecular

Table 1. A daily balance sheet of photosynthesis, respiration and exudation for *Fucus vesiculosus* (Spring).

	mg C/100 g
Photosynthesis (Ghr immersed illumination)	
Net C fixed = Ghr @ 170 mg C/100 g/hr =	1020
Respiration = Ghr @ 13 mg C/100 g/hr =	78
Total C fixed minus =	1098
Total respiration = Net C fixed =	882
Respiration	
Immersed = 12 hr @ 13 mg C/100 g/hr =	156
Emersed (partially desiccated) = 12 hr @ 10 mg C/100 g/hr =	120
Total respiration	276
Exudation	
Immersed = Ghr @ 42 mg C/100 g/hr =	252
Emersed, 1 desiccation @ 39 mg C/100 g =	39
1 rain @ 46 mg C/100 g =	46
Total exudation	337

30.7% total carbon fixed.
41.0% net carbon fixed.

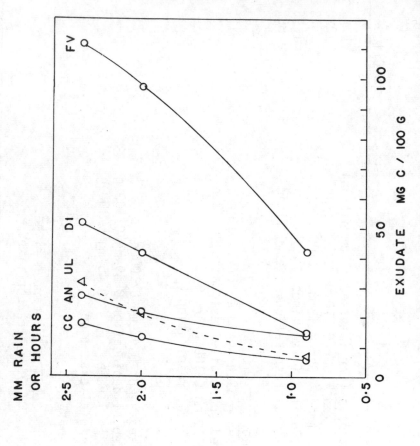

Fig. 4. The rate of exudation of organic matter during a light natural rain from *Chondrus crispus* (CC), *Ascophyllum nodosum* (AN), *Ulva lactuca* (UL), *Dumontia incrassata* (DI) and *Fucus vesiculosus* (FV).

carbohydrates found in *Fucus vesiculosus* are a monoacetate, a monoglucoside and a diglucoside of mannitol (Lindberg, 1953). The ratio of reducing to non-reducing and low to high molecular carbohydrates in the exudates has not been determined.

A highly variable constituent of the exudate is ninhydrin-reacting material. Smith and Young (1953) found that in *Fucus vesiculosus* the total organic nitrogen content varied between 1 and 3% of total solids. Of this, volatile nitrogen compounds (ammonia, methylamine and trimethylamine) were 2 to 3%, free amino acids 10% and peptides 7 to 8%. The remaining 80% appeared to be hard-to-extract protein. One would expect that the nitrogenous constituents of the exudates would be largely the 20% fraction of lower molecular compounds, especially the amino acids and peptides.

Colorimetric tests for carbohydrates (phenol-sulfuric) expressed as glucose, nitrogenous compounds (ninhydrin) expressed as α-alanine, and polyphenols (brentamine fast red 2G) expressed as phloroglucinol were carried out in all the exudate experiments only as an indication of the nature of the exudates. Exudates obtained during photosynthesis had nitrogenous concentrations below the detectable level. The ratio of carbohydrates to polyphenols varied from 4:1 to 1:1 in the browns. Exudates resulting from desiccation had carbohydrate:nitrogenous:polyphenol ratios ranging from 3:2:1 in moderately desiccated plants to 2:3:1 after severe desiccation. Exudates resulting from rain water extraction had a carbohydrate:nitrogenous:polyphenol ratio of 2:1:1.5 while the ratio for exudates obtained upon thawing in sea water after freezing at -30 C for 4 hours was 1:4.5:1. It appears that carbohydrate and polyphenolic materials are the more usual products of exudation while nitrogenous compounds are liberated in greater concentrations during conditions which are injurious to the plant.

TRANSFORMATION TO GELBSTOFF

The constituents of normal exudation appear to be partly consumed by bacterial activity of the epiphytic and planktonic microflora. The transformation of a lightly colored exudate to a dark tea-colored solution is shown by the chromatograms in Fig. 5. A bucket of *Fucus vesiculosus* covered with sea water for 24 hours produced a sea water extract rich in phenols, which could be detected by direct paper chromatography. A large wet spot of the exudate on thick prewashed paper was developed first in water then in acetic acid — ethyl acetate — water (2:6:2). After the chromatogram was examined for yellow color visible in natural light and areas visible under UV light, it was stained with bis-diazotized benzidine, a polyphenolic reagent. At 1 day, 3 phenolic areas but no visible or UV spots were detected. By the third day material in areas 1 and 3 was yellow-brown in color and UV quenching. Deeply staining polyphenols streaked from the origin to near the front. The phenolic area to the right behaved similarly to phloroglucinol. A very complex picture was obtained on day 7. After 16 days only 2 lightly staining phenolic but visibly colored areas remained. Apparently, the slowly staining combined or precursor form of the

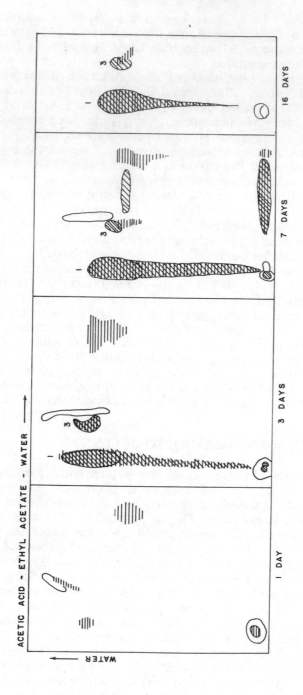

ACETIC ACID – ETHYL ACETATE – WATER ⟶

WATER ⟵

1 DAY   3 DAYS   7 DAYS   16 DAYS

Fig. 5. A series of paper chromatograms showing the change in a sea water extract of *Fucus vesiculosus* from colorless to highly yellow pigmented with humic material (Gelbstoff). The colorless polyphenolic precursors underwent a series of transformations to form the visible yellow pigmented areas 1 and 3. (Reprinted from Sieburth and Jensen, 1969.)

polyphenols was quickly transformed into rapidly staining polyphenols which apparently reacted with other substances to form lightly staining yellow substances (Gelbstoff) in areas 1 and 3.

SYNTHESIS OF GELBSTOFF

Ascophyllum nodosum was used since this alga showed a simple polyphenol composition initially in extracts of the thallus and in the exudates. Two-day sea water exudates (extracts) were separated on a column of G-15 Sephadex to yield fractions containing only detectable proteinaceous material, polyphenol precursor, or carbohydrates. Each fraction was mixed or diluted so that equal concentrations were achieved alone and in combination. The solutions were adjusted to pH 8.0. The resulting development of yellow color on standing is shown in Table 2. After 4 days the individual fractions were still quite colorless, while the addition of either the proteinaceous or the carbohydrate fractions to the polyphenol fraction measurably increased discoloration. The combination of all three was nearly additive. Similar results were obtained after 7 days. This and other experiments suggest that the Gelbstoff or humic fractions are condensates caused by the polyphenolic binding of carbohydrate and nitrogenous material under the mildly alkaline conditions of sea water and aided by natural solar radiation.

The polyphenol in fresh exudates appears to be in a precursor or combined form and as such is non-toxic to plaice larvae. Under alkaline conditions, such as in sea water, it is present as free polyphenol and has an LD_{50} of 0.32 mg/liter for young plaice larvae. In this free form, it rapidly tans either or both proteinaceous and carbohydrate material to form colored Gelbstoff material. This fraction is non-toxic for plaice larvae.

COMPARISON OF NATURAL GELBSTOFFS

Some 70% recovery of the humic material (Gelbstoff) in bog water, river water and sea water was achieved by the percolation of acidified samples through a column consisting of a rolled white crepe-nylon stocking. After rinsing with distilled water the larger humic materials were eluted with 0.1N sodium hydroxide, neutralized, and evaporated *in vacuo* to yield a 1:7000 concentration. This material was chromatographed in the same wet-spot manner as the exudates. This method, although not ideal, permits the separation of humic materials from various sources even when co-chromatographed. A composite chromatogram is shown in Fig. 6. The darker shaded areas are the Gelbstoff components. This procedure has shown that bog water material enters the rivers and that these terrestrial materials quickly disappear when they enter sea water. Humic material prepared from various phaeophyte species coincided closely with that obtained from inshore sea water samples. There is little doubt that marine Gelbstoff is primarily derived from extracellular substances exuded by brown seaweeds in the waters tested, thus confirming the speculations of Khailov (1963) and Craigie and McLachlan (1964).

Table 2. Synthesis of Gelbstoff by recombination of colorless Sephadex G-15 fractions of a 2-day sea water exudate of *Ascophyllum nodosum* (from Sieburth and Jensen, 1969).

Fraction (ml)	Dominant Component	Flask					
		1	2	3	4	5	6
90-95	Nitrogenous	X			X		X
115-123	Polyphenolic		X		X	X	X
55-62	Carbohydrate			X		X	X
O.D. 450 nm pH 8.0		0.006	0.007	0.005	0.023	0.019	0.039

X = yellow color

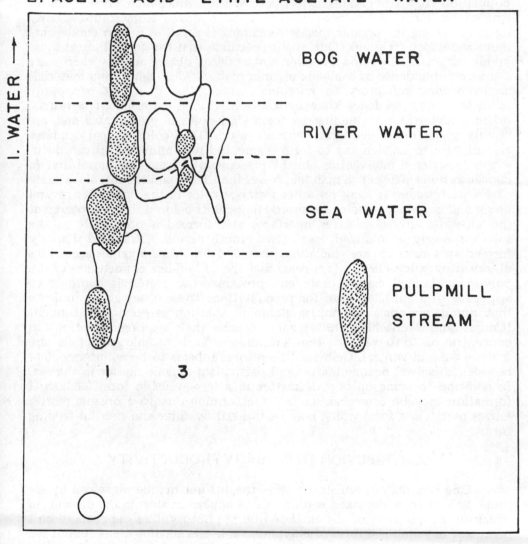

2. ACETIC ACID - ETHYL ACETATE - WATER ⟶

1. WATER →

BOG WATER

RIVER WATER

SEA WATER

PULPMILL
STREAM

1   3

Fig. 6.   Composite two-dimensional paper chromatogram shows the positions of the yellow pigments (Gelbstoff) from different sources (shaded areas). (Reprinted from Sieburth and Jensen, 1968.)

FATE OF EXUDATES AND CONDENSATES

The suggested transformation of phaeophyte extracellular organic matter by bacterial activity and chemical condensation is shown in a hypothetical diagram in Fig. 7. In the presence of a moderate bacterial population (5×10^5 organisms/ml) part of the extracellular organic matter exuded by *Fucus vesiculosus* appears to be removed from solution fairly rapidly. Among the organic matter remaining is a yellow-brown condensate more refractory to attack. One might speculate that the formation of these humic materials slows down organic matter decay during periods when there is an over-abundance of available organic matter. Although humic materials are somewhat refractory to microbial attack, this does not necessarily indicate a long residence time in solution. Humic materials of terrestrial origin decolorize on standing to form dark-colored precipitates and are rapidly precipitated on contact with sea water. Dark-colored algal exudates also decolorize on standing to form pigmented precipitates. This can occur without bacterial intervention. In the presence of 10 mg thiomersal/liter (a concentration sufficient to maintain fewer than 10 organisms/ml) an exudate of *Fucus vesiculosus* took on a deep orange color in the light after several hours and deepened in color for several days. Buff-colored flakes appeared at the air-water and glass-water interfaces and formed a precipitate as the solution slowly decolorized over a two-month period. These and similarly formed precipitates are indistinguishable from the organic aggregates observed by Riley (1963). It appears that the colloid-like condensates of the polyphenol-tanned carbohydrate and proteinaceous materials continue to aggregate to a sufficient size for precipitation. These observations indicate that humic materials are not as stable in solution as previously thought (Craigie and McLachlan, 1964) and explains their seasonal variations in concentration observed in the Trondheimsfjord (humic materials are undetectable in winter). Gelbstoff, therefore, appears to be an intermediate between dissolved organic matter and particulate organic matter in the sea. In addition to tying up organic matter in a less available form, Gelbstoff formation may be a mechanism for transforming dissolved organic matter into a particulate form which may be utilized by filter and detrital feeding forms.

CONTRIBUTION TO PRIMARY PRODUCTIVITY

One can only speculate on why the littoral marine algae can exude some 40% of their net fixed carbon. Rates appear greatest in the browns, in which up to a quarter of the exudate during photosynthesis appears to be a precursor or combined form of polyphenols. In the alkaline menstrum of sea water, these substances form free polyphenols toxic to algal (McLachlan and Craigie, 1964), bacterial (Conover and Sieburth, 1964), and larval forms (Sieburth and Conover, 1965; Sieburth and Jensen, 1969). However, plant protection (Sieburth, 1968) seems only a partial answer. Most organisms shed a certain amount of extracellular material. The leaky nature of these seaweeds may be a reflection of a poor mechanism of conservation due to

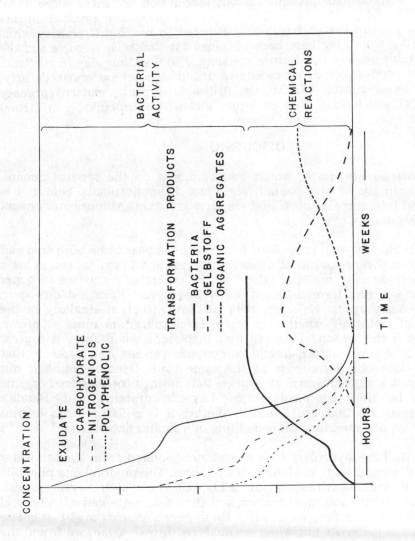

Fig. 7. This diagram suggests the transformation of extracellular organic matter by bacterial activity and photo-chemical condensation. This is a closed system in which an exudate is added at the start of the observation period.

very efficient photosynthesis which can be 20 times the rate of respiration (Kanwisher, 1966). Whatever the reason, extracellular organic matter production in *Fucus* and *Laminaria* appears to be some 30% of total carbon fixed. The standing crops of these algae are 1000 to 2000 g C/m^2 (Blinks, 1955) which can fix up to 20 g C/m^2/day (Blinks, 1955; Kanwisher, 1966). Therefore, extracellular organic matter production in these algae must approach 7 to 14 g C/m^2/day. The theoretical maximum production rate possible for phytoplankton has been calculated to be 25 g C/m^2/day while yields of 10 g C/m^2/day have been obtained for *Chlorella* cultures and the maximum rates observed in Nature are some 3 to 6 g C/m^2/day (Strickland, 1965). The production of extracellular organic matter by seaweeds may, therefore, be a source of directly utilizable organic matter (primary productivity) which may rival or equal that of phytoplankton in littoral waters.

DISCUSSION

CHRISTMAN: Dr. Sieburth, would you comment on the type of phenol, i.e., the specificity of the phenol, for your different plants before it is incorporated into this Gelbstoff and whether you think the original phenol could be liberated on hydrolysis?

SIEBURTH: No, the polyphenols of brown algae appear to be both acid and alkali sensitive. Every species of algae that Jensen and I have looked at has a different polyphenolic material. They can be separated by means of paper chromatography and have different RF values. Some have just one spot; some have many spots; however, they all seem to react similarly in the formation of Gelbstoff whether they are from sphagnum moss or brown algae. What is the reason? I believe that in periods when there is a great liberation of organic matter, humic compounds can act as a brake so that everything does not decompose at the same time. Decomposition is not stopped but it is slowed down. It appears that most of the dissolved organic matter is in the combined form. Degen's proteins and Handa's polysaccharides are tied up, I think. Whether it is a clathrate, as Degens contends, I am not sure, but it is something of a similar nature.

DEGENS: We have hydrolyzed these materials isolated from the sea water with both alkali and acids to identify the phenols. The predominate phenolic acids were p- and m-hydroxybenzoic acids, salicylic acid and syringic acid. We also analyzed the sediments below, and they also contained salicylic acid and phenolic acid. At first we thought these phenolic acids might originate from terrestrial materials but when we analyzed brown algae, we found the three benzoic acids, p- and m-hydroxybenzoic acids and syringic acids.

SIEBURTH: Which browns did you look at?

DEGENS: I do not know the species. The biologist told me it was brown algae.

SIEBURTH: You're no help.

NATARAJAN: Did you observe differences in the exudation rate as the age of the plant varied?

SIEBURTH: We did this in spring when there was actively growing tissue and we used the whole plants wherever possible. We could have compared old and young tissues or stipe and frond and so on, but I am a bacteriologist and all I want to know is how fast my substrate is coming in so I can determine flux rates. I now have a system that I think works; and I hope the botanists will do more work on exudation. I only want to know what the bacteria are doing.

BLUMER: It bothers me that only these phenolic precursors come out of the cells. Do you know what else, if anything, is exuded?

SIEBURTH: The predominate substances in the exudates, of course, are the carbohydrates. They are about four times as plentiful as the nitrogenous substances and polyphenols. There are equal amounts of nitrogenous and polyphenolic material. Under conditions which are potentially injurious to the plant, such as extreme desiccation, rain and freezing, the nitrogenous material just pours out.

BLUMER: Lipids, steroids?

SIEBURTH: Lipids cannot be much of a problem since you only have 4% to start with; I discussed this with Dr. Jeffrey yesterday. We agreed that these could not amount to too much. In the diatoms, yes, but in other phytoplankton and the seaweeds, no.

BELSER: When the bacteria use your Gelbstoff, do they leave the polyphenol behind or do they crank those around too?

SIEBURTH: There may be a release of soluble Gelbstoff, polyphenolic material, I don't know.

JONES: What level of Gelbstoff do you get in your local waters in spring?

SIEBURTH: In Norway we had 1.0 to 8 mg/liter. Around Rhode Island, I guess we do not have enough browns to achieve 1 mg/liter. This is a good project to work on in Norway; it is not as good a project in Rhode Island. I think that up around your country, it would be much better. By the time you get up to Canada, I think that it is even better.

HOOD: Do green and red algae produce exudates?

SIEBURTH: Yes, they do. *Ulva lactuca* exudes about 20 mg C/100 g/hr; *Chondrus crispus* about 4 mg C/100 g/hr. In the case of something like

Polysiphonea harveyii, the filamentous red, which water cannot permeate too well, and which is just loaded with epiphytic bacteria, then exudation gets down to 0.4 mg C/100 g/hr.

HOOD: How is the effect of pH recognized in these systems?

SIEBURTH: Sea water is pretty well buffered, but we have not examined the effects of pH excursions which we know occur in highly productive systems.

BELSER: I have two questions. The first is on the G-15 column, where you showed the temporal sequence of aggregation and the faster migrating things. You had one peak which you are calling nitrogenous material. That was retarded which means it was fairly small molecularly. Do you have any information as to whether the aggregated material which appeared was a specific product or a non-specific aggregation?

SIEBURTH: This I would like to know. I think that my next step, though, is to try to get something like 80% recovery of the products and find out what the major components are. Is it mainly mannitol? What are the amino acids? I hope to put a handle on the polyphenol, and then start recombining so that we can trace the structure of this condensate. We have no idea, and the only way we will be able to get an idea is to isolate the individual components and resynthesize them.

BELSER: What I am really asking is whether you are talking about one compound or about something which is essentially a non-specific aggregation of a whole complex.

SIEBURTH: We are talking about a family of compounds. I think the best thing to call it is a P-3 condensate composed of polyphenol, polysaccharide and protein or amino acids which keep building on and building on until the complex precipitates. Gelbstoff really is an intermediate between the exudate and the organic aggregates.

BELSER: Now I would like to shift to the bacterial information. You indicated that you thought bacteria were using a lot of the material that was exuded. I wondered whether you have followed the increase in bacterial density.

SIEBURTH: No, we are in the process of doing that now with flux rates and generation periods. This is an area we want to explore further.

WRIGHT: Your finding of active bacterial uptake is something that we ought to consider with respect to the phytoplankton. This is something I have been afraid of for a long time. We measure the rates of excretion of dissolved organic carbon in the phytoplankton. We are missing what the bacteria are getting during the course of our measurement. You say 40% and possibly a great deal higher?

SIEBURTH: What I am actually saying is that the primary production rates are 40% too low and times for an annual crop to grow are 40% too short, at least. These are minimal values.

DUURSMA: Have you made an attempt to apply your theory or your results to the old Gelbstoff measurements made by means of light absorption and fluorescence studies? Do they agree?

SIEBURTH: No. This stuff is UV-absorbing. I do not want to go into detail, but we also get the blue fluorescing substance Kalle observed (1966). We have passed water samples through a nylon column with about 70% recovery. With this method we have been able to estimate the seasonal variations. We have not really tried to correlate our work with that of other people. It is very impressive that in the winter when exudation is minimal or non-existent the Gelbstoff disappears from the water. In the spring when the algae become active the Gelbstoff returns.

SIEBURTH (note added in proof): Khailov and Burlakova (1969), using different procedures, have shown rates of release of dissolved organic matter from seaweeds equal (browns) and higher (reds) than ours.

REFERENCES

BIDWELL, R. G. S. 1967. Photosynthesis and metabolism in marine algae. VII. Products of photosynthesis in fronds of *Fucus vesiculosus* and their use in respiration. Can. J. Bot., *45*: 1557-1565.

BLINKS, L. R. 1955. Photosynthesis and productivity of littoral marine algae. J. Mar. Res., *14*: 363-373.

CONOVER, J. T., and J. McN. SIEBURTH. 1964. Effect of *Sargassum* distribution on its epibiota and antibacterial activity. Bot. Mar., *6*: 147-157.

CRAIGIE, J. S., and J. McLACHLAN. 1964. Excretion of colored ultraviolet absorbing substances by marine algae. Can. J. Bot., *42*: 23-33.

FOGG, G. E. 1966. The extracellular products of algae. Oceanogr. Mar. Biol. Annu. Rev., *4*: 195-212.

HELLEBUST, J. A. 1965. Excretion of some organic compounds by marine phytoplankton. Limnol. Oceanogr., *10*: 192-206.

KALLE, K. 1937. Meereskundliche chemische Untersuchen mit Hilfe des Zeisschen Pulfrich Photometers. Ann. Hydrogr. Berl., *65*: 276-282.

KALLE, K. 1966. The problem of the Gelbstoff in the sea. Oceanogr. Mar. Biol. Annu. Rev., *4*: 91-104.

KANWISHER, J. 1957. Freezing and drying in intertidal algae. Biol. Bull., *113*: 275-285.

KANWISHER, J. 1966. Photosynthesis and respiration in some seaweeds, p. 407-420. *In* H. Barnes [ed.], Some contemporary studies in marine science. Allen and Unwin Ltd., London.

KHAILOV, K. M. 1963. Some unknown organic substances in sea water. Dokl. Akad. Nauk SSSR (Transl.), *147*: 1355-1357.

LINDBERG, B. 1953. Low molecular carbohydrates in algae. I. Investigation of *Fucus vesiculosus*. Acta Chem. Scand., 7: 1119-1122.

LUCAS, C. E. 1961. On the significance of external metabolites in ecology, p. 190-206. *In* F.C. Milthrope [ed.], Mechanisms in biological control, Symp. Soc. Exp. Biol., *15*. Academic Press, New York.

MAUTNER, H. G. 1954. The chemistry of brown algae. Econ. Bot., *8*: 174-192.

McLACHLAN, J., and J. S. CRAIGIE. 1964. Algal inhibition by yellow ultraviolet-absorbing substances from *Fucus vesiculosus*. Can. J. Bot., *42*: 287-292.

NIGRELLI, R. F. 1958. Dutchmans "baccy juice" or growth-promoting and growth-inhibiting substances of marine origin. N.Y. Acad. Sci., Trans., Ser. II, *20*: 248-262.

RILEY, G. A. 1963. Organic aggregates in sea water and the dynamics of their formation and utilization. Limnol. Oceanogr., *8*: 372-381.

SIEBURTH, J. McN. 1968. The influence of algal antibiosis on the ecology of marine microorganisms, p. 63-74. *In* M.R. Droop and E.J.F. Wood [ed.], Advances in microbiology of the sea. Academic Press, London and New York.

SIEBURTH, J. McN. 1969. Studies on algal substances in the sea. III. Production of extracellular organic matter by littoral marine algae. J. Exp. Mar. Biol. Ecol., *3*: 290-309.

SIEBURTH, J. McN., and J. T. CONOVER. 1965. *Sargassum* tannin, an antibiotic which retards fouling. Nature, *208*: 52-53.

SIEBURTH, J. McN., and A. JENSEN. 1968. Studies on algal substances in the sea. I. Gelbstoff (humic material) in terrestrial and marine waters. J. Exp. Mar. Biol. Ecol., *2*: 174-189.

SIEBURTH, J. McN., and A. JENSEN. 1969. Studies on algal substances in the sea. II. Gelbstoff (humic material) formation in phaeophyte exudates. J.Exp. Mar. Biol. Ecol., *3* : 275-289.

SMITH, D. G., and E. G. YOUNG. 1953. On the nitrogenous constitutents of *Fucus vesiculosus*. J.Biol. Chem., *205*: 849-858.

STRICKLAND, J. D. H. 1965. Phytoplankton and marine primary production. Annu. Rev. Microbiol., *19*: 127-162.

VALLENTYNE, J. R. 1957. The molecular nature of organic matter in lakes and oceans, with lesser reference to sewage and terrestrial soils. J. Fish. Res. Bd. Canada, *14*: 33-82.

THE UPTAKE AND UTILIZATION OF ORGANIC SUBSTANCES BY MARINE PHYTOPLANKTERS

Johan A. Hellebust
The Biological Laboratories
Harvard University
Cambridge, Massachusetts 02138

ABSTRACT

Melosira nummuloides takes up amino acids through active transport systems. Some amino acids, when present in the external medium at 1×10^{-4} M, are concentrated by a factor exceeding two orders of magnitude. The uptake of arginine follows the laws of saturation kinetics with a transport constant, K_t, as low as 7.7×10^{-6} M, which compares favorably with the transport constants of many bacteria for the uptake of organic substrates. Valine appears to be taken up by two transport systems — one with high affinity and low capacity, and another with low affinity and high capacity.

From studies of interactions of amino acids for uptake sites in *M. nummuloides* there appear to be more than three transport systems available: one for basic amino acids, one for acidic amino acids and probably several for neutral amino acids.

Amino acids may contribute a large part of the cell's carbon at low rates of photosynthesis. However, amino acids do not support growth in the absence of light. A possible explanation for this is that *M. nummuloides* is incapable of gluconeogenesis in the dark. Several amino acids inhibit the growth of *M. nummuloides* when present singly in the medium. The growth inhibition by threonine is partly relieved by serine, alanine and glycine.

Cyclotella cryptica, when grown photosynthetically, has very low capacity for glucose transport. Formation of the glucose transport system is not induced by the presence of glucose, but rather by the absence of light of moderate to high intensities.

A survey of the uptake capacities and specificities of a limited number of marine phytoplankters has been made. *Coccolithus huxleyi*, *Isochrysis galbana*, *Dunaliella tertiolecta*, *Pyramimonas* sp. and *Skeletonema costatum* did not take up any of the substrates offered at measurable rates. Two dinoflagellate species, *Gymnodinium nelsonii* and *Peridinium trochoideum*, took up glucose as well as the amino acids lysine and alanine.

INTRODUCTION

Strickland (1965) recently claimed that one of the outstanding problems in the study of marine primary productivity is the production of dissolved organic matter and its subsequent fate. The importance of marine algae as producers of dissolved organic matter has been demonstrated by several investigators (Guillard and Wangersky, 1958; Wangersky and Guillard, 1960; Steward, 1963; Marker, 1965; Hellebust, 1965 and 1967; Sieburth and Jensen, in press). With regard to the utilization of dissolved organic substances, heterotrophic bacteria undoubtedly play a major role since they depend on preformed organic substances for growth. Kinetic studies of the uptake of various substrates by aquatic bacteria have been published both for freshwater (Hobbie and Wright, 1965; Wright and Hobbie, 1965 and 1966) and for marine populations (Vaccaro and Jannasch, 1966 and 1967; Hamilton, Morgan and Strickland, 1966; Jannasch, 1967; Hamilton and Austin, 1967; Hobbie, Crawford and Webb, 1968). What role algae play as consumers of dissolved organic substances is much less obvious, and very few studies have been devoted to this problem.

Photosynthetic phytoplankters within the euphotic zone do not depend on the uptake of dissolved organic substances for growth, except for possible requirements of minute quantities of certain vitamins such as B_{12}, thiamine and biotin, and/or of the presence of organic substances to serve as chelators for trace metals of low solubility. Photosynthetic—or at least pigmented—phytoplankters occurring at depths far below the euphotic zone (Wood, 1956; Bernard and Lecal, 1960; Bernard, 1964), where light cannot possibly support their growth may, however, depend on dissolved organic matter for growth. Non-photosynthetic phytoplankters, such as the numerous colorless dinoflagellates, small colorless flagellates of uncertain taxonomic position, and some colorless cryptomonads, definitely need preformed organic matter for growth. They may either use particulate organic matter through phagotrophy, or take up dissolved organic substances. However, practically nothing is known regarding the kinetics or nature of utilization of organic matter for either photosynthetic algae within or below the euphotic zone, or heterotrophic phytoplankters.

Studies of the nutrition of photosynthetic phytoplankters show, at least in an indirect way, that these algae often take up and utilize dissolved organic substances. Phytoplankters frequently need extremely low concentrations of vitamins for growth (Provasoli, 1963). Many dinoflagellates (Provasoli and Gold, 1962; Provasoli and McLaughlin, 1963), chrysomonads (Pintner and Provasoli, 1963) rock pool flagellates (Droop, 1961), and some diatoms (Guillard, 1963) are able to use certain amino acids as sources of nitrogen. Some organic substances allow growth in the dark, or at least stimulate the respiration of a limited number of littoral diatoms (Lewin, 1963). Although these studies clearly demonstrate that organic substrates penetrate and are utilized by the algae, they yield no information about the nature of the uptake process. Since the concentration of amino acids, sugars and organic acids utilized is quite high (10^{-3} to 10^{-2} M), penetration through the cell membrane by diffusion might supply the cell with substrate at sufficiently high concentrations for their further metabolism.

Wright and Hobbie (1966) compared the uptake kinetics for various substrates of bacterial and algal populations from freshwater lakes, and concluded that specific transport systems (permeases) effective at very low substrate concentrations were made available by the bacteria, and a diffusion mechanism, effective only at higher substrate concentrations, to the algae. It is important to find out whether this situation applies in general to the competition for organic substrates by planktonic bacteria and algae or whether some planktonic algae possess effective transport systems that take up substrates from the surrounding medium at very low concentrations and supply them inside the cells at concentrations sufficiently high for their effective introduction into the cell's metabolic pathways. Studies by Taylor (1960a,b) indicate that *Scenedesmus quadricauda* may take up glucose by an active process, although the kinetic aspects of the work are not convincing. Shrift (1966) has more recently demonstrated that another freshwater alga, *Chlorella vulgaris*, takes up methionine through an active transport system. Hellebust and Guillard (1967) showed that the marine diatom *Melosira nummuloides* is highly selective in its ability to take up organic substrates. It does not take up sugars, sugar alcohols or organic acids to a significant extent, but readily takes up any amino acid present in the medium at relatively low concentrations. The uptake of amino acids is strongly depressed by 2,4-dinitrophenol, an uncoupler of oxidative phosphorylation, which indicates that the uptake process requires metabolic energy.

The present paper reports on further work on the nature of the amino acid transport system in *Melosira nummuloides*, and on the glucose transport system of another marine centric diatom, *Cyclotella cryptica*. The results of a brief survey of the uptake abilities of a number of other phytoplankters are also included.

METHODS AND MATERIALS

The algae used in this investigation were obtained from Dr. R.R.L. Guillard's culture collection at the Woods Hole Oceanographic Institution. A list of the algae with clone symbols and information regarding their original isolation is given below:

Species	Clone symbol	Original isolation
Skeletonema costatum	Skel	Long Island Sound, N.Y.
Melosira nummuloides	0-8	Oyster Pond, Martha's Vineyard, Mass.
Thalassiosira norden-skioldii	T. nord	Woods Hole Harbor, Mass.
Chaetoceros pelagicus (?)	Ch4	Sargasso Sea
Chaetoceros simplex (?)	BBsm	Sargasso Sea
Cyclotella nana	13-1	Sargasso Sea
Cyclotella cryptica	0-3A	Oyster Pond, Martha's Vineyard, Mass.

Isochrysis galbana	Iso	? Probably inshore environment
Coccolithus huxleyi	BT-6	Sargasso Sea
Gymnodinium nelsonii (?)	GSBL	Great South Bay, N.Y.
Peridinium trochoideum	Peri	? Probably inshore environment
Dunaliella tertiolecta	Dun	? Probably inshore environment
Pyramimonas sp.	Pyr I	San Francisco Bay, N.Y.

The algae were grown in medium f/2 (Guillard, 1963) with about 5 lumens of continuous illumination from cool-white fluorescent tubes at 18 C. The cultures were axenic, and checks for bacterial contaminants were made by inoculations into liquid tryptone media.

The general technique for determining rates of substrate uptake was as follows: 0.1 μc of uniformly ^{14}C-labeled substrate (New England Nuclear Corp.) and 0.1 $\mu mole$ of unlabeled substrate were added to 1 ml of algal suspension taken from an exponentially growing culture of medium density. The final substrate concentration was 1 x 10^{-4} M in most of the experiments. Changes in concentration or conditions are described in the presentation of the experimental data. For studies of uptake rate as a function of substrate concentration (Fig. 1 to 4) the incubation time was 10 min. Each experimental culture was contained in a 5 ml stoppered vial. Duplicates were always used, and an additional sample containing iodine-killed cells was run simultaneously. During the incubation period the vials were swirled at frequent intervals. At the end of an uptake experiment the samples were filtered through MP filters (HA; diam. 25 mm, pore size 0.45 μ) and rinsed 5 times with 1 ml portions of f/2 medium. The filters were then put on planchets with a small amount of vacuum grease, dried *in vacuo* for 1 hr or longer, and the radioactivity determined with a Nuclear-Chicago gas-glow detector of known counting efficiency. The amount of radioactivity taken up by the iodine-killed sample was subtracted from that taken up by the live samples. Heat-killed and iodine-killed samples took up about the same amount of radioactivity which usually was not greater than 5% of the radioactivity taken up by live samples. It is assumed that most of the radioactivity observed in killed samples is due to adsorption rather than uptake, and therefore should be subtracted from that of live samples.

To determine the fate of ^{14}C-labeled substances taken up by the cells, the filters supporting the algae were extracted for approximately 5 min with several portions of hot 80% aqueous ethanol. The combined extracts (total volume: 5 ml) were evaporated to dryness under a hairdryer; the labeled

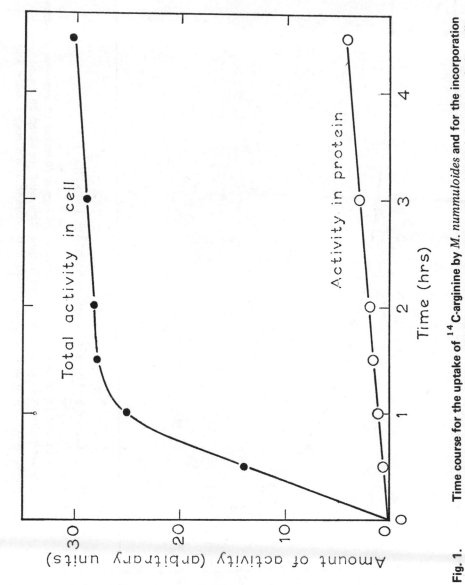

Fig. 1. Time course for the uptake of ^{14}C-arginine by *M. nummuloides* and for the incorporation of radioactivity into the protein (trichloroacetic acid-insoluble) fraction of the cells. *Conditions:* 18 C and 5 klux. Arginine concentration: 1×10^{-4} M.

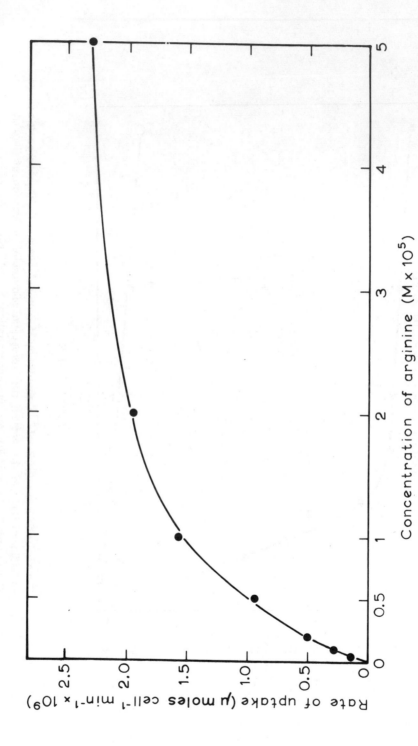

Fig. 2. Rate of uptake of arginine by *M. nummuloides* as a function of external substrate concentration. *Conditions:* 18 C and 5 klux. The rates are based on measurements of radioactivity taken up by the cells 10 min after addition of the labeled amino acid.

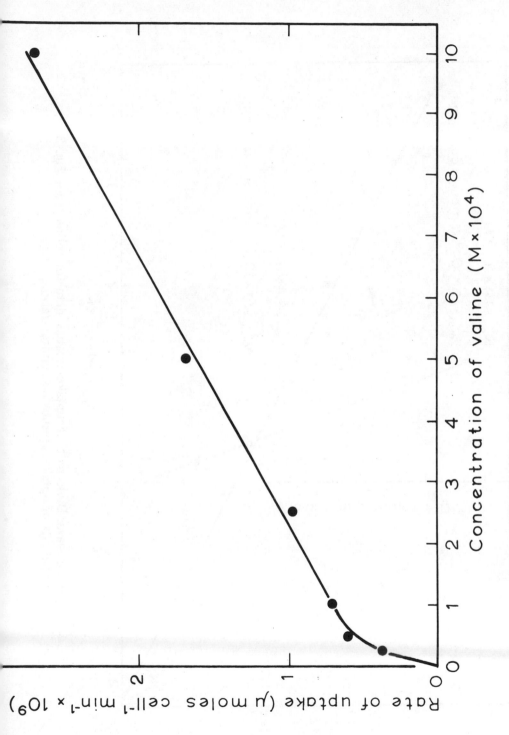

Fig. 3. Rate of uptake of valine by *M. nummuloides* as a function of external substrate concentration. *Conditions:* 18 C and 5 klux. The rates are based on measurements of radioactivity taken up by the cells 10 min after addition of the labeled amino acid.

Concentration of valine $(M \times 10^4)$

Rate of uptake (μ moles cell^{-1} min$^{-1} \times 10^9$)

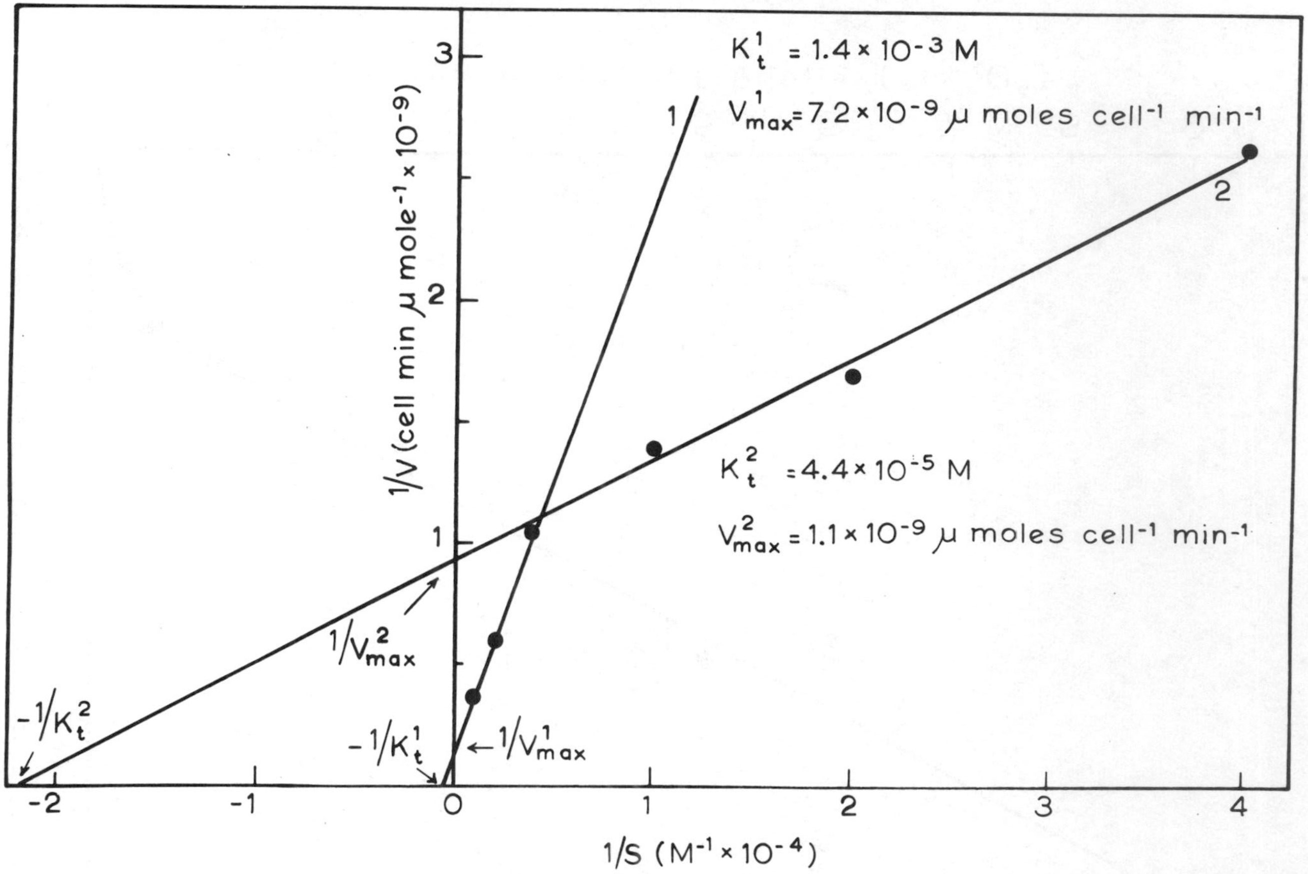

$K_t^1 = 1.4 \times 10^{-3}$ M
$V_{max}^1 = 7.2 \times 10^{-9}$ μ moles cell^{-1} min^{-1}
$K_t^2 = 4.4 \times 10^{-5}$ M
$V_{max}^2 = 1.1 \times 10^{-9}$ μ moles cell^{-1} min^{-1}
1
2
$1/V_{max}^2$
$-1/K_t^2$
$-1/K_t^1$
$1/V_{max}^1$
1/V (cell min μ mole^{-1} × 10^{-9})
1/S ($M^{-1} \times 10^{-4}$)

Fig. 4. **Lineweaver-Burk plot of uptake-kinetics data for valine from Fig. 3. v = initial rate of uptake, s = substrate concentration.**

residue was taken up in 100 μliter of water and chromatographed. The techniques for chromatography, autoradiography, and identification of the labeled substances extracted in this way have been described earlier (Hellebust and Bidwell, 1963). The residue after ethanol extraction was hydrolyzed with 1N H_2SO_4 at 100 C for 6 hr. The hydrolysates were neutralized with $BaCO_3$, and the resulting $BaSO_4$ was removed by centrifugation. The sulfate-free hydrolysates were then evaporated to dryness. The residue was taken up in small volumes of distilled water and subjected to chromatography and autoradiography.

Cell counts were made with an improved Neubauer hemacytometer (Brightline)®, except for *Melosira nummuloides* which was counted with a 0.1 ml Palmer Mahoney cell. For growth experiments with *M. nummuloides* the cells were inoculated into 50 ml of f/2 containing the appropriate amino acids in 125 ml erlenmeyers.

The amount of radioactivity incorporated into the trichloroacetic acid-insoluble (protein) fraction of the cells was determined as follows: after rinsing the cells on MP filters with f/2 medium as described above, the cells were extracted 3 times with 5 ml portions of cold 10% trichloroacetic acid. The total filtration time for the trichloroacetic acid extraction was about 10 min. The filters were then dried and their radioactivity was determined as described.

In the case of cells incubated with labeled amino acids, one may assume that most of the radioactivity found in trichloroacetic acid fraction is actually contained in proteins (Britten and McClure, 1962). However, in the case of photoassimilation of $^{14}CO_2$, a considerable amount of the activity found in this fraction is probably due to other compounds such as lipids which are not soluble in cold trichloroacetic acid.

RESULTS

The time course for uptake of ^{14}C-arginine by *M. nummuloides* cells, and for incorporation of radioactivity into the protein (trichloroacetic acid insoluble) fraction of the cells is shown in Fig. 1. The time courses for uptake of other amino acids and their incorporation into proteins were quite similar, although the initial linear portion of the uptake curves differed markedly in duration. The minimum duration of the initial linear uptake, at an external amino acid concentration of 1 x 10^{-4} M, was about 1 hr (arginine), and the maximum duration almost 3 hr (proline and leucine). This means that measurements of uptake rates at this amino acid concentration, as late as 1 hr after the addition of the radioactive amino acid, can be expected to be close to the initial uptake rates.

If the amino acids are taken up by an active transport process, one should be able to demonstrate a higher concentration of the amino acid inside than outside the cell. Cells were allowed to take up various ^{14}C-labeled amino acids supplied at 1 x 10^{-4} M concentration in the medium for 1 hr. The amount of radioactivity in the same free amino acid in the cell as that supplied in the medium, as a percentage of the total amount of radioactive amino acid taken up, was determined, and is recorded in Table 1.

Table 1. Estimate of concentration factors for various amino acids accumulated by *M. nummuloides* after 1 hr incubation at 18 C and 5 klux. (Radioactive amino acid concn in medium: 1×10^{-4} M)

Amino acid	% of total radio-activity of cell in free amino acid	Concn of free amino acid in cell (M)	Concn factor: C_{cell}/C_{medium}
Arginine	43	2.2×10^{-2}	220
Proline	68	2.0×10^{-2}	202
Glutamic acid	8	5.0×10^{-4}	5
Aspartic acid	64	2.5×10^{-3}	25
Leucine	81	1.1×10^{-2}	107
Valine	85	1.2×10^{-2}	120
Glutamine	37	5.5×10^{-3}	55
Alanine	25	7.2×10^{-3}	72

Knowing the total amount of radioactivity in the free amino acid in the cell, and the specific activity of the same amino acid in the medium, it was possible to calculate the concentration of the amino acid in the cell after 1 hr incubation. Concentration factors (C_{cell}/C_{medium}) for the various amino acids were also calculated and are given in Table 1. The external amino acid was taken up and concentrated from 5 times (glutamic acid) to as much as 220 times (arginine) under the given conditions.

The effect of external amino acid concentration on initial uptake rate is shown for arginine in Fig. 2. By plotting the inverse of the rate of uptake against the inverse of substrate concentration (Lineweaver-Burke plot, not shown here) a straight line resulted from which the following parameters for the uptake kinetics were determined: K_t (transport constant = concentration at which the uptake rate is half the maximum rate) = 7.7 x 10^{-6} M, and V_{max} (maximum rate of uptake, i.e., at substrate saturation of uptake sites) = 2.5 x 10^{-9} μmole cell^{-1} min^{-1}. The transport system for this amino acid has thus a very high substrate affinity, and exhibits saturation (Michaelis-Menten) kinetics. The kinetics for valine uptake (Fig. 3) are quite different than for arginine uptake, and no saturation of the uptake rate is seen at the highest substrate concentration used (1 x 10^{-3} M). A Lineweaver-Burke plot from these data (Fig. 4) makes it possible to fit two straight lines to the points obtained indicating the operation of (at least) two transport systems for the uptake of valine with different substrate affinities and maximum velocities (Christensen, 1966). The high affinity system (represented by line 2 in Fig. 4) has a K_t = 4.4 x 10^{-5} M, and a relatively low V_{max} (1.1 x 10^{-9} μmole cell $^{-1}$ min^{-1}), and the low affinity system (line 1 in Fig. 4) has a K_t = 1.4 x 10^{-3} M, and a high V_{max} (7.2 x 10^{-9} μmole cell^{-1} min^{-1}). However, it is possible that free diffusion plays a significant part in the uptake at the highest substrate concentration. A more complete study of the uptake kinetics for amino acids by *M. nummuloides* will be published elsewhere (Hellebust, in preparation).

Several experiments were performed to investigate possible interactions of amino acids for the transport systems in *M. nummuloides*. It can be seen from Fig. 5 that the uptake of ^{14}C-α-aminoisobutyric acid is strongly reduced by the presence of an equal concentration of unlabeled valine. The results of a relatively long-term experiment on the effects of glutamic acid and arginine on the uptake of ^{14}C-glutamine and incorporation of ^{14}C into the protein (trichloroacetic acid insoluble) fraction of the cells are presented in Table 2. While the presence of unlabeled glutamic acid (5 x 10^{-4} M) in the medium reduced both the total uptake of ^{14}C-glutamine and the incorporation of radioactivity into the carbon fraction, arginine had little effect on the total ^{14}C-glutamine uptake during the 3-hr period, but reduced significantly the incorporation of activity into protein. This may be interpreted to mean that glutamic acid competes with glutamine both at the transport level and at the level of biochemical conversions of glutamine into other compounds, e.g., proline, aspartic acid and arginine, while arginine has an effect primarily at the metabolic level. However, even in case of the inhibition by glutamic acid of the total uptake of ^{14}C-glutamine, it is possible—because of the long incubation time—that

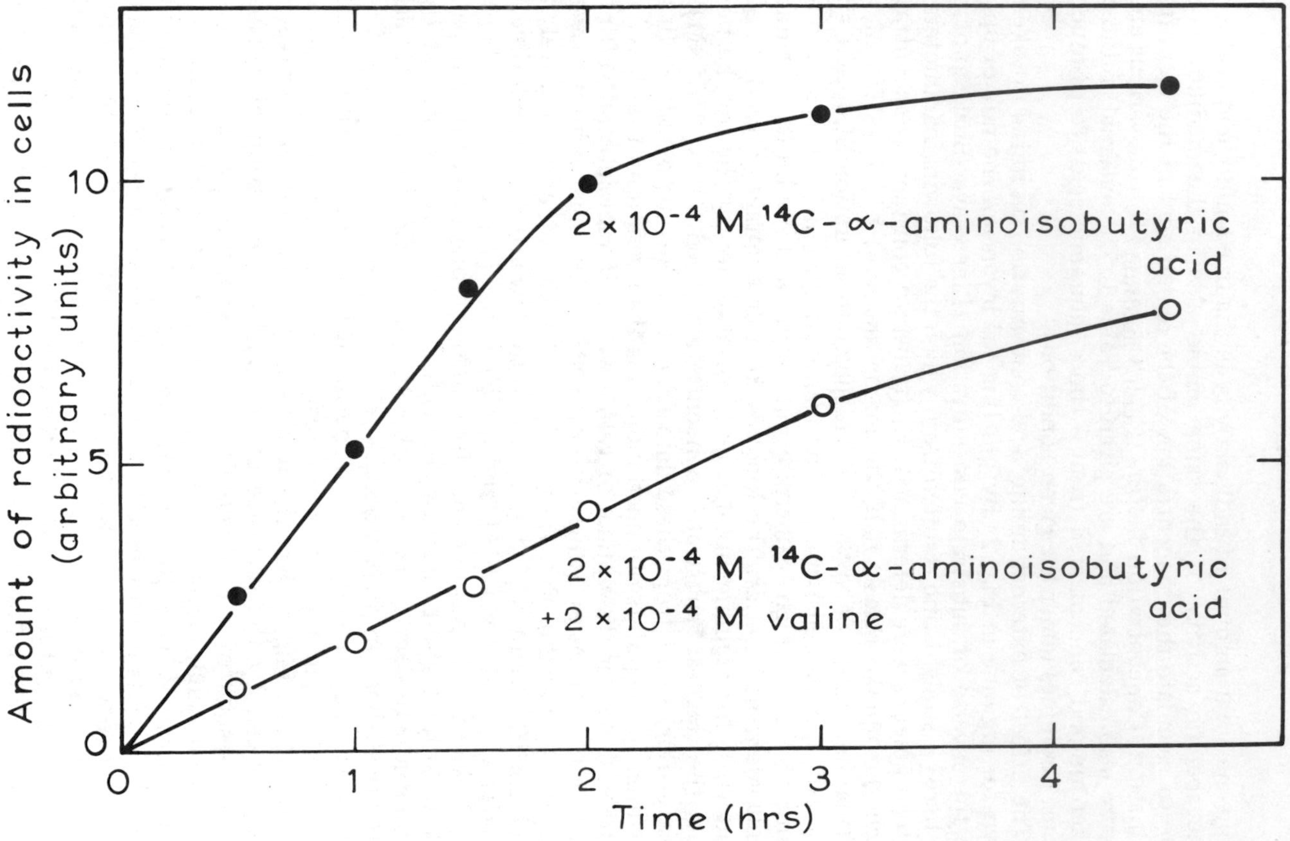

Fig. 5. Time course for the uptake of ^{14}C-aminoisobutyric acid in the presence or absence of unlabeled valine. *Conditions:* 18 C and 5 klux.

Table 2. Uptake of ^{14}C-glutamine by *M. nummuloides* and the incorporation of radioactivity into protein in the absence or presence of glutamic acid or arginine after 3 hr incubation at 18 C and 5 klux.

(Amino acid concn: 5 x 10^{-4} M)

Amino acids added to medium	Rate of uptake (μmoles ^{14}C-glutamine cell^{-1} min^{-1} x 10^9)	
	Total	Protein*
^{14}C-glutamine	0.28	0.14
^{14}C-glutamine + glutamic acid	0.13	0.04
^{14}C-glutamine + arginine	0.27	0.08

*Trichloroacetic acid-insoluble fraction. Rate expressed as if all the radioactivity entered this fraction as ^{14}C-glutamine.

the main effect occurs at the level of assimilation, since the two amino acids likely will be channeled into the same metabolic pools.

Short-term studies (10 min or 1 hr) of the effects of a large number of unlabeled amino acids on the uptake of ^{14}C-amino acids at a concentration of 1 x 10^{-4} M have been made. Some of the main findings from these studies are presented in Table 3. There appears to be one transport system in common for the basic amino acids: arginine, lysine and histidine; one for the acidic amino acids: glutamic acid and aspartic acid; and at least two for the neutral amino acids. These are minimum numbers for the amino acid transport systems. Cysteine and cystine did not inhibit any of the other amino acids, and are probably taken up by a separate transport system. A more detailed report and discussion of the results of investigations of amino acid interactions at the transport level will be published elsewhere (Hellebust, in preparation).

A comparison of relative rates of photoassimilation of CO_2, and uptake and assimilation of glutamic acid into *M. nummuloides* cells, and into the protein (trichloroacetic acid insoluble) fraction of the cells, is presented in Table 4. The total amount of ^{14}C-glutamic acid taken up is not much lower in the dark than at 0.5 lumen or 10 lumens. However, the relative amount incorporated into protein increases markedly with increasing light intensity. At 0.5 lumen the rate of glutamic acid uptake and assimilation is much higher than the rate of photoassimilation of CO_2 (on a carbon basis). At 10 lumens, however, the rate of photoassimilation of CO_2 is almost double that of glutamic acid uptake over the 3-hr period. It can be seen that 5 x 10^{-4} M unlabeled glutamic acid depresses the rate of photoassimilation of $^{14}CO_2$ from 190 to 160 x 10^{-9} μmole carbon cell^{-1} hr^{-1}.

Since amino acids are taken up so efficiently by *M. nummuloides* both in light and dark (Table 4; Hellebust and Guillard, 1967) one might expect that the presence of amino acids at a concentration of about 1 x 10^{-4} M should allow the cells to grow in the dark, or at least enhance growth at very low light intensities. However, no growth has been obtained in complete darkness in the presence of alanine, glutamic acid or arginine. Some stimulation of growth by glutamic acid and arginine was apparent at about 1 lumen, but no growth took place below 0.5 lumen and 18 C with or without the presence of these amino acids.

An experiment was designed to compare the uptake and assimilation of ^{14}C-alanine in complete darkness and at 5 lumens in an attempt to find out why this amino acid will not support growth of *M. nummuloides* in the dark. After 4 hr incubation in the presence of 5 x 10^{-4} M of the labeled amino acid, the cells were extracted with hot 85% ethanol, and the residue was hydrolyzed. The results of chromatography and autoradiography of the ethanol extracts and the hydrolysates are presented in Table 5. Radioactivity from ^{14}C-alanine appeared in aspartic acid and glutamic acid in the ethanol extract both in the light and dark, but radioactive proline was found only in the presence of light. In the hydrolysate the key difference between the two samples is the presence of radioactivity in glucose only in the light sample. Protein synthesis from alanine and other amino acids evidently occurred in the dark as well as in the light sample, although the total amount of radioactivity in protein was much higher in the light sample.

Table 3. Interactions of amino acids for transport sites in *M. nummuloides*.

Test-^{14}C-amino acid	Uptake of test-^{14}C-amino acid inhibited by the following unlabeled amino acids
Aspartic acid	Glutamic acid
Glutamic acid	Aspartic acid
Arginine	Lysine, (histidine)
Histidine	Lysine, arginine
Lysine	Arginine, (histidine)
Leucine	Isoleucine, valine, proline, phenylalanine, tryptophan, methionine
Valine	Leucine, proline, isoleucine, phenylalanine, tryptophan, alanine, methionine
Serine	Proline, isoleucine, valine, leucine, threonine, alanine, hydroxyproline, methionine
Alanine	Proline, phenylalanine, tryptophan, leucine, methionine, valine, hydroxyproline, glycine, asparagine, isoleucine, serine, tyrosine

Table 4. Comparison of rate of photoassimilation of $^{14}CO_2$ and of uptake and assimilation of ^{14}C-glutamic acid by *M. nummuloides* at different light intensities after 4 hr incubation at 18 C.

(Glutamic acid concn when present: 5 x 10^{-4} M; HCO$_3^-$ concn: 2 x 10^{-3} M.)

Experimental system	Rates of uptake and assimilation (μmoles C cell^{-1} hr^{-1} x 10^9)					
	Dark		0.5 klux		10 klux	
	Total	Protein*	Total	Protein	Total	Protein
$^{14}CO_2$ + glutamic acid	-**	-	15	12	160	75
$^{14}CO_2$	-	-	-	-	190	92
CO_2 + ^{14}C-glutamic acid	85	12	110	25	100	45

*Trichloroacetic acid-insoluble fraction

**Not determined

Table 5. Radioactive compounds detected by chromatography of extracts and hydrolysates of *M. nummuloides* previously incubated with ^{14}C-alanine in the dark and at 5 klux for 4 hr at 18 C.

(Alanine concn: 5×10^{-4} M)

Cell fraction	Dark	5 klux
Ethanol extract	Alanine, aspartic acid, glutamic acid	Alanine, aspartic acid, glutamic acid, proline
Hydrolysate of ethanol-insoluble fraction	Alanine, and traces of activity in aspartic acid and glutamic acid	Alanine, aspartic acid, glutamic acid, proline, glycine
		Glucose

While testing the suitability of various amino acids as nitrogen sources for the growth of *M. nummuloides*, it was noticed that several amino acids acted as potent growth inhibitors when supplied singly in the medium even at very low concentrations. Strong growth inhibition was obtained with isoleucine and lysine at 1×10^{-5} M, and in some cases even at 1×10^{-6} M (Hellebust and Guillard, unpublished data). Threonine almost completely inhibits growth at 1×10^{-4} M, while the same concentration of alanine, serine or glycine allows normal growth to take place. If serine, alanine or glycine is added to the medium at 1×10^{-4} M simultaneously with 1×10^{-4} M threonine, the growth inhibiting effect of threonine diminishes and the cells grow at approximately half their normal rate (Table 6). Addition of leucine, glutamic acid or arginine together with threonine did not relieve the growth inhibition.

Lewin (1963) demonstrated that the centric diatom *Cyclotella cryptica* (0 to 3A) can grow on glucose as the only carbon source in the dark at about half its light saturated growth rate. Glucose was supplied in the medium at a fairly high concentration — about 1×10^{-2} M — and might, therefore, have entered the cells by diffusion rather than through an active uptake mechanism. However, the lag phase observed in these growth experiments when the cells were placed in the dark with glucose indicates an induction period during which the cells synthesize either a necessary transport system for glucose, or the necessary enzymes for the metabolism of glucose, or both. Assays for the uptake of ^{14}C-glucose showed that cells grown photosynthetically had very low capacities for glucose uptake (Table 7). The capacity to transport glucose increased about tenfold during 24 hr in darkness in a medium containing no glucose, and increased only a little more during two more days in the dark. No glucose was necessary for the induction of the glucose transport system. High concentrations of glucose actually inhibited the formation of the transport system in the dark, and did not cause its induction in the light (Table 8). Further work has demonstrated that the uptake of glucose follows the laws of saturation kinetics, and that the capacity to transport glucose induced in cells kept in the dark is rapidly lost when the cells are subsequently exposed to light of intensities higher than about 4 lumens (Hellebust, unpublished data).

A general survey of the uptake capacities and specificities of various marine phytoplankters was made to find out how widely distributed transport systems for organic substances are in marine photoautotrophs (Table 9). The rates of uptake after a 4 hr incubation period are expressed as a percentage (on a carbon basis) of the light saturated rate of photoassimilation of CO_2. Rates below 0.5% could not be measured accurately, in most cases, and were considered negligible. Fructose, glycerol and mannitol were not taken up to a measureable extent by any of the phytoplankters. The two members of the *Chrysophyceae*, *Coccolithus huxleyi* and *Isochrysis galbana*, and the two members of the *Chlorophyceae*, *Dunaliella tertiolecta* and *Pyramimonas* sp., did not take up any of the seven substrates offered. The two dinoflagellate species, *Gymnodinium nelsonii* and *Peridinium trochoideum*, took up glucose as well as the amino acids lysine and alanine. Most of the diatoms took up acetate at fairly low rates.

Table 6. Growth of *M. nummuloides* in the presence or absence of various amino acids after incubation at 18 C and 5 klux.
(Amino acid concn: 1 x 10^{-4} M)

Additions to medium	Cell count (cells/ml x 10^{-5})	
	Initial	After 7 days
None	0.039	1.4
Alanine	0.039	1.3
Serine	0.039	1.0
Glycine	0.039	1.3
Threonine	0.039	0.045
Threonine + serine	0.039	0.23
Threonine + alanine	0.039	0.15
Threonine + glycine	0.039	0.17

Table 7. Effect of light and darkness on the glucose transport system in *C cryptica* grown at 18 C in absence of glucose.
(Glucose concn in assay system: 1 x 10^{-4} M)

Pretreatment	Rate of glucose uptake (10^{10} μmoles cell^{-1} min^{-1})
Cells grown at 5 klux	0.2
After 1 day in the dark	1.9
After 2 days in the dark	2.5
After 3 days in the dark	2.3

Table 8. Effect of glucose concentration on formation of the glucose transport system in *C. cryptica* incubated at 18 C in the dark and at 5 klux. Cells kept for 24 hr under conditions described below before determination of uptake rates.

Culture conditions	Relative uptake rates
5 klux, no glucose	7
5 klux, 1 x 10^{-2} M glucose	4
5 klux, 1 x 10^{-1} M glucose	2
Dark, no glucose	100
Dark, 1 x 10^{-2} M glucose	48
Dark, 1 x 10^{-1} M glucose	13

Table 9. Uptake capacities and specificities for organic substrates of some marine phytoplankers from different algal classes and isolated from various marine environments, all incubated for 4 hr at 18 C and 5 klux. (Substrate concn: 1×10^{-4} M. All rates are expressed as a percentage of the light-saturated rate of photoassimilation of CO_2.)

Alga	Environment from which isolated	Rate of uptake of substrate						
		Glucose	Fructose	Glycerol	Mannitol	Acetate	Lysine	Alanine
Bacillariophyceae								
S. costatum	Inshore	*	–	–	–	–	–	–
T. nordenskioldii	Inshore	–	–	–	–	–	–	–
C. simplex	Open ocean	–	–	–	–	12	–	–
C. pelagicus	Open ocean	–	–	–	–	4	–	–
C. nana	Open ocean	–	–	–	–	13	14	8
C. cryptica	Salt-water pond	75	–	–	–	2	75	11
M. nummuloides	Salt-water pond	–	–	–	–	11	86	64
Chrysophyceae								
C. huxleyi	Open ocean	–	–	–	–	–	–	–
I. galbana	Probably inshore	–	–	–	–	–	–	–
Dinokontae								
G. nelsonii	Polluted bay	6	–	–	–	–	11	6
P. trochoideum	Probably inshore	9	–	–	–	–	110	86
Chlorophyceae								
D. tertiolecta	Probably inshore	–	–	–	–	–	–	–
Pyramimonas sp.	Inshore	–	–	–	–	–	–	–

*Rates lower than 0.5% of the rate of photoassimilation.

Only the two diatoms from a saltwater pond, *Cyclotella cryptica* and *Melosira nummuloides*, took up amino acids rapidly. The open ocean diatom *Cyclotella nana* (13 to 1) took up amino acids to a measurable extent, but no uptake could be demonstrated for the other open ocean or inshore diatoms.

CONCLUSION

This investigation has mainly dealt with the kinetics of amino acid transport in *M. nummuloides*. From the data presented here, and those obtained in an earlier study of substrate specificity and amino acid transport in the same species (Hellebust and Guillard, 1967), it seems safe to conclude that this diatom takes up amino acids through processes requiring metabolic energy, and that the evidence from amino acid interactions for uptake sites (Table 3) and the complex kinetics for uptake of valine (Fig. 4) indicates that the amino acid transport systems involved are probably as complex as those reported for any other microorganism (Britten and McClure, 1962; Kepes and Cohen, 1962), or cell types (Oxender and Christensen, 1963).

Some amino acids, when present in the medium at 1×10^{-4} M, can be concentrated by a factor of two orders of magnitude by *M. nummuloides* (Table 1). Even higher degrees of concentration can be expected at lower external amino acid concentrations (Britten and McClure, 1962). The formation of steep concentration gradients across the cell membrane is further evidence for the active nature of the uptake processes.

The rate of uptake remains constant for quite a long time after addition of amino acid at 1×10^{-4} M, in most cases for more than 1 hr (Fig. 1 and unpublished data). This is in sharp contrast to the very short duration — often only a few minutes — of linear uptake of amino acids observed with bacteria. This is probably in part due to the relatively large amino acid pools formed in the diatoms (5×10^{-4} M to 2×10^{-2} M, Table 1), and in part to their lower rate of metabolism. Temperature also affects the rate of uptake and therefore the duration of the linear uptake (Britten and McClure, 1962). The incubation temperature of the present experiments (18 C) was somewhat lower than that commonly used in uptake experiments with bacteria (25 to 37 C), and is, thus, a contributing factor to the relatively slow rates of pool formation in the diatom.

The uptake of arginine followed saturation kinetics (Fig. 2), and yielded a transport constant, K_t, as low as 7.7×10^{-7} M. The transport constants for uptake of organic substrates by fungi, bacteria or bacterial populations from various natural environments have been determined by several investigators. For example, the K_t for alanine and glycine transport by *Streptococcus faecium* is about 1×10^{-4} M (Brock and Moo-Penn, 1962), for valine uptake by *Escherichia coli* about 3×10^{-6} M (Cohen and Rickenberg, 1956), for tryptophan uptake by *Neurospora crassa* about 5×10^{-5} M (Wiley and Matchett, 1966) and for a marine bacterium (*Achromobacter aquamarinus* ?) isolated from Vineyard Sound, Mass. 1.5×10^{-7} M at 6 C and 1×10^{-6} M at 20 C (Vaccaro and Jannasch, 1966). The K_t for arginine transport in *M. nummuloides* compares very favorably with these values. Similarly, North and Stephens (1967) have reported on a glycine transport system in the marine alga, *Platymonas subcordiformis*, with a K_t of about 7×10^{-6} M. This alga, a member of the Volvocales, is occasionally abundant in the phytoplankton (Margaleff, 1946) and is also found in high concentration in tidepools (Lewis and Taylor, 1921).

Recent reports on the kinetics of substrate uptake by samples of natural sea water demonstrate the existence of aquatic bacterial populations possessing transport systems with considerably higher substrate affinities (inverse of K_t) than those mentioned above. Thus, Hobbie, Crawford, and Webb (1968) found K_t's for amino acid transport by bacterial populations in an estuary (York River estuary, Virginia) ranging from 4×10^{-9} M to 1×10^{-6} M (majority of values: 2 to 5×10^{-7} M), and Vaccaro and Jannasch (1966) obtained a K_t for glucose transport by an inshore (Woods Hole, Mass.) bacterial population of about 2×10^{-8} M at 6 C. It appears that microorganisms possess transport systems of widely varying affinities depending on the substrate concentrations of their natural environments. For example, Ehrlich ascites (mammalian tumor) cells, which are naturally exposed to very high amino acid concentrations, have amino acid transport systems with K_t's as high as 1×10^{-3} M (Oxender and Christensen, 1963).

The uptake of valine by *M. nummuloides* exhibits a rather complicated kinetic picture (Fig. 3 and 4), which can be interpreted as consisting of two transport systems: one with high affinity ($K_t = 4.4 \times 10^{-5}$ M) and low capacity, and another with low affinity ($K_t = 1.4 \times 10^{-3}$ M) and high capacity. However, one cannot ignore the possibility that uptake at high substrate concentrations includes a component of passive diffusion. Similar complex kinetics have been reported by Ames (1964) for histidine transport by *Salmonella typhimurium*: one high affinity system, $K_t = 1.7 \times 10^{-7}$ M, and one low affinity system, $K_t = 1.1 \times 10^{-4}$ M, and by Britten and McClure (1962) for proline transport by *E. coli*: one high affinity system, $K_t = 2.5 \times 10^{-6}$ M, and one low affinity system, $K_t = 4 \times 10^{-5}$ M. The high affinity system has always low capacity and conversely.

It is clear from studies of interactions of amino acids for uptake sites in *M. nummuloides* that several transport systems are available, and that each of these systems will serve a limited number of structurally similar amino acids. There appears to be one system for basic amino acids, one for acidic amino acids, and several systems for the neutral amino acids (Table 3). The complex kinetics for valine uptake indicate that this amino acid is taken up by more than one transport system (Fig. 4). Further studies of amino acid interactions indicate that several amino acids are taken up by at least two transport systems: one system with high affinity and specificity for the amino acid, and another with low affinity and specificity which serves a limited number of structurally similar amino acids (Hellebust, unpublished data). Amino acids which are closely related to each other through metabolic pathways, e.g., glutamic acid, glutamine and arginine, may compete with each other for uptake by the cells in long-term experiments at the level of assimilation rather than of transport (Table 2). Arginine, which is structurally very different from glutamic acid, but which can be synthesized, at least in part, from glutamic acid, will cause less incorporation of glutamate carbon into proteins if supplied in the medium simultaneously with glutamic acid. Glutamine, which does not compete with glutamic acid for uptake in short-term experiments (Table 3), will cause a decrease in glutamic acid uptake in long-term experiments (Table 2) by filling the same amino acid pools through common metabolic pathways after entry into the cell.

Earlier studies of amino acid transport by M. nummuloides (Hellebust and Guillard, 1967) have already shown that this diatom has very high capacities for the uptake of amino acids. The initial rate of uptake of several amino acids at an external concentration of 1×10^{-4} M is of the same order of magnitude as that of photoassimilation of CO_2. The present work shows that glutamic acid supplied in the medium at this concentration may supply a major fraction of the cell's carbon at very low light intensities, and a considerable fraction even at high light intensities (Table 4). The rate of uptake of glutamic acid is quite similar in the light and the dark in experiments of a few hours duration, but light stimulates the incorporation of glutamate carbon into proteins.

Attempts to grow M. nummuloides in the dark in the presence of several amino acids, alanine, glutamic acid and arginine, which are all rapidly taken up by the cells in the dark as well as in the light, did not succeed. Chromatographic and autoradiographic investigations of the conversions of ^{14}C-alanine into other metabolites and macromolecular components in the light and dark (Table 5) suggest one reason why amino acids fail to support heterotrophic growth in this diatom. In the light, a considerable amount of radioactivity appeared in glucose from the hydrolyzed residue, while no radioactivity could be detected in glucose in cells kept in the dark. A requirement for glucose formation from alanine is the reversal of the Embden-Meyerhof pathway from pyruvic acid, the deamination product of alanine, to glucose. Several steps of this reversed pathway are energy requiring (ATP, GTP and $NADH_2$), and it seems likely that light is necessary for the photosynthetic generation of a cellular environment with sufficiently high ATP/ADP and $NADH_2$/NAD ratios for a reversal of the Embden-Meyerhof pathway to take place. It seems likely that the citric acid cycle operates in the dark, since labeled aspartic acid and glutamic acid, which must have been derived from the corresponding members of the citric acid cycle, oxaloacetic and α-ketoglutaric acid, were formed from ^{14}C-alanine. However, the operation of the citric acid cycle and oxidative phosphorylation appears to be insufficient to allow gluconeogenesis to occur in this diatom. The situation with glutamic acid and arginine, which also did not support growth in the dark, is essentially the same, since oxaloacetic acid derived from these amino acids would have to enter, and follow the reverse of the Embden-Meyerhof pathway to produce triose-phosphate and hence carbohydrates. For amino acids to support heterotrophic growth it is essential that carbohydrates can be synthesized from their deamination products, and the failure of gluconeogenesis to take place in the dark is a sufficient—if not the only—reason why heterotrophic growth of M. nummuloides did not occur on alanine, glutamic acid and arginine.

Amino acids may, in addition to serving as nitrogen and carbon sources for M. nummuloides, act as strong growth inhibitors when supplied in the medium at very low concentrations (Table 6, and unpublished observations). The inhibitions by 1×10^{-4} M threonine could in part be relieved by the simultaneous presence of the same concentration of serine, alanine or glycine. The reason for growth inhibition by threonine is not known, but it is possible that it interferes with the biosynthesis of serine. Serine relieves the growth inhibiting effect of threonine considerably; alanine and glycine, which may give rise to serine through different biosynthetic pathways, also relieve threonine inhibition, but to a lesser extent. Hayward (1965) observed growth inhibition of another marine diatom, *Phaeodactylum tricornutum*, by aspartic acid and glutamic acid at relatively high concentrations (4×10^{-3} M). Threonine, at 4×10^{-3} M, did not inhibit growth of this diatom.

Formation of the glucose transport system in *Cyclotella cryptica* is not induced by the presence of glucose in the medium, but rather by the absence of light of moderate to high intensities (Table 7, and unpublished observations). Glucose, if present at high concentrations in the medium, inhibits formation of the glucose transport system in the dark (Table 8). It may be ecologically advantageous to have this transport system controlled by light intensity rather than by the presence or absence of glucose in the environment. At light intensities allowing rapid photosynthesis there is no need for an additional carbon source and the transport system, if already present, is destroyed (Hellebust, unpublished data). In the dark, or at low light intensities, an external organic carbon source is needed, and the transport system is formed. If the synthesis of the transport system depended on external glucose for its induction, a relatively high concentration would be necessary for the induction in cells lacking a transport system, since glucose could only enter such cells by passive diffusion.

Investigations of a number of other photoautotrophic phytoplankters from various taxonomic classes and isolated from different marine environments show that the ability to take up organic compounds from rather low concentrations is quite limited (Table 9). Five of the thirteen species studied did not take up measurable amounts of any of the seven substrates offered. The two dinoflagellates took up significant amounts of glucose as well as the amino acids, lysine and alanine. Only the two diatoms, *Melosira nummuloides* and *Cyclotella cryptica*, which were originally isolated from salt water ponds where they may encounter relatively high concentrations of organic substrates compared with the open ocean environment, exhibited high capacities for uptake of organic substrates. This agrees with the findings of Sloan and Strickland (1966) for three open ocean phytoplankters, *Skeletonema costatum*, *Coccolithus huxleyi* and *Thalassiosira rotula*, which did not take up significant quantities of acetate, glucose or glutamate supplied at 1×10^{-5} M to 1×10^{-6} M.

Undoubtedly, some marine algae possess transport systems effective in concentrating external organic substrate at very low concentration levels to levels sufficiently high for their further assimilation (Hellebust and Guillard, 1967; North and Stephens, 1967; present investigation), but we need much more information about how widely distributed such transport systems are among marine phytoplankters. It seems likely that many algae found in environments with relatively high concentrations of organic substances, such as rock pools, salt ponds and various polluted inshore environments, possess such transport systems. However, it would be most interesting to find out whether certain photosynthetic algae reported to occur at great depths have the necessary transport systems to live heterotrophically, and furthermore, to obtain information about the kinetic parameters and substrate specificities of transport systems in colorless phytoplankters from marine environments with very low concentrations of organic substrates. A recent report (Neujahr, 1966) demonstrates that thiamine is taken up through an active process in the bacterium *Lactobacillus fermenti*. It is therefore possible that vitamins, which are present in extremely low concentrations in the open ocean, may be taken up by phytoplankters through transport systems of very high affinities.

DISCUSSION

WRIGHT: I have two questions for you. First, have you noted any effect of light or dark or relative light intensities on the magnitude of the transport constants? Second, at natural concentrations of amino acids, I think you would agree that the amount that any of these organisms might obtain would be rather small. Do you think this may be a source of nitrogen rather than of carbon?

HELLEBUST: The importance of these amino acids as a nitrogen source has been indicated already and published by myself and Guillard. I think probably they are more important as a nitrogen source than as a carbon source, but as has been shown here also, the capacity for amino acid utilization is very high. It, of course, depends upon the concentration outside. A large amount of carbon can also be taken up under certain circumstances. The immediate effect of light on the glucose transport system is quite apparent. I have a lot more data on this and it is definitely a light intensity effect. This is quite clear. The light effect on the amino acid transport system is quite different in that the transport system is there. It is non-inducible; it is constitutive. However, there is a long-term light effect which affects the metabolism of the compounds rather than the transport itself.

MALCOLM: I was curious to learn that you believe that amino acids are the factor limiting increase in growth with the uptake of this high nutrient material.

HELLEBUST: As I mentioned, I think it has something to do with biosynthetic pathways and product regulation. I really have no hard evidence on this.

MALCOLM: How much conservation of energy is there in adsorption of the free assimilated carbon source as opposed to making the carbon?

HELLEBUST: I think there is no doubt that the uptake of almost any carbon source is well worth the energy expended taking it up. It certainly is very clear in the case of glucose. A cell may get 30 to 40 times as much energy out of it as is used in taking it up. This is true for many other compounds too.

MALCOLM: Given this and the high nitrogen source, it is surprising that you don't get a rapid increase in growth, because nitrogen is one of the principal growth limiting elements for many of these organisms.

HELLEBUST: Of course, these were grown in media where there was no limiting supply of nitrogen. Therefore, they may be equivalent to nitrate as nitrogen sources. A number of amino acids, such as arginine, glutamic acid and proline are excellent nitrogen sources if present in sufficient concentrations.

PRAKASH: After listening to Dr. Sieburth's paper on Gelbstoff and to Dr. Hellebust's presentation, I wish to comment on our work at the Bedford Institute. For the last 18 months we have been looking into the ecological implications of the dissolved yellow stuff for phytoplankton production in coastal and oceanic waters. Our results are preliminary, but we find that these compounds, especially humic compounds in small amounts, exert a stimulating influence on the production of the phytoplankton which is reflected in increased growth and increased ^{14}C uptake. We believe that this is partly due to increased uptake of the nutrients in the presence of humic compounds, and partly to stimulation of physiological processes within the algal cell.

ACKNOWLEDGMENTS

This study was supported by National Science Foundation Grant GB-7087.

I wish to thank Miss Christine Spielvogel for able technical assistance with many of the experiments.

REFERENCES

AMES, G. F. 1964. Uptake of amino acids by *Salmonella typhimurium*. Arch. Biochem. Biophys., *104*: 1-18.

BERNARD, F. 1964. La nanoplancton en zone aphotique des mèrs chaudes. Pelagos, *2*: 1-32.

BERNARD, F., and J. LECAL. 1960. Plancton unicellulaire recolté dans l'ocean Indien par le *Charot* (1950) et le *Norsel* (1955-56). Int. Oceanogr. Bull., Monaco., *1166*: 1-59.

BRITTEN, R. J., and F. T. McCLURE. 1962. The amino acid pool in *Escherichia coli*. Bact. Rev., *26*: 294-335.

BROCK, T. D., and G. MOO-PENN. 1962. An amino acid transport system in *Streptococcus faecium*. Arch. Biochem. Biophys., *98*: 183-190.

CHRISTENSEN, H. N. 1966. Methods for distinguishing amino acid transport systems of a given cell or tissue. Fed. Proc., *25*: 850-853.

COHEN, G. N., and H. V. RICKENBERG. 1956. Concentration spécifique réversible des amino acids chez *Escherichia coli*. Annu. Inst. Pasteur, *91*: 693-720.

DROOP, M. R. 1961. *Haematococcus pluvialis* and its allies. III. Organic nutrition. Rev. Algo., *4*: 247-259.

GUILLARD, R. R. L. 1963. Organic sources of nitrogen for marine centric diatoms, p. 93-104. *In* C.H. Oppenheimer [ed.], Symp. on Marine microbiology. C. Thomas, Springfield, Ill.

GUILLARD, R. R. L., and P. J. WANGERSKY. 1958. The production of extracellular carbohydrates by some marine flagellates. Limnol. Oceanogr., *3*: 449-454.

HAMILTON, R. D., and K. E. AUSTIN. 1967. Assay of relative heterotrophic potential in the sea: the use of specifically labelled glucose. Can. J. Microbiol., *13*: 1165-1173.

HAMILTON, R. D., K. M. MORGAN, and J. D. H. STRICKLAND. 1966. The glucose uptake kinetics of some marine bacteria. Can. J. Microbiol., *12*: 995-1003.

HAYWARD, J. 1965. Studies on the growth of *Phaeodactylum tricornutum* (Bohlin). I. The effect of certain organic nitrogeneous substances on growth. Physiol. Plant., *18*: 201-207.

HELLEBUST, J. A. 1965. Excretion of some organic compounds by marine phytoplankton. Limnol. Oceanogr., *10*: 192-206.

HELLEBUST, J. A. 1967. Excretion of organic compounds by cultured and natural populations of marine phytoplankton, p. 361-366. *In* G.H. Lauff [ed.], Estuaries. Amer. Ass. Adv. Sci. Pub. 83.

HELLEBUST, J. A., and R. G. S. BIDWELL. 1963. Protein turnover in wheat and snapdragon leaves. Can. J. Bot., *41*: 969-983.

HELLEBUST, J. A., and R. R. L. GUILLARD. 1967. Uptake specificity for organic substances by the marine diatom *Melosira nummuloides*. J. Phycol., *3*: 132-136.

HOBBIE, J. E., C. C. CRAWFORD, and K. L. WEBB. 1968. Amino acid flux in an estuary. Science, *159*: 1463-1464.

HOBBIE, J. E., and R. T. WRIGHT. 1965. Bioassay with bacterial uptake kinetics: glucose in freshwater. Limnol. Oceanogr., *10*: 471-474.

JANNASCH, H. W. 1967. Enrichments of aquatic bacteria in continuous culture. Arch. Mikrobiol., *59*: 165-173.

KEPES, A., and G. COHEN. 1962. Permeation, p. 179-221. *In* I.C. Gunsalus and R. Y. Stanier [ed.], The bacteria, v. 4. Academic Press, New York.

LEWIN, J. C. 1963. Heterotrophy in marine diatoms, p. 229-235. *In* C.H. Oppenheimer [ed.], Symp. on Marine microbiology. C. Thomas, Springfield, Ill.

LEWIS, F., and W. R. TAYLOR. 1921. Notes from the Woods Hole Laboratory. Rhodora, *23*: 249-256.

MARGALEFF, R. 1946. Contribution al conocimiento del genero *Platymonas*. Collect. Bot., I (1), *8*: 95-105.

MARKER, A. F. H. 1965. Extracellular carbohydrate liberation in the flagellates *Isochrysis galbana* and *Prymnesium parvum*. J. Mar. Biol. Ass. U.K., *45*: 755-772.

NEUJAHR, H. Y. 1966. Transport of B-vitamins in microorganisms. II. Factors affecting the uptake of labelled thiamine by non-proliferating cells of *Lactobacillus fermenti*. Acta Chem. Scand., *20*: 771-785.

NORTH, B. B., and B. C. STEPHENS. 1967. Uptake and assimilation of amino acids by *Platymonas*. Biol. Bull., *133*: 391-400.

OXENDER, D. L., and H. N. CHRISTENSEN. 1963. Distinct mediating systems for the transport of neutral amino acids by the Ehrlich cell. J. Biol. Chem., *238*: 3686-3699.

PINTNER, I. J., and L. PROVASOLI. 1963. Nutritional characteristics of some chrysomonads, p. 114-121. *In* C. H. Oppenheimer [ed.], Symp. Marine microbiology. C. Thomas, Springfield, Ill.

PROVASOLI, L. 1963. Organic regulation of phytoplankton fertility, p. 165-219. *In* M.N. Hill [ed.], The sea, v. 2. Interscience, New York.

PROVASOLI, L., and K. GOLD. 1962. Nutrition of the American strain of *Gyrodinium cohnii*. Arch. Mikrobiol., *42*: 196-203.

PROVASOLI, L., and J. J. A. McLAUGHLIN. 1963. Limited heterotrophy of some photosynthetic dinoflagellates, p. 105-113. *In* C.H. Oppenheimer [ed.], Symp. on Marine microbiology. C. Thomas, Springfield, Ill.

SHRIFT, A. 1966. Methionine transport in *Chlorella vulgaris*. Plant Physiol., *41*: 405-410.

SIEBURTH, J. McN., and A. JENSEN. 1969. Studies on algal substances in the sea. II. Gelbstoff (humic material) formation in phaeophyte exudates. J. Exp. Mar. Biol. Ecol., *3*: 275-289.

SLOAN, P. R., and J. D. H. STRICKLAND. 1966. Heterotrophy of four marine phytoplankters at low substrate concentrations. J. Phycol., *2*: 29-32.

STEWARD, W. D. P. 1963. Liberation of extracellular nitrogen by two nitrogen fixing blue-green algae. Nature, *200*: 1020-1021.

STRICKLAND, J. D. H. 1965. Phytoplankton and marine primary production. Annu. Rev. Microbiol., *19*: 127-162.

TAYLOR, F. J. 1960a. The absorption of glucose by *Scenedesmus quadricauda*. I. Some kinetic aspects. Roy. Soc., Proc., *B.151*: 400-418.

TAYLOR, F. J. 1960b. The absorption of glucose by *Scenedesmus quadricauda*. II. The nature of the absorptive process. Roy. Soc., Proc., *B.151*: 483-496.

VACCARO, R. F., and H. W. JANNASCH. 1966. Studies on heterotrophic potential in the sea: the use of specifically labelled glucose. Can. J. Microbiol., *13*: 1165-1173.

VACCARO, R. F., and H. W. JANNASCH. 1967. Variations in uptake kinetics for glucose by natural populations in sea water. Limnol. Oceanogr., *12*: 540-542.

WANGERSKY, P. J., and R. R. L. GUILLARD. 1960. Low molecular weight organic base from the dinoflagellate *Amphidinium carteri*. Nature, *185*: 689-690.

WILEY, W. R., and W. H. MATCHETT. 1966. Tryptophan transport in *Neurospora crassa*. J. Bact., *92*: 1698-1705.

WOOD, E. J. F. 1956. Diatoms in the ocean deeps. Pacific Sci., *10*: 377-381.

WRIGHT, R. T., and J. E. HOBBIE. 1965. The uptake of organic solutes in lake water. Limnol. Oceanogr., *10*: 22-28.

WRIGHT, R. T., and J. E. HOBBIE. 1966. Use of glucose and acetate by bacteria and algae in aquatic ecosystems. Ecology, *47*: 447-464.

RELEASE OF DISSOLVED ORGANIC COMPOUNDS BY MARINE AND FRESH WATER INVERTEBRATES

R. E. Johannes and Kenneth L. Webb
Department of Zoology
University of Georgia
Athens, Georgia 30601

Virginia Institute of Marine Science
Gloucester Point, Virginia 23062

ABSTRACT

Aquatic invertebrates release a variety of dissolved organic compounds into the water. Per unit weight, rates of release of some of these compounds have been shown to decrease with starvation, decreasing temperature, decreasing salinity and increasing body weight. Published data on uptake of radioactively labeled dissolved organic compounds by aquatic invertebrates do not constitute evidence for the *net* uptake of these compounds. The possibility that aquatic animals are a quantitatively significant source of dissolved organic matter in aquatic ecosystems is discussed.

INTRODUCTION

Studies of the release of dissolved organic compounds by aquatic invertebrates are numerous and the literature extends back into the 19th century. Most of these investigations focused on comparative aspects of the physiology of excretion, particularly nitrogenous excretion. These studies are no less interesting when examined in the context of energy flow through aquatic ecosystems.

Dissolved organic nitrogen compounds have been reported in the release products of all major invertebrate phyla from Protista through Chordata. Free amino acids (FAA) are released by a wide variety of aquatic invertebrates (see below). Urea and uric acid are released by most major groups (e.g., Nicol, 1967), and purines by a number of groups, including crustaceans (Delaunay, 1934) and Protozoa (Soldo and van Wagtendonk, 1961). Octopus urine reportedly contains a large number of organic N compounds (Emmanuel, 1957). The ciliate, *Tetrahymena pyriformis*, releases hypoxanthine and pyrimidines (Leboy et al., 1964).

Dissolved organic phosphorus is released by a wide variety of marine invertebrates (e.g., Pomeroy and Bush, 1959; Satomi and Pomeroy, 1965) although specific compounds were not identified. Glucose has been reported in the urine of *Octopus dofleini*, (Harrison and Martin, 1965).

Probably almost any soluble, reasonably stable organic compound present in an aquatic organism could be found in the soluble release products of an animal which feeds upon this organism. Even readily assimilable components of food do not appear to be completely assimilated, but are released in part from the gut (see below). We suspect that the only reason a much wider variety of compounds has not been reported is simply that no one has looked for them yet.

METHODOLOGICAL PROBLEMS

A number of uncertainties make it difficult to accept at face value data reported in many papers on the release of dissolved organic nitrogen, especially data on rates. Incubations often lasted as long as 24 hours, during which time the animals were not fed. We have found that rates of release of dissolved organic materials by small invertebrates may decrease considerably when they are deprived of food. For example, Johannes (1964a) reported that the rate of release of dissolved organic phosphorus by the amphipod *Lembos intermedius* decreased by 50% after only two hours of starvation. In what may be an extreme case, we found that the rate of release of dissolved free amino acids by the planarian' *Dugesia dortocephala* fed on liver, decreases by almost two orders of magnitude during 24 hours of starvation (Johannes, Coward and Webb, unpublished manuscript).

The microbial removal of released substances is also liable to influence results during such long incubation periods. It is well known that marine bacteria multiply rapidly when sea water is enclosed in a small container (e.g., ZoBell and Anderson, 1936). Johannes (1963) observed that within 24 hours marine bacteria removed from solution almost all of the dissolved organic phosphorus released by a group of marine amphipods. More recently we added single fecal pellets from the copepod *Acartia* sp. to two sea water samples containing mixed FAA at a total concentration of 510 μg α-amino N/liter. After 24 hours of incubation of the samples at 10 C, bacteria reached a density of 0.5 x10^6/ml and 29 to 31% of the dissolved FAA had disappeared from solution (Webb and Johannes, 1969). Corner and Newell (1967) reported finding no dissolved FAA released by copepods incubated for 24 hours under similar conditions. It is possible that bacteria introduced with the copepods and their fecal pellets reduced these compounds to levels beneath the sensitivity of the analysis.

Some investigators have not filtered incubation media prior to analysis for dissolved organic release products. Such analyses are open to question qualitatively as well as quantitatively since they probably include particulate material such as feces and mucus.

Crowding is a problem common to all release experiments with aquatic animals. Crowding may bring about either an increase or a decrease in the metabolic rates of different zooplankton species (see Satomi and Pomeroy, 1965, for discussion). This problem can be minimized by keeping densities of animals in incubation vessels just high enough to obtain a measurable change in the concentration of the substance being studied. Difficulties of measuring small changes in water chemistry caused by most animals when incubated at their natural densities make the complete elimination of this problem unlikely.

To obtain the most realistic estimates of *in situ* release rates of dissolved materials, therefore, animals should be incubated as soon after capture as possible (or, if the animals are from cultures, they should not be starved), densities should be kept as low as possible, the duration of incubation should be as short as possible and the incubation medium must be filtered when the experiment is terminated even if no particulate matter is visible.

Clean equipment is essential. A single misplaced fingerprint can ruin an experiment (e.g., Hamilton, 1965). Membrane filters should be rinsed before use with hot distilled water to remove soluble organics (e.g., Cahn, 1967) or ashed metallic or glass fiber filters may be used.

RELEASE OF FREE AMINO ACIDS

Taxa

Free amino acids (FAA) have been reported in the release products of aquatic protozoa, coelenterates, molluscs, crustaceans, annelids, echinoderms and brachiopods (see review in Nicol, 1967). In addition to measuring FAA release rates of representatives of most of these groups, we have measured FAA release by aquatic insect larvae, tunicates, sponges and turbellarians (Table 1; Webb and Johannes, 1967; Johannes, Coward and Webb, 1969). Collectively, these compounds appear to be the largest component of the dissolved organic nitrogen released by aquatic crustaceans (Parry, 1960), echinoderms (Nicol, 1967; Lewis, 1967) and a number of other invertebrate groups. In only one published case we are aware of, i.e., the marine copepod *Calanus helgolandicus*, were investigators unable to detect FAA in release products (Corner and Newell, 1967). The related species, *Calanus chilensis*, is reported to release FAA (Webb and Johannes, 1967).

Qualitative studies

Webb and Johannes (1967) made the first qualitative study of FAA release by marine zooplankton. Using a wide variety of populations of mixed net zooplankton, we found that taurine and ornithine, in addition to most of the amino acids commonly occurring in protein, were released. FAA patterns of taxonomically diverse zooplankton were characterized less by their differences than by their similarities. Glycine, alanine and taurine were usually the most abundant amino acids. Since that time, we have measured FAA released by a number of individual invertebrate species from marine, estuarine and fresh waters (e.g., Table 1).

Considerable variation in relative abundance of different amino acids was found although glycine was generally among the largest components. Taurine was conspicuously missing from five analyses of the release products of *Artemia salina* and this compound seems less abundant in the release products of fresh water invertebrates than marine ones. Taurine is generally found in high concentrations in the tissues of marine invertebrates while it is usually absent from the tissues of fresh water species (Awapara, 1962).

Relative concentrations of free amino acids in release products of a number of aquatic invertebrates are shown in Table 1. Incubation times

Table 1. Composition of dissolved free amino acids released by some aquatic invertebrates (mole per cent)[1].

	Artemia salina, adult (yeast)[2]	Artemia salina, nauplii (yeast)[2]	Clymenella torquata[3]	Acanthopleura granulata[4]	Nerita versicolor[5]	Acropora muricata[6]	Daphnia magna[7]	Chaoborus punctipennis[8]
cysteic acid	-	-	5.5	3.3	1.3	3.1	-	2.2
taurine	-	-	9.6	7.7	32.8	3.9	3.5	1.2
meth. sulf.	-	-	2.0	2.7	0.9	2.5	0.8	-
aspartic acid	7.9	4.5	6.0	4.1	1.3	3.9	5.7	14.7
threonine	8.3	4.1	4.3	2.2	1.7	-	5.2	6.8
serine	15.1	14.2	20.5	1.6	2.1	6.7	25.6	1.1
glutamic acid	1.0	0.8	2.5	34.9	4.0	11.6	2.7	-
proline	3.0	1.5	4.7	6.2	3.9	2.2	3.6	-
glycine	10.3	50.2	9.2	15.5	38.0	54.5	15.9	10.8
alanine	8.3	5.9	9.9	5.3	4.6	2.4	8.4	8.2
valine	4.8	2.0	2.5	1.5	1.8	0.8	2.9	4.3
cystine	0.8	-	-	2.6	-	-	-	tr.
methionine	-	-	-	0.3	-	-	-	-
isoleucine	2.8	1.2	1.6	1.0	1.3	0.3	2.4	3.4
leucine	4.2	1.6	1.9	2.0	2.3	0.4	2.8	4.9
tyrosine	5.0	0.8	-	0.9	0.7	0.4	1.9	2.1
phenylalanine	2.9	0.4	1.3	1.1	0.8	0.02	1.3	2.6
ornithine	10.7	7.8	11.8	1.1	-	3.4	10.2	3.1
lysine	7.7	2.2	3.8	2.7	1.4	1.5	2.7	7.2
histidine	4.5	2.1	2.3	1.0	-	1.8	3.0	5.5
arginine	2.8	0.6	0.7	2.9	1.1	0.4	1.4	6.1
unidentified ninhydrin positive	trace	trace	-	-	-	-	-	15.9

[1]The food of animals from cultures is shown in parentheses immediately under their names. Other species were incubated at *in situ* temperatures immediately after their removal from their natural environment, except for *Nerita versicolor*, which was held without food for three hours prior to incubation.

[2]hypersaline crustacean   [3]estuarine annelid   [4]marine chiton   [5]marine gastropod
[6]marine scleractinian coral   [7]freshwater crustacean   [8]freshwater dipteran larva

ranged from 1 to 3 hours. Methods are given in Webb and Johannes (1967) and Webb and Wood (1967).

Temperature relations

Webb and Johannes (1967) report that release rates of mixed marine net zooplankton are linearly correlated with temperature. This report is based on incubations at *in situ* temperatures between 6.9 C and 25.5 C. If this linear relationship remains unaltered at lower temperatures, it can be inferred that FAA release ceases at about 6 C. This seems unlikely but the possibility should be examined.

Size relations

The greater importance per unit biomass of small animals in the production of dissolved FAA (e.g., Table 2) is not surprising. Per unit biomass, rates of oxygen consumption, dissolved phosphorus release and food ingestion of aquatic animals are also negatively correlated with body weight (Zeuthen, 1947; Johannes, 1964b; Sushchenya and Khmeleva, 1967). These and other observations (e.g., Wieser and Kanwisher, 1961; Beers and Stewart, 1967; Pomeroy and Johannes, 1968) indicate that the importance of microzooplankton and microzoobenthos in aquatic trophic dynamics is probably often underrated.

Release mechanisms

In aquatic invertebrates dissolved FAA may conceivably be released by true excretion, by egestion, or by diffusion. The presence of FAA as well as a number of other dissolved organic compounds in urine taken directly from the animals has been reported for a number of marine invertebrates (Emmanuel, 1957; Delaunay, 1931; Binns and Peterson, 1969) and provides direct evidence for the true excretion of these compounds. It has been noted, however, that the urinary release of various nitrogenous compounds seems to account for a comparatively small fraction of the total release of these materials in some invertebrates (e.g., Binns and Peterson, 1969).

Release directly from the gut may be important since release rates may drop considerably after the gut is emptied of food. This might be attributed simply to a starvation-mediated decrease in metabolic rate with a concomitant decrease in true excretion rate. However, we have found that FAA release rates decrease faster than respiration rates during starvation. A striking example of this is the planarian *Dugesia dortocephala*, where, as noted above, the FAA release rates decreased by almost two orders of magnitude during 24 hours of starvation, while respiration rates decreased by only about 50% (Johannes, Coward and Webb, unpublished). In addition, the release products of recently fed *Dugesia* contained eight prominent unidentified ninhydrin positive compounds which gave peaks on chromatograms identical to those found in extracts of the liver on which they had been fed. Ethanolamine, glucosamine and β-aminoisobutyric acid

Table 2. Increase in FAA release rate per gram dry tissue with decreasing body weight in marine invertebrates.

Species	Mean dry wt (mg)	FAA release rate (mg FAA/g dry wt/day)
Acanthopleura granulata	3600	0.044
Clymenella torquata	92	0.53
Palaemonetes pugio	50	0.56
Artemia salina adult	0.28	3.9
nauplii	0.01	12.7

were also found in their food and their release products. None of these eleven compounds were found in the release products of *Dugesia* starved for 24 hours or more. These observations indicate that these release products of fed *Dugesia* were derived in part from ingested, unassimilated food. It should be noted, however, that these compounds may not be present in *Dugesia's* normal food.

Baldwin (1947) suggested that the release of FAA by marine invertebrates may take place by diffusion across permeable membranes, and Delaunay (1931), Mollitor (1937) and others have demonstrated the release of urea by diffusion in a number of marine invertebrates. If Baldwin's hypothesis is correct, FAA release rates should increase with increasing salinity since there is a marked increase in tissue FAA in estuarine invertebrates as the salinity rises (e.g., Florkin, 1966). This is indeed the case with the marine-estuarine turbellarian *Bdelloura candida* (Johannes, Coward and Webb, 1969). However, tissue FAA levels increase faster than FAA release rates in *Bdelloura*, suggesting that simple diffusion does not account for all the FAA released by this species.

It appears then that egestion, leakage across the body wall and true excretion are all involved in the release of dissolved organic compounds by aquatic animals. Experimental conditions and species differences undoubtedly determine the relative importance of these three processes.

FAA release by corals

It is of some interest to determine whether or not invertebrates containing zooxanthellae release free amino acids in the water like other aquatic invertebrates. It has been suggested that zooxanthellae may remove animal release products from their hosts' tissues (Yonge and Nicholls, 1931) and McGlaughlin and Zahl (1959) have shown that zooxanthellae are capable of utilizing FAA. Accordingly, we attempted to measure the release of FAA by the zooxanthellae-containing scleractinian corals *Acropora muricata* (Table 1), *Montastrea annularis, Manicina areolate* and *Porites asteroides*.

The incubations were run in the dark at *in situ* temperatures. There was a net release of small amounts of FAA into the medium by all four species. Weight specific release rates were not calculated since we could not determine tissue weights directly, and measured nitrogen contents, which have been used as an index of coral biomass, proved in our experience to be too variable. Our observations suggest that if zooxanthellae do utilize FAA that would otherwise be released into the water by the coral host, this utilization is not 100% efficient.

NUTRITIVE VALUE TO INVERTEBRATES
OF DISSOLVED ORGANIC COMPOUNDS

Pütter (1909) first suggested that marine animals may utilize dissolved organic matter as a source of nutritional energy. Moore et al. (1912) critically reviewed Pütter's claims and his methods and were unable to verify his hypothesis experimentally. Their experiments invariably indicated a net loss of dissolved organic matter from marine animals, but their long incubation times rendered their own results subject to criticism. Krogh (1931) also pointed out the inadequacy of Pütter's techniques and concluded that no valid evidence existed to support Pütter's ideas. Like Moore et al. (1912), he found a net loss of dissolved organic matter to the water by a number of fresh water animals (Krogh, 1930).

A few years ago Stephens reopened this controversy, reporting the uptake of labeled FAA from solution by a wide variety of soft-bodied marine invertebrates (e.g., Stephens and Schinske, 1961). These and similar subsequent observations have been interpreted by their authors as indicating that there is a net removal of FAA from sea water and that these compounds may constitute a significant energy source for marine invertebrates (e.g., Stephens, 1967; Virkar, 1963; McWhinnie and Johanneck, 1966; Ferguson, 1967; Chapman and Taylor, 1968; Little and Gupta, 1968; Southward and Southward, 1968). However, in none of these experiments were release rates of total dissolved FAA measured. Consequently, it cannot be claimed that these data demonstrate even the direction of net flow of dissolved amino acids (i.e., into or out of the animal) let alone the net rate of flow of these compounds.

Clymenella torquata, a maldanid polychaete, was one of the animals most extensively studied by Stephens (1963). In an effort to reconcile our observations on FAA release by marine invertebrates with Stephens' observations on FAA uptake, we reran some of Stephens' experiments on *Clymenella*, using C^{14} labeled FAA. But whereas Stephens measured only changes in the concentration of *labeled* amino acids in the medium, we also measured changes in the concentration of total (i.e., labeled and unlabeled) dissolved amino acids in the medium. Our results confirm those of Stephens; there was a measurable, reproducible uptake of labeled FAA from the medium. However, there also was a net increase in total dissolved FAA in solution (e.g., Table 3). (This and additional experiments will be reported more fully elsewhere.) In other words, there was a bidirectional movement of FAA between animal and medium but the net flow was into the medium. We have obtained similar results with the turbellarian *Bdelloura candida* (Johannes, Coward and Webb, 1969) and the tunicate *Molgula manhattanensis* (Webb and Johannes, unpublished.)

The two-way movement of free amino acids across biological membranes is a well documented phenomenon in mammals (e.g., Christensen, 1962), and an excellent discussion of this phenomenon as it relates to amino acid transport between internal organs of starfish is given by Ferguson (1964). Ussing (1949) warned that the isotope method for measuring movement of materials from one compartment to another can lead to erroneous conclusions if the bidirectional nature of the flux of small molecules across permeable membranes is not taken into consideration. Unfortunately, some unwarranted assumptions concerning the net direction of flow of dissolved phosphorus in aquatic organisms are also based on an apparent lack of awareness of this phenomenon (e.g., Slater and Tremor, 1962; Parker and Olson, 1966).

Table 3. Uptake and release of dissolved free amino acids by 15 *Clymenella torquata* incubated in 50 ml for 32 min at 24 C. Salinity, 22°/oo.

Initial glycine – C^{14} level (cpm/ml)	1470
Final glycine – C^{14} level (cpm/ml)	740
Initial DFAA level (NM/ml)	1.7
Final DFAA level (NM/ml)	2.9
Net FAA release rate (NM/hr/g fresh wt)	102

ENERGETICS

One of the major goals of ecology is to discover the routes and rates of energy flow through ecosystems. Tracing each of the myriad pathways of energy transfer to and from all the components of these systems does not seem feasible. We must therefore focus our attention on quantitatively significant pathways and be satisfied with sketching in only the important features of ecosystem energetics. Hence, we must ask whether or not the release of dissolved organic materials by aquatic animals is really worth investigating in this context; is this pathway of energy flux an important one in aquatic ecosystems?

Total dissolved organic carbon

Speculation concerning the origins of dissolved organic matter in natural waters has concerned algae and detritus almost exclusively (e.g., Fogg, 1966; Duursma, 1961). It has been suggested by some that animals cannot play a major role in the production of these compounds because algae and bacteria account for a greater proportion of the total metabolism of aquatic communities (e.g., Khailov, 1965). This hypothesis is based on the untested assumption that, per unit of total metabolism, rates of release of dissolved organic metabolites by plants and bacteria are similar to or greater than these rates in animals.

In the case of plankton, for example, there is room for the opposite speculation. It has been stated by several investigators that plankton ecosystems appear to be dominated by grazing food chains; that is, in contrast to salt marsh or forest communities, most plant life in the plankton is eaten while alive and thus does not undergo a "natural death" to form detritus (Odum, 1962; MacFadyen, 1964). The observation that marine phytoplankton populations are more often controlled by grazing than by nutrients (e.g., Nielsen, 1958) seems to support this contention. If we assume that zooplankton ingest an average of 80% of primary production, and if 10% of the ingested organic material is subsequently excreted, egested and leaked into the water in solution, then 8% of the energy fixed by primary producers will have found its way, via zooplankton, into the dissolved organic matter pool. This would indeed be a significant contribution to the pool.

Unfortunately, data are available for the ratio of dissolved organic matter released to organic carbon ingested for only one aquatic invertebrate. Johannes and Satomi (1967) reported a ratio of 3.3:1 for *Palaemonetes pugio*. Determinations of the ratio of dissolved organic carbon released to organic carbon ingested by a wide variety of animals would clearly help to determine the quantitative significance of animals in the production of dissolved organic matter. In addition, such determinations are an integral part of determining the amount of organic carbon ingested by aquatic animals which is unavailable for maintenance and growth (Johannes and Satomi, 1967).

Free amino acids

Under steady state conditions the flux of free amino acids in the water is equal to either the rate of supply (release by organisms) or the rate of removal (uptake by organisms). Significance of this flux may be evaluated in terms of the replacement time or the proportion of primary production partitioned to this pathway.

Webb and Johannes (1967) have estimated that dissolved FAA replacement time due to release by net zooplankton is about one month in marine waters. Microzooplankton, which escape zooplankton nets and were thus not included in this estimate, would be expected to shorten this replacement time significantly. On the other hand, crowding of animals in incubation vessels may have increased FAA release rates in these experiments as Corner and Newell (1967) have suggested, although we found no correlation between density and release rate over an order of magnitude of test densities. Estimates using labeled amino acids suggest that the FAA flux brought about by the activities of all planktonic organisms results in an FAA replacement time of about one day in an estuary (Hobbie et al., 1968).

Johannes and Webb (1965) reported data indicating that net zooplankton in the Sargasso Sea and Gulf Stream release dissolved FAA carbon at a rate equivalent to 22 to 25% of the rate of primary production of organic carbon. These surprisingly high values may result from erroneously high release estimates, erroneously low production estimates or both. In an estuary, Hobbie et al. (1968) estimated the flux of FAA carbon due to all planktonic organisms to be between 1 and 10% of the rate of primary production of organic carbon.

CONCLUSIONS

A variety of challenges to the physiological ecologist exist in connection with the release of dissolved organic substances by aquatic animals. What are the non-nitrogenous constituents of these release products? Are there significant qualitative or quantitative differences in the release products of marine and fresh water animals, animals of different taxa, carnivores and herbivores? Why are some valuable compounds "wasted" in this fashion by marine animals? Evidence discussed here suggests that the release of dissolved organic carbon by marine animals may be an important pathway of flow of reduced carbon in aquatic ecosystems. This evidence is fragmentary and considerably more research is required before the question is settled. In the past few years the analytical tools necessary to provide detailed answers to some of these questions have become commonly available. Hopefully this paper will encourage their use.

DISCUSSION

SIEBURTH: In the beginning you mentioned that you have to take precautions against bacterial effects, but you did not mention how you do this.

JOHANNES: We incubate the animals for as short a time as is consistent with obtaining measurable increases in dissolved free amino acids. Bacteria are introduced initially with the sample, of course, but we are dealing with zooplankton which are concentrated out of many cubic meters of water. We are, of course, not concentrating bacteria in the sea water simultaneously. Initially, then, there will not be enough bacteria present to remove significant quantities of dissolved amino acids. If the experiments are run immediately and kept brief, significant bacterial growth will not occur. The longest experiment we ran lasted about four hours, which I feel now was too long. I like to keep experiments down to one hour. In the case of animals other than zooplankters, we simply rinse them carefully several times before we incubate them and use filtered water, again holding the incubation down to an hour or two.

SIEBURTH: How do you filter the water?

JOHANNES: We filter it with washed 0.45 μ Millipore filters, which let a few bacteria through, right? But not enough to cause any problems for the first couple of hours.

SIEBURTH: You are also introducing a lot of bacteria with your fecal pellets. I think it might be possible for you to use a flow-through cell like we do. I think there are advantages to it.

JOHANNES: There are advantages to it. I agree with you. I think there are also disadvantages insofar as the products that are released are diluted in a system like this.

SIEBURTH: You can still concentrate it?

JOHANNES: Yes, you can. With fresh water you can do so easily, but concentration from sea water is laborious and accuracy is reduced — sometimes prohibitively.

SIEBURTH: You are looking for specific products. You have not been looking for totals. I would like to see you quantify this by measuring the total carbon rather than just looking at individual products.

JOHANNES: Total dissolved organic carbon? I could talk at great length about the Beckman Carbonaceous Analyzer that we have had for 16 months and from which we have very little data.

SIEBURTH: I sympathize. It took me two years to get mine working; service is heart breaking and expensive.

DEGENS: You determined the release rate for the individual organisms on the basis of the free amino acids. Do you have any idea of the quantity of small peptides and proteins released and when they are released? If so, what is the ratio of the amount of free amino acids released and the amount of small peptides and proteins?

JOHANNES: We have rarely looked for proteins. In a couple of cases with fresh water insect larvae, in which we looked for proteins, we found none, using a fairly insensitive method. As far as unidentified ninhydrin positive substances like some of your dipeptides, we very rarely get anything more than traces, less than 1% of the total amount, none of which we have attempted to identify.

PARSONS: Have you, by any chance, studied the release of organics during molting? I know this is probably difficult since you are dealing with short term experiments, but with euphausiids, for example, which molt very frequently, the release of dissolved organics might be quite appreciable.

JOHANNES: No, we have not; it would be an interesting thing to do. You might expect that the release rate would go up as a result of increased permeability.

ACKNOWLEDGMENTS

This research was supported in part by National Science Foundation grants BG6550 and GB6064.

This is contribution No. 160 from the University of Georgia Marine Institute and Contribution No. 289 from the Virginia Institute of Marine Science.

REFERENCES

AWAPARA, J. 1962. Free amino acids in invertebrates: a comparative study of their distribution and metabolism, p. 158-175. *In* J.T. Holden [ed.], Amino acid pools. Elsevier, Amsterdam.

BALDWIN, E. 1947. Dynamics aspect of biochemistry. Cambridge Univ. Press, New York.

BEERS, J. R., and G. L. STEWART. 1967. Microzooplankton in the euphotic zone at five locations across the California current. J. Fish. Res. Bd. Canada, *24*: 2053-2068.

BINNS, R., and A. J. PETERSON. 1969. Nitrogen excretion by the spiny lobster *Jasus edwardsi* (Hutton): the role of the antennal gland. Biol. Bull., *136*: 147-153.

CAHN, R. D. 1967. Detergents in membrane filters. Science, *155*: 195-196.

CHAPMAN, G., and A. G. TAYLOR. 1968. Uptake of organic solutes by *Nereis virens*. Nature, *217*: 763-764.

CHRISTENSEN, H. N. 1962. Biological transport. Benjamin, New York. 133 p.

CORNER, E. D. S., and B. S. NEWELL. 1967. On the nutrition and metabolism of zooplankton. IV. The forms of nitrogen excreted by *Calanus*. J. Mar. Biol. Ass. U.K., *47*: 113-120.

DELAUNAY, H. 1931. L'excrétion azotée des Invertébrés. Biol. Rev., *6*: 265-301.

DELAUNAY, H. 1934. Le métabolisme de l'ammoniague d'après les recherches relative aux Invertébrés. Annu. Physiol. Physiochim. Biol., *10*: 695-729.

DUURSMA, E. K. 1961. Dissolved organic carbon, nitrogen and phosphorus in the sea. Nethl. J. Sea Res., *1*: 1-148.

EMMANUEL, C. F. 1957. The composition of octopus renal fluid. II. A chromatographic examination of the constituents. Z. Vergl. Physiol., *39*: 477-482.

FERGUSON, J. C. 1964. Nutrient transport in starfish. II. Uptake of nutrients by isolated organics. Biol. Bull., *126*: 391-406.

FERGUSON, J. C. 1967. Utilization of dissolved exogenous nutrients by the starfishes, *Asterias forbesi* and *Henricia sanguinolenta*. Biol. Bull., *132*: 161-173.

FLORKIN, M. 1966. Nitrogen metabolism, p. 309-351. *In* K. M. Wilbur and C. M. Yonge [ed.], Physiology of mollusca, v. 2. Academic Press, New York.

FOGG, G. E. 1966. The extracellular products of algae. Oceanogr. Mar. Biol. Annu. Rev., *4*: 195-212.

HAMILTON, P. B. 1965. Amino acids on hands. Nature, *205*: 284-285.

HARRISON, F. M., and A. W. MARTIN. 1965. Excretion in the cephalopod, *Octopus dofleini*. J. Exp. Biol., *42*: 71-98.

HOBBIE, J. E., C. C. CRAWFORD, and K. L. WEBB. 1968. Amino acid flux in an estuary. Science, *159*: 1463-1464.

JOHANNES, R. E. 1963. Uptake and release of phosphorus by representatives of a coastal marine ecosystem. Ph.D. Thesis, University of Hawaii, (Diss. Abstr., *24*: 3812).

JOHANNES, R. E. 1964a. Uptake and release of phosphorus by a benthic marine amphipod. Limnol. Oceanogr., *9*: 235-242.

JOHANNES, R. E. 1964b. Phosphorus excretion and body size in marine animals: microzooplankton and nutrient regeneration. Science, *146*: 923-924.

JOHANNES, R. E., S. J. COWARD, and K. L. WEBB. 1969. Are dissolved amino acids an energy source for marine invertebrates? Comp. Biochem. Physiol., *29*: 283-288.

JOHANNES, R. E., and M. SATOMI. 1967. Measuring organic matter retained by aquatic invertebrates. J. Fish. Res. Bd. Canada, *24*: 2467-2471.

JOHANNES, R. E., and K. L. WEBB. 1965. Release of dissolved amino acids by marine zooplankton. Science, *150*: 76-77.

KHAILOV, K. M. 1965. Dynamic marine biochemistry—development prospects. Oceanology, *5*(1): 1-9.

KROGH, A. 1930. Über die Bedentung von gelösten organischen Substanzen bei der Ernährung von Wassertieren. Z. Vergl. Physiol., *12*: 668-681.

KROGH, A. 1931. Dissolved substances as food of aquatic organisms. Bio. Rev., *6*: 412-442.

LEBOY, P. S., S. G. CLINE, and R. L. CONNER. 1964. Phosphate, purines, and pyrimidines as excretory products of *Tetrahymena*. J. Protozool., *11*: 217-222.

LEWIS, J. B. 1967. Nitrogeneous excretion in the tropical sea urchin *Diadema antillarum* Philippi. Biol. Bull., *132*: 34-37.

LITTLE, C., and B. L. GUPTA. 1968. Pogonophora: uptake of dissolved nutrients. Nature, *218*: 873-874.

MacFADYEN, A. 1964. Energy flow in ecosystems and its exploitation by grazing, p. 3-20. *In* D.J. Crisp [ed.], Grazing in terrestrial and marine environments. Blackwells, Oxford.

McGLAUGHLIN, J. J. A., and P. A. ZAHL. 1959. Axenic zooxanthellae from various invertebrate hosts. Annu. N.Y. Acad. Sci., *77*: 55-72.

McWHINNIE, M. A., and R. JOHANNECK. 1966. Utilization of inorganic and organic carbon compounds by Antarctic zooplankton. Antarctic J.U.S., *1*: 210.

MOLLITOR, A. 1937. Beiträge zur Untersuchung des Exkretsstoffwechsels und der Exkretion von *Eriocheir sinensis*. Zool. Jb. Allgem. Zool., *57*: 323-354.

MOORE, B., E. S. EDIE, E. WHITELY, and W. J. DAKIN. 1912. The nutrition and metabolism of marine animals in relation to (a) dissolved organic matter and (b) particulate organic matter of sea water. Biochem. J., *6*: 255-296.

NICOL, J. A. C. 1967. The biology of marine animals. 2nd ed. Interscience, New York. 699 p.

NIELSEN, E. STEEMANN. 1958. The balance between phytoplankton and zooplankton in the sea. J. Cons., *23*: 178-188.

ODUM, E. P. 1962. Relationship between structure and function in the ecosystem. Jap. J. Ecol., *12*: 108-118.

PARKER, R. A., and M. I. OLSON. 1966. The uptake of inorganic phosphate by *Daphnia schodleri* Sars. Physiol. Zool., *39*: 53-65.

PARRY, G. 1960. Excretion, p. 341-366. *In* T.H. Waterman [ed.], The physiology of crustacea, v. 1. Academic Press, New York.

POMEROY, L. R., and F. M. BUSH. 1959. Regeneration of phosphate by marine animals, p. 893-895. *In* Mary Sears [ed.], Preprints Int. Oceanogr. Congr., Amer. Ass. Adv. Sci., Washington, D.C.

POMEROY, L. R., and R. E. JOHANNES. 1968. Occurrence and respiration of ultraplankton in the upper 500 meters of the ocean. Deep-Sea Res., *15*: 381-391.

PÜTTER, A. 1909. Die Ernährung der Wassertiere und der Stoffhaushalt der Gewässer. Fischer, Jena, Germany.

SATOMI, M., and L. R. POMEROY. 1965. Respiration and phosphorus excretion in some marine populations. Ecology, *46*: 877-881.

SLATER, J. V., and J. W. TREMOR. 1962. Radioactive phosphorus accumulation and distribution in *Tetrahymena*. Biol. Bull., *122*: 298-309.

SOLDO, A. T., and W. J. VAN WAGTENDONK. 1961. Nitrogen metabolism in *Paramecium aurelia*. J. Protozool., *8*: 41-55.

SOUTHWARD, A. J., and E. C. SOUTHWARD. 1968. Uptake and incorporation of labelled glycine by Pogonophores. Nature, *218*: 875-876.

STEPHENS, G. C. 1963. Uptake of organic materials by aquatic invertebrates. II. Accumulation of amino acids by the bamboo worm, *Clymenella torquata*. Comp. Biochem. Physiol., *10*: 191-202.

STEPHENS, G. C. 1967. Dissolved organic material as a nutritional source for marine and estuarine invertebrates, p. 367-383. *In* G.H. Lauff [ed.], Estuaries. Amer. Ass. Adv. Sci. Pub. *83*.

STEPHENS, G. C., and R. A. SCHINSKE. 1961. Uptake of amino acids by marine invertebrates. Limnol. Oceanogr., *6*: 175-181.

SUSHCHENYA, L. M., and N. N. KHMELEVA. 1967. Consumption of food as a function of body weight in crustaceans. Akad. Nauk SSSR. Doklady, Biol. Sci. Sect., *176*: 559-562.

USSING, H. H. 1949. Transport of ions across cellular membranes. Physiol. Rev.. *29*: 127-155.

VIRKAR, R. A. 1963. Amino acids in the economy of the sipunculid worm, *Golfingia gouldii*. Biol. Bull., *125*: 396-397. (Abstr.)

WEBB, K. L., and R. E. JOHANNES. 1967. Studies of the release of dissolved free amino acids by marine zooplankton. Limnol. Oceanogr., *12*: 376-382.

WEBB, K. L., and R. E. JOHANNES. 1969. Do marine crustaceans release dissolved amino acids? Comp. Biochem. Physiol, *29*: 875-879.

WEBB, K. L., and L. WOOD. 1967. Improved techniques for analysis of free amino acids in sea water, p. 440-444. *In* Automation in analytical chemistry, Technicon Symposium 1966, v. 1. Mediad, White Plains, New York.

WIESER, W., and J. KANWISHER. 1961. Ecological and physiological studies on marine nematodes from a salt marsh near Woods Hole, Massachusetts. Limnol. Oceanogr., *6*: 262-270.

YONGE, G. M., and A. G. NICHOLLS. 1931. Studies on the physiology of corals. IV. The structure, distribution and physiology of zooxanthellae. Sci. Rep. Gr. Barrier Reef Exped. 1928-29. Br. Mus. (Nat. Hist.), *1*: 135-176.

ZEUTHEN, E. 1947. Body size and metabolic rate in the animal kingdom, with special regard to the marine micro-fauna. Compt. Rend. Trav. Lab. Carlsberg, Ser. Chim., *26*: 17-161.

ZOBELL, C. E., and D. Q. ANDERSON. 1936. Observations on the multiplication of bacteria in different volumes of stored sea water and the influence of oxygen tension and solid surface. Biol. Bull., *71*: 324-342.

OCCURENCE, POSSIBLE SIGNIFICANCE AND METABOLISM
OF OBLIGATE PSYCHROPHILES IN MARINE WATERS

Richard Y. Morita and Sheril D. Burton
Molecular Biology Section
National Science Foundation
Washington, D.C. 20550

Department of Microbiology
Brigham Young University
Provo, Utah 84601

INTRODUCTION

For convenience obligate psychrophiles may be defined as organisms whose optimum temperature for growth is below 20 C (Stokes, 1963). This thermal class of bacteria has been neglected not only by the marine microbiologists but by others because they were thought to be non-existent. As late as 1962, Ingraham (1962) stated in a review on temperature relationship among microorganisms the following: "Other authors have felt that the term psychrophile should be reserved for bacteria whose growth temperature optima are below 20 C, if and when such organisms are found." However, in the last five years several investigators have isolated bacteria whose optimum temperature for growth is below 20 C [Morita and Haight, 1964; Eimjhellen (see Hagen et al., 1964); Harder and Veldkamp, 1966; Stanley and Rose, 1967; Sieburth, 1967].

This paper pertains mainly to cold waters, such as found below the thermocline and in both polar regions. Although the authors recognize that much of the organic turnover occurs above the thermocline, the large volume of the oceans below the thermocline should not be neglected.

OCCURRENCE OF OBLIGATE PSYCHROPHILES
IN MARINE WATERS

Many obligate psychrophiles have been isolated by various investigators taking the necessary precautions (Morita, 1966). However the actual distribution of this thermal type has not been determined because of the lack of facilities aboard research vessels, personnel and ship time.

Microorganisms already isolated from below the thermocline (e.g., Kriss, 1963) cannot be classified as obligate psychrophiles. Enumeration studies alone cannot elucidate the "metabolism of the sea" in terms of the microbial population. Conditions such as temperature, pressure, availability of an energy source, pH and Eh, as well as the type of microorganism present vary constantly. The result is continuous changes in the dynamic equilibrium which exists between bacteria and their environment.

Soil microbiologists have long recognized that numbers of bacteria in soil do not necessarily correlate with their activities. This is well illustrated by Starkey's (1968) statement:

Little of value has resulted from determination of numbers for the purpose of making census of the populations of soils. The older literature of soil microbiology is replete with data on numbers that are ignored.... Consciously or unconsciously one assumes an implicit direct correlation between numbers and activity, although this may be unjustified. It may be recalled that some years ago Jensen presented evidence that, at low temperatures, there was an inverse relation between numbers and activity. Accordingly, there are advantages in determining activity directly in preference to determining numbers where information on activity is actually the information sought.

If only low temperature is considered then the number of non-psychrophilic bacteria in cold waters may not be an accurate index of their importance. Because psychrophiles (Table 1) can rapidly outgrow non-psychrophiles, the activities of psychrophiles must be considered in cold environments.

Although no serious effort has been made to elucidate the numbers and distribution of obligate psychrophiles in the marine environment, we did study a few water samples at Station NH-65 (Oregon State University). Employing the MPN methods, 79 and 27 psychrophiles were found per 100 ml of sea water at 350 and 2800 meters. Bacteria capable of oxidizing ammonia at an appreciable rate at 2 C have also been isolated off the Bering Straits. Elucidation of psychrophilic bacteria at a few stations in the Arctic has also been undertaken (Table 2).

POSSIBLE SIGNIFICANCE OF PSYCHROPHILES

Stabilization of organic matter content of sea water

When studying marine bacteria other than obligate psychrophiles, Waksman and Carey (1935) found that approximately 50% of the total organic matter in sea water readily decomposed. According to Waksman and Carey (1935) and Waksman and Renn (1936) the main factor limiting bacterial multiplication was the amount of organic matter present in sea water. When 2.5 mg glucose was added to natural sea water, they found 2,005,000 bacteria/ml of water after 24 hours whereas the control had only 625,000 bacteria/ml. Enriching the sea water with ammonium sulfate boosted the plate count to 3,850,000 bacteria/ml in 24 hours.

When only 0.1 mg/liter of peptone was added to a mineral medium, ZoBell and Grant (1943) found that most of the marine bacteria they studied multiplied, but the rate of multiplication was low.

According to Vaccaro and Jannasch (1966) glucose can be effectively assimilated by certain marine bacteria that have half maximum uptake velocities at glucose concentrations as low as 4×10^{-8} M.

Low temperatures are not inimical to the growth of psychrophiles (Morita and Albright, 1965). Under optimum conditions cell yields of 10^{11} and 10^9 cells/ml were obtained in 24 hours at 15 and 4 C respectively. Although we cannot expect such high yields in the open ocean below the

Table 1. Comparison of growth of *Vibrio marinus* MP-1 (obligate psychrophile) and *Pseudomonas enalia* when grown together at 4 C.

Organism	Initial inoculum (cells/ml)	After incubation for 60 hr (cells/ml)
V. marinus	17,500	4,840,000
P. enalia	24,500	35,500

Replicate spread plates were made and incubated at 22 C for *P. enalia* and 4 C for *V. marinus*. SDB medium (broth or agar) (Haight and Morita, 1966) was employed in this study (Robison and Morita, unpublished data).

Table 2. Elucidation of psychrophilic bacteria at various University of Alaska stations.

Station	Depth (m)	No. bacteria/50 ml
1048	surface	10750
1048	50	181
1049	surface	213
1049	75	293
Deadman's Cove	surface	TMC[*]
Deadman's Cove	20	550
Deadman's Cove	30	302
Plume, Silver Bay	surface	2000
1052	surface	12865
1052	75	115
1041	surface	60
1041	50	140
1041	surface film	TMC
1041	20	273
1041	30	107

[*]TMC = too many to count

The number of bacteria was determined by the spread plate method employing medium composed of 25 g NaCl, 1 g $MgSO_4$, 1 g succinic acid, 0.5 g yeast extract, 1 g casamino acids, 1 g malt extract, 100 ml sea water, 900 ml distilled water and 15 g Noble agar. The pH of the medium was 7.2 after autoclaving. Incubation temperature was 0 C. None of the organisms counted grew at 25 C.

thermocline, the psychrophiles could become numerous if sufficient energy were available.

The degradation of organic matter in cold areas by psychrophilic bacteria should also be considered. The relatively low concentration of organic matter below the thermocline and in both polar regions could be due partly to the presence of psychrophiles. The metabolic activities of these bacteria may contribute to the stabilization of the amount of organic matter found. As noted earlier, obligate psychrophiles are not abundant below the thermocline, but they are capable of handling large amounts of substrate in natural unpolluted water. Substrate, not low temperature, may become the limiting factor. In polluted areas, generally oxygen becomes the limiting factor in the multiplication of bacteria. The uptake of oxygen in the presence of glucose is very rapid at low temperatures when the obligate psychrophile, *V. marinus* MP-1, is employed in Warburg studies (Robison, 1965).

Parsons and Strickland (1961), Vaccaro and Jannasch (1966) and Hobbie and Wright (1968) used rate of glucose uptake as an indicator of the natural heterotrophic behavior of microplankton in water. Hobbie and Wright found that the maximum rate of uptake varied from lake to lake and was greatest where pollution was greatest. Vaccaro and Jannasch, studying radioactive glucose uptake by indigenous microflora in natural waters, found that the data was not amenable to analysis by the Michaelis-Menton equation. The Lineweaver-Burk plot of uptake velocity vs. substrate concentrations resulted in a linear function. However the function is probably non-linear because the constants for the uptake kinetics presumably differ for each species of microorganism. Vaccaro and Jannasch concluded that either the differences between constants are too small to be resolved, or the uptake response is largely due to a single predominate species. They favored the latter conclusion. Preliminary studies in Alaskan waters employed the methods mentioned above. The rate of uptake of C^{14}-glycine was greatest at a temperature equal to the ambient temperature of the water. For example, in Taku Harbor in March, 1966, the surface temperature was 2.5 C and the rate of uptake at 10 C was only 60% of the rate at 2.5 C. Thus, it appears that psychrophilic bacteria are very important in the "metabolism of the arctic waters" since more activity was evident at 2.5 C. If more activity had occurred at 10 C, the facultative psychrophilic mesophiles would be more implicated.

Production of micronutrients

Provasoli (1961) states that bacteria are the main synthesizers of vitamins under natural conditions. He argues that thiamine and biotin as well as vitamin B_{12} should be considered in possible bloom situations. The production of antibiotics must also be considered in marine waters. The interdependency of growth factors among bacteria is well known but awareness of the interdependency between bacteria and other forms of life in the sea is just beginning (Droop, 1957; Provasoli, 1963). Burkholder (see Provasoli, 1963) has demonstrated the exchange of vitamins between marine bacteria. Belser (1963) has looked at amino acids, purines and pyrimidines — especially the bases adenine, xanthine, guanine, hypoxanthine, cytosine, thymine and urasil — as possible micronutrients.

Thermally induced leakage in bacteria has been noted by Strange and Shon (1964) and in marine psychrophilic bacteria by Hagen et al. (1962) and Haight and Morita (1966). It is possible that certain vitamins are released along with proteins, amino acids, ribonucleic acid, and deoxyribonucleic acid. This brings up the question of what types of ectocrine compounds are released by obligate psychrophiles when certain water masses are upwelled in tropical and subtropical regions. Although death occurs before lysis (Kenis and Morita, 1968), lysis does occur. Furthermore, cryptic growth and natural die-off probably result in the release of other cellular constituents, some of which may be ectocrine compounds for other organisms. Following leakage in *V. marinus* MP-1, Haight and Morita (1966) identified 17 amino acids and monomeric and polymeric nucleic acids. The latter could easily be the source of pyrimidines and purines.

Colwell and Chapman (personal communication) have demonstrated by means of electron micrographs that cells of *V. marinus* MP-1 leak DNA when exposed to 26.5 C for 1 minute. Membrane integrity can be easily destroyed by heat; leakage of malic dehydrogenase (part of the cell membrane) occurs when the cells are exposed to moderate temperatures (Kenis and Morita, 1968). This suggests that phospholipids are released into the suspending menstruum, be it a natural body of water or the test tube. Glucose-6-phosphate dehydrogenase can also be thermally induced to leak from the cells (Kenis and Morita, 1968; Miller, 1968).

Thermally induced leakage products of cells must be taken into account when sea water is analyzed for amino acids, fatty acids, etc.

METABOLISM OF OBLIGATE PSYCHROPHILIC BACTERIA

The well-being of microorganisms in the sea is directly related to their activities. The abnormal thermolability of enzymes in obligate psychrophiles is consistent with their metabolism at low temperatures. Examples of this thermolability include malic dehydrogenase in a facultative psychrophile (Morita and Burton, 1963) and in an obligate psychrophile (Langridge and Morita, 1966); and succinic dehydrogenase, hexokinase, phosphoglucose isomerase and lactic dehydrogenase (Mathemeir, 1966). It is not yet known what other enzymes of psychrophiles are thermolabile at moderate temperatures (20 to 30 C).

Extrapolation from the laboratory to the marine environment requires that cells be grown in the laboratory at temperatures similar to those in the environment from which they were isolated. For example, Haight and Morita (1966) demonstrated that the respiration rate of cells grown at 5 C is different from that of cells grown at 15 C. Differences in thermal leakage and ability to withstand moderate temperatures were also demonstrated. Albright (1966) observed a difference in the ability of the cells grown at 4 C and 15 C to deaminate L-serine at various temperatures and hydrostatic pressures. Substrate saturation occurred at 3 and 50 μmoles at 4 and 15 C respectively. This as well as limited organic matter may be important when cells are growing at low temperatures.

The effect of low temperature and hydrostatic pressure (Morita, 1967) on microbes and other organisms needs more attention. Basic problems of cellular metabolism of marine forms in terms of the Ideal Gas Law and salts also remain to be solved (Stanley and Morita, 1968).

DISCUSSION

SIEBURTH: In talking about the natural occurrence of psychrophiles, you keep talking about Antarctic waters and waters below the thermocline. There are great areas of temperate waters which are very productive and cold. I do not know if you have ever read my paper on the subject (Sieburth, 1967). As soon as water gets below 10 C, the dominant organisms in the population are obligate psychrophiles. Not 100 organisms/ml as you see it, but as many as 5×10^5 organisms/ml.

MORITA: I have a table on this matter in the manuscript based on work by Burton here in Alaska. On the occurrence of psychrophiles in the Antarctic there are some data by Stanley. We obtained our Antarctic isolates from Stanley, who was a postdoctorate with my group.

BELSER: It seems to me that if you are really looking for a way to firm up the definition of a psychrophile you have got it in your hands, and that is the temperature optimum for given enzymes. When Burton and I examined tryptophane synthetase in some of the Alaskan psychrophiles that he isolated locally, we found that the optimum was 12 to 15 C. We could not pin it down exactly because we worked with a whole cell assay.

MORITA: I do not know if you have seen the latest paper by N. L. Malcolm (1968) in the Journal of Bacteriology, but he has an obligate psychrophile, *Micrococcus cryophilus*, in which he cannot demonstrate any abnormally thermolabile enzymes. He states that loss of viability due to heat is not temperature-induced membrane damage, inhibition of respiration or energy metabolism or the depletion of intracellular reserves but rather correlates with the inhibition of protein synthesis. In view of this I believe we will have to leave the definition as it now stands.

NATARAJAN: What are the pressure effects on these psychrophiles?

MORITA: We have not looked at the pressure effects on this organism to any great extent, but we do know that it grows well at 200 to 300 atm. Some studies on certain enzymes of obligate psychrophiles have been made. The difficulty with pressure experiments is that techniques have not been worked out sufficiently. What we are presently looking at in the laboratory is not precisely related to the problem of psychrophily. The effect of pressure on the conformation of a model protein is currently being investigated (especially in terms of hydrophobic bonding). We hope that we can translate some of the data obtained to organisms under pressure. However, I do not know if we will be able to do this. We have run into all kinds of problems because when we start talking about a model protein we must go back and worry about the pH effect, the various salt effects, temperature effects and many other parameters. Our latest difficulty is that our stainless steel pressure cylinders give off ions which affect the model protein that we have. We are in difficulty and we cannot afford to gold-plate the pressure cylinder.

ALLEN: Your electron micrograph looks like something which pertains directly to the cell wall.

MORITA: The cell wall looks as if it is peeling off and the membrane gives way. If this be the case you may have high concentrations of phospholipids in the water which is another thing one would have to worry about in terms of the organic matter in natural waters.

ACKNOWLEDGMENTS

The research data originating from Oregon State University were supported by NSF grant GB 6548, USPHS grant AM 06752 and USPHS training grant 5 T1 GM 704 from the Institute of General Medical Sciences.
Data originating from the University of Alaska were supported by NSF grant GB 4661 from the Institute of Marine Science at the University of Alaska.

REFERENCES

ALBRIGHT, L. J. 1966. The effect of temperature and hydrostatic pressure on deamination of L-serine by *Vibrio marinus*, an obligate psychrophile. M.S. Thesis, Oregon State Univ., Corvallis.

BELSER, W. L. 1963. Bioassay of trace substances, p. 220-231. *In* M. N. Hill [ed.], The sea, v. 2. Interscience, New York.

DROOP, M. R. 1957. Auxotrophy and organic compounds in the nutrition of marine phytoplankton. J. Gen. Microbiol., *16*: 286-293.

HAGEN, P. D., D. J. KUSHNER, and N. E. GIBBONS. 1964. Temperature induced death and lysis in a psychrophilic bacterium. Can. J. Microbiol., *10*: 813-823.

HAIGHT, J. J., and R. Y. MORITA. 1966. Some physiological differences of *Vibrio marinus* grown at environmental and optimal temperatures. Limnol. Oceanogr., *11*: 470-474.

HAIGHT, R. D., and R. Y. MORITA. 1966. Thermally induced leakage from *Vibrio marinus*, an obligately psychrophilic bacterium. J. Bacteriol., *92*: 418-423.

HARDER, W., and H. VELDKAMP. 1966. Observations on marine obligately psychrophilic bacteria, p. 390. *In* 9th Int. Congr. Microbiol. (Abstr.).

HOBBIE, J. E., and R. T. WRIGHT. 1968. A new method for the study of bacteria in lakes. Mitt. Intern. Ver. Limnol., *14*: 64-71.

INGRAHAM, J. L. 1962. Temperature relationships, p. 265-296. *In* I. C. Gunsalus and R. Y. Stanier [ed.], The bacteria, v. 4. Academic Press, New York and London.

KENIS, P. R., and R. Y. MORITA. 1968. Thermally induced leakage of cellular material and viability in *Vibrio marinus*, a psychrophilic marine bacterium. Can. J. Microbiol., *14*: 1239-1244.

KRISS, A. E. 1963. Marine microbiology (deep-sea). Translation by J. M. Shewan and Z. Kabata. Oliver and Boyd, London. 536 p.

LANGRIDGE, P., and R. Y. MORITA. 1966. Thermolability of malic dehydrogenase from the obligate psychrophile, *Vibrio marinus*. J. Bacteriol., *92*: 418-423.

MATHEMEIER, P. F. 1966. Thermal inactivation studies on some enzymes from *Vibrio marinus*, an obligately psychrophilic marine bacterium. Ph.D. Thesis, Oregon State Univ., Corvallis.

MILLER, W. W. 1968. Studies on glucose-6-phosphate dehydrogenase obtained from *Vibrio marinus*, an obligate psychrophile. M.S. Thesis, Oregon State Univ., Corvallis.

MORITA, R. Y. 1966. Marine psychrophilic bacteria. Oceanogr. Mar. Biol. Annu. Rev., *4*: 105-121.

MORITA, R. Y. 1967. Effects of hydrostatic pressure on marine microorganisms. Oceanogr. Mar. Biol. Annu. Rev., *5*: 187-203.

MORITA, R. Y., and L. J. ALBRIGHT. 1965. Cell yields of *Vibrio marinus*, an obligate psychrophile, at low temperatures. Can. J. Microbiol., *11*: 221-227.

MORITA, R. Y., and S. D. BURTON. 1963. Influence of moderate temperature on growth and malic dehydrogenase activity of a marine psychrophile. J. Bacteriol., *86*: 1025-1029.

MORITA, R. Y., and R. D. HAIGHT. 1964. Temperature effects on the growth of an obligately psychrophilic marine bacterium. Limnol. Oceanogr., *9*: 103-106.

PARSONS, T. R., and J. D. H. STRICKLAND. 1961. On the production of particulate organic carbon by heterotrophic processes in sea water. Deep-Sea Res., *8*: 211-222.

PROVASOLI, L. 1961. Micronutrients and heterotrophy as possible factors in bloom production in natural waters, p. 48-56. *In* Trans. 1960 seminar on algae and metropolitan waters. Robt. A. Taft Sanitary Engineering Center, Cincinnati, Ohio. Tech. Rep. W61-3.

PROVASOLI, L. 1963. Organic regulation of phytoplankton fertility, p. 165-219. *In* M. N. Hill [ed.], The sea, v. 2. Interscience, New York.

ROBISON, S. M. 1965. Studies on the effect of moderate temperature on *Vibrio marinus*. M.S. Thesis, Oregon State Univ., Corvallis.

SIEBURTH, J. McN. 1967. Seasonal selection of estuarine bacteria by water temperature. J. Exp. Mar. Biol. Ecol., *1*: 98-121.

STANLEY, S. O., and R. Y. MORITA. 1968. Salinity effect on the maximal growth temperature of some bacterial environments. J. Bacteriol., *95*: 169-173.

STANLEY, S. O., and A. H. ROSE. 1967. Bacteria and yeasts from lakes on Deception Island. Roy. Soc. (London) Phil. Trans., *B. 252*: 199-207.

STARKEY, R. L. 1968. The ecology of soil bacteria: discussion and concluding remarks, p. 635-646. *In* T. R. G. Gray and D. Parkingson [ed.], The ecology of soil bacteria. Univ. Toronto Press, Toronto.

STOKES, J. L. 1963. General biology and nomenclature of psychrophilic bacteria, p. 187-192. *In* N. E. Gibbons [ed.], Recent progress in microbiology. Univ. Toronto Press, Toronto.

STRANGE, R. E., and M. SHON. 1964. Effects of thermal stress on viability and ribonucleic acid of *Aerobacter aerogenes* in aqueous suspension. J. Gen. Microbiol., *34*: 99-114.

VACCARO, R. F., and H. W. JANNASCH. 1966. Studies on heterotrophic activity in sea water based on glucose assimilation. Limnol. Oceanogr., *11*: 596-607.

WAKSMAN, S. A., and C. L. CAREY. 1935. Decomposition of organic matter in sea water by bacteria. II. Influence of addition of organic substances upon bacterial activity. J. Bacteriol., *29*: 545-561.

WAKSMAN, S. A., and C. E. RENN. 1936. Decomposition of organic matter in sea water by bacteria. III. Factors influencing the rate of decomposition. Biol. Bull., *70*: 472-483.

ZOBELL, C. E., and C. W, GRANT. 1943. Bacterial utilization of low organic matter. J. Bacteriol., *45*: 555-564.

DETERMINATION OF MICROBIAL BIOMASS IN DEEP OCEAN WATER

Osmund Holm-Hansen
Institute of Marine Resources
University of California
Box 109
La Jolla, California 92037

ABSTRACT

The content of ATP in the particulate fraction has been determined in four profiles in the Pacific Ocean down to 3500 m. The ATP values are converted to cellular organic carbon values, and compared to the total organic carbon in the particulate fraction. The microbial biomass as estimated by the ATP data is very high in the euphotic zone and decreases rapidly to 1 to 2 μg cellular C/liter at about 200 m. At the lower depths sampled, the calculated biomass contained about 0.1 μg organic C/liter.

Microscopic examination of deep samples showed the presence of large numbers of small flagellated algal-like cells. The numbers and sizes of these cells have been determined and their biomass is compared to that estimated by the ATP data.

INTRODUCTION

Our interest in the distribution of microbial life in the oceans is related primarily to the importance of these organisms in bathypelagic food chains. Most studies involving the marine food chain are restricted to the production and conversion of energy rich materials in the upper 200 m of the ocean. We know, however, that the ocean bottoms also possess a rich and diversified flora and fauna, and that the entire water column is populated with a wide assortment of zooplankton and fish. The lower trophic levels of the food chain which supports these populations of macroscopic organisms in deep water are not known, but the following hypotheses have been suggested. (1) Food materials may be conveyed to deep water by a series of migrating zooplankton populations, each of which feeds on food reserves in the water column above them and in turn is consumed by a deeper living migratory population (Vinogradov, 1962). (2) Filter feeding zooplankton may feed directly on the non-living particulate organic material which was formed in the euphotic zone and is slowly settling toward the bottom. (3) The detrital organic material which may serve as food for zooplankton can also originate through equilibrium reactions between dissolved organic compounds and particles in suspension (Riley et al., 1964; Sheldon et al., 1967). This represents a vast reservoir of potential energy, as the detrital organic carbon (ca. 10 to 20 μg C/liter) and the dissolved organic carbon (ca. 500 μg C/liter) account for more than 98% of all the organic carbon in the oceans. (4) Heterotrophic microorganisms may subsist on the dissolved and detrital organic material, and in turn be consumed by filter feeding organisms.

In order to evaluate these possibilities, it is important to determine the distribution and concentration of heterotrophic microorganisms at any depth in the ocean. The estimation of microbial biomass has been very difficult, however, because of lack of suitable methods. The methods most commonly used involve plating on agar and counting of colonies, or direct counting of cells by microscopic examination. Both these methods suffer from serious inherent drawbacks. More reliable estimates of biomass can be obtained by quantitative determination of certain cell constituents which are not found to any significant degree in detrital matter. Methods have recently been developed for routine determination of adenosine triphosphate (ATP) and of deoxyribonucleic acid (DNA) in samples of one to four liters of deep water. This paper reports the results obtained by using these analytical methods for the determination of microbial biomass down to 3500 m in the ocean.

METHOD

Samples for ATP determination were obtained from sterile disposable Niskin bags, while samples for DNA were obtained from Van Dorn bottles made of polyvinyl chloride. All glassware and sample receptacles were thoroughly cleaned and all feasible precautions were employed to minimize any contamination of the samples. The salinity of every sample was determined and compared to the salinity profile as determined in samples from Nansen bottles; any sample in which a misfire was indicated by the salinity value was discarded. Each sample was passed through 150 μ-mesh nylon netting, and then one to two liter aliquots were filtered through a 47 mm HA (0.45 μ pore size) Millipore filter for subsequent analysis of ATP or DNA, or through a 25 mm glass fiber filter for total particulate organic carbon analysis. The filters for DNA and total organic carbon were placed in appropriate containers and stored at -20 C. The sample for ATP analysis was quickly immersed in boiling Tris buffer to inactivate all enzymes, and then kept at 100 C for five minutes to extract all cellular ATP. This extract was then stored at -20 C.

The ATP in the extracted samples was subsequently determined by measurement of the light emitted upon incubation with firefly luciferin-luciferase. The instrumentation and procedures used in this determination of ATP have been described by Holm-Hansen and Booth (1966).

The DNA content of the particulate fraction was determined by a fluorometric procedure. After removing the Millipore filter by extraction with absolute acetone, the particulate matter was extracted with 90% acetone, cold 10% trichloroacetic acid, and 95% ethanol. The extracted pellet was then dried, and the DNA content determined by measurement of fluorescence after hydrolysis of the sample at 60 C for one hour with a solution of 3, 5-diaminobenzoic acid. The details of this procedure have been published by Holm-Hansen et al., (1968).

The organic carbon content of the particulate fraction was determined by infrared gas analysis of the CO_2 liberated during wet combustion of the sample. The procedure is that described by Menzel and Vaccaro (1964) with a few minor modifications (Holm-Hansen et al., 1967).

Microscopic examination of the particulate material was performed on samples in one profile down to 3500 m. Aliquots of 100 to 500 ml of each sample were put through a 25 mm GS Millipore filter, which was dried and then cleared in immersion oil. Visual examination for recognizable cells was done under a phase-contrast oil immersion microscope as described by Hamilton et al. (1968).

RESULTS

The distribution of ATP from the surface down to 1000 meters at two stations off the California coast is shown in Fig. 1. Both curves show high concentrations of ATP (more than 200 mμg ATP/liter) at 200 m, secondary maxima at about 400 m, and then decreasing concentrations with depth down to a few mμg ATP/liter in the deepest samples.

A similar ATP profile with depth is shown in Fig. 2, which shows the concentration of ATP down to 2400 m at a station off the coast of Peru. Again there was a minimum at close to 200 m, higher concentrations between 300 and 500 m, and decreasing amounts down to the lowest value of about 0.05 mμg ATP/liter at 2400 m.

On the basis of a survey of the ATP content of a variety of bacteria and algae, cellular ATP may be extrapolated to total cellular carbon by multiplying the ATP content by a factor of 250. This has been done for the data shown in Fig. 2, and the resulting values for cellular organic carbon are shown as a per cent of the total particulate organic carbon at each depth (Fig. 3). The fraction of the total particulate organic carbon that is found in living cells is very high in the euphotic zone (approaching 100%), fluctuates from 0.5 to 4% between 200 and 2000 m and then falls to about 0.1% at 2400 m.

A profile of ATP concentration down to 3500 m has also been made off the coast of Baja California; in this work we also attempted to discern the nature of the cells responsible for the observed ATP. The ATP data, again converted to cellular organic carbon, are shown in Fig. 4 (solid circles). Results are similar to those in the preceding figures, with the cellular organic carbon being estimated at less than 0.5 μg/liter at most depths below 600 m, and reaching a minimum of 0.1 μg/liter at 3500 m. These samples between 300 and 3500 m were examined microscopically and viable bacterial cells were detected by counting colonies on filters which had been placed on nutrient agar. The observed concentrations of viable bacteria were converted to organic carbon in bacterial cells by assuming an average carbon content of about 5×10^{-7} μg C/cell. The values so obtained were at least three orders of magnitude smaller than the biomass indicated by the ATP data. Although this suggests that the bacterial population comprises an insignificant fraction of the estimated biomass, one cannot be certain on this point. Jannasch and Jones (1959) demonstrated that viable bacterial counts may yield very low

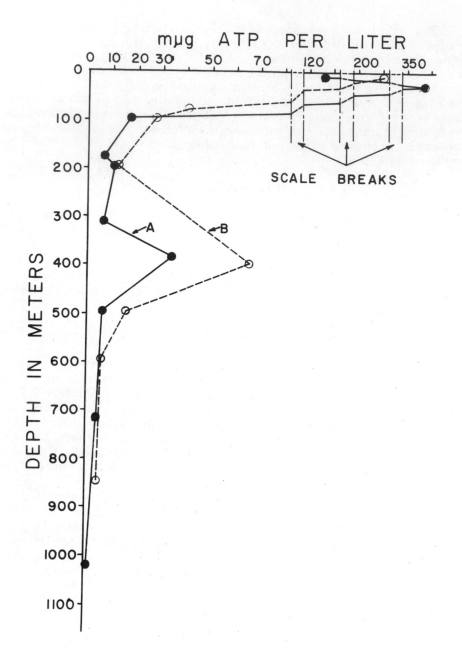

Fig. 1.   Vertical distribution of ATP at two stations off the California coast. Curve A, 33° 18.5'N lat, 118° 40'W long. Curve B, 32° 37'N lat, 117° 21.8'W long. (Reprinted from Holm-Hansen and Booth, 1966).

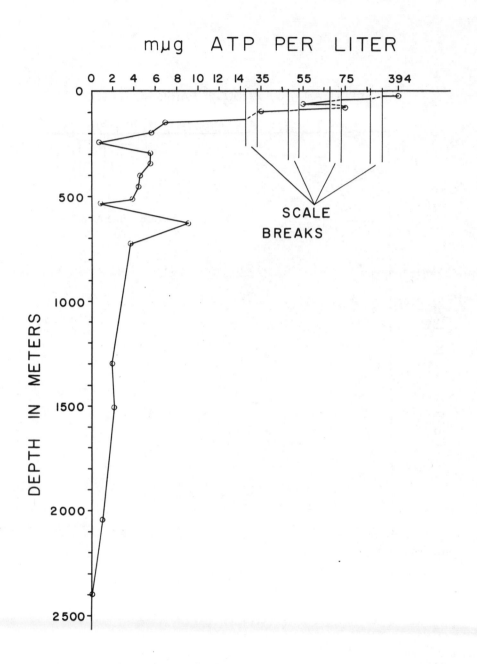

Fig. 2.   Vertical distribution of ATP off the coast of Peru (09° 04′S, 83° 37′W).

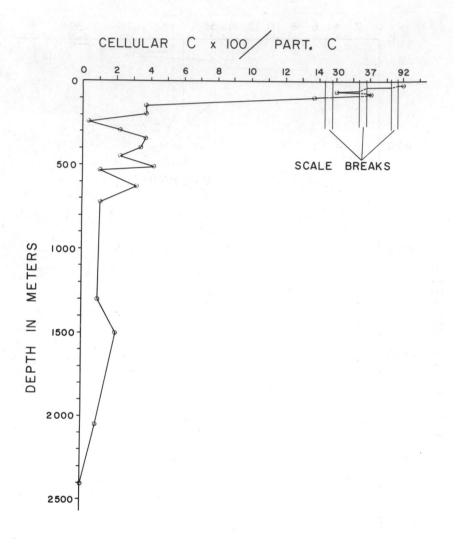

Fig. 3.   The distribution of organic carbon in living cells as a percent of the total particulate organic carbon in a deep profile off the coast of Peru. The cellular organic carbon was calculated from the ATP data shown in Fig. 2.

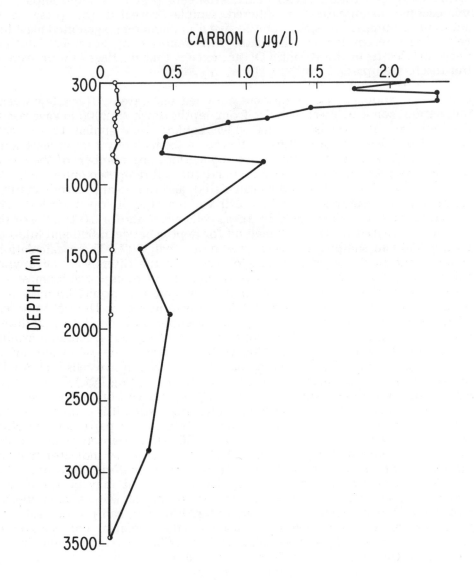

Fig. 4. The distribution of cellular organic carbon predicted from ATP concentration (solid circles) and the estimated carbon in cells ranging from one to four microns in diameter. The station position was 31° 45′N, 120° 30′W. (Reprinted from Hamilton et al., 1968.)

estimates of the total number of bacterial cells present in any sample. The microscopic examination of filtered samples revealed the presence of substantial numbers of small (one to five μ in diameter) pigmented algal-like cells. These resembled the flagellated cells reported by Fournier (1966) in deep samples from the Atlantic Ocean, except that no flagella were seen on our filtered samples.

At the time of filtration of the samples, small volumes from each depth were added to sterile nutrient enriched sea water. After a few weeks' incubation, some of these samples from depths down to 2000 m gave rise to live cultures of flagellated cells which looked very similar to the cells counted on the Millipore filters. It therefore seems likely that at least some of these cells were alive at the time of collection. The numbers of these cells on the Millipore filters were counted and the cell diameters measured. The total volume of the cells was then calculated, and the organic carbon content estimated by assuming 0.1 g C/cc cell volume (Fig. 4, open circles). The estimated biomass contributed by these cells accounts for 10 to 30% of the biomass estimated by the ATP method for depths between 600 and 3000 m; in the 3500 m samples the value was more than 80%. These calculations assume that all the pigmented cells observed on the filters were alive when filtered, which will result in some over-estimation of their actual biomass.

The results of our first attempt to estimate microbial biomass in a deep ocean profile by measuring DNA is shown in Fig. 5. The DNA content of the particulate fraction was high in the euphotic zone (1 to 2 μg/liter), decreased to a minimum of 0.1 μg/liter at 1000 m, and fluctuated around 0.2 μg/liter between 1000 and 3000 m. Laboratory studies of a wide variety of phytoplankton indicate that the amount of DNA in live cells is about 1% of the total cellular organic carbon. The value of 0.2 μg DNA/liter in deep water thus indicates a value of about 20 μg organic carbon in living cells per liter. This latter value is obviously much too high when it is compared to the reported values of 10 to 30 μg organic carbon in the particulate fraction from deep water (Menzel and Goering, 1966; Holm-Hansen et al., 1966). These data indicate that the use of DNA as a biomass indicator may be limited by the presence of DNA in detrital organic material. Recent studies of DNA concentrations in the ocean indicate that it may be useful as a biomass indicator in the euphotic zone or in coastal waters. Its potential usefulness in deep samples of ocean water, however, can not be evaluated until further analyses have been made of the chemical composition of particulate matter in deep samples. It is possible that something in the particulate fraction interferes in the fluorometric analysis of DNA, although there is no such evidence available at the present time.

CONCLUSION

The validity of estimating microbial biomass from the ATP concentrations in ocean water is dependent upon several factors. First, the cellular ATP levels must not change significantly during obtaining of the sample. Temperature and pressure changes affect ATP levels to a small degree, but these effects are not considered large enough to be very

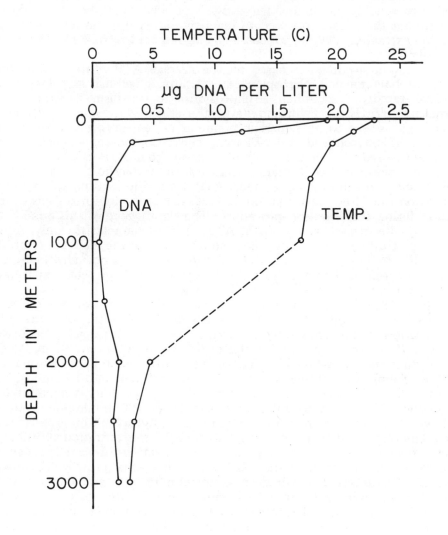

Fig. 5.   Profile of DNA concentration and of temperature off the coast of North
          Carolina. The station position was approximately 33° 18′N, 75° 25′W.
          (Reprinted from Holm-Hansen et al., 1968.)

important in this work. The only practical way to eliminate these effects, an *in situ* ATP analyzer, is not feasible at the present time. Second, when the sample has been filtered, any live cells in the particulate fraction must be killed very quickly to eliminate hydrolysis of ATP. Our laboratory studies indicate that the procedures used to inactivate all enzymatic activity and to store the extracted ATP do not cause any significant loss of ATP. Third, the extrapolation of ATP values to cellular organic carbon values is of necessity a fairly rough approximation based on the average ATP content of a wide variety of bacteria and phytoplankton. Although cellular ATP levels can fluctuate rapidly (e.g., when a photosynthetic organism is exposed to alternating periods of light and dark) the steady-state concentration of cellular ATP seems to be remarkably similar under varying environmental conditions (Hamilton and Holm-Hansen, 1967; Coombs et al., 1967). The factor 250, used to calculate organic carbon from ATP values, has been remarkably consistent in all marine and fresh water microorganisms we have investigated. Fourth, as we extract ATP from the particulate material retained on the filter, we would not detect ATP from any organisms which rupture during the filtration procedure. The significance of this possibility has not yet been investigated. Fifth, ATP must be characteristic only of live cells, and must not be found as a constituent of the detrital fraction. Laboratory studies have shown that ATP in solution is not adsorbed onto detrital material, and that there is no detectable ATP in cells which have lysed or have been killed by excessive heat or cold.

Fig. 1, 2 and 4 all show basically the same features of ATP concentration with depth. From high values in the euphotic zone, the ATP concentration falls to a low value at about 200 m and then steadily decreases to values of less than 1 mμg ATP/liter at depths of 2000 to 3000 m. We do not yet have enough detailed profiles of ATP with concomitant information on other chemical constituents of the particulate fraction to be sure of the validity and significance of the ATP concentrations commonly encountered at 200 and 400 m. It is possible, however, that the 200 m minimum reflects the lower zone in which remineralization of the phytoplankton crop is more or less complete, and that the zone of higher ATP concentration at 400 m is being enriched by the excretory products of migrating zooplankton species, the organic matter serving as the substrate for microbial growth. The lower levels of ATP detected in our deep samples indicate a biomass containing about 0.1 μg organic C/liter. This value seems fairly reasonable when compared to the reported values of total organic carbon in the particulate fraction of deep water. If we assume an average of about 10 μg detrital organic C/liter, the microbial biomass for deep ocean water would contain about 1% of the total particulate organic carbon content. The dissolved organic compounds, which contain about 500 μg C/liter on the average, must also be considered as potential substrates for microbial growth.

Several investigators have reported the occurrence of plant cells in deep water (Bernard, 1963; Kimball et al., 1963; Wood, 1956; Fournier, 1966) and commented on their possible ecological significance. The measurement of ATP furnishes the first chemical evidence that there is a substantial biomass of microbial cells in deep water, and thus lends support to these reports. It is particularly interesting that we detected large numbers of small pigmented cells that appear to be very similar to those reported by Fournier. The biomass of these cells plus the bacterial biomass do not account for all of the biomass as estimated by the ATP method. It is possible that there are many small colorless cells which are not detected by our microscopic examination, or many fragile organisms which are distorted beyond recognition by the filtration and fixation procedures. Further studies are required to close this gap between the biomass as estimated by ATP measurements and that estimated by direct microscopic examination.

DISCUSSION

SIEBURTH: It is very interesting that you have cultured the spherical yellow cells that Fournier (1966) talks about. What kind of nutrient medium did you use and was it in the light or the dark?

HOLM-HANSEN: These were cultured in nitrate and phosphate enriched sea water in low light.

SIEBURTH: You should be able to culture them in the dark.

HOLM-HANSEN: You should be, but we have not tried that.

SIEBURTH: Have you tried to extract pigments?

HOLM-HANSEN: Yes, I did. The trouble here is that we never got a unialgal culture so a sample would contain some cells with two flagella, some with four. We always dealt with mixed populations of these small pigmented cells. In one sample that we looked at, we had lots of chlorophylls a and c.

BELSER: From which organisms did you derive your factor for ATP computation?

HOLM-HANSEN: We used seven or eight bacterial strains and about 30 marine and fresh water algal forms.

BELSER: Was there any possibility of a factorial error between bacterial or algal derivation of the ATP?

HOLM-HANSEN: This is one of the rough factors you are forced into in this sort of oceanographic work. All my data for ATP conform generally to a normal distribution curve, averaging about 0.2% of the dry weight as ATP. I worked with bacteria and algae under all sorts of extremes of temperature, light and nutrients, and with chemostatic cultures, batch cultures from the early log phase through the very old stagnant phase and dying cultures. These extremes were 0.03% and 0.4%, but the great majority of the ATP values lie between 0.1 and 0.25%. This is rough, but in this kind of oceanographic work I am very happy with such an approximation.

JOHANNES: Did you look at the pigments of these cells right after they had been collected? Larry Pomeroy, Bill Wiebe and I have been looking at some of these deep water flagellates with fluorescence microscopy right after we collect them in the Sargasso Sea off the Carolinas. (Pomeroy and Johannes, 1968, and subsequent unpublished observations extending into deeper waters.) We find that many of them do not fluoresce at all. I wonder if incubation of your flagellates in the light might bring about the development of chlorophyll pigments that were not there initially.

HOLM-HANSEN: That is always possible. Our data are very speculative at the present time. There is always the possibility of contamination. All our sampling is done with Niskin bags, which are sterile, sealed, disposable, plastic bags sent down closed. They are cut open by a little guillotine gadget at the desired depth, sealed at the depth by a plunger which comes down and smacks the rubber tubing, and raised closed. When we get them on deck, we slice the rubber tubing between a clamp and the bag, so there is no contamination by water adhering to the cut end of the rubber tubing. Our methods and aseptic procedures are as controlled as possible, and I have great assurance that we are not dealing with artifacts, but to answer your question, we do not really know what these things are doing at depth. If they are colorless at depth, they might develop chlorophyll in our culture system. However, they are pigmented on our filters. Our filter samples are filtered, fixed and dried, and then examined later in the lab under a microscope. This is oil immersion phase contrast microscopy. The cells are pigmented but we have done no microphotometric determinations of the chlorophyll content of these cells. They are green and look like typical small *Chlorella* cells, for instance.

NATARAJAN: Is it by any chance *Nannochloris*?

HOLM-HANSEN: It is hard to say. It is one to four μ in size. You can see various organelles, and in a large portion you can see flagella. We never got flagella on the fixed specimens which Fournier also noted; apparently during the filtration and the fixing of the cells we lost the flagella for some reason. I hesitate to put any names on these at all.

RICHARDS: Have you looked at any pigments other than chlorophyll?

HOLM-HANSEN: No.

NORRIS: Could you tell us the culture conditions or the bacterial counts?

HOLM-HANSEN: Hamilton did this (Hamilton and Holm-Hansen, 1967). The samples are filtered onto small HA filters and placed on nutrient pads.

NORRIS: At what temperature?

HOLM-HANSEN: Room temperature. Unfortunately, in all this work, you get temperature and pressure effects which most of us do not control very well. This might be a serious thing in the interpretation of our data.

ACKNOWLEDGMENTS

This research was supported by the U.S. Atomic Energy Commission Contract AT(11-1)GEN 10, PA 20.

REFERENCES

BERNARD, F. 1963. Vitesse de chute en mèr des amas palmelloides de *Cyclococcolithus*. Ses consequence pour le cycle vital des mèrs chaudes. Pelagos, *1*: 5-34.

COOMBS, J., P. J. HALICKI, O. HOLM-HANSEN, and B. E. VOLCANI. 1967. Changes in concentration of nucleoside triphosphates in silicon-starvation synchrony of *Navicula pelliculosa* (Bréb.) Hilse, Exp. Cell Res., *47*: 315-328.

FOURNIER, R. O. 1966. North Atlantic deep-sea fertility. Science, *153*: 1250-1252.

HAMILTON, R. D., and O. HOLM-HANSEN. 1967. Adenosine triphosphate content of marine bacteria. Limnol. Oceanogr., *12*: 319-324.

HAMILTON, R. D., O. HOLM-HANSEN, and J. D. H. STRICKLAND. 1968. Notes on the occurrence of living microscopic organisms in deep water. Deep-Sea Res., *15*: 651-656.

HOLM-HANSEN, O., and C. R. BOOTH. 1966. The measurement of adenosine triphosphate in the ocean and its ecological significance. Limnol. Oceanogr., *11*: 510-519.

HOLM-HANSEN, O., J. COOMBS, B. E. VOLCANI, and P. M. WILLIAMS. 1967. Quantitative micro-determination of lipid carbon in microorganisms. Anal. Biochem., *19*: 561-568.

HOLM-HANSEN, O., J. D. H. STRICKLAND, and P. M. WILLIAMS. 1966. A detailed analysis of biologically important substances in a profile off southern California. Limnol. Oceanogr., *11*: 548-561.

HOLM-HANSEN, O., W. H. SUTCLIFFE, Jr., and J. SHARP. 1968. Measurement of deoxyribonucleic acid in the ocean and its ecological significance. Limnol. Oceanogr., *13*: 507-514.

JANNASCH, H. W., and G. E. JONES. 1959. Bacterial populations in sea water as determined by different methods of enumeration. Limnol. Oceanogr., *4*: 128-139.

KIMBALL, J. R., Jr., E. F. CORCORAN, and E. J. F. WOOD. 1963. Chlorophyll-containing microorganisms in the euphotic zone of the oceans. Bull. Mar. Sci. Gulf Caribbean, *13*: 574-577.

MENZEL, D. W., and J. J. GOERING. 1966. The distribution of organic detritus in the ocean. Limnol. Oceanogr., *11*: 333-337.

MENZEL, D. W., and R. F. VACCARO. 1964. The measurement of dissolved organic and particulate carbon in sea water. Limnol. Oceanogr., *9*: 138-142.

RILEY, G. A., P. J. WANGERSKY, and D. VAN HEMERT. 1964. Organic aggregates in tropical and subtropical waters of the North Atlantic Ocean. Limnol. Oceanogr., *9*: 546-550.

SHELDON, R. W., T. P. T. EVELYN, and T. R. PARSONS. 1967. On the occurrence and formation of small particles in sea water. Limnol. Oceanogr., *12*: 367-375.

VINOGRADOV, M. E. 1962. Feeding of the deep-sea zooplankton. Rapp et Procesverb. J. Cons., *153*: 114-120.

WOOD, E. J. F. 1956. Diatoms in the ocean deeps. Pacific Sci., *10*: 377-381.

METAL ORGANIC COMPLEXES FORMED BY MARINE BACTERIA

Galen E. Jones
Jackson Estuarine Laboratory
University of New Hampshire
Durham, New Hampshire 03824

INTRODUCTION

In the aerobic seas of today, marine organisms excrete organic compounds into the water (Lucas, 1961; Hellebust, 1965; Fogg, 1966). Most of these substances have an affinity for heavy metal ions to a greater or lesser extent, depending upon their stability constants (Dwyer and Mellor, 1964; Johnston, 1964; Duursma and Sevenhuysen, 1966). Fogg and Westlake (1955) pointed out that extracellular polypeptides may be of biological importance because of their metal complexing properties. Saunders (1957) realized the importance of organic matter in sea water as a chelating agent for trace metal ions and postulated that the interaction of the organic matter and metal ions could produce either inhibitory or stimulatory ecological relationships, depending on the environment. The levels of amino acids, approximately 100 μg/liter in sea water (Siegel and Degens, 1966), are sufficient to interact with heavy metals in the transition series. Evidence for organically bound copper in sea water has been suggested from the non-dialyzable nature of copper in the sea (Slowey et al., 1967). Perlman (1965) reviewed the literature on the microbial production of metal-organic compounds in Nature and concluded that our knowledge is fragmentary and unsystematic.

Escherichia coli does not grow in sea water supplemented with glucose, ammonium and phosphate ions unless the sea water is treated with chelating agents or autoclaved (Jones, 1964). This inhibitory effect of sea water for *E. coli* was attributed to the heavy metal ions in sea water (Jones, 1964 and 1967). Fresh water bacteria are more susceptible to the adverse effects of sea water than microbes indigenous to the marine environment (Jones, 1963). The following paper is based on a series of studies designed to yield insight into how marine bacteria cope with metal ions in sea water (Roche, 1966; Wirsen, 1966; Cobet, 1968).

METHOD

Sampling

Sea water samples were obtained using a Cobet or Niskin bacteriological water sampler. In littoral environments, sterile milk dilution bottles were often used to collect sea water samples which were treated immediately for the enumeration of marine bacteria.

Organisms

The marine bacteria were isolated by picking colonies from sea water agar plates obtained from samples in the vicinity of Woods Hole, Massachusetts. The organisms were picked from a modified 2216E medium (Oppenheimer and ZoBell, 1952) to which various concentrations of $CuSO_4$ or $NiCl_2$ were added. The fresh water bacteria were obtained from the American Type Culture Collection (ATCC), Washington, D.C. and were: *E. coli* (9637), *E. coli* (4157), *Proteus morgani* (8019), *Staphylococcus aureus* (6538), *Bacillus cereus* (9637), *Aerobacter aerogenes* (12650-T9A), and *A. aerogenes* (15619).

Media and sea water

The following media were prepared with 75% synthetic sea water (Lyman and Fleming, 1940) or 100% double distilled water.

1. Modified 2216E medium (Oppenheimer and ZoBell, 1952) with the following composition per liter: Bacto-peptone, 1.0 g; Bacto-yeast extract, 1.0 g; ferric ammonium citrate, 0.005 g; and Bacto-agar, 15.0 g.

2. Glucose medium with the following composition per liter: glucose, 5.0 g; NH_4Cl, 1.0 g; NH_4NO_3, 1.0 g; K_2HPO_4, 1.0 g; and Bacto-agar, 15.0 g.

3. Synthetic medium with the following composition per liter: glucose, 5.0 g; NH_4NO_3, 0.5 g; K_2HPO_4, 0.02 g; and L-asparagine, 0.01 g.

Plating procedure

The pour plate technique was employed to determine ecological effects of metal ions on heterogeneous populations of marine bacteria. Immediately after collection, the sea water samples were pipetted into disposable plastic petri dishes at appropriate dilutions made in either synthetic sea water or distilled water. The appropriate agar was cooled to 42 C and approximately 10 ml were poured over the sample and swirled. After solidifying, all plates were incubated in 18 C and colonies were counted after various periods of time.

RESULTS

Effect of metal ion concentrations in media on bacterial development

Copper ions added to 2216E medium at varying molar concentrations were toxic to the mixed bacterial flora from 39 sea water samples at the higher concentrations (Fig. 1). There was no visible growth on any of the plates containing 10^{-2} M $CuSO_4$. Growth was visible on the rest of the plates after 3 or 4 days and reached a maximum in 3 or 4 weeks at 18 C. Colony size varied from pinpoint to several mm in diameter. Many had a glistening, mucoid appearance. Large numbers of pigmented colonies were observed, especially at the lower copper concentrations. The predominate colors were yellow and orange; red, tan, and dark brown colonies occurred occasionally.

COPPER TOLERANCE BY MARINE BACTERIA

average of ecological surveys

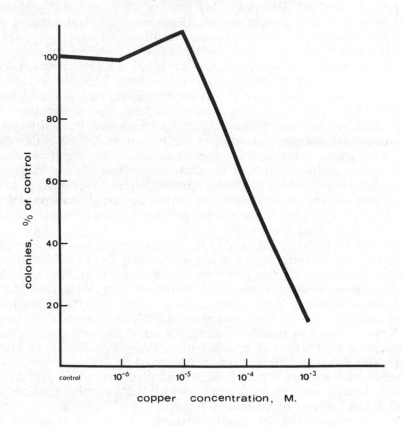

Fig. 1.   Ecological survey including a percentage average of 39 sea water samples in which $CuSO_4$ was added to 2216E medium at various molar concentrations and colonies were counted after 3 to 4 weeks incubation at 18 C.

The red-brown "copper colonies" reported by Waksman et al. (1943) to develop optimally on media containing 25 mg Cu/liter were rarely observed. At 10^{-3} M copper (64 mg/liter), the colonies were generally off-white or yellow. Since the distribution of these "copper colonies" varies with location, depth, season and other factors (Taga, 1955), their infrequent occurrence in these samples may be due to unfavorable environmental conditions.

There was no inhibition of colony development at copper concentrations of 10^{-6} and 10^{-5} M, but at 10^{-4} and 10^{-3} M copper suppression became increasingly severe. There was sufficient organic matter in the 2216E medium to chelate the amount of added copper through 10^{-4} M level. The slight stimulation of growth at 10^{-5} M copper may be due, in part, to displacement by added copper of other micronutrients originally complexed by the organic matter. Microorganisms from the littoral zone were able to tolerate higher concentrations of copper, 10^{-3} and 10^{-4} M, than bacteria from the open ocean. The copper content of sea water, determined by the method of Riley and Sinhaseni (1958), was higher in the littoral zone than at sea. (Water samples collected in the harbor at Woods Hole averaged about 15 μg Cu/liter, whereas the copper content of samples from the Gulf of Maine varied with depth and location from 2 to 10 μg/liter). Some correlation apparently exists between copper tolerance by marine bacteria and the copper content of sea water. It should be noted, however, that the organic content of littoral sea water was undoubtedly higher than the organic content of oceanic sea water.

The effect of nickel ions added to 2216E medium at different molar concentrations of bacteria from the sea was similar to the effect of copper ions. The bacterial populations were markedly reduced at 10^{-4} and 10^{-3} M nickel. No colonies developed on 2216E medium containing 10^{-2} M $NiCl_2$.

Sea water samples from Salem Harbor, Massachusetts, (March, 1966; water temperature, 3.5 C) were plated on 2216E or glucose medium made with 75% sea water and distilled water. The colonies were counted after 6 days incubation at 18 C. The number of colonies developing on the four different media using one ml dilutions is presented in Table 1.

Stimulation was evident in most of the media to which 10^{-6} M nickel was added. Drastic reductions in the number of colonies relative to the untreated control were not evident in either of the 2216E media even with 10^{-4} M nickel present. In the glucose medium, the chelating power of the medium decreased to a point where 10^{-4} M nickel became toxic. Where 10^{-3} M nickel was present the toxic effect of the nickel ions was evident in all cases although the presence of sea water was beneficial. Generally, the 2216E medium prepared with 75% synthetic sea water was almost an order of magnitude better at supporting growth of marine bacteria. Glucose was a much poorer substrate than the complex proteins, peptone and yeast extract contained in the 2216E medium as indicated by Ostroff and Henry (1939). In addition to the nutrient effects of the amino acids and proteins in the medium, the chelating power of the medium is important to the growth of marine bacteria (Jones, 1964).

Table 1. The effect of nickel concentrations added to Salem Harbor, Massachusetts, sea water on bacterial populations per ml and as percentages of 2216E medium controls in four media after 6 days incubation at 18 C.

Addition NiCl$_2$ (M)	2216E, 75% sea water		2216E, Distilled water		Glucose, 75% sea water		Glucose, Distilled water	
	No. colonies	%	No. colonies	%	No. colonies	%	No. colonies	%
none	1205	100	134	11	60	5	51	4
10^{-6}	1596	132	168	14	76	6	48	4
10^{-5}	1050	87	186	15	83	7	27	2
10^{-4}	1041	86	108	9	8	0.7	7	0.6
10^{-3}	7	0.6	2	0.2	0	0	0	0

One ml of a $1/10^5$ dilution of greenhouse soil was plated on each of the four media to observe the effects of nickel on terrestrial bacteria. The number of colonies after 7 days incubation at 18 C on 2216E medium prepared with distilled water as a standard is indicated in Table 2. The 2216E medium prepared with distilled water supported almost 3 times as many colonies as the 2216E medium prepared with 75% synthetic sea water. Below concentrations of 10^{-4} M, nickel had no marked effect; at that level the population declined 20 to 40% in both media. Marked reductions in population occurred when the nickel concentrations were increased to 10^{-3} M. More colonies survived in the sea water medium than in the distilled water medium, indicating that competition of nickel for sights on the ligands present had a synergestic effect in making required nutrients available to the organisms. This phenomenon was noted in several other experiments of this type. Soil bacteria colonies were 4 to 7 times more numerous on glucose media in which distilled water was used than when sea water was used. No colonies developed in the presence of 10^{-3} M nickel in this medium. Fresh water and soil bacteria were not significantly more susceptible to nickel toxicity than marine bacteria. The results emphasize the importance of a high capacity of chelates in a medium where large amounts of metal ions are present.

Tolerance of marine and freshwater bacteria to nickel ions

All 12 isolates of marine bacteria grew luxuriently when streaked on 2216E medium with up to 10^{-4} M $NiCl_2$ (Wirsen, 1966). The marine isolates tolerated 10^{-3} M nickel, although growth was somewhat reduced. There was no visible growth in plates containing 10^{-2} M nickel but most of the marine bacteria remained viable. Terrestrial bacteria were at least an order of magnitude less nickel tolerant when similarly streaked in the complex 2216E medium and were even less tolerant in the simple glucose medium. The terrestrial bacteria tested were listed in the method section.

Study of metal tolerant organisms

Two marine bacteria were isolated for special study. One, a highly copper-tolerant bacterium identified as *Pseudonomas x* (Roche, 1966), is a gram-negative rod, averaging 1 x 2.3 μ. It is highly motile and has a single polar flagellum observed in electron micrographs (Fig. 2) and by Leifson's flagella staining technique (Leifson, 1930).

Spores are not produced and the India ink technique (Dugoid, 1951) and $CuSO_4$ stains failed to show the presence of definitive capsules. *Pseudomonas x* is an obligate aerobe that grows at temperatures of 4, 18 (optimal), 25 but not at 37 C. The pH range is approximately 6 to 9. The upper limit of copper tolerance in 2216E broth with this organism was 2 to 2.5 x 10^{-3} M copper.

An interesting phenomenon was noted during the characterization of *Pseudomonas x*. When liquid cultures containing 10^{-4} M copper were removed from the shaking incubator 20 to 24 hours after inoculation and

Table 2.   The effect of nickel concentrations added to 10^5 dilution of a gram of greenhouse soil on bacterial populations and as percentages of 2216E medium prepared with distilled water in four media after 7 days incubation at 18 C.

Addition NiCl$_2$ (M)	2216E, 75% sea water		2216E, Distilled water		Glucose, 75% sea water		Glucose, Distilled water	
	No. colonies*	%	No. colonies*	%	No. colonies*	%	No. colonies*	%
none	99	38	262	100	21	8	96	37
10^{-6}	106	40	257	98	11	4	74	28
10^{-5}	110	42	240	92	13	5	48	18
10^{-4}	81	31	162	62	3	1	6	2
10^{-3}	5	2	0	0	0	0	0	0

* Number multiplied by 100,000 = microbes per g of soil.

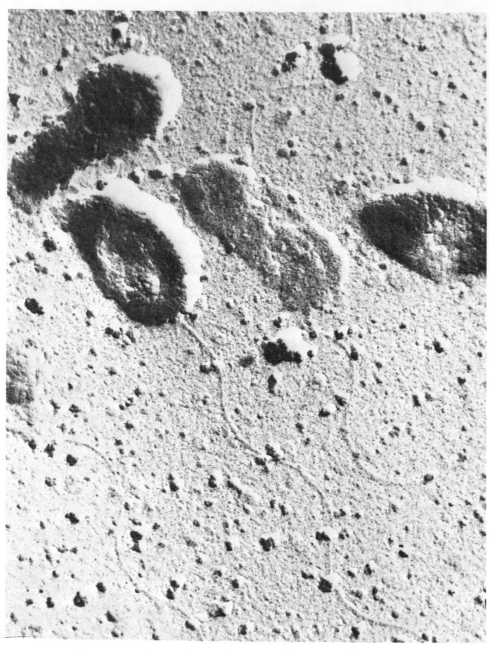

Fig. 2.   Electron micrograph of *Pseudomonas x* showing single polar flagellum. 20,000 magnification. (Taken by John Albright of Boston University.)

allowed to stand, a pink color developed within 45 minutes to an hour. Upon centrifugation of the cultures, the pink color was observed to be entirely associated with the cell pellet. If the culture of *Pseudomonas x* was allowed to stand for some time after color development, the color faded completely in two or three days. Fading was retarded by keeping the culture at 4 C. Putting colored cultures back on a shaking incubator resulted in a rapid loss of color, but the color could be restored to some extent if flasks were again removed and allowed to stand. No morphological changes in the cells were associated with this phenomenon. Attempts to extract the color complex using organic solvents chloroform, methanol, dimethylsulfoxide (DMSO) and dilute HCl and NaOH were unsuccessful, resulting only in loss of color. Adding sodium hydrosulfite, a strong reducing agent, to a 20 to 24 hour culture containing 10^{-4} M copper after removal from the shaking incubator also produced the pink complex. Other reducing agents such as ascorbic acid and hydrogen gas failed to produce any color, indicating that hydrosulfite itself may be active in the formation of the color. It was critical to take the cells from the shaking machine at a precise point in the growth cycle, which varies slightly from batch to batch, to obtain the pink copper-organic complex. The nature of the organic portion of the complex is still unknown. However, in a high-energy situation such as exists in these flasks, metal-organic complexes are formed.

The nickel tolerant organism isolated for special study was originally identified as an *Achromobacter* sp. by Wirsen (1966). It has been re-identified as *Arthrobacter marinus*, a new species, by Cobet (1968). The growth response of *A. marinus* to increasing concentrations of nickel was determined by increasing the concentration from 1×10^{-4} to 5×10^{-4} M in half-nutrient modified 2216E medium (Fig. 3). The sterile medium was inoculated and shaken and optical density readings were made at 13, 24, 48, 72, 96, 120 and 144 hours. Increasing concentrations of nickel resulted in an increase in the lag phase from about 3 hours in the untreated control without added nickel to more than 70 hours in the case of media containing 4×10^{-4} M nickel. In media containing 5×10^{-4} M nickel the culture did not grow during a 144 hour period. The slope of the line during the logarithmic phase of growth was depressed with each increase in nickel concentration, so the time required for the culture to attain maximum optical density increased at the higher concentrations of nickel. Increased nickel concentrations in these cells was associated with the formation of enlarged megalomorphic cells. These cells were most evident at 4×10^{-4} M nickel. Fig. 4 presents photomicrographs comparing the maximum size of the megalomorphs developing in the various nickel concentrations with the control culture. The most dramatic change in morphology occurred between 2×10^{-4} and 3×10^{-4} M nickel. Considerable vacuolation of the megalomorphs developed with increased time and nickel concentrations. The cells were generally round to oval, and a crescent of cytoplasm was pushed over to one side of the cell. As the cells became older the cytoplasm became more vacuolated and the shape more irregular. In the stationary phase the cells became smaller but the vacuoles and crescent shaped cytoplasm persisted.

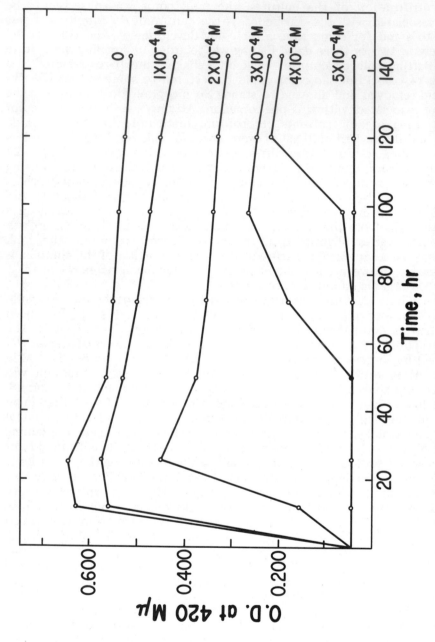

Fig. 3. Growth response of *A marinus* to increasing molar concentrations of $NiCl_2$ in 2216E medium inoculated with 18 hr culture and shaken at 3000 rpm at 25C.

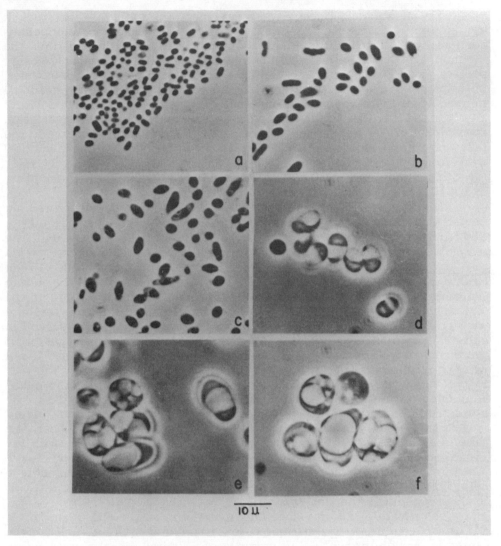

Fig. 4.   Morphological changes in *A. marinus* grown with 4 x 10⁻⁴ M NiCl₂ in
2216E medium. At indicated times, aliquots were removed, wet mounts
prepared and photomicrographs made by phase contrast with a Zeiss WL
microscope.

a. Inoculum, 18 hr culture from 2216E agar slant.
b. After 1.5 hr at 25 C.
c. After 2.5 hr at 25 C.
d. After 4.5 hr at 25 C.
e. After 6.5 hr at 25 C.
f. After 10 hr at 25 C.

The membrane permeability of these megalomorphic cells was studied. An indirect assessment was made by studying the leakage of compounds particularly 260 to 280 mμ absorbing material from the cell into the medium. The synthetic medium containing glucose and asparagine as energy sources was prepared with 1×10^{-5} to 1×10^{-4} M nickel. At various times, portions of the cultures were removed and centrifuged at 3000 rpm for 10 minutes. The twice centrifuged supernatant was placed in matched quartz cuvettes and the optical density read in a Bausch and Lomb dual beam spectrophotometer against the uninoculated medium as a reference in the range of 230 to 320 mμ (Fig. 5). The values plotted in stationary cultures were from cultures at maximum optical density. Growth during the early logarithmic phase in 2×10^{-5} M nickel and during the late logarithmic phase in 1×10^{-5} M nickel is also presented.

The culture in the synthetic medium without nickel showed an increased absorbance over the uninoculated medium with a sharp drop from 230 to 250 mμ and a more gradual drop thereafter to 320 mμ. The supernatant from the early logarithmic culture in 2×10^{-5} M nickel showed a response similar to that of the control. Absorbance increased from 245 mμ to 320 mμ in the late logarithmic stage in the supernatant from the culture grown in 1×10^{-5} M nickel. The stationary cultures grown in media containing 1×10^{-5} and 2×10^{-5} M nickel demonstrated this same response with greater absorbance across the curve. There was very slight growth in cultures grown in media containing 4×10^{-5} M nickel, the supernatant producing a high absorbance at 230 mμ followed by a rapid drop to 245 mμ where it remained essentially negative.

During the early stages of growth the supernatant from the nickel containing cultures produced an ultraviolet absorption pattern similar to the untreated culture. As growth progressed, absorbing material in the 230 mμ range was released. This release became marked by the stationary phase. The time of release of the 260 mμ material coincided to some degree with the formation of the megalomorphic cells, i.e., the mid-logarithmic phase. How much of this absorbance was due to release resulting from membrane permeability and disruption and how much was due to cytolysis was difficult to assess without further analysis.

The release of 230 mμ absorbing material in all the phases and under all growth conditions was attributed to carbohydrate release. Cells in the synthetic medium grown in the presence of a limited nickel concentration were not as large as those from half nutrient 2216E medium which were 2 to 3 μ in diameter.

Under the stress of metal in the medium, the cells of A. marinus released large amounts of organic material which had considerable potential for metal complexing. There is no evidence to date that nickel actually penetrates the membrane on the cells of A. marinus although large amounts of nickel (8.4 μg Ni/mg cell nitrogen at 10^{-4} M nickel) are adsorbed by the cells. No electron dense areas have been observed in these cells.

In the case of Pseudomonas x, electron dense areas within the cells have been observed (Fig. 6). Copper is taken up to a great extent by Pseudomonas x (369 ppm dry weight). These metal tolerant marine bacteria

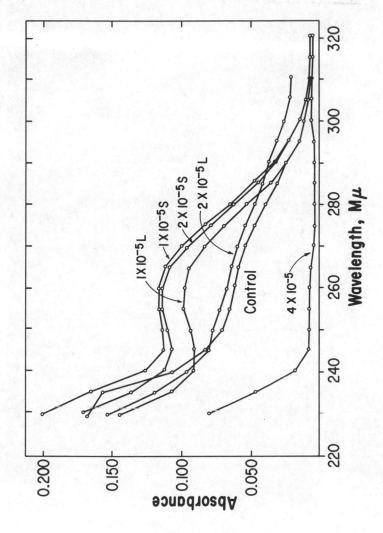

Fig. 5. 260 to 280 mμ absorbance of culture supernatant of *A marinus* grown in synthetic medium containing increasing concentrations of nickel at 25 C. Control: no added nickel; the culture was in stationary phase after 36 hr. 1 x 10^{-5} L: late logarithmic phases of growth after 36 hr. 1 x 10^{-5} S: stationary growth after 44 hr. 2 x 10^{-5} S: stationary phase of growth after 68 hr. 2 x 10^{-5} L: early logarithmic phase of growth after 44 hr. 4 x 10^{-5} : after 68 hr.

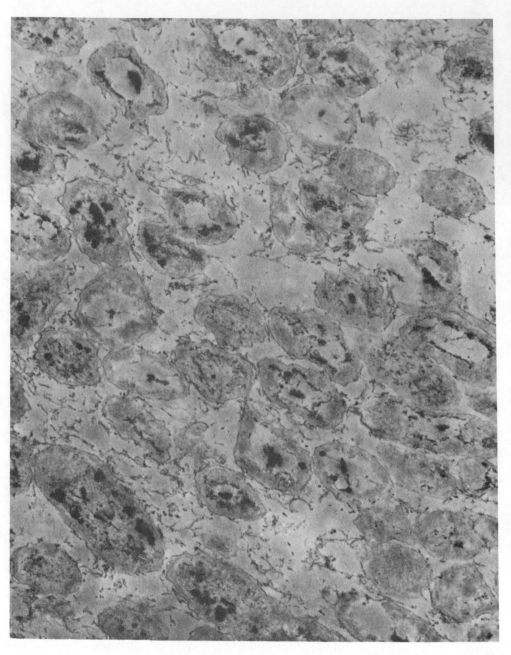

Fig. 6. Electron micrograph of this section of *Pseudomonas x* showing electron dense inclusions. 20,000 magnifications. (Taken by John Albright of Boston University.)

bacteria have various mechanisms for living with large concentrations of metal ions. Evidence indicates the excretion of organic compounds into the medium by marine bacteria to complex the metals.

CONCLUSION

Metal organic complexes are of geochemical and biogeochemical importance in the sea. Trace elements accumulate in various bioliths (Bowen, 1966). Thus, crude oil is often rich in Mo, Ni or V and asphalt is rich in Ni. Breger (1963) has suggested that Ni and V form strong complexes with porphyrins in organic debris and that these complexes accumulate in petroleum. The concentration of trace elements such as Cu, Ni, Co, Cd and other transition elements by plants, animals and bacteria may be a principal mechanism by means of which these elements are concentrated in geological deposits.

It is difficult to study the interaction of organic compounds and trace metals in the sea due to the low concentrations of both the organic matter and the trace elements in this complex environment. When microorganisms are brought into the laboratory and exposed to 10^2 to 10^3 times as much organic matter as they encounter in Nature, zymogenous organisms are selected for and the concentrations of both the organic matter and the metal ions in the water must be raised to obtain a balanced reaction. Ecological balances in the ratios of elements, organic nutrient requirements and production of extracellular organic matter are disturbed.

The formation of organic compounds by marine bacteria may be important during the formation of small particles in the sea (Sheldon et al., 1967), during the formation of ferromanganese nodules (Jones, 1965), as food for algae (Fogg, 1966), as energy for other bacteria (Jannasch, 1965), as growth factors or inhibitory substances for algae (Saunders, 1957), and as metal chelating substances (Johnston, 1963).

DISCUSSION

SIEBURTH: Both of these bugs are polysaccharide producing, so this is one possibility.

JONES: This was our initial idea with *Pseudomonas x*. It has no capsule and produces very little polysaccharide material. *Arthrobacter marinus* does produce some.

SIEBURTH: I am glad that you can recognize an *Arthrobacter*. However, I am shocked by the way you report your data. In your Fig. 1, Table 1 and Table 3, the data are given in terms of per cent of colonies. You are not kidding anybody; we all know that the variation in plate counts is approximately 100%.

JONES: Well, I do not think that it is that high — say 10%.

SIEBURTH: Really you are talking about 85 to 100%. This is a very poor way of doing it. You have about a 4 log difference in your ion concentration and yet only a fraction of a log change in bacteria. It is either a plus or minus effect on growth because you are within the margin of experimental error.

JONES: We used triplicate plates on these.

SIEBURTH: I do not care if you used fifty plates, you are still going to be within the error.

JONES: Not by 100%. I disagree with you on the order of magnitude of the error. I will agree that plate counts are not the best way to do it. Another of the difficulties is that when one is dealing with these enriched media and much larger amounts of metal than occur in the ocean, the environment is extremely artificial. The reason for doing this is that the methodology for working at natural concentrations of organic matter and metals make it extremely difficult for a microbiologist to get this kind of data and see if he can make a little more of it. These are high energy media relative to sea water; low energy media compared to most microbiological media. But they do set up artificial situations in contrast to direct ecological interpretation.

MORGAN: I did not fully understand the difference between the log growth and the stationary data. I gather that is a relatively important point in the case of nickel. What interpretation are you placing on the two different stages of growth?

JONES: We have not overly interpreted it. The point in doing both the log and stationary analyses is that no autolysis should take place during the log phase while there may be some autolysis during the early stationary phase.

MORGAN: Which of the two stages gave you the greatest repression of the metal ion activity site?

JONES: All we were looking for at these levels was the expression of ultraviolet absorbing material. These nickel concentrations are about an order of magnitude lower than is needed to stop growth. I might also point out that 4×10^{-4} M nickel, under these nutrient conditions, is the nickel concentration necessary to stop growth. But it does not kill the cell; the cell is not killed until the nickel concentration increases to 3×10^{-3} M. It just stops growing. We know that the nickel inhibits growth by interfering with the cell division mechanism, but it does not affect respiration.

ACKNOWLEDGMENTS

This work was supported in part by Research Grant WP-00650 from the Federal Water Pollution Control Administration and Office of Naval Research Contract N-00014-68-C-0269.

REFERENCES

BREGER, I. A. 1963. Organic geochemistry. Pergamon, New York.

COBET, A. B. 1968. The effect of nickel ions on *Arthrobacter marinus*, a new species. Ph.D. Thesis, Univ. New Hampshire, Durham, N. H., 212 p.

DUGOID, J. P. 1951. The demonstration of bacterial capsules and slime. J. Pathol. Bacteriol., *63*: 673-685.

DUURSMA, E. K., and W. SEVENHUYSEN. 1966. Note on chelation and solubility of certain metals in sea water at different pH values. Nethl. J. Sea Res., *3*: 95-106.

DWYER, F. P., and D. P. MELLOR. 1964. Chelating agents and metal chelates. Academic Press, New York. 530 p.

FOGG, G. E. 1966. The extracellular products of algae. Oceanogr. Mar. Biol. Annu. Rev., *4*: 195-212.

FOGG, G. E., and D. F. WESTLAKE. 1955. The importance of extracellular products of algae in fresh water. Verh. Int. Ver. Limnol., *12*: 219-232.

HELLEBUST, J. A. 1965. Excretion of some organic compounds by marine phytoplankton. Limnol. Oceanogr., *10*: 192-206.

JANNASCH, H. W. 1965. Continuous culture in microbial ecology. Lab. Practice, *14* (83 Special Article): 1162-1167.

JOHNSTON, R. 1963. Sea water, the natural medium of phytoplankton. I. General features. J. Mar. Biol. Ass. U. K., *43*: 427-456.

JOHNSTON, R. 1964. Sea water, the natural medium of phytoplankton. II. Trace metals and chelation, and general discussion. J. Mar. Biol. Ass. U. K., *44*: 87-109.

JONES, G. E. 1963. Suppression of bacterial growth by sea water, p. 572-579. *In* C. H. Oppenheimer [ed.], Symp. Marine microbiology. C. Thomas, Springfield, Ill.

JONES, G. E. 1964. Effect of chelating agents on the growth of *Escherichia coli* in sea water. J. Bact., *87*: 483-499.

JONES, G. E. 1965. The living economy of the sea. Bull. At. Sci., p. 13-17.

JONES, G. E. 1967. Growth of *Escherichia coli* in heat- and copper-treated synthetic sea water. Limnol. Oceanogr., *12*: 167-172.

LEIFSON, E. 1930. A method of staining bacterial flagella and capsules together with a study of the origin of flagella. J. Bact., *20*: 203-211.

LUCAS, C. E. 1961. Interrelationships between aquatic organisms mediated by external metabolites, p. 499-518. *In* M. Sears [ed.], Oceanography. Amer. Ass. Adv. Sci., Pub. 67.

LYMAN, J., and R. H. FLEMING. 1940. Composition of sea water. J. Mar. Res., *3*: 134-146.

OPPENHEIMER, C. H., and C. E. ZOBELL. 1952. The growth and viability of sixty-three species of marine bacteria as influenced by hydrostatic pressure. J. Mar. Res., *11*: 10-18.

OSTROFF, R., and B. S. HENRY. 1939. The utilization of various nitrogen compounds by marine bacteria. J. Cell. Comp. Physiol., *13*: 353-371.

PERLMAN, D. 1965. Microbial production of metal-organic compounds and complexes, p. 103-138. *In* W. W. Umbreit [ed.], Advances in applied microbiology, v. 7. Academic Press, New York.

RILEY, J. P., and P. SINHASENI. 1958. The determination of copper in sea water, silicate rocks and biological materials. Analyst, *83*: 299-304.

ROCHE, P. M. 1966. The effect of copper on marine bacteria. M.A. Thesis, Boston Univ., Boston, Mass., 74 p.

SAUNDERS, G. W. 1957. Interrelationships of dissolved organic matter and phytoplankton. Bot. Rev., *23*: 389-410.

SHELDON, R. W., T. P. T. EVELYN, and T. R. PARSONS. 1967. On the occurrence and formation of small particles in sea water. Limnol. Oceanogr., *12*: 367-375.

SIEGEL, A., and E. T. DEGENS. 1966. Concentrations of dissolved amino acids from saline waters by ligand-exchange chromotography. Science, *151*: 1098-1101.

SLOWEY, J. F., L. M. JEFFREY, and D. W. HOOD. 1967. Evidence for organic complexed copper in sea water. Nature, *214*: 377-378.

TAGA, N. 1955. Studies on the effect of copper upon the marine bacteria. I. The depressing activities of copper sulfate upon the development of bacteria in sea water. Bull. Jap. Soc. Sci. Fish., *20*: 280-285.

WAKSMAN, S. A., D. D. JOHNSTONE, and C. L. CAREY. 1943. The effect of copper on the development of bacteria in sea water, and the isolation of specific bacteria. J. Mar. Res., 5: 136-152.

WIRSEN, C., JR. 1966. The effects of nickel on marine bacteria. M.A. Thesis, Boston Univ., Boston, Mass., 122 p.

THRESHOLD CONCENTRATIONS OF CARBON SOURCES LIMITING BACTERIAL GROWTH IN SEA WATER

Holger W. Jannasch
Woods Hole Oceanographic Institution
Woods Hole, Massachusetts 02543

ABSTRACT

Growth experiments with marine bacterial isolates in a chemostat reveal the existence of threshold concentrations of some limiting carbon sources (lactate, glucose, glycerol). The phenomenon is explained in terms of the elimination of a positive feedback effect below a critical population density.

INTRODUCTION

In dealing with the occurrence and cycling of organic matter in sea water, the abundance and presumable activities of heterotrophic microorganisms present a still unsolved puzzle. While the population size of higher organisms more or less reflects the nutritional characteristics of their environment, the abundance of microorganisms is a much less reliable indicator. The reason is the enormous versatility of microorganisms in producing dormant stages of life as a means of survival whenever unfavorable environmental conditions occur, or, in other words, the difficulty of assessing the metabolic activity of a microbial cell in its natural habitat.

Yet, when considerable quantities of organic carbon are found in waters where no other factor appears to limit microbial growth, the question arises: why is this energy source for heterotrophic metabolism not utilized by microorganisms? Explanations have been sought by assaying for substances resistant or inhibitory to microbial metabolism. For a long time, the highly dilute nutrient concentrations of sea water prevented another and more direct approach: the study of microbial growth in sea water at extremely low concentrations of a limiting substrate.

In 1942, Monod did a thorough study of bacterial growth with regard to the concentration of a limiting carbon and energy source. He observed a pleasing similarity between this relationship and the well-known kinetic model of enzyme reactions described in Michaelis-Menten's substrate saturation curve containing two constant parameters, (a) the maximum growth rate, μ_m, and (b) the saturation constant, K_s (Fig. 1) and (c) the yield coefficient, y. There was no doubt that this curve could be continued through the origin. Growth data obtained at low substrate concentrations indicated that even minute amounts of the substrate utilized for endogenous respiration or maintenance metabolism could not be detected. Later, with more accurate techniques, changes in the ratio of biosynthetic and respiratory metabolism at low growth rates have been found (e.g., Herbert, 1958; Marr et al., 1963). As a corollary, the curve of the relationship growth rate versus substrate concentration may intersect the abscissa at a positive value.

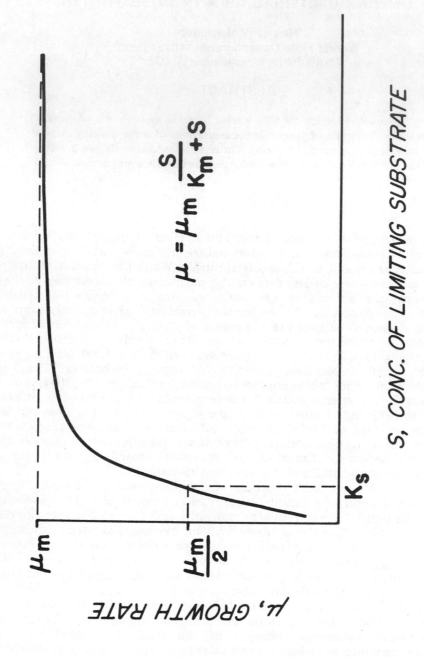

$$\mu = \mu_m \frac{S}{K_m + S}$$

Fig. 1. Relationship between growth rate and concentration of the limiting substrate, Monod's (1942) data-fitting mathematical description.

When this problem came up again during microbial ecology studies, those general results had to be reexamined for two reasons. First, bacteriologists commonly use well-supplemented media in order to meet all growth requirements and to approach maximum growth, transformation rates and yields. Sea water certainly is different from a rich bacteriological medium. Second, work with stationary microbial cultures, "batch cultures" or "closed culture systems", becomes extremely difficult at low substrate concentrations where, in addition to the inconstancy of growth conditions with time, the partial autolysis of the population greatly influences the limiting concentration of the chosen substrate. This problem could be solved by applying a continuous culture procedure where microbial growth can be studied as a function of minute concentrations of the limiting substrate.

The chemostat was chosen for another reason too. If a natural habitat is considered an open system, rather than a closed one (where growth is time dependent), the *in situ* concentration of the limiting substrate(s) will be the difference between the amount continuously produced (s_0) by one part of the population and the amount continuously consumed by another ($\frac{x}{y}$; biomass divided by a yield coefficient):

$$s = s_0 - \frac{x}{y} \tag{1}$$

This simple relationship presupposes a steady state and demonstrates that the concentration of the limiting substrate in the habitat will not be zero as long as growth occurs. Thus, available dissolved organic carbon in sea water may represent s, the steady state concentration of the limiting substrate. When sampled in a bottle, a closed system, s will become s_0, the initial concentration of the limiting substrate which will be reduced to zero during growth at a decreasing rate.

In mixed populations this change of an open into a closed system often is followed by periodic increases of cell counts in the sample bottles, most likely indicating the successive decomposition of a complex substrate by a variety of species. Experiments with samples of sea water in closed systems are suitable for studying the biochemical availability of organic material rather than its actual utilization under natural conditions.

In the chemostat at steady state, the growth constants, μ_m, and K_s, of a pure culture can be used for the calculation of s according to:

$$s = K_s \frac{D}{\mu_m - D} \tag{2}$$

where D is the dilution rate which is equal to the growth rate (e.g., Herbert et al., 1956).

Several isolates of marine bacteria (of the genera *Achromobacter*, *Pseudomonas*, *Spirillum* and *Vibrio*) were studied in pure culture using glucose, glycerol and lactate as limiting substrates (Jannasch, 1967). When s_0 was lowered stepwise in the reservoir of the chemostat at a given dilution rate, washout occurred much sooner than expected (Fig. 2) and in the presence of a steady state substrate concentration larger than its theoretical value. There was a definite minimum population density dependent on the

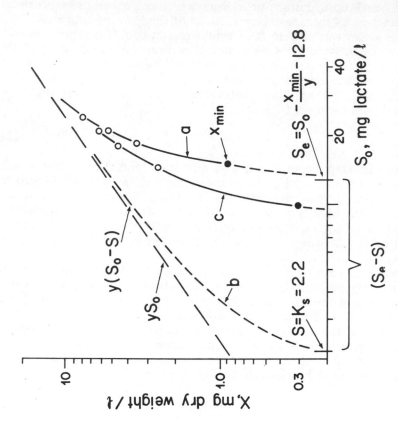

Fig. 2.

Steady state population density, x, plotted versus concentration of limiting substrate, S_0, of the reservoir of the chemostat. Organism: *Spirillum serpens*; growth rate = $\mu_m/2$ = 0.185; x_{min} = minimum population density; a = experimental data; b = theoretical curve; c = experimental data after the addition of ascorbic acid. (Reprinted from Jannasch, 1965.)

particular growth rate at which the experiment was conducted. The higher this growth rate, the lower the minimum population density and the value of s, the leftover substrate concentration. In accordance with an earlier study of *Spirillum serpens*, this experimental value for s was designated s_e and could be estimated by the equation:

$$s_e = K_s \frac{D}{\mu_m - D} + \frac{1}{A + Bx} \tag{3}$$

where A and B are parameters obtained from a linear plot of x versus $1/s - s_e$ (Jannasch, 1965).

Equation 3 indicates that s_e increases (or that growth is increasingly inhibited) with decreasing population density (x). This implies the internal production of a growth factor which, as reflected by the growth response, appears as an integral part of the environmental conditions. With decreasing steady state population densities, the concentration of this proposed growth factor decreases accordingly causing a decline in the growth rate and an increase in s_e. Washout occurs when the growth rate becomes unable to balance the dilution rate. At this point, s_e becomes identical with s_o and can be termed the threshold concentration of the limiting substrate below which no growth will occur.

Two facts indicate that this phenomenon cannot be explained by endogenous respiration: (1) it has also been observed when organic nitrogen was growth limiting, and (2) the yield coefficient is hardly affected.

The phenomenon can be described as a population effect. The initial growth limitation by a defined substrate changes at a certain point during a decrease of the population density. This is typical for microbial growth in a suboptimal medium. The actual mechanism may differ with the species and with the limiting substrate. In the case of a micro-aerophilic bacterium (*Spirillum serpens*, Jannasch, 1965) it has been shown that growth limitation by lactate changes due to a rising redox potential as soon as the population drops below a critical density. This critical population density could be lowered by the addition of ascorbic acid. Assuming that, in a similar fashion, a reducing power exerted by the growing culture overcomes the suboptimal redox potential, the effect can be described as positive feedback.

Microbial growth has often been found to require the presence of a minimal population density (Meyrath and McIntosh, 1963) in order to overcome initially unfavorable environmental conditions. It is common knowledge in applied microbiology that certain microbial transformations can only be initiated by the addition of a "starter" population of an empirically predetermined size.

The data in Table 1 suggest a similar phenomenon in sea water with regard to certain substrates and their marine bacterial decomposers. The threshold concentrations for several growth rates (in decimal fractions of the maximum growth rate) appear to be unrealistically high when compared to the concentrations of organic carbon reported for sea water, especially in view of the general assumption that only a fraction of this material is available for microbial attack. It must be realized, however, that these values were obtained in pure culture experiments. In the presence of a variety of

Table 1. Threshold concentrations of lactate, glycerol and glucose in sea water in chemostat experiments with three marine bacterial isolates at several growth rates (given in decimal fractions of the maximum growth rates). D = dilution rate (at steady state equal to growth rate); μ_m = maximum growth rate (both in hr^{-1}).

	D/μ_m	Lactate (mg/liter)	Glycerol (mg/liter)	Glucose (mg/liter)
Achromobacter *aquamarinus* (strain 208)	0.5	0.5	1.0	0.5
	0.1	0.5	1.0	0.5
	0.05	1.0	5.0	1.0
μ_m		0.15	0.20	0.34
Spirillum *serpens* (strain 101)	0.5	5	5	no growth
	0.3	10	10	
	0.2	20	100	
	0.1	50		
μ_m		0.45	0.60	
Pseudomonas sp. (strain 201)	0.5	20	50	20
	0.3	50	50	50
	0.2	100	>100	>100
	0.1	>100	-	-
μ_m		0.80	0.65	0.80

species, exhibiting a variety of growth constants, an increased metabolic diversity and a more efficient uptake and consumption of substrates must be expected. The present experiments emphasize the existence of threshold concentrations in sea water as a principle rather than stipulating their actual values.

Whenever organic substrates are found in sea water presumably available to but not utilized by microorganisms, the explanation resulting from this study is an alternative to the proposed presence of inhibitory or antibiotic materials.

DISCUSSION

HOLM-HANSEN: How do you measure growth in cultures?

JANNASCH: We run dry weight or protein analyses. If the population is high, even turbidity may be measured. If we determine maximum growth rates, we have high population densities, and are able to compare cell counts with dry weight measurements. From there we can extrapolate in some cases to fairly low concentrations of 10^3 to 10^4 cells/ml.

BELSER: How do you prevent clumping in the experiment thus far? Do you ever see clumping?

JANNASCH: Yes, so we have to select organisms which do not clump for this type of experiment. Sometimes clumping is a matter of growth rate. We have organisms which are suspended nicely at high growth rates, but clump at low growth rates. We found this with an anaerobic form, *Desulphovibrio*, where clumping was associated with the formation of polysaccharide slimes which appeared only at low growth rates. The whole enzyme system shifted according to the growth rate.

BELSER: Would you predict, based on a lot of evidence that has been published previously, that if these organisms clump, your threshold values might shift downward because they were able to transport the large concentrations across a much smaller gradient?

JANNASCH: It could very well be. The problem is that under such conditions it is hard to use the chemostat. It will depend on the degree of clumping and on whether you are able to retain complete mixing. Clumping may also mean wall growth, of course. Without any experimental evidence a prediction on the effect of clumping on the threshold values is difficult.

WRIGHT: Given some of the similarities between the chemostat and the natural environment, I have a lot of trouble understanding what in the natural environment corresponds to dilution and washout in the chemostat. How do you compare these?

JANNASCH: You can never reproduce natural populations in the chemostat. The chemostat is an artificial and highly selective system. You can say only that the organisms in nature, as in continuous culture, are growing under conditions of an open system. The chemostat is a very well defined open system. It has been described as a homo-continuous culture system as compared to hetero-continuous cultures. An open tray with an inflow and an outflow would represent a hetero-continuous open system, leading to the development of a heterogenous population mostly of attached forms. The dilution rate of a chemostat eliminates all species from the system but those competing sucessfully for the limiting substrate. In a natural population, grazing, sedimentation, forming of spores, etc., eliminate cells and are comparable to the dilution rate of the chemostat. I do not think, however, that such an analogy is very useful. The values of the chemostat system lie in its quality as an experimental tool for measuring growth of microorganisms under defined conditions.

ACKNOWLEDGMENTS

Contribution No. 2170 from the Woods Hole Oceanographic Institution.

This work was supported by National Science Foundation Grant GB 7747.

REFERENCES

HERBERT, D. 1958. Some principles of continuous culture, p. 381-396. *In* 7th Int. Congr. Microbiol. Symp., Stockholm. 381-396.

HERBERT, D., R. ELSWORTH, and R. C. TELLING. 1956. The continuous culture of bacteria: a theoretical and experimental study. J. Gen. Microbiol., *14*: 601-622.

JANNASCH, H. W. 1965. Starter populations as determined under steady state conditions. Biotech. Bioeng., 7: 279-283.

JANNASCH, H. W. 1967. Growth of marine bacteria at limiting concentrations of organic carbon in sea water. Limnol. Oceanogr., *12*: 264-271.

MARR, G. A., E. H. NILSON, and D. J. CLARK. 1963. The maintenance of *Escherichia coli*, p. 536-548. *In* C. Lamanna [ed.], Endogenous metabolism with special reference to bacteria. Annu. New York Acad. Sci., *102*.

MEYRATH, J., and A. F. McINTOSH. 1963. Size of inoculum and carbon metabolism in some *Aspergillus* species. J. Gen. Microbiol., *33*: 47-56.

MONOD, J. 1942. Recherches sur la croisance des cultures bacteriennes. 2nd ed., Hermann, Paris, 1958.

GENERAL DISCUSSION AFTER SESSION II

ALLEN: This is directed to Dr. Sieburth, Dr. Prakash or both, perhaps. Is there any evidence for or against utilization of complexes of phenolic compounds, carbohydrates and nitrogenous materials by phytoplankton as nutrients rather than as growth stimulating factors?

PRAKASH: There is some work done on the assimilation of these compounds, mostly by Prát in Czechoslovakia (Prát and Pospisil, 1959; Prát et al., 1961). He found evidence that humic compounds get into the plant cell and presumably participate in plant cell metabolism. We feel that the same thing is happening in phytoplankton cells, that some of these compounds are activating certain enzymes which enable the cell to take up nutrients rapidly.

ALLEN: Assuming your point, these things are not going directly into the carbon chain. I wonder whether they have to go by way of the bacteria. Is there any chance that they go directly into the phytoplankton?

SIEBURTH: I keep wondering whether the bacterial utilization is as great as I think it is. Perhaps the algae are recycling it and taking some of it back. In this regard, Provasoli (Provasoli and Pinter, 1966) has been using Craigie and McLaughlan's Gelbstoff preparations (Craigie and McLaughlan, 1964) and showing that this material will restore normal morphogenesis to axenic cultures of seaweed which would otherwise go haywire.

PARSONS: A new word has been introduced here, exudation. I think this is probably a good word. We have been talking about "excretions" from phytoplankton for a long time and I am sure that "excretion" is the wrong word. It has a precise physiological meaning. I suggest that Dr. Sieburth's word "exudation" is a good word when we want to talk about "the release of extracellular products" by algae, which is rather a long phrase.

NATARAJAN: Exudation has something to do with osmotic pressure.

ALLEN: Yes, it does have another meaning in higher plant physiology. It has to do with the adherence of little droplets of liquid to the surface of a plant.

NATARAJAN: Yes, that is right.

MENZEL: Dr. Sieburth, the excretion rates you obtained upset me. It really bothers me to think that an organism fixes carbon and then excretes 40% of what it fixes. We have been working with this plant for some time and the highest excretion rate we have measured is something like 2%. I wonder where our differences could come from.

SIEBURTH: With the same plant?

MENZEL: With *Fucus*.

SIEBURTH: If you did not get any greater excretion rate, then it was because the bacteria were chomping it up as fast as it was appearing.

MENZEL: That is possible, but the way I looked at it at the time these were monitored — at the same time we were monitoring pH, oxygen, C^{14} uptake as determined by direct combustion and measurement in an electrometer and also the dissolved fraction — was, if a plant is photosynthesizing very rapidly and if there is respiration due to bacteria going on, you cannot accumulate a lot of oxygen and other by-products of photosynthesis or the respiration rate will cut it down and the two will balance out.

SIEBURTH: Right, but we add the amount of exudation to the photosynthesis to correct for this. Even taking this into consideration, the growth rate is such that you get a doubling time of 65 days with our values. As Kanwisher has rightly pointed out, these weeds can really grow. Respiration is only something like 5% of photosynthesis. So under continued illumination the plant has only got to be slightly more than 5% efficient, if you do not include emersion and darkness. If you include emersion and darkness, then it is 20%. And if you include 30% for exudation of the total carbon, which was my value this morning, then only half is lost. For any organism this is about par. A bacterium synthesizing an essential metabolite loses 50% of it immediately. I think they are efficient in that they do not leak in the dark; this amazes me.

MENZEL: It is efficient in reference to other organisms but it is not an efficient system.

SIEBURTH: It has to be efficient. Look at their great standing biomass. Kanwisher's work with such organisms as *Ulva*, *Fucus* and *Chondris crispus*, without emersion or darkness obtained a doubling time of 20 to 120 hours. He also cut off the actively growing tip and measured this. Under these conditions he calculated doubling time of 3 1/2 days for *Fucus*. In our system with whole plants, otherwise similar to his, it was seven days. Our values are not too far off as far as respiration and metabolism are concerned. Even taking into account exudation, the tissue doubles in 65 days, which coincides with published field data. The plant may be extravagant, but it is nice for the bacteria.

SESSION III. ORGANIC MATTER AND WATER QUALITY

Chairman: A.A. Rosen
Chief, Waste Identification and Analysis Activities
Cincinnati Water Research Laboratory
Federal Water Pollution Control Administration
Cincinnati, Ohio 45226

The subject of this session can be paraphrased as "Organic matter as water pollutants." It is, therefore, appropriate to introduce this group of presentations with a definition of pollutants and a brief survey of their origins.

For practical purposes, a pollutant is any substance that interferes with a generally accepted water use, whether the pollutant is man-caused or natural. According to this definition, visible natural coloring matter in tap water is a pollutant. Low levels of minerals that necessitate the purification of water to be used in electronic manufacture are not pollutants, if that is the only adverse effect.

In terms of pollution effect, organic chemicals in surface waters fall into two general classes. The first class consists of easily oxidized substances. They are important pollutants when their concentration is high enough to seriously reduce the dissolved oxygen (DO) in a stream. Because oxidation rapidly eliminates these compounds, they are not ordinarily important pollutants in terms of specific individual properties. The other class of organic chemical pollutants consists of compounds which are oxidized slowly, if at all. They do not consume oxygen rapidly enough to reduce the DO significantly. Any important pollution effect caused by these substances is due to some property other than oxygen consumption.

The origin of organic substances important for reasons other than BOD can be associated with the composition of the pollutants and, consequently, with the type of pollution problem they present.

Natural

Natural organic substances arise during the decay of vegetation and the consequent runoff of decay products into surface waters, as well as from aquatic algae and other microorganisms.

Muncipal

This pollutant class consists of organic matter introduced via raw or treated municipal wastes.

Agricultural

Pollutants from this source include pesticides, fertilizers, animal wastes, the soluble biological components of decaying crops and crop trimmings and the organic components of soil washed into surface water because of agricultural activity, causing conspicuous turbidity.

Industrial

Food and biological industries produce wastes chemically similar to sewage since they are readily oxidized animal and vegetable products.

Heavy industries comprise the most important source of serious pollution by non-BOD organic chemicals. Characteristic industrial pollution sources are: coal coking, heavy chemicals including petrochemicals, manufacturing, petroleum refining, metallurgy and the manufacture of consumer chemical products such as paint, drugs, plastics, pesticides, detergents, etc.

Transportation

The various forms of transportation cause pollution of surface waters by organic matter, largely through accident. Barge and vessel transport on rivers and the seas is a major source of organic chemicals through the cleaning of tanks and bilges, spills and leaks, and accidents resulting in sinking. Rail and road transportation contributes organics through collisions and other incidents that result in spills which run off into lakes and streams. Pipelines, particularly those transporting petroleum products, are sources of stream pollution when they leak or are accidently ruptured. Then, large volumes of organic chemical material flow into streams and other surface waters.

INSTRUMENTAL TECHNIQUES FOR THE IDENTIFICATION OF POLLUTANTS

Ihor Lysyj
Environmental Sciences and Technology
R O C K E T D Y N E
6633 Canoga Avenue
Canoga Park, California 91303

ABSTRACT

A pyrographic method for analysis and identification of water pollutants is described. The technique consists of (1) direct pyrolysis of water samples containing organic pollutants, (2) gas chromatographic separation and hydrogen flame ionization measurement of pyrolytic fragments produced and (3) application of mathematical techniques for the interpretation of resulting complex pyrograms. No sample preconcentration or preanalysis handling is required.

The technique has potential application in rapid tracing of pollutants to their sources, ascertaining the pollution load contributed by each upstream source and measuring the degradation rates of pollution during downstream travel.

INTRODUCTION

The composition of industrial waste is characteristic of the source industry or plant. In the food processing industry, wastes are predominately carbohydrates and their degradation products. On the other hand, meat packing wastes contain larger amounts of proteins and fats with correspondingly smaller quantities of carbohydrates. Pulp and paper processing effluents contain large quantities of materials such as lignins, resin acids, terpenes, spent sulfite liquor, and fibers. Wastes from petroleum production and refining are predominately hydrocarbons and related compounds. In general, the wastewaters from a chemical industry contain materials peculiar to the particular processes involved.

PYROGRAPHIC METHODS OF ANALYSIS

Pyrolytic analysis, combined with gas chromatographic or mass spectroscopic detection and characterization of produced fragments, has been used on a number of occasions for qualitative and quantitative determination of organic materials. It was decided to assess the usefulness of such techniques for direct (without preconcentration or separation) analysis of dissolved organics. The ability of such techniques to differentiate between naturally occurring organics and man-made pollutants and between the different classes of pollutants was studied.

In pyrolysis, an organic molecule subjected to an elevated temperature decomposes into several preferential fragments. At high temperatures, the compound fragments mainly into methane, hydrogen, carbon monoxide and a few other small molecules. When the pyrolysis is conducted at lower temperatures, short chain organic fragments are obtained with a corresponding decrease in methane, hydrogen and other simple molecules.

In general, organic fragments obtained during pyrolysis are related to the molecular structure of the parent material. Certain fragments are obtained only from particular organic materials. Thus, the organics in a homologous series or class of compounds may have pyrolytic patterns with one or more peaks characteristic of the class or series. The chromatograms of the pyrolytic fragments from such materials exhibit magnitude differences in the common peaks as well as some characteristic peaks.

The studies described here applied gas chromatographic pyrolytic technique (called, in short, "pyrographic method") to the characterization and differentiation of natural organics present in various water sources and intruded organic pollutants of man-made origin. The feasibility of direct (without separation or preconcentration) pyrography of water samples containing organic matter of different kinds has been demonstrated by the author and K. H. Nelson (1968) in previous studies.

These studies demonstrate the utility of such a technique when applied to the differentiation between natural organics and man-made pollutants in natural water bodies.

INSTRUMENTATION

The pyrographic instrumentation used in this study consists of several subsystems: sample injector, pyrolytic unit, carrier gas source, fragment separator, detector and readout (Fig. 1).

Sample injector

The sample injector for the pyrograph must permit injection of optimum size samples without alteration of sample composition or introduction of contaminants. Prior experience in pyrolytic water analysis has shown that introduction of water samples by conventional injection through the gas chromatographic septa yields pyrolytic patterns with large nonreproducible peaks. It was found that these peaks originate from the minute septum particles which adhere to the syringe needle and are carried into the pyrolysis zone. A three-way injection valve was incorporated in the pyrograph to overcome this difficulty.

Carrier gas generator

The commercial steam generator used in initial investigations performed poorly in terms of temperature control and steam flow so a custom built generator was designed. This consisted of a 1.7 liter stainless steel sphere heated with a heating tape. The thermal conditions were regulated by a thermocouple sensor. The generator was equipped with a pressure gauge and was connected by 1/8 inch OD heated tubing through a check valve to the pyrolysis subsystem.

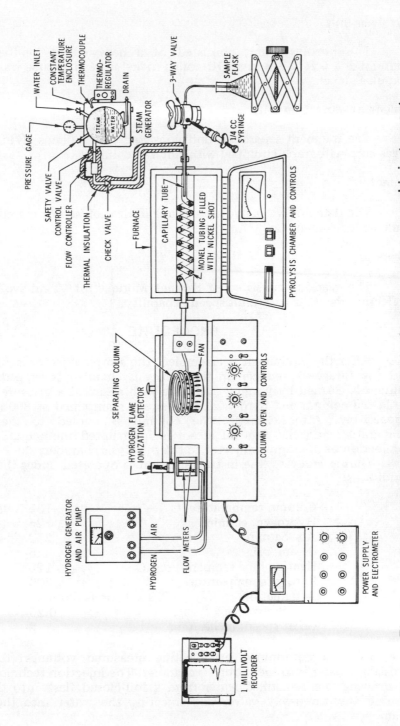

Fig. 1. Relationship of the subsystems in the prototype pyrographic instrument.

Pyrolysis unit

The pyrolysis unit consisted of a heavy duty Lindberg furnace containing a 5 ft x 3/8 inch OD coiled nickel tube. The tube was filled with granular nickel.

Fragment separation unit

The fragment separation unit consisted of a Wilkens HyFi Model 600 C gas chromatograph equipped with suitable columns.

Detector

The detector was a hydrogen flame ionization sensor manufactured by Wilkens Instrument Co.

Readout

The readout consisted of Sargent Model "SR" 1-millivolt full scale deflection recorder with multispeed capability.

PROCEDURE

After the equipment is assembled, the sample injector is disconnected and the Swagelok reducer on the pyrolysis chamber is capped. Then the column is cleaned by purging overnight with steam at a pressure of 10 psig while the column and pyrolysis chamber are maintained at 300 and 800 C, respectively. After cleaning, the column is cooled to the operating temperature and the flow of steam is interrupted momentarily to allow connection of the sample injector to the pyrolysis chamber.

During analyses, the instrumentation is operated under the following conditions:

Column temperature, C	135
Hydrogen, cc/min	25
Air, cc/min	250
Steam, psig	5.5
Heating tape temperatures, C	125
Pyrolysis temperature, C	700
Attenuation	10 x 1, or as required
Sample size, cc	0.25
Chart speed, inches/min	2

The blank is determined by injecting measured volumes (0.25 cc) of redistilled water into the pyrolysis chamber. The injection technique consists of drawing the redistilled water from a foil-closed flask into the syringe, turning the three-way valve, and injecting the water into the pyrolysis chamber.

COLUMN EVALUATION

Characterization of the dissolved organics places stringent requirements on the operating parameters. Steam must be used as the carrier gas to minimize the effects of injected samples on the hydrogen flame ionization detector. In addition, the column must be stable at temperatures above 100 C.

A concentrated effort was made to evaluate all potentially promising gas chromatographic columns. The evaluation was based on several criteria: (1) the resolution of the pyrolytic fragments, (2) the stability of the column in the temperature range from 100 to 200 C and (3) the extent of column bleeding at elevated temperatures.

Column substrates were selected for investigation on the basis of reported stability at high temperatures and their resolution of different classes of compounds. These substrates included SE-30, Carbowax 20M, silicone oil 710 and m-phenylether (five ring). Porous glass was used as the support for SE-30. The other substrates were coated on 60 to 80 mesh Chromosorb W which had been acid washed and treated with dimethyldichlorosilane to minimize peak tailing. Soluble starch, gelatin and heptanoic acid were used as standard test materials in the initial investigations.

The pyrograms obtained with SE-30 on porous glass afforded poor sensitivity and reproducibility. The silicone oil column exhibited only moderate temperature stability. Although this column resolved gelatin fragments fairly well, neither heptanoic acid nor starch fragments were notably separated. Both Carbowax 20M and m-phenylether (five ring) substrates exhibit very good temperature stability and separation of pyrolytic fragments.

To complete the column evaluation, three additional substrates were investigated: ethylene glycol adipate, diethylene glycol malonate and Apiezon L. Pyrograms obtained at 600 to 800 C for starch, gelatin and heptanoic acid did not show these substrates to be superior to the Carbowax 20M. As with the substrates investigated previously, these three substrates were deficient in either stability or in resolution of the fragments from the three materials used. Because the Carbowax 20M substrate provided reasonable separation of pyrolytic fragments and was temperature stable, it was further investigated.

Temperature conditions for pyrolysis were also studied. The pyrograms for aqueous solutions of gelatin, starch and heptanoic acid were obtained at 500, 600 and 700 C. More complex spectra were obtained in all cases at higher pyrolysis temperatures. This would provide a better basis for subsequent mathematical treatment of the data.

To illustrate differences in the pyrolytic patterns, pyrograms were obtained at 700 C for aqueous solutions of starch, gelatin and heptanoic acid. The pyrograms in Fig. 2 through 4 show the similarities and differences obtained for materials of different molecular structure. These pyrograms revealed a total of 14 peaks discernable in the pyrolysis of a water sample containing all three materials. The retention times and heights of these peaks are presented in Table 1.

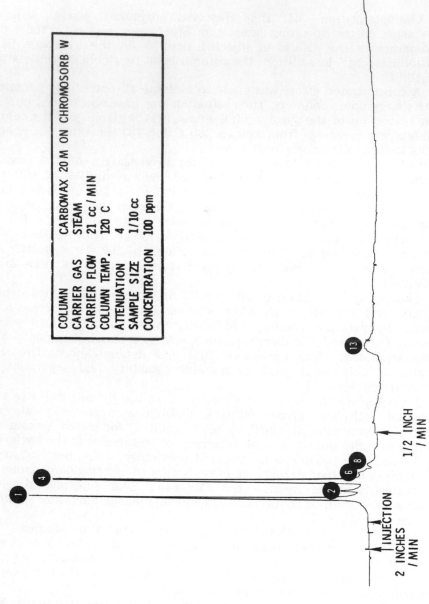

COLUMN   CARBOWAX 20 M ON CHROMOSORB W
CARRIER GAS   STEAM
CARRIER FLOW   21 cc / MIN
COLUMN TEMP.   120 C
ATTENUATION   4
SAMPLE SIZE   1/10 cc
CONCENTRATION   100 ppm

1/2 INCH / MIN

INJECTION
2 INCHES / MIN

Fig. 2.   Pyrogram of aqueous starch solution.

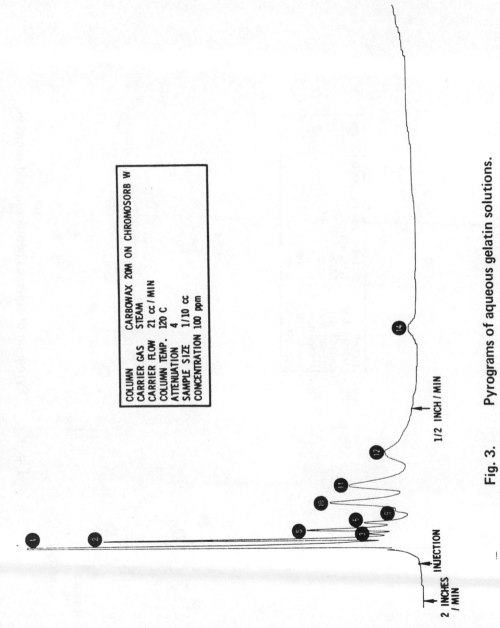

COLUMN   CARBOWAX 20M ON CHROMOSORB W
CARRIER GAS   STEAM
CARRIER FLOW   21 cc / MIN
COLUMN TEMP.   120 C
ATTENUATION   4
SAMPLE SIZE   1/10 cc
CONCENTRATION   100 ppm

1/2 INCH / MIN

INJECTION

2 INCHES / MIN

Fig. 3.   Pyrograms of aqueous gelatin solutions.

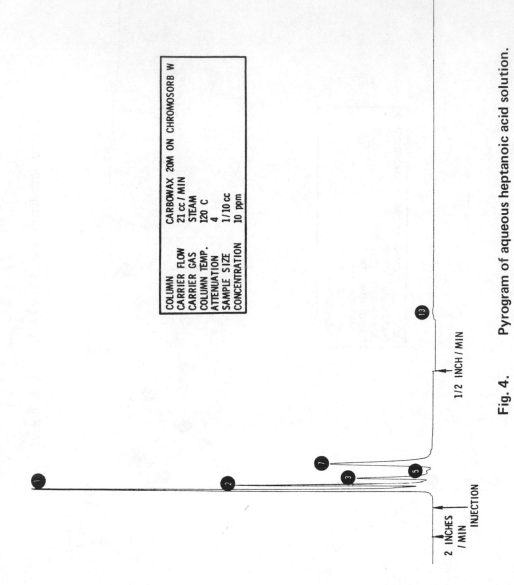

Fig. 4. Pyrogram of aqueous heptanoic acid solution.

COLUMN	CARBOWAX 20M ON CHROMOSORB W
CARRIER FLOW	21 cc / MIN
CARRIER GAS	STEAM
COLUMN TEMP.	120 C
ATTENUATION	4
SAMPLE SIZE	1/10 cc
CONCENTRATION	10 ppm

1/2 INCH / MIN

2 INCHES / MIN

INJECTION

Table 1.   Pyrographic data for three organic materials.

Peak no.	Retention time (min)	Peak height		
		Starch	Gelatin	Heptanoic acid
1	0.22	66	100+	100+
2	0.29	5.5	74.5	46
3	0.34		11.5	18
4	0.38	61.5		
5	0.41		26.5	1.5
6	0.46	2	13	
7	0.49			24
8	0.54	1		
9	0.59		5	
10	0.70		21	
11	0.89		16.5	
12	1.24		8	
13	4.10	2.5		1
14	5.34		2	

In a water sample containing a mixture of these organics, all three materials would contribute to most of the major peaks. However, there would also be some distinctive peaks which would originate from only one of the materials (blocked numbers in Table 1). As Table 1 indicates, starch produces the fully distinctive peak 4 at a retention time of 0.38 min and peak 8 at a retention time of 0.54 min. Gelatin is characterized by a group of distinctive peaks 9 through 12 with retention times of 0.59, 0.70, 0.89 and 1.24 min, respectively, and peak 14 at a retention time of 5.39 min. Heptanoic acid produced distinctive peak 24 at a retention time of 0.49 min.

CHARACTERIZATION OF NATURAL WATER SOURCES

The pyrographic technique was applied to the pyrolytic characterization of natural water sources. In the initial experiment, the instrumentation and procedure were used as described previously. The separation column was 6 ft long and was filled with a packing of 20% Carbowax 20M on Chromosorb W.

Although it was possible to characterize pyrolytically natural water sources using this column, the peak resolution was of a low order. Therefore, a Porapak column was used for subsequent analyses of natural water sources. The Porapak substrate does not contain a liquid phase, and was superior to Carbowax 20M in resolving the organic fragments obtained from natural water sources.

The instrumental conditions used with the Porapak column were as follows:

Column	7 1/2 ft x 3/16 inch OD filled with 50 to 80 mesh Porapak Q preceded by a 2 1/2 ft x 3/16 inch OD column filled with 60 to 80 mesh glass beads
Column temperature	120 C
Pyrolysis temperature	700 C
Carrier gas	Steam
Carrier flowrate	22 cc/min
Detector	Hydrogen flame ionization
Hydrogen flowrate	40 cc/min
Air flowrate	250 cc/min
Chart speed	1/2 in/min
Sample size	0.20 cc

Water samples of natural origin came from streams in localities removed from habitation and other sources of contamination. These localities also differed in geographic and climatic aspects. The pyrographic spectrum of each water sample was obtained with the Porapak column at an attenuation of 10 and the preceding instrumental conditions. These pyrograms are shown in Fig. 5 and 6 and the data are presented in Table 2. A comparison of the pyrograms reveals differences and similarities. The

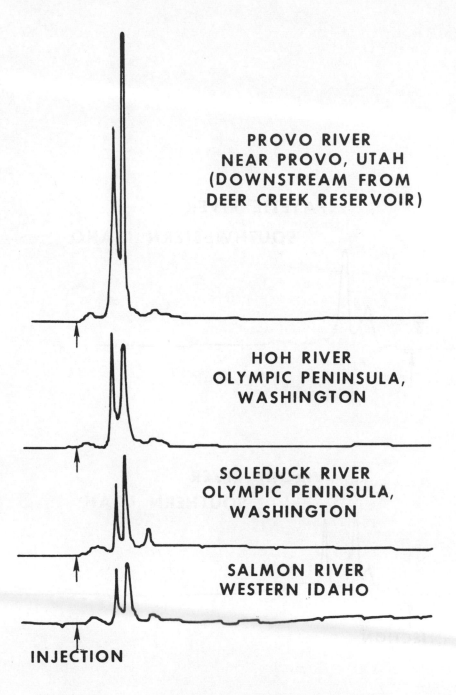

PROVO RIVER
NEAR PROVO, UTAH
(DOWNSTREAM FROM
DEER CREEK RESERVOIR)

HOH RIVER
OLYMPIC PENINSULA,
WASHINGTON

SOLEDUCK RIVER
OLYMPIC PENINSULA,
WASHINGTON

SALMON RIVER
WESTERN IDAHO

INJECTION

Fig. 5.   Pyrograms of some natural river waters.

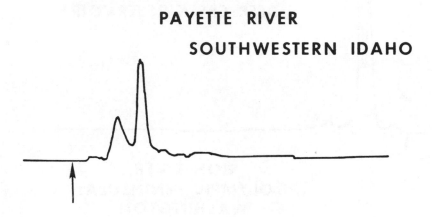

PAYETTE RIVER

SOUTHWESTERN IDAHO

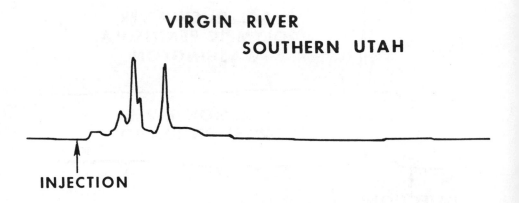

VIRGIN RIVER

SOUTHERN UTAH

INJECTION

Fig. 6.   Pyrograms of two river waters.

Table 2. Pyrographic data for waters of natural origin.

Retention time (min)	Peak height (arbitrary units)					
	Hoh River	Soleduck River	Salmon River	Provo River	Virgin River	Payette River
0.5	27	32	22		3	14
0.7				26		
1.3	213	138	133		32	83
1.5	105	180	140		60	
1.6				200+		
1.8						178
1.9					8	112
2.0				22		
2.1						47
2.3	39	55	29		28	
2.4				104		
2.5						22
2.6				28		
3.3						16
8.0			19			
9.0				4		

pyrograms obtained (Soleduck River, Washington; Hoh River, Washington; Salmon River, Idaho; Provo River, Utah) are similar in that they contain four main peaks. The relative magnitudes of these peaks differ but the retention volumes are the same. The other two pyrograms of natural waters (Fig. 6) differ between themselves and from the other four pyrograms (Fig. 5).

MATHEMATICAL TREATMENT OF PYROGRAMS

While specific and distinctive peaks provide means for the identification of certain organic groups, the pyrogram considered as a whole represents considerably more information. This information can be abstracted mathematically by the application of the least-squares method.

Instead of interpretation only by means of distinctive peaks, the calculation of the concentrations of individual components can be best carried out by relating all pyrographic peaks to the concentration of each component. For this, the area or height of a peak can be utilized. Using a least-squares technique, the mathematical models are developed along the following general lines. In the pyrogram, the area y_i or other parameter of a peak i in a determination for an organic component j is directly related to the concentration of that component by a proportionality constant a_{ij}. The linear equation relating these quantities is:

$$y_i = a_{ij}c_j \tag{1}$$

where

> y = area of peak i
> a = area per unit concentration of the jth component in a peak i
> c = concentration of the jth component
> i = the peak
> j = the component

In samples containing more than one organic compound, the total area of a peak on the pyrogram may be assumed to be the sum of the contributions from each component. Therefore, c_1, c_2, ..., c_m can represent the concentrations of the components in the sample and y_1, y_2, ..., y_n are the observed peak areas in the pyrogram. Assuming that equations of type (1) are valid for all components and that interactions between components are negligible, the total peak area y_i at peak i will be:

$$y_i = \sum_{j=1}^{m} a_{ij}c_j \tag{2}$$

Thus, the equation relating the area of the first peak to the unknown concentrations would be:

$$y_1 = a_{11}c_1 + a_{12}c_2 + \ldots + a_{1m}c_m \tag{3}$$

With the proportionality constants a_{ij} determined by calibration and the peak areas y_i observed for the sample, the pyrogram can be completely defined by a set of n equations in the m unknown concentrations:

$$y_1 = a_{11}c_1 + a_{12}c_2 + \ldots + a_{1m}c_m$$

$$y_2 = a_{21}c_1 + a_{22}c_2 + \ldots + a_{2m}c_m$$

$$y_3 = a_{31}c_1 + a_{32}c_2 + \ldots + a_{3m}c_m$$

.

.

.

$$y_n = a_{n1}c_1 + a_{n2}c_2 + \ldots + a_{nm}c_m \qquad (4)$$

Because the number of components m is less than the number of peaks n, this represents an overdetermined set of equations. There exist no values for the unknowns $c_1, c_2, \ldots, c_m$ that will satisfy all n equations exactly. The least-squares technique produces a solution $c_1, c_2, \ldots, c_m$ which in a sense most nearly satisfies all n equations simultaneously. The least-squares technique is applied to the residuals which are given by:

$$r_1 = y_1 - a_{11}\hat{c}_1 - a_{12}\hat{c}_2 - \ldots - a_{1m}\hat{c}_m$$

$$r_2 = y_2 - a_{21}\hat{c}_1 - a_{22}\hat{c}_2 - \ldots - a_{2m}\hat{c}_m$$

$$r_3 = y_3 - a_{31}\hat{c}_1 - a_{32}\hat{c}_2 - \ldots - a_{3m}\hat{c}_m$$

.

.

.

$$r_n = y_n - a_{n1}\hat{c}_1 - a_{n2}\hat{c}_2 - \ldots - a_{nm}\hat{c}_m \qquad (5)$$

The method selects the values $\hat{c}_1 \ldots \hat{c}_m$ that minimize the sum of the squares of the residuals, defined by the equation:

$$Q = \sum_{i=1}^{n} r_i^2 = r_1^2 + r_2^2 + \ldots + r_n^2 \qquad (6)$$

It is believed that application of the pyrographic mathematical technique to the indentification and characterization of dissolved organics, when backed by computized analysis of pyrograms, provides a powerful tool for the chemical characterization of organic pollutants in natural waters.

DISCUSSION

SIEBURTH: Do you have any data at all on natural waters?

LYSYJ: Yes.

SIEBURTH: Does it make sense?

LYSYJ: We are not in position, at this time, to make a very detailed evaluation. We just obtained some data from several rivers from the state of Washington down to New Mexico. I did not attempt to explain them in any great detail.

SIEBURTH: Those of us who do not have Rocketdyne's facilities have to work with test tubes. I think you were awfully hard on the rest of us in your opening remarks.

LYSYJ: I hope I was not.

SIEBURTH: Be sure you can produce as well as you imply you can.

BLUMER: I think in your introduction you said something like, "If you try to isolate pure compounds from a natural mixture, you find that everything that can be there, is, and in addition, some things that you may have thought are not, are also present." I think I tried to make the point that this is not so, and you can, contrary to what you say, extract useful information from that. For instance, if we look at the isoprenoid acids in ancient sediments, we find a very wide range from 11 to 22. In recent sediments, we find only 16, 19 and 20. This is a difference. The limitation in the recent sediment comes from a source which has a limited carbon number distribution; in an ancient sediment, you have a much wider range. This leads you to processes, geochemical processes. I do not see how you can get information like this in any other way than by isolating single compounds and seeing where they come from and where they go. I am fully aware of the value of pyrolysis, but there are many characteristics of natural organic mixtures which can no longer be recognized after pyrolysis.

LYSYJ: Maybe I overstated my case. I agree that there is a place for molecular chemistry and that it provides us with a useful handle on special problems, such as identification of insecticides, for example. You can go directly after them, but you must admit that what you will find on a molecular level in natural waters is a very broad spectrum of materials.

BLUMER: But the point is that organisms do not produce as wide a spectrum of materials as does petroleum for instance. This gives you the handle to distinguish petroleum pollution from the natural hydrocarbons in the water.

LYSYJ: This you can do by pyrolytic means.

BLUMER: You can also do it by isolation.

LYSYJ: It is a matter of choice.

CHRISTMAN: You present this technique as a very valuable aid for characterizing effluents of plants into streams. Do you have a similar technique for effluents which are not largely organic?

LYSYJ: No, the technique relates strictly to the organic pollutants. We are considering going to electrochemical methods for inorganic materials, but this step and this approach are still in the thinking stages. We are referring now to inorganic pollutants.

CHRISTMAN: Well, for plating wastes, for instance, your instrument would be useless.

LYSYJ: We are concentrating, at this time, on industries such as pulp processing, food industries, industries which do produce a substantial demand on the dissolved oxygen in water.

BREGER: Once you start computerizing your information, you are automatically freezing all the conditions under which you have to operate from that point on.

LYSYJ: That is correct. You must develop a system and then freeze it into that condition. You can, of course, make a flexible program compensating for the special situation, but that is in the future.

ACKNOWLEDGMENTS

This work was supported by the Office of Saline Water, U.S. Department of the Interior, under Contract No. 14-01-0001-965.

REFERENCES

BIRGE, E. A., and C. JUDAY. 1934. Particulate and dissolved organic matter in inland lakes. Ecol. Monogr., 4(4): 440-474.

LYSYJ, I., and K. H. NELSON. 1968. Pyrographic method for the analysis of organics in aqueous solution. Anal. Chem., 40: 1365-1367.

AIR TRANSPORT OF ORGANIC CONTAMINANTS TO THE MARINE ENVIRONMENT

Edward D. Goldberg
Scripps Institution of Oceanography
University of California, San Diego
La Jolla, California 92037

INTRODUCTION

Homo sapiens is responsible more than any other species for causing substantial alterations to the chemical makeup of the oceans. Such changes are perhaps related to the destiny of man. The world population continues to increase with a consequential larger demand for the material resources of the earth. Although the early stages of society can be described as accumulative — the industrial and agricultural products were maintained mainly near the residences of man; today, essentially all that is acquired must be disposed, often in degraded forms. These metabolic wastes of civilization often increase the levels of chemical species already a part of the environment, as in the case of carbon dioxide. Sometimes they are alien to the surroundings, the pesticides or synthetic detergents for example. When such *contaminants* cause a loss or restricted use of an environmental resource, they become *pollutants*.

The chemical invasion of the oceans by man involves time periods quite different from those encountered in terrestrial water systems. Where a river essentially renews itself annually, lakes in periods of decades or centuries, the residence times of dissolved chemical species in the oceans are of the order of hundreds through hundreds of millions of years. These periods are related to the chemical reactivities of the substances. Species intimately involved in biological or inorganic reactions, for example copper or manganese, have shorter passage times through ocean waters to the sedimentary deposits than those of such ions as sodium or calcium, that enjoy a relatively inert existence in solution. It is important to realize that contaminants, introduced by man today into the marine environment, in principle will be detectable by many, many generations in the future.

Most of the concern with the contaminants in the oceans has involved materials in solution. However, the industrial, social and agricultural activities of society introduce such refractory phases as fly-ash, talc, and glass, solids that rapidly pass through the water column to the sediments. Their importance in altering the overall chemical composition of the oceans may result from their acting as reaction sites for precipitation or oxidation-reduction processes involving the dissolved species in sea water. Practically no considerations have been given to these possibilities as yet.

The transport of erosion products from continental weathering processes, as well as that of the contaminants, takes place through wind systems, through rivers, or through glacial ice movements. In addition, sewage systems and discharges from sea going vessels now provide additional means of transferring waste products to the seas.

There are many frameworks in which an entry of the impingement of man upon the oceans might be made. As a result of time restrictions, it appears worthwhile to address ourselves to the principal parameters involved in such an interaction through a discussion of a limited part of the general problem — the atmospheric transport of organic contaminants to the marine environment.

Wind systems

In each of the hemispheres of the earth there are three main global air mass movements — the equatorial easterlies (the trades); the temperate westerlies (the jets); and the polar easterlies. Each of these zones of air circulation can accommodate discharges from the continents and can carry them over large distances. Fission products resulting from a low yield nuclear explosion in Nevada subsequently were found over Paris, Cairo and Asahikawa with the fallout in Japan occurring two weeks after the event (Miyake et al, 1956). Transport took place in the jet stream. Freshwater diatoms and dust, as well as pesticides (the chlorinated hydrocarbons) have been carried by the Northeast Trades from the European-African continents to the Island of Barbados, 5000 km away (Delaney et al., 1967; Risebrough et al., 1968).

Types of materials and injection rates into the atmosphere

The rates of introduction of organic contaminants into the atmosphere (Table 1) appear to be approaching the net rate of primary production of organic matter, 10^{16} grams of carbon per year (Nielsen, 1960). While the rates of contaminant entry increase, the primary productivity is presumed to remain more or less constant. All of the material injected into the atmosphere does not enter the marine environment, however, approximations to the relative fallouts of aerosols can be made on the basis of relative areas of land and of ocean under the wind system being considered. For gases the relative importance of the sea water compared to other sinks for their removal from the atmosphere must be evaluated.

The United States appears to be responsible for around one-third of the contaminants introduced into the atmosphere in comparison with the rest of the world. The automobile is the major source of the carbon monoxide, hydrocarbons and lead tetraethyl combustion products.

Petroleum products may also be introduced during their transport across the oceans on ships. The present rate of transfer is 10^{15} grams/year and this amount is increasing at a rate of 4% annually. A loss of a fraction of a percent of these materials to the sea would be of a similar order of magnitude to that introduced by wind systems. Such chronic inputs may be compared to the *Torrey Canyon* accident in which the breakup of a tanker off the west coast of Cornwall, England introduced 10^{10} grams of hydrocarbons to the marine environment.

Table 1. Estimated rates of injection of materials into the atmosphere.

Material	U.S. rate (gm/yr)	World rate (gm/yr)
CO	7×10^{13}	2×10^{14}
Sulphur oxides	2×10^{13}	8×10^{13}
Hydrocarbons	2×10^{13}	8×10^{13}
Nitrogen oxides	8×10^{12}	5×10^{13}
CO_2		9×10^{15}
Smoke particles	1×10^{13}	2×10^{13}
Tetraethyl lead combustion products*	3×10^{11}	7×10^{11}
Pesticides*	4×10^{11}	

* Production rates are given rather than atmospheric injection rates.

Removal of contaminants from the atmosphere to the ocean

Knowledge about the mechanisms that transfer atmospheric contaminants into the oceans is in general poorly defined, however there are some broad considerations (see Junge, 1963, for a general discussion). Several processes appear to be of importance: (1) direct solution into the ocean, especially for gases; (2) dry fallout of particulate phases, including impaction; and (3) removal with atmospheric precipitation such as rain or hail.

Absorption in the world ocean can account for the entry of such gaseous species as CO, CO_2 and the low molecular weight hydrocarbons which have low solubilities in water and whose atmospheric contents would not be seriously affected by precipitation processes.

Scavenging by aqueous fallout is an efficient process to remove suspended phases from the atmosphere. Recent studies on the dry sedimentation of sodium chloride and of aerosols containing artificially produced radionuclides suggest that this mechanism can be responsible for the transfer up to perhaps one-third to one-fourth of the solid materials.

Monitoring of the contaminant entry rate into the oceans

The rates of man's chemical impingement upon the oceans can be categorized on the basis of the time periods over which the measurements are averaged. Nearly all of the inputs that substantially alter the composition of the marine environment have taken place since the Industrial Revolution, say the last 150 years.

Measurements of the standing crop of the contaminant in the atmosphere, coupled with sedimentation or removal rates, allow the computation of input, integrated over fractions of years. Such a method has been applied to the introduction of chlorinated hydrocarbons to the equatorial Atlantic by the Northeast Trades (Risebrough et al., 1968). Daily samples of dusts, collected from several million cubic meters of air, were pooled such that they represented time periods from 2 days to 2 weeks, before analyses for the pesticides. It was assumed that the chlorinated hydrocarbons, attached to the dust particles, sedimented out of the atmosphere through gravitational settling.

Glacial snowfields are natural receptacles of dust and can maintain a record of fallout. They are especially attractive inasmuch as they are found at all latitudes and can hence monitor the wind systems bringing materials to the oceans. The use of firn stratigraphy or radiometric methods of glacial ice dating based on lead-210 (Goldberg, 1963) provide the time parameter. Glacial snowfields accumulate at rates of tens of centimeters per year. Since the ages of various levels can usually be determined to within a year or two over the past 100 years, the integrated time period one can study span the period of a year to a hundred years. This technique has been used to consider the input of talc, a diluent and carrier for pesticides, in a Washington glacier (Windom et al., 1967).

The rapidly accumulating near shore marine sediments may also provide a useful log of the entry of solid materials, unaffected in their sea water passage to the deposits, or of soluble contaminants scavenged upon the natural sedimentary components. This possibility has received so far scant attention.

Insight into the entry rates of substances accumulated by members of the marine biosphere may be obtained by analyses upon accurately dated museum specimens. Although this technique has not been applied to a contaminant involved in marine systems, it has been most effectively used in the terrestrial dissemination of mercury compounds used as fungicidal seed dressings (Berg et al., 1966). The introduction of alkyl-mercury compounds in Sweden as fungicides in 1938 to 1940 has been recorded by the rise in the mercury content of bird feathers which increased 10 to 20 times over the pre-1940 levels. The metallo-organic mercury compounds have been extracted from the feathers of birds captured in 1961. The dispersion of mercury prior to 1940 through its use in the chlorine-alkali industry and in seed dressings as inorganic salts or as phenyl mercury compounds was not extensive enough to alter the mercury levels in the bird feathers.

To translate such findings into quantitative rates, several assumptions must be invoked. The organism must be a closed system to gains and losses of the compound in question since its death. Enrichment factors in the organism or in the parts analyzed over the environment must be known. Nonetheless, the marine museums probably hold a most impressive record of man's history in altering the seas.

Finally, measurement of the contaminant in sea water as a function of time and space can lead to introduction rates. Tatsumoto and Patterson (1963) found lead in higher concentrations in surface sea waters as opposed to samples from greater depths. On the basis of a two-box model of the oceans, they concluded that the present rate of entry of lead to the oceans is twenty-seven times greater than the rate for the Pleistocene as a result of industrial contamination, mainly lead tetraethyl combustion products. Further, they indicated that marine organisms effectively transport the lead from surface waters to the sediments and that the half-life of the common lead in the upper layers of the oceans is about seven years.

An example

DDT and other chlorinated hydrocarbons are probably the most widely disseminated man-made chemicals in the marine environment. At the present time they must be considered contaminants although there is evidence they may affect populations in natural communities. Sea water concentrations of DDT in the parts per billion range reduced the rate of photosynthesis in laboratory cultures of four species of coastal and oceanic phytoplankton (Wurster, 1968). Residues of DDT in the eggs of the Bermuda petrel were implicated in the decline of their reproductive rate (Wurster and Wingate, 1968).

High concentrations of DDT residues found in Pacific and Antarctic Ocean pelagic birds indicate that coastal areas are not the sites of ingestion and directed Risebrough and his coworkers (1968) to investigate atmospheric transport. Chlorinated hydrocarbons are known to co-distill with water and could enter the atmosphere directly. They had been detected in the atmosphere, in atmospheric dusts, and in rainwater over the continents. Windom et al. (1967) found abnormally high concentrations of talc in airborne particulate matter over the sea. The fact that talc is a carrier and diluent for pesticides suggested a link with the global dispersion of pesticides, later confirmed by the work of Risebrough et al. (1968).

These latter investigators put forth a lower limit of 0.6 tons of chlorinated hydrocarbons per year contributed to the tropical Atlantic by trade winds. The atmospheric rate is considered an underestimate inasmuch as the method of collection of the dusts fractionates against materials carried on particles of less than several microns or in the gas phase. The input of pesticides into San Francisco Bay from the San Joaquin River amounts to about 1.9 tons per year, while the Mississippi discharged about 10 tons to the Gulf of Mexico. Such rates show the relative importance of wind and river transport to the marine environment, but perhaps of greater significance indicate that the atmosphere may provide conveyance of pesticides from the continents where ocean currents and river drainage are unable to explain their presence.

CONCLUDING REMARKS

The organic effluents of civilization reaching the ocean are attaining input levels comparable to those of the oceanic community. The number of different chemicals is probably less than the very large number indicated by Dr. Blumer (1970) to arise from natural populations. Insight into the materials entering the marine environment may be gained by a survey of the production rates of organic materials and by coupling such information to chemical properties and uses. For example, the widespread utilization of the poly-chlorinated biphenyls in the plastics industry may explain their recently observed occurrences in marine organisms (Risebrough et al., 1968). Perhaps, the finding of acetone in surface sea waters, reported at these meetings by Professor Corwin (1970) may be linked to its extensive use in the chemical industry and to its volatility.

The interpretations of the occurrences and concentrations of organic materials in the marine chemical system cannot disregard potential contributions from man. Especially of concern may be the materials found in petroleum.

Finally, the spectre that these organic compounds introduced to the oceans may negatively affect ecological systems, including that occupied by man, is before us. The text-book example of an organic chemical contaminant becoming a pollutant in Minimata Bay may be either a warning or a prelude as to what can happen. Neurological disorders occurred among residents of this area in Japan following the consumption of fish and shellfish. The "Minimata Disease" took its toll among many species of animals including waterfowl. The cause of these troubles was isolated to the introduction of methyl mercury compounds, byproducts in the synthesis of acetaldehyde, in waters upstream from the Minimata Bay area (Irukayama, 1966).

DISCUSSION

NOAKES: Where did you get your figure of ten tons per year from the Gulf coast of the Mississippi?

GOLDBERG: This is a figure from Page Nicholson's paper in *Science* (Nicholson, 1967).

ROSEN: That figure is very close to right for the period at which the study was made. Some of the input happens to be my own analyses, so I know. I am not sure it is still true; I think the high level at that time scared enough people so that it has been reduced. That could be your theme, of course: we scare enough people and some of the residues will be reduced, we hope.

GOLDBERG: No, this is not my theme. My theme is that we must study this general problem and get the Washington policy makers to support research along these lines.

ROSEN: That is what I meant by scare enough people, with just cause.

ACKNOWLEDGMENTS

This work was supported by a research grant from the National Center for Air Pollution Control, Department of Health, Education, and Welfare, Public Health Service.

REFERENCES

BERG, W., A. JOHNELS, B. SJOSTRAND, and T. WESTERMARK. 1966. Mercury content in feathers of Swedish birds from the past 100 years. Oikos, *17*: 71-83.

BLUMER, M. 1970. Dissolved organic compounds in sea water. *In* D.W. Hood [ed.], Proc. Symp. Organic matter in natural waters. Occa. Pub. No. 1, Inst. Mar. Sci., Univ. Alaska, this volume.

CORWIN, J. F. 1970. Volatile organic materials in sea water. *In* D. W. Hood [ed.], Proc. Symp. Organic matter in natural waters. Occa. Pub. No. 1, Inst. Mar. Sci., Univ. Alaska, this volume.

DELANEY, A. C., MRS. A. C. DELANEY, D. W. PARKIN, J. J. GRIFFIN, E. D. GOLDBERG, and B. E. F. REIMANN. 1967. Airborne dust collected at Barbados. Geochim. Cosmochim. Acta, *31*: 885-909.

GOLDBERG, E. D. 1963. Geochronology with Pb-210, p. 121-131. *In* Radioactive dating. Intern. At. Energy Agency, Vienna.

IRUKAYAMA, K. 1966. The pollution of Minamata Bay and Minamata disease. Adv. Water Poll. Res., *3*: 153-180.

JUNGE, C. E. 1963. Air chemistry and radioactivity. Academic Press, New York and London. 382 p.

MIYAKI, Y., Y. SUGIURA, and Y. KATSURAGI. 1956. Radioactive fallout at Asahikawa, Hokkaido in April, 1955. J. Met. Soc. Japan, Ser. 2, *34*: 226-230.

NIELSEN, E. STEEMANN. 1960. Productivity of the oceans. Annu. Rev. Plant. Physiol., *11*: 341-362.

RISEBROUGH, R. W., R. J. HUGGETT, J. J. GRIFFIN, and E. D. GOLDBERG. 1968. Pesticides: transatlantic movements in the Northeast Trades. Science, *159*: 1233-1236.

TATSUMOTO, M., and C. C. PATTERSON. 1963. The concentration of common lead in sea water, p. 74-89. *In* J. Geiss and E. D. Goldberg [ed.], Earth science and meteoritics. North-Holland Publishing Co., Amsterdam.

WINDOM, H., J. GRIFFIN, and E. D. GOLDBERG. 1967. Talc in atmospheric dusts. Environ. Sci. Technol., *1*: 923-926.

WURSTER, C. F. 1968. DDT reduces photosynthesis by marine phytoplankton. Science *159*: 1474-1475.

WURSTER, C. F., and D. B. WINGATE. 1968. DDT residues and declining reproduction in the Bermuda petrel. Science, *159*: 979-981.

IDENTIFICATION OF ORGANIC MATTER IN POLLUTED WATER

A. A. Rosen
U. S. Department of the Interior
Federal Water Pollution Control Administration
Cincinnati Water Research Laboratory
4676 Columbia Parkway
Cincinnati, Ohio 45226

ABSTRACT

Organic chemical pollutants have to be identified when they exert specific adverse effects on water quality beyond the consumption of dissolved oxygen. Pollutants of this class may affect human physiology, aquatic life, industrial applications, and esthetic and recreational uses. The proportion of industrial wastes in waterborne organic matter is determined by carbon isotope assay. A general analytical system starts with the recovery of organic matter from large volumes of polluted water. The available wide array of organic analytical methods, most of which are suitable only for isolated substances in a non-aqueous environment, can then be applied to the recovered organics. Isolation of individual pollutants makes use of solubility group separations, adsorption chromatography and specific separation techniques. The most rewarding of these have proved to be the many variants of gas chromatography and spectrophotometry. When the pollutants have been identified, it is important to correlate them with the adverse effects observed in the original water sample.

INTRODUCTION

At the start of this session, it was stated that identification of organic pollutants is important in the case of those that produce specific adverse effects other than reduction of dissolved oxygen. The purpose of identification is not only to elucidate pollution effects, but also to trace contaminants to their many potential sources, in order to abate them.

ADVERSE EFFECTS OF ORGANIC MATTER

Our first concern must be with effects on human physiology, particularly with those substances which have the potential to produce cancer through exposure to or consumption of polluted water. Carcinogenic hydrocarbons have been detected in all types of waters, ranging from relatively pure ground water to heavily contaminated surface waters. Borneff and Fischer (1961, 1962) reported that surface waters heavily contaminated with wastes may contain 50 to 100 micrograms of carcinogenic hydrocarbons per cubic meter, and that in extreme cases river waters may contain 10 times this concentration. Domestic sewage has been found to contain up to 6000 micrograms of these carcinogens per cubic meter, and sewage containing industrial wastes has ranged up to 130,000 micrograms per cubic meter. Hueper and Ruchhoft (1954) detected carcinogenic capability in the organic chemicals recovered from surface water heavily contaminated with petroleum refinery wastes. These data indicate that such pollutants are widespread and can attain alarming levels. This is an open-ended problem. Substances not formerly considered as carcinogens are now being reclassified in that category which extends the possibilities of cancer-producing pollutants in surface waters, derived from industries using substances such as aromatic amines. Because extremely low concentrations of carcinogens can be hazardous, sensitive analytical capabilities are demanded that are not yet available.

Some organic chemicals are hazardous, not because of the risk of cancer but because they are toxic to warm-blooded animals in other ways. The most significant class of such organics is the pesticides. Other organics, classified as coal-tar chemicals, are also potentially toxic. An example is the o-nitrochlorobenzene that was discovered in the Mississippi River (Middleton, 1959).

Posing still another pollution problem related to human physiology are the substances causing taste and odor in drinking water and in water used in the food and beverage industries. Such substances are in general extremely persistent and have a high potential for polluting streams.

Another class of problems is caused by those organic substances that affect aquatic animal and plant life. Notorious are the pesticides which can kill fish or affect their reproduction through destruction of food organisms. Some organic chemicals produce an offensive taste in the flesh of fish in the stream. This reduces the desirability of fish for food and discourages a major recreational use of streams, sport fishing.

Organic chemicals also affect industries using surface waters. The most widely cited example of this problem is the fouling of ion-exchange resins. Less well understood is the damage to boilers and high pressure steam turbines caused by volatile, stable organic contaminants (J. K. Rice, personal communication).

Esthetic and recreational uses of water are hampered by effects other than reduction of DO, such as offensive color or foam in the water. The incidence of detergent-caused foam has been markedly reduced by product changes in the detergent industry. The most spectacular esthetic damage is a result of floating oil and tar which produce unsightly slicks, foul shorelines and damage recreational boats and other watercraft.

IDENTIFICATION PROCEDURES

Proportion of non-BOD wastes

Clearly, the more important organic substances in polluted waters are those that produce effects other than consumption of oxygen. Since these are ordinarily products derived from industrial processes based on coal, gas or petroleum, they can be distinguished as a group from the substances exerting a pronounced BOD. In the latter class are municipal wastes and the wastes from food and biological industries, consisting of recently-living vegetable and animal matter. The proportion of these two broad classes of substances can therefore be determined by an assay for the natural radioactive isotope, C^{14}, which is present in biological materials but not in the fossil raw materials of heavy chemical industry (Rosen and Rubin, 1964 and 1965). Very recently, a similar method for determining the proportion of industrial organic materials in aquatic systems has been based on the ratio of the stable isotopes C^{13}/C^{12} (Calder and Parker, 1968). This general parameter of origin of organic matter can be extremely informative in establishing a pollution control policy for a particular watershed, based on the relative abundance of industrial and municipal wastes.

Choice of analytical approach

In developing a system for identifying organic contaminants, the choice lies between developing new sensitive, specialized analytical procedures appropriate to the extremely low concentrations of specific contaminants as they exist in water, or converting the water sample into a form suitable for the commonly available methods of organic qualitative and quantitative analysis.

A few methods are sufficiently specific and sensitive to be applied directly to a water sample, for example, the determination of phenol, COD and (with the use of specialized instruments) pesticides. Other standard analytical procedures can be used after the water sample is concentrated. Such concentration has been carried out both by vacuum evaporation and by fractional freezing. Fractional freezing has made possible the identification and measurement of phenols and organic acids in surface waters (Baker, 1965).

Procedures for identifying and determining organic compounds are generally based on reactions that must be carried out in the absence of water and that lead to determinations of the physical properties of isolated pure substances and their derivatives. These methods are the most promising approach to the identification of organic contaminants in water. To use them, the contaminant must be separated from water. Isolation of the contaminants from large volumes of water yields adequate quantities of sample for conventional methodology.

Methods for recovering organic materials from water may be classified according to the quantity of water that must be processed to supply an adequate sample. A convenient method for water samples of 1 to 4000 liters is liquid-liquid extraction. In this method the water sample is equilibrated with an immiscible organic solvent. A wide range of extraction selectivity can be attained by proper choice of the polarity of solvent (ranging from aliphatic hydrocarbons to very polar liquids), pH, and inorganic salt concentration. Where the partition coefficient is not sufficiently favorable for the substance to be extracted, continuous extractors involving multiple stages of extraction are used (Hoak, 1962; Bunch and Ettinger, 1966).

To concentrate large volumes of water containing extremely low concentrations of organic matter, the carbon filter is the most useful method

(Braus et al., 1951). Organic matter is adsorbed from aqueous solution upon the active carbon and then desorbed by one or more organic solvents. The advantage of this method is the large amount of water than can be put through a small filter; the disadvantages lie in the lack of quantitative adsorption and desorption. The carbon filter, like liquid extraction, is selective. In general, non-polar compounds are strongly adsorbed and polar compounds are weakly adsorbed, e.g., petroleum is more strongly adsorbed than amino acids. Other variables control both the efficiency and selectivity of adsorption: method of activation, adsorbent particle size, flow velocity, pH, column shape and contact time.

The adsorbed organic substances are recovered by desorption with organic solvents. Desorption, the reverse of adsorption, is affected by the same variables. Furthermore, it is possible to use a variety of desorption solvents. The selectivity shown by these solvents is an additional tool in the identification process. Generally, two solvents — chloroform and ethanol — are used for extraction, yielding fractions identified as Carbon Chloroform Extract (CCE) and Carbon Alcohol Extract (CAE). Most analytical attention has been given to the CCE fraction, because this usually contains the contaminants responsible for the adverse effects mentioned at the beginning of this discussion.

General analytical separations

The organic contaminants from water as extracted from carbon or concentrated by liquid extraction usually form exceedingly complex mixtures for which there is no one satisfactory separation procedure (Middleton et al., 1959). A useful and generally applicable preliminary separation may be made on the basis of relative acidities. By extracting an ether solution of the recovered sample with water, then with dilute hydrochloric acid, then sodium bicarbonate and finally sodium hydroxide, a separation into water-soluble, basic, strongly acidic, weakly acidic and neutral fractions may be made. The portion insoluble in ether may also be recovered as an additional fraction. This method is obviously not suited to very volatile substances nor to substances unstable in water or dilute acid or base. This procedure constitutes one of the best preliminary steps in analyzing any unknown organic sample. It may be profitably teamed with steam distillation, fractional crystallization, etc. Qualitative organic tests such as the tests for nitrogen, halogen, sulphur and phosphorus may be applied to the separated fraction.

The neutral fraction consists of substances insoluble in water under both acidic and basic conditions. This group may range widely from simple aliphatic hydrocarbons to quite complex polar substances containing oxygen, nitrogen, halogen or sulphur atoms. This neutral group is therefore subdivided into classes with similar polar properties by adsorption chromatography on a column of active inorganic adsorbent, such as alumina or silica gel. This widely used procedure yields three sub-fractions of the neutral group: aliphatics, aromatics and oxys.

After concentration by separation from water, solubility group separation and adsorption chromatography, the sample has been reduced to much less complex sub-groups that are more amenable to identification and analytical procedures. If, for example, odor is being studied, the odor intensity of each fraction is determined. Results indicate which fraction contains the organic chemical responsible for odor in the sample. We thus have an excellent clue to the chemical nature of the responsible compound, for example, whether it is an aliphatic hydrocarbon or a weak acid. Substances toxic to fish can be pinpointed in the same way by bioassay procedures.

Infrared spectrophotometry is often applicable to such mixtures. This technique is routinely applied to all the fractions obtained from the carbon extracts of waters containing organic substances. The infrared often reveals useful information about the general class of substances in each fraction. In special cases it has yielded sufficient information to provide an identification, even of complex fractions. For example, infrared analysis of the oxy fraction of a carbon filter extract served to identify o-nitrochlorobenzene in the Mississippi River (Middleton, 1959). Infrared spectroscopy of the aromatic fraction of extracts recovered from the Great Lakes provided the first recognition of chlorinated insecticides as environmental pollutants in waters not known in advance to be thus polluted (Middleton and deLaporte, 1956).

SPECIALIZED IDENTIFICATION PROCEDURES

The generalized sample treatment and instrumental survey described above does not frequently result in identification of organic pollutants. Usually, the mixture of organic contaminants is far too complex to be resolved by the limited steps described. The industrial stretches of some rivers may contain numerous industries producing 500 to 1000 or more different organic products. The industries' waste streams contain not only these products but also all the corresponding raw materials and by-products of the production processes. Therefore, in most cases highly specialized analytical procedures are necessary to identify the significant organic substances. These procedures apply the principles of conventional organic analysis, namely, the isolation of individual components and the measurement of their specific properties.

Separation methods

A specific precipitation reaction is an ideal direct way to separate specific organic compounds and determine physical constants for identification. Examples are not very common. However, successful use has been made of precipitation of fatty acids as their silver salts, of organic bases in the form of chloroplatinates or tetraphenylboron derivatives, and of ketones and aldehydes in the form of various phenylhydrazine derivatives. It is possible to determine various crystalline and optical properties of these precipitates in order to arrive at an identification.

Following the group separations just described, more powerful fractionation methods are applied. The procedure that comes immediately to mind is fractional distillation. This has been used with limited success in characterizing petroleum contaminants. By far the most widely useful fractional separation procedure in studying organic contaminants in water is gas chromatography, which has fulfilled the almost impossible dream of an extremely micro fractional distillation system with extremely high fractionating efficiency. This analytical system, furthermore, produces a quantitative "distillation curve" and permits the large number of separated components to be recovered, even in quantities of less than a milligram. Furthermore, the separated components can be readily related to the more serious manifestations of pollution, by running fish toxicity or odor tests on each of the isolated fractions for example, even before any of them is chemically identified. The other chromatographic procedures, such as thin-layer and column adsorption chromatography, serve similar purposes. These also yield separated components for additional analytical testing and are, furthermore, applicable to substances which cannot be gas chromatographed. These solid chromatography procedures have been particularly widely used in the analysis of insecticides.

Specialized instrumental procedures

Gas chromatography accomplishes more than separation — it also determines unique physical properties leading to the identification of organic substances. The retention time of a given gas chromatographic peak is a clue to its identity. Several such values obtained using a variety of chromatographic columns frequently provide sufficient information to accomplish identification. More properly, when we are dealing with complex samples, it is necessary to isolate the gas chromatographic peak from one column and then to determine its retention time on other columns in order to be sure that the values obtained all apply to the same substance and therefore constitute an identification.

The variations of gas chromatography that help identify an unknown organic substance are numerous and constitute a field in themselves. Two will be discussed here. One is the combination with pyrolysis. A non-volatile sample is subjected to high temperature in an inert atmosphere and immediately injected into the gas chromatograph. The pattern of decomposition products thus obtained can sometimes be empirically correlated with the kinds of organic pollutants originally recovered. A more versatile modification is the use of multiple selective detectors. An example of an effective combination selected from the many detectors available is the simultaneous use of an electron capture detector and a sodium thermionic detector. The ratio of detector response is characteristic of every organic substance and is coupled to the characteristic retention time on the column used. This method has proved very powerful in the analysis of chlorinated insecticides (which respond primarily to the electron capture detector) and phosphorus insecticides (which respond primarily to the thermionic detector).

The infrared technique described earlier as a general survey tool is much more powerful when applied to isolated pure substances. The procedure can be adapted readily to samples of the order of 10 micrograms; in this variation it has been used with great success to identify the pesticides isolated from the tissues of poisoned fish (Boyle et al., 1966).

A number of other spectrometric methods are widely used in identifying organic matter. These include mass spectrometry, nuclear magnetic resonance and ultraviolet spectrometry. These three methods were teamed with gas chromatographic isolation and infrared spectrometry to accomplish the identification of the microbial metabolite, "geosmin," most frequently responsible for the earthy-musty odors of surface waters (Gerber, 1968). Another method in this group is fluorescence spectrometry. Both activation and emission fluorescence spectra are useful in the identification of aromatic compounds, particularly polynuclear carcinogenic hydrocarbons.

X-ray methods have not been widely used in water pollution analysis. X-ray fluorescence spectrometry is mainly applicable to the determination of inorganics. But X-ray diffractometry is eminently suitable to identification of organic substances. Since this is a measurement of crystalline properties of a solid, it can be applied in any case in which the organic analyst would ordinarily determine a melting point. However, the X-ray diffraction pattern is much more informative and specific. The method has been applied to the identification of fatty acids from sewage in the form of their silver salts and to the identification of organic bases in the form of chloroplatinates (Burttschell et al., 1957) or tetraphenylboron compounds.

Many of the organic substances in water are extremely complex in structure and cannot be identified by the more common physical procedures. One means of identifying complex biological organic matter is specific serological tests; these have been applied to identify the waste of antibiotic manufacture discharged into surface waters (Bunch and Barth, Jr., 1958). Another approach is to simplify the organic substance into a form more readily identifiable. The carbon skeleton analyzer is one way to accomplish this objective. The unknown substance is hydrogenated before gas chromatographic analysis. Complex substituent groups are removed and the molecule is converted to its saturated hydrocarbon analog. This procedure has only recently been applied to the water field. An example of its use is to distinguish between chlorinated hydrocarbons that are not separated by gas chromatography but whose corresponding hydrocarbons are separable and have characteristic retention times.

Correlation with pollutional effects

It is not practical to attempt to identify the countless individual organic substances to be found in typical polluted surface waters. The choice of substances to be identified is based on the kind and extent of their damage to water quality. Accordingly, all the separation procedures are teamed with tests for pollutional effects, such as odor and taste, fish toxicity, carcinogenicity and interference with water purification.

FUTURE RESEARCH NEEDS

The foregoing discussion emphasizes that identification succeeds best with organic matter separable into individual compounds that are relatively simple in structure and low enough in molecular weight to permit gas chromatography. The main sources of such substances are industrial wastes. To identify industrial waste organics, the chemist should be armed with knowledge about the location of industries in each watershed, the products they make, the processes they employ and the composition of the wastes they discharge. This information constitutes an industrial waste inventory.

The methodology described in this presentation is much less useful for complex, non-volatile, high molecular weight organic materials such as those in municipal waste waters and other biological wastes. This field urgently demands expanded capability. As treatment of municipal waste progresses from no treatment or minimal primary treatment to advanced tertiary treatment methods before discharge into natural waters, the need to know which organics respond and which remain untouched by each treatment becomes more important. Approaches to this problem will have to rely on the methods most commonly used in biochemical investigations: liquid and gel permeation chromatography, electrophoresis, immunodiffusion and serological and enzymatic characterization. A vast field for research is opened by these needs and the field calls for important additional professional qualification on the part of the investigators still to be recruited for the battle against water pollution.

REFERENCES

BAKER, R. A. 1965. Microchemical contaminants by freeze concentration and gas chromatography. J. Water Poll. Cont. Fed., *37*: 1164.

BORNEFF, J., and R. FISCHER. 1961. Cancerogene Substanze in Wasser und Boden. Arch. Hyg. Bakteriol., *145*: 241.

BORNEFF, J., and R. FISCHER. 1962. Cancerogene Substanzen in Wasser und Boden. Arch. Hyg. Bakteriol., *146*: 183.

BOYLE, H. W., R. H. BURTTSCHELL, and A. A. ROSEN. 1966. Infrared identification of chlorinated insecticides in tissues of poisoned fish, p. 207-218. *In* Organic pesticides in the environment. Adv. Chem. Ser. No. 60.

BRAUS, H., F. M. MIDDLETON, and G. WALTON. 1951. Organic chemical compounds in raw and filtered surface waters. Anal. Chem., *23*: 1160-1164.

BUNCH, R. L., and E. F. BARTH, JR. 1958. Serological detection of fermentation wastes. Nature, *182*: 1680.

BUNCH, R. L., and M. B. ETTINGER. 1966. A field countercurrent extractor for water pollutants, p. 93-97. *In* Proc. 20th Purdue Ind. Waste Conf., Eng. Ext. Ser. No. 118.

BURTTSCHELL, R. H., A. A. ROSEN, J. G. WELLS, and E. S. YUNGHANS. 1957. Characterization of organic contaminants of ground waters. Presented at 131st Nat. Meeting of Amer. Chem. Soc., Miami.

CALDER, J. A., and P. L. PARKER. 1968. Stable carbon isotope ratios as indices of petrochemical pollution of aquatic systems. Environ. Sci. Technol., *2*: 535-539.

GERBER, N. N. 1968. Geosmin, from microorganisms, is *trans*-1, 10-dimethyl-*trans*-9-decalol. Tetrahedron Letters, *25*: 2971.

HOAK, R. D. 1962. Recovery and identification of organics in water. Int. J. Water Poll., *6*: 521.

HUEPER, W. C., and C. C. RUCHHOFT. 1954. Carcinogenic studies of adsorbates of industrially polluted raw and finished water supplies. Arch. Ind. Hyg. Occup. Med., *9*: 488.

MIDDLETON, F. M. 1959. Report on the recovery of orthonitrochlorobenzene from the Mississippi River. U. S. Public Health Service, Dept. Health, Educ., Welfare, Cincinnati, Ohio. 12 p.

MIDDLETON, F. M., and A. V. DE LAPORTE. 1956. A study of organic contaminants in boundary waters using carbon filter techniques, Lake Huron - Lake Erie, 1953-1955. Prepared for Int. Joint Comm., United States and Canada, on boundary waters. 34 p.

MIDDLETON, F. M., A. A. ROSEN, and R. H. BURTTSCHELL. 1959. Manual for recovery and identification of organic chemicals in water. U. S. Public Health Service, Dept. Health, Educ., Welfare, Cincinnati, Ohio. 48 p.

ROSEN, A. A., and M. RUBIN. 1964. Natural carbon-14 activity of organic substances in streams. Science, *143*: 1163.

ROSEN, A. A., and M. RUBIN. 1965. Discriminating between natural and industrial pollution through carbon dating. J. Water Poll. Cont. Fed., *37*: 1302.

GENERAL DISCUSSION AFTER SESSION III

BLUMER: Can I make two remarks about pollution? One: many things which are now classified as pollutants, namely, among others, carcinogens and other hydrocarbons, are not only introduced by man into the environment, they also occur naturally and have occurred naturally since before man was present on the earth. I would like to make a plea that this is about the last chance we have to establish what the natural levels are. This we must know if a) we want to trace pollution and b) we want to know the effects of these compounds on living organisms. The second remark: it appears more and more to me that the effects of pollution occur at two entirely different levels. About one, we have a good bit of knowledge and about the other, we have none. One is the high level, and much of what Dr. Rosen has mentioned regarding the fouling of industrial water supplies and aesthetic considerations happens at this level. At much, much lower levels pollution may interfere with the reproduction and migration of organisms. Dr. Whittle will say more about this tomorrow. There is a growing conviction that pollution by a very wide range of compounds may interfere with the marine food chains, and, therefore, in a rather direct way with human nutrition. Again I want to repeat the plea that we should know much more than we do about the low level pollution effects.

ROSEN: It is for that reason that I started out by making my operational definition. I have argued with a lot of people about this, but I include in the word "pollution" effects which are not man-made, provided they have any adverse effects on man's use of this world. Your point is, of course, that you are not going to understand anything if you do not understand the baseline before it occurred.

SESSION IV. INORGANIC-ORGANIC ASSOCIATIONS IN NATURAL WATERS

Chairman: F. A. Richards
Department of Oceanography
University of Washington
Seattle, Washington 98103

In recent years it has become increasingly apparent to me as an inorganic chemist trying to understand the chemistry of the oceans that sea water does not act as a simple inorganic solution. For years we have been attempting to explain phenomena such as the apparent supersaturation of sea water with a variety of inorganic compounds, apparent non-equilibrium states, and successions in biological populations, on the basis of the total inorganic composition of sea water or the availability or non-availability of inorganic nutrients. The history of chemical oceanography has been primarily a history of inorganic, analytical chemistry, so perhaps it is not surprising that we were baffled by questions which it now becomes apparent must be answered in terms of the organic constituents of sea water. Until we began to elucidate the qualitative and quantitative organic chemistries of sea water, we simply were not looking at the right properties so the questions we asked were insoluble. I think this symposium is a good indication that we are beginning to look at the things that are important in controlling both what we have thought of as the inorganic nature of the oceans and the life cycles at sea. Although I speak as an oceanographer, I think most of the things that I am saying also apply to fresh water systems. This session addresses some of the problems that we have begun to feel intuitively can be solved only when we understand better how the organic content of sea water influences the inorganic constituents. Many phenomena may well yield to a logical explanation once the organic nature of sea water is understood. Among these phenomena are lags in plankton blooms in upwelling regions that may somehow be associated with the complexing or binding of trace metals by organic materials, the apparent supersaturation of the upper layers of the oceans with calcium carbonate, and the much higher concentrations of certain trace metals in sulfide-bearing environments than one would expect from the solubility of inorganic sulfides.

CARBONATE-ORGANIC INTERACTIONS IN SEA WATER

K.E. Chave
Department of Oceanography
University of Hawaii
2525 Correa Road
Honolulu, Hawaii 96822

Three features of the calcium carbonate-sea water system have puzzled marine geochemists for many years. These features are:

1. The supersaturation of most surface and near-surface sea waters with respect to $CaCO_3$ (Wattenberg and Timmermann, 1936; MacIntyre and Platford, 1964).
2. The complex mineralogy of shelf carbonate sediments (Land, 1967, Fig. 1).
3. The occurrence of $CaCO_3$ in pelagic sediments from all depths of the ocean (Bramlette, 1961; Smith et al., 1968).

These features of the carbonate-sea water system are indicators of disequilibrium. A solution should not remain supersaturated indefinitely. A complex of $CaCO_3$ mineral phases cannot be in equilibrium with a single aqueous phase. Deep ocean waters are undersaturated with respect to $CaCO_3$ (Buch and Gripenberg, 1932; Pytkowicz, 1965; Petersen, 1966), and carbonates should therefore be absent in deep pelagic sediments.

In the past, lack of equilibrium in the carbonate-sea water system has been generally accounted for on the basis of reaction kinetics (Cloud, 1962; Berner, 1966; Schmalz, 1967). Yet, it is easily demonstrated, using the method of Weyl (1961), or a slight modification of this method (Chave and Schmalz, 1966), that any sea water sample will equilibrate with at least the surface of any marine carbonate mineral within about one hour. Thus, the puzzling features of this natural system must be the result of something other than the slow reaction between inorganic components of the system. Recent studies of the interaction of dissolved organic molecules with carbonate minerals (Chave, 1965; Chave and Suess, 1967; Suess, 1968), appear to shed some light on the causes of this chemical disequilibrium.

Chemical interactions between skeletal carbonate minerals and sea water were reported by Chave and Schmalz (1966). It was demonstrated that the equilibrium state in the carbonate-sea water system is determined by carbonate mineralogy, particle size and the grinding history of the solid. Throughout the study, rapid equilibration was observed.

The suspended carbonate-natural sea water system was reported on by Chave (1965) and Chave and Suess (1967). These studies were undertaken with the idea that perhaps chemical equilibrium exists in a dilute suspension of fine grained solids near the ocean surface. The results indicated that this is not the case. A typical X-ray diffraction pattern for suspended minerals in Bermuda surface sea water (Fig. 1a) indicates a mixture of aragonite and a spectrum of magnesium calcites having a range of more than 10 per cent $MgCO_3$ in composition.

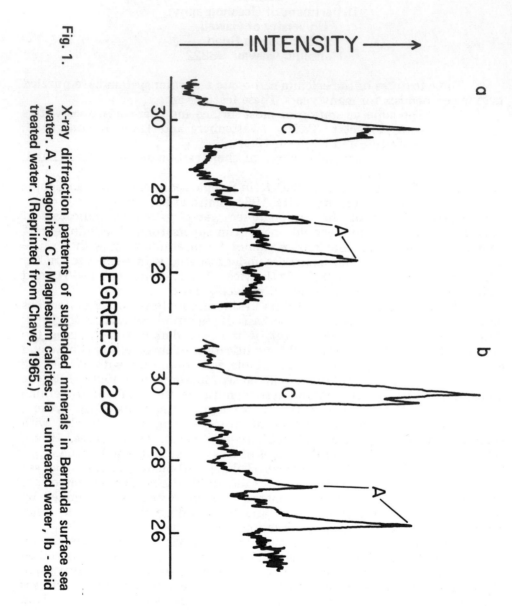

Fig. 1. X-ray diffraction patterns of suspended minerals in Bermuda surface sea water. A - Aragonite, C - Magnesium calcites. Ia - untreated water, Ib - acid treated water. (Reprinted from Chave, 1965.)

Suspended carbonate minerals, with a complex mineralogy, were found to occur in both under- and over-saturated sea water (Chave and Suess, 1967). They were found to be resistant to acid attack down to a pH of 6.0. Fig. 1b is the X-ray diffraction pattern of Bermuda suspended minerals after one hour's treatment with HCl-spiked sea water.

Suspended carbonate minerals, on microscopic examination, were observed to be coated with or enclosed in brownish, amorphous organic aggregates (Chave, 1965). The organic coatings appear to explain the lack of reactivity of the suspended particles.

During the laboratory studies of carbonate mineral-sea water interactions, it was observed that the steady state composition of the system was influenced by the solid-to-water ratio. As illustrated in Fig. 2 (from Chave and Suess, 1967), 100 ml supersaturated sea water do not react with 13 to 300 mg $CaCO_3$, react somewhat with 500 and 700 mg, and equilibrate with 1000 and 1300 mg. Dotted curve "A" indicates the lack of reaction of 300 mg $CaCO_3$, previously stirred with 100 ml sea water, stirred with 50 ml of the same sea water. It is evident that the expected 300 mg:50 ml (i.e., 600 mg:100 ml) reaction does not occur. After treatment of the same 300 mg $CaCO_3$ with hot 30% H_2O_2, the expected reaction with 50 ml of sea water takes place (dotted curve B).

The interpretation of this series of experiments is that the surface area of up to 300 mg of this specific $CaCO_3$ sample is rapidly coated with dissolved organic molecules before carbonate precipitation can take place. Large amounts of carbonate — 1000 and 1300 mg — have a large enough surface area to be essentially unaffected by the dissolved organics in 100 ml of sea water. Five hundred and 700 mg yield intermediate results. Removal of the organic coating by oxidation allows the inorganic reaction to take place.

A model of carbonate-organic association has been developed by Suess (1968). He demonstrated the rapid formation of organic monolayers and multilayers in experiments with pure surface active molecules on carbonate minerals from aqueous solutions. He also showed that carbonate-organic aggregates, similar to those seen in Nature, could be formed by stirring finely ground carbonate with filtered sea water. The carbonates apparently scavenge dissolved organics from the water.

Suess demonstrated, using methylene blue stain, that shallow water carbonate sediment particles were organically coated, and that the coatings could be removed by oxidation. Coated particles would not react with sea or interstitial waters, but oxidized particles would.

PRELIMINARY OBSERVATIONS ON CaCO₃ SUPERSATURATION IN SEA WATER

Our recent experiments indicate that dissolved organic compounds in sea water are one of the regulators of the non-skeletal precipitation of carbonate minerals. In the presence of normally occurring organics, and in the pH range of sea water, precipitation should not occur.

Our experiments involve increasing the degree of supersaturation by addition of Ca^{++} or $Co_3^{=}$ and observing reactions if and when they occur.

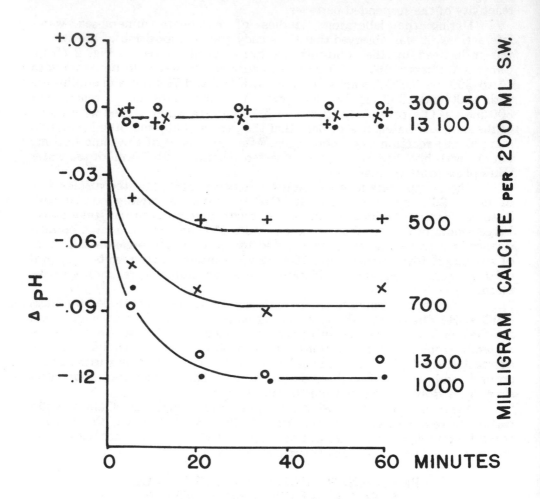

Fig. 2. Reaction of 100 ml supersaturated sea water with different amounts of CaCO₃, of constant surface area. (Reprinted from Chave and Suess, 1967.)

I. **Addition of Ca^{++}**. Addition of Ca^{++}, as 1.0 M CaCl$_2$, to increase the Ca^{++} concentration two to three times, produces a precipitate only after several days. The precipitate formed contains both gypsum and aragonite, with the ratio of the two solids varying from experiment to experiment. The first gypsum precipitated contains organic material. The pH of the Ca^{++} enriched sea water is between 7.5 and 8.0.

II. **Addition of CO$_3$$^=$**. Addition of CO$_3$$^=$, as 0.1 M Na$_2CO_3$, to increase the CO$_3$$^=$ concentration 2 or 3 times, to a pH above 9, causes precipitation of CaCO$_3$, as aragonite, after a period of time. Typical precipitation curves, expressed in terms of change in pH, are shown in Fig. 3. In these experiments the Na$_2$CO$_3$ solution is added dropwise to a 50 ml, Millipore HA-filtered sea water sample, while it is being stirred, until a pH of 9.50 is reached. Stirring is continued and the change in pH is monitored. The time for precipitation of CaCO$_3$, as indicated by a rapid pH drop, is correlated with the dissolved organic content of the water as indicated in Fig. 3 and summarized in Fig. 4.

CaCO$_3$ precipitation is preceded by precipitation of a portion of the dissolved organics in the water, presumably as calcium compounds.

The composition of the precipitate in the solution during a typical experiment is shown in Fig. 5. After the pH of the sea water was raised to 9.44 by addition of Na$_2$CO$_3$, a portion was withdrawn periodically and analyzed for CaCO$_3$ carbon and organic carbon. Organic carbon is precipitated just prior to the initiation of rapid carbonate precipitation.

Our interpretation of these experiments is that CaCO$_3$ precipitates very slowly from sea water containing normally occurring organics at normal pH's (around 8.0). Ca^{++} addition produces largely gypsum. CaCO$_3$ precipitation occurs at high pH's, but only after reactive organics have been precipitated.

If our interpretation of these data is correct, it is unlikely that CaCO$_3$ will precipitate from normal sea water, and thus, as long as the rate of addition of Ca^{++} from land is greater than the rate of uptake of Ca^{++} by organisms, the sea will remain supersaturated with CaCO$_3$.

CONCLUSIONS

Evidence has been presented that each of the three puzzling features of the geochemistry of the carbonate-sea water system — the evidence for disequilibrium — can be explained on the basis of regulation of the reactions by surface active organic molecules.

(1) Precipitation from highly supersaturated sea water occurs very slowly in the presence of dissolved organics, at sea water pH's. When these organics are removed, at higher pH's, precipitation proceeds rapidly. Precipitation does not take place on pre-existing nuclei because they are coated with organics.

(2) Complex mineralogy of shallow sediments is explained by organic coatings on mineral grains which prevent contact between the mineral and the water.

(3) Occurrence of carbonates in the deep sea is explained by the resistance of organic coatings to acid attack.

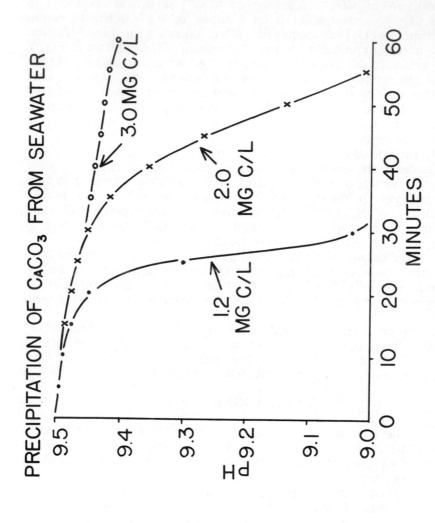

Fig. 3. Reaction of three sea water samples after the pH was raised to 9.5 by addition of 0.1 M Na_2CO_3. The precipitation of $CaCO_3$, as indicated by a rapid drop in pH, appears to be regulated by the amount of dissolved organic carbon in the sea water (mg C/liter).

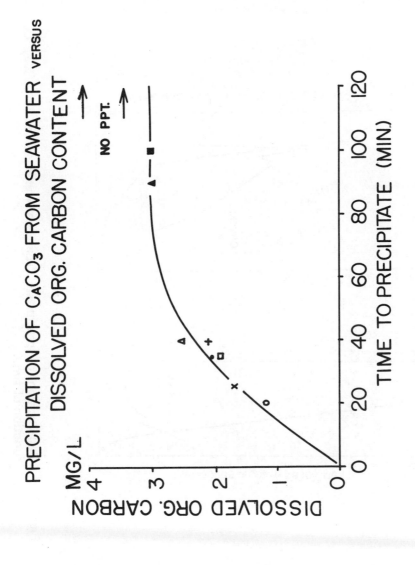

Fig. 4.

Summary of 10 precipitation experiments in which 0.1 M Na_2CO_3 was added to various sea waters to pH of 9.5. Time to precipitate is time until rapid pH drop. See Fig. 3. No precipitation ocurred in 4 hours above 3 mg/liter dissolved organic carbon.

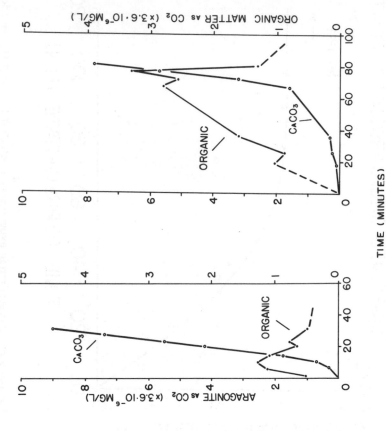

Fig. 5. Composition of precipitate from sea water spiked with Na_2 CO_3 as a function of time.

DISCUSSION

DUURSMA: First, how do you obtain littoral sea water from 1 to 30 mg C/liter? Second, since these are short-term experiments they are probably related to a first order formation of anything which can precipitate; how can you extrapolate to the long times which are normally involved in seas?

CHAVE: To answer the first question, I went all around the lab and asked for different kinds of sea water. I ran the experiments and then the dissolved organics. You get a musty old aquarium here and you get some nice stuff out of the tap, then go out in a boat, and you end up with quite a range of things. I do not know that I am extrapolating them to long periods; the most significant feature is that when calcium is added to sea water maintaining the normal pH of sea water, gypsum precipitates before carbonate, or gypsum precipitates and carbonate does not. Running the pH up to 9.5 is just a convenience to get some reaction to take place before you get tired of waiting for it. You can run them up to pH 10, or to 9.2; you get the same sort of thing, but at pH 8, you do not.

ROSEN: I have two comments. As far as how you get these waters to different organic levels, I suggest you start with the worst, varying the amounts of the same organic matter. I think that would be, in a way, more intellectually satisfying on a graph, although it is beautiful that you got such a nice, smooth curve even though you have water from different sources. My other comment concerns the phosphate. As many of you are aware, one of the important moves going on in the pollution area is to reduce the phosphate in waste effluents in order to cut down on the growth of plankton, and precipitation with lime is one of the favorite methods. I know that people who are working on this have been troubled by the fact that they are getting an unexplainable phenomenon of supersaturation and have to use much higher loadings of lime than any equilibria data indicate they would have to have. It would appear the same phenomenon applies to phosphate precipitation.

CHAVE: In regard to your first comment, Dr. Seuss, in his thesis, did a great deal of work with your compounds at different concentrations, so now we feel we are on a firm basis and can go ahead with sea water; they are all from the general area and the data suggest that as you increase or decrease the amount of total dissolved organic, you are increasing or decreasing essentially similar things.

ROSEN: I would like to prove my point from the opposite direction, i.e., remove the organic matter in successive increments rather than depend on a fortuitous circumstance of a series of waters from different sources.

MORGAN: I may have missed this, because I came a little late, but is there any evidence to tell you whether the organic matter in your system is more associated with a solid phase at the beginning, or whether it is really in operation in true solution?

CHAVE: In this experiment, the water is initially Millipore filtered, and then filtered at various later points. These are analyses of the particulate material from the sample and the ratio of carbonate to organic material, so this is material which goes from the dissolved to the particulate state.

MORGAN: So there is a high degree of association apparently between the organic matter and particulates.

HOOD: I do not think you have done this yet, but do you have any evidence indicating the speciation of organic sorption?

CHAVE: No, I do not. I think the reactions which we observed would fit very well for the general lipid material that we have heard about at this meeting and it would form insoluble calcium compounds at high pH's. It seems, from listening to you people, that lots of things would undergo this reaction.

GARRETT: Have you made any calculations from your data that would lead you to be able to guess whether this is a simple monomolecular film acting as sort of a protective colloid or whether you need something a little more bulky than that?

CHAVE: Dr. Seuss's experiments with stearic acid suggest that it is not a monolayer of stearic acid which forms on these things but rather a relatively highly hydrated calcium bicarbonate stearate compound of some sort. You get about 0.01 of the C^{14} reactivity in the water system that you do in the benzene system where you get a nice simple monolayer formed, so something more complicated is going on.

GARRETT: Something between a chemical bond and a physical bond perhaps?

CHAVE: Yes, I will buy that.

SIEBURTH: In reading the early papers by Drew (1914) on the precipitation of calcium carbonate by bacterial action, I was very skeptical. Greenfield (1963) more recently has shown that bacteria are able to precipitate calcium and magnesium salts. I can argue which is first, particularly whether the calcium is precipitating the organic matter or the organic matter is precipitating the calcium.

CHAVE: There is certainly a great deal more calcium present. If the organic material precipitated all the calcium it could, it would not materially affect the total calcium in the water.

SIEBURTH: I mean these organic aggregates like the things we see, where there is about 30% ash. Are they spontaneous or are they mediated by bacterial activity?

CHAVE: We have observed from many parts of the ocean that these contain minerals derived from land and they have the mineralogy of the shallow sediments, even hundreds of miles from shore, so this is in skeletal carbonate. I do not know that we can say that for all of the ocean.

GOLDBERG: I would like to make a couple of comments on my experience in precipitating calcium carbonate from sea water. The very simple technique involves reducing the water content by evaporation with an infrared lamp at low temperature while passing nitrogen gas through the system. The solution is allowed to reach a precipitation temperature. CO_2 is then bubbled through to produce the beautiful aragonite needles. I have not been able to do this, but it works beautifully — pure aragonite needles. I want to couple this comment with the observation made by many people who study oolites, that they contain a lot of organic matter. An inorganic precipitation of calcium carbonate from sea water may scavenge quantities of organic matter. I have always wondered why only the argument that they are biologically produced is accepted.

CHAVE: Half of the people in the world think they are biologically produced.

MITTERER: In connection with the oolites, I have just been carrying out some analyses of the organic matter and I find that it is very proteinaceous. I have sampled oolites from three different localities, and the organic matrix has a high acidic amino acid content, similar to that of shell protein.

HOOD: Have you looked at the molecular ratio of calcium carbonate in enough detail to see if the calcium might be tied up organically, or in fact, the carbon dioxide might be tied up organically?

CHAVE: Initially the material is nondescript under the microscope, as is the gypsum we get in the same way. It seems to have organic material associated with it, but it is crystallographically aragonite. As you go on and as you get up to the higher ratios, you get nice pure needles of aragonite.

HOOD: Careful analysis of the calcium and the carbonate might lead you to suspect the presence of calcium, stearate salts or organic carboxylates.

CHAVE: This is something that we have more to do on.

MENZEL: Have you ever looked for or found particles of carbonate in what you call undersaturated water? If surface waters are saturated everywhere, when this stuff goes down into the deep ocean then undersaturation must be a function of pressure. Do you really know what the effects of pressure are on this? Can you really say it is undersaturated when you take pressure into consideration?

CHAVE: We do not have the thermodynamic data on the dissociation in the carbon dioxide system.

MENZEL: My question is this. Could it be saturated?

CHAVE: I think we have various bits of evidence that somewhere down there it is undersaturated, whether it is at 4000, 3000, 6000 or 100 meters, I do not think anybody knows quite satisfactorily.

DUURSMA: Yes, they do know. They know this kind of thing from, I think, 1919, Buch's calculations in relation to solubility.

CHAVE: These are inferences from 1 atm data. We do not really have good data on the dissociation constants in the system at high pressure.

RICHARDS: I think Pytkowicz and Kester are doing this at Oregon State; I have not seen the results. I am not sure that Buch's work was experimental.

DUURSMA: Buch in the literature has done it to very high pressures (Buch and Gripenberg, 1932).

CHAVE: I think it is safe to say that it is undersaturated down there somewhere.

HOOD: Pressure would work the other way anyway, wouldn't it?

RICHARDS: That is a very complex function, Dr. Hood.

CHAVE: The solubility product goes up with pressure as the dissociation constants for carbonic acid and bicarbonate decrease with temperature. How much, we do not know.

ACKNOWLEDGMENTS

This work was supported by the Office of Naval Research Contract N00014-67-A-0387-0002.

Contribution No. 290 from the Hawaii Institute of Geophysics.

REFERENCES

BERNER, R. A. 1966. Chemical diagenesis of some modern carbonate sediments. Amer. J. Sci., *264*: 1-36.

BRAMLETTE, M. N. 1961. Pelagic sediments, p. 345-366. *In* M. Sears [ed.], Oceanography. Amer. Ass. Adv. Sci. Pub. 67.

BUCH, K., and S. D. GRIPENBERG. 1932. Ueber den Einfluss des Wasserdruckes auf pH und das Kohlensauergleichgewicht in grossern Meerestiefen. J. Cons., 7: 233-245.

CHAVE, K. E. 1965. $CaCO_3$: association of organic matter in surface sea water. Science, 148: 1723-1724.

CHAVE, K. E., and R. F. SCHMALZ. 1966. Carbonate-sea water interactions. Geochim. Cosmochim. Acta, 30: 1037-1048.

CHAVE, K. E., and E. SUESS. 1967. Suspended minerals in sea water. N.Y. Acad. Sci., Trans., 29: 991-1000.

CLOUD, P. E. 1962. Environment of $CaCO_3$ deposition west of Andros Island, Bahamas. U.S. Geol. Surv. Prof. Paper 350. 138 p.

LAND, L. S. 1967. Diagenesis of skeletal carbonates. J. Sed. Petr., 37: 914-930.

MacINTYRE, W. G., and R. F. PLATFORD. 1964. Dissolved $CaCO_3$ in the Labrador Sea. J. Fish. Res. Bd. Canada, 21: 1475-1480.

PETERSEN, M. N. 1966. Calcite: rates of dissolution in a vertical profile in the central Pacific. Science, 154: 1542-1544.

PYTKOWICZ, R. M. 1965. $CaCO_3$ saturation in the ocean. Limnol. Oceanogr., 10: 220-225.

SCHMALZ, R. F. 1967. Kinetics and diagenesis of carbonate sediments. J. Sed. Petr., 37: 60-67.

SMITH, S. V., J. A. DYGAS, and K. E. CHAVE. 1968. Distribution of $CaCO_3$ in pelagic sediments. Mar. Geol., 6: 391-400.

SUESS, E. 1968. Calcium carbonate interaction with organic compounds. Ph.D. Thesis, Lehigh University, Bethlehem, Pa.

WATTENBERG, H., and E. TIMMERMANN. 1936. Ueber die Sattigung des Seiwasser an $CaCO_3$, und die anorganogene Bildung von Kalksedimenten. Ann. D. Hydrogr. U. Mar. Meter., 23-31.

WEYL, P. K. 1961. The carbonate saturometer. J. Geol., 69: 32-44.

ORGANIC CHELATION OF ^{60}Co AND ^{65}Zn BY LEUCINE IN RELATION TO SORPTION BY SEDIMENTS

E. K. Duursma
International Laboratory of Marine Radioactivity, IAEA
Musée Océanographique
Monaco-Ville
Principality of Monaco

ABSTRACT

The sorption of ^{60}Co and ^{65}Zn, as determined for one fresh water and two marine sediments, is reduced by the addition of 10^{-3} to 10^{-2} M leucine. This reduction is almost equal to that calculated from their stability constants with leucine, if the chelation of Ca^{++}, Mg^{++} and H^+ by leucine is also taken into account.

Extrapolation of the results to sea conditions shows that no chelation of Co^{++} and Zn^{++} is possible at the μg/liter concentrations of leucine. These elements could be chelated if stronger chelating agents occur in the sea at concentrations of some tenths of a mg C/liter. This is illustrated with two examples using quinoline-2-carboxylic acid and EDTA, from which it can be concluded that specific competition between different metal complexes is very important.

INTRODUCTION

Chelation of trace metals in sea and fresh water by natural dissolved organic substances is repeatedly mentioned as a possible explanation of biological and geochemical phenomena. Evidence for the existence of the trace metal organic compounds has been found in that the metals are partly in a non-dialysable state, which state disappears after oxidation (Hood, 1966). Whether these compounds are formed by reversible processes which have a characteristic chemical equilibrium or are stable organic complexes produced by marine organisms is still a question. The fact that these Zn and Cu complexes are found in the water layers where the largest amount of decay of living material occurs may indicate the second possibility.

Duursma and Sevenhuysen (1966) tried to find some method for determining the chelation of trace metals in the sea by natural and artificial organic substances, but no significant chelation could be found. Only with added amounts of isoleucine were results obtained for Fe and Zn which could have been due to chelation.

In this paper a more recent investigation is reported in which the concurrence between chelation and sorption is used to determine the influence of chelation. The results are compared with those that can be calculated on the basis of the stability constants of leucine.

EXPERIMENTS

^{60}Co, ^{65}Zn, sediment and extra leucine were added to sea and fresh water using methods described by Duursma and Bosch (in press) to determine the distribution coefficient of sorption. (Definition of distribution coefficient:

$$K = \frac{\text{amount of metal sorbed per ml sediment, at equilibrium}}{\text{amount of metal in 1 ml solution}}).$$

1)   **Sediment:** Mediterranean sediment, off Nice, from 1000 m depth.
     Water: Sea water (Mediterranean).
     Method: Suspension technique, using 375 mg sediment/liter.
     Chelating ligand: Leucine: 0, 1.9 x 10^{-3} and 7.6 x 10^{-3} M.
     Trace metal: ^{60}Co: 0.9 to 1.0 μg Co/liter (1.5 to 1.7 x 10^{-8} M), being about 0.1 μg natural Co/liter and 0.8 to 0.9 μg added carrier Co/liter.
     Results:

Concentration leucine	Distribution coefficient
0	3.24 x 10^3
1.9 x 10^{-3} M	2.52 x 10^3
7.6 x 10^{-3} M	7.56 x 10^2

2)   **Sediment:** Pacific 18° 16′N, 131° 16′W, 5210 m depth (provided by W.R. Riedel, La Jolla, California).
     Water: Sea water (Mediterranean).
     Method: Sedimentation technique, using 40 mg sediment/liter.
     Chelating ligand: Leucine: 0, 1.52 x 10^{-3}, 3.04 x 10^{-3}, 4.56 x 10^{-3} and 6.08 x 10^{-3} M.
     Trace metals: a)^{60}Co: carrier and natural cobalt: 0.9 to 1.0 μg Co/liter (1.5 to 1.7 x 10^{-8} M);
     b)^{65}Zn: 110 μg Zn/liter (1.7 x 10^{-6} M), mainly carrier (the natural concentration is 5 μg/liter).
     Results:

Concentration leucine	Distribution coefficient ^{60}Co	^{65}Zn
0	3.8 x 10^4	8.5 x 10^3
1.52 x 10^{-3} M	1.8 x 10^4	6.7 x 10^3
3.04 x 10^{-3} M	8.5 x 10^3	4.2 x 10^3
4.56 x 10^{-3} M	5.3 x 10^3	3.0 x 10^3
6.08 x 10^{-3} M	4.0 x 10^3	2.2 x 10^3

3)   **Sediment:** Fine clay sediment from the Var River (near Nice, France).
     Water: Var River water. Ca^{++}: 1.3 x 10^{-3} M

pH = 8.18

Mg^{++}: 4.45 x 10^{-4} M

     Method: Sedimentation technique, using 40 mg sediment/liter per treatment.

Chelating ligand: Leucine: 0, 1.52×10^{-4}, 3.04×10^{-4}, 1.52×10^{-3} and 3.04×10^{-3} M/liter.

Trace metals: a)^{60}Co: 0.9 to 1.0 μg Co/liter (1.5 to 1.7×10^{-8} M), mainly carrier;

b)^{65}Zn: 110 μg Zn/liter (1.7×10^{-6} M), mainly carrier.

Results:

Concentration leucine	Distribution coefficient	
	^{60}Co	^{65}Zn
0	1.2×10^{4}	1.5×10^{4}
1.52×10^{-4} M	9.4×10^{3}	1.3×10^{4}
3.04×10^{-4} M	7.2×10^{3}	1.0×10^{4}
1.52×10^{-3} M	4.2×10^{3}	7.2×10^{3}
3.04×10^{-3} M	3.4×10^{3}	6.0×10^{3}

THEORETICAL

Basic data: Organic ligand = L

Metal (Co and Zn) = M

Sediment = S

Stability constants for leucine: (Logarithmic values) from Martell and Sillén (1964)

Co^{++} :	$K_1 = 4.5$	$K_2 = 3.6$
Zn^{++} :	$K_1 = 4.0$	$K_2 = 3.4$
Ca^{++} :	$K_1 = 1.24$	estimated from alanine
Mg^{++} :	$K_1 = 1.96$	estimated from alanine
H^{+} :	$K_1 = 9.6$	$K_2 = 2.37$

Reactions:

$$M^{++} + L^{-} \rightleftharpoons ML^{+}: K_1 = \frac{[ML^{+}]}{[M^{++}][L^{-}]} \tag{1}$$

$$ML^{+} + L^{-} \rightleftharpoons ML_2 : K_2 = \frac{[ML_2]}{[ML^{+}][L^{-}]} \tag{2}$$

$$M^{++} + S \rightleftharpoons MS: K = \frac{[MS]}{[M^{++}]} \tag{3}$$

In the experiment the distribution coefficient of sorption is measured, that is

$$K' = \frac{[MS]}{([M^{++}] + [ML^{+}] + [ML_2])} \tag{4}$$

where $K' = K$ when no leucine is added.

Calculations: From (1), (2), (3) and (4) K' can be calculated as a function of K_1, K_2 and L^{-}, being

$$\frac{1}{K'} = \frac{1}{K}(1 + K_1[L^{-}] + K_1 K_2 [L^{-}]^{2}) \tag{5}$$

where L^- is the free, not chelated, leucine concentration. The value L^- can be found from the following equations:

$$\sum_{n=0}^{n=2} [H_n L^{(1-n)-}] + \Sigma([ML^+] + 2[ML_2]) = [L_{total}] \tag{6}$$

$$[M^{++}] + [ML^+] + [ML_2] = [M_{total}] \tag{7}$$

$$pH = 8 \tag{8}$$

The expressions for the stability constants of the bivalent metals like (1) and (2), and for H^+ result in the combinations

$$K_1 = \frac{[HL]}{[H^+][L^-]} \text{ and } K_2 = \frac{[H_2 L^+]}{[H^+][HL]} \tag{9}$$

From these equations equation 10 results when the leucine concentration is 10^{-2} M.

$$-1 + 4.50 \times 10^3 [L^-] + 4.52 \times 10^5 [L^-]^2 - 6.47 \times 10^6 [L^-]^3 = 0 \tag{10}$$

L^- was graphically estimated to be 2.2×10^{-4} M. These computations were repeated for other values of L_{total}.

The same calculation was made for the Var River conditions, using the Ca, Mg and pH values determined in the third experiment.

The values derived for the free leucine (L^-) were used to calculate $\frac{1}{K}$, from formula (5).

Results: The calculated values for $\frac{1}{K}$, for Co with the two sea sediments and for Zn with Pacific sediment are given in Fig. 1, and for both metals with Var sediment in Fig. 2 (dotted lines).

In the case of Co with Mediterranean sediment two curves are also shown to illustrate the effect when the binding to leucine of either H^+ or Ca^{++}, Mg^{++} and H^+ (pointed lines) was absent.

For the Var sediment results, the calculated chelation of the leucine was mainly due to the H^+, and not to Ca^{++} and Mg^{++}.

DISCUSSION

Relatively high amounts of leucine must be added if any change in the sorption of cobalt and zinc by sediments either under sea water or fresh water conditions is to be detected. If the natural leucine concentration in sea water is taken as 0.9 to 3.8 μg/liter (6.86×10^{-9} to 2.90×10^{-8} M) (Riley and Skirrow, 1965), the effect is measurable only at concentrations of at least 10^4 times the natural concentration.

At these excess concentrations, it is striking that the calculated sorption distribution coefficients (as $\frac{1}{K}$,) agree quite well with the

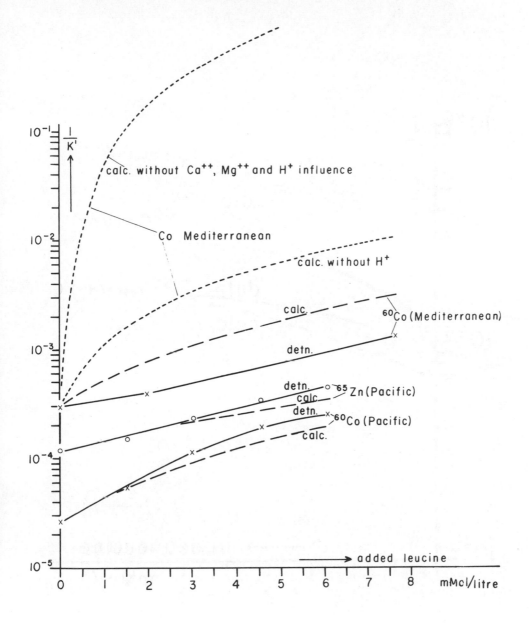

Fig. 1. Determined and calculated reciprocals of the distribution coefficients of sorption in relation to the amount of leucine added to sea water. Trace metals, Co and Zn; sediments from the Mediterranean and Pacific.

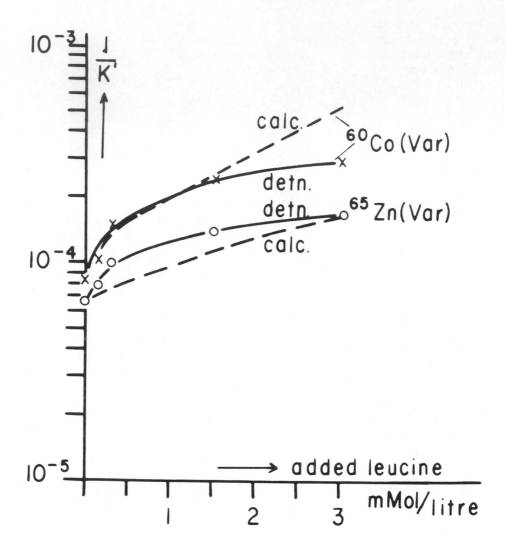

Fig. 2.   Determined and calculated reciprocals of the distribution coefficients of sorption in relation to the amount of leucine added to freshwater. Trace metals, Co and Zn; sediment from the Var River (near Nice, France).

experimentally found values, and that in general the chelation can be approached on the basis of the stability constants of the present cations and ligand. If so, it is also possible to calculate the chelation of, for example, cobalt and zinc with leucine at their natural concentrations. This can be done with the help of the same equations as (1), (2), and (6) to (10). If the mean leucine concentration is assumed to be 1.80×10^{-8} M, the "free" leucine concentration is 3.91×10^{-10} M. The rest is mainly bound to Ca^{++}, Mg^{++} and H^+. For the trace metals Co and Zn this free leucine concentration is too low for chelation to be important and it can be calculated from their stability constant expressions (1) and (2) that ZnL^+ and ZnL_2 are 3.9×10^{-6} and 9.8×10^{-3} times the Zn^{++} concentration, respectively, and that CoL^+ and CoL_2 are 1.2×10^{-5} and 4.9×10^{-2} times the Co^{++} concentration. At these low concentrations of leucine in sea water, this means almost *no* chelation of the trace metals by leucine.

It would be interesting to evaluate the results for a somewhat stronger chelating compound present in the sea at some higher concentration, for example, a few tenths or even several milligrams per liter. Envisaged are the humic compounds with melanine structures which might have chelating properties.

An example will illustrate what might happen. A calculation was made for a compound whose stability constants are known (Martell and Sillén, 1964), and whose structure relates best to humic acid structures (Riley and Skirrow, 1965). Quinoline-2-carboxylic acid was chosen and the calculations made from concentrations of 0.2 and 2.0 mg C/liter of this compound.

The results indicate that at concentrations of 0.2 to 2.0 mg C/liter the chelation of trace metals can be important although the majority of this ligand is bound to Ca and Mg (Table 1). What this suggests in regard to the dissolved organic matter in the sea, which is present at concentrations between 0.2 and 2.0 mg C/liter, is another problem, but perhaps chelating "humic" substances are present in the fraction of compounds which are resistant to bacterial breakdown.

This leads us to the point from which the problem should be investigated. Only quantitative data on the stability constants of identified compounds can give the exact information. These stability constants should be known not for only one trace metal, but for all those metals in the sea which compete in the chelation of the organic matter. This competition is very important, as is illustrated in Fig. 3, where the metal-ligand concentrations for EDTA and the major trace metals in the sea are calculated as functions of the EDTA concentration. The figure shows that at EDTA concentrations lower than 1.7×10^{-7} M (which is 0.02 mg C as EDTA/liter) there is chelation only of Fe^{+++} and Cr^{+++}. This in turn indicates that Fe^{+++} regulates the chelation of all the other metals at low concentrations, due to its relatively high stability constant. Changing the iron concentration or including activity coefficients in the calculation shifts the curves of Fig. 3 to the right or to the left without changing this fact importantly.

Clearly chelation between trace metals and dissolved organic matter in both the sea and in fresh water is not a simple process. We have much to learn about the chemical composition of the dissolved organic matter, and about their chelating stability constants in relation to all present cations.

Table 1. Calculated percentage of H^+, Ca^{++}, Mg^{++}, Co^{++} and Zn^{++} ions chelated and the percentage of ligand bound to each of the ions. The ligand (L) is quinoline-2-carboxylic acid, in concentrations of 0.2 and 2.0 mg C/liter (1.67×10^{-6} and 1.67×10^{-5} M respectively) in sea water. (Sample calcultions.)

Stability constants (logarithmic values)		Concentration in sea water (M)	Percentage chelated			
			of total cation		of total ligand	
			0.2 mg C/liter	2.0 mg C/liter	0.2 mg C/liter	2.0 mg C/liter
H^+	$K_1 = 4.92$	H^+	10^{-8}	95.0	64.7	*	
	$K_2 = 1.9$	HL		5.0	35.3	0.03	0.03
		H_2L^+		0.0	0.0	0.00	0.00
Ca^{++}	$K_1 = 1.42$	Ca^{++}	10^{-2}	100.0	100.0		
	$K_2 = 2.99$	CaL^+		1.7×10^{-3}	1.7×10^{-2}	10.13	10.09
		CaL_2		1.1×10^{-6}	1.1×10^{-4}	0.01	0.12
Mg^{++}	$K_1 = 1.37$	Mg^{++}	5.55×10^{-2}	100.0	100.0		
	$K_2 = 2.55$	MgL^+		1.5×10^{-5}	1.5×10^{-4}	50.10	49.91
		MgL_2		3.6×10^{7}	3.6×10^{-5}	0.03	0.23
Co^{++}	$K_1 = 4.49$	Co^{++}	8.5×10^{-10} (0.05 µg/liter)	30.5	0.44		
	$K_2 = 8.23$	CoL^+		0.6	0.09	3×10^{-4}	4×10^{-6}
		CoL_2		68.9	99.47	0.01	0.01
Zn^{++}	$K_1 = 5.1$	Zn^{++}	7.65×10^{-8} (5 µg/liter)	92.2	48.9		
	$K_2 = 4.6$	ZnL^+		7.6	40.5	0.33	0.18
		ZnL_2		0.2	10.6	0.02	0.09
			Free ligand:			39.34	39.34
			Total:			100.0	100.0

* The pH remains 8

-394-

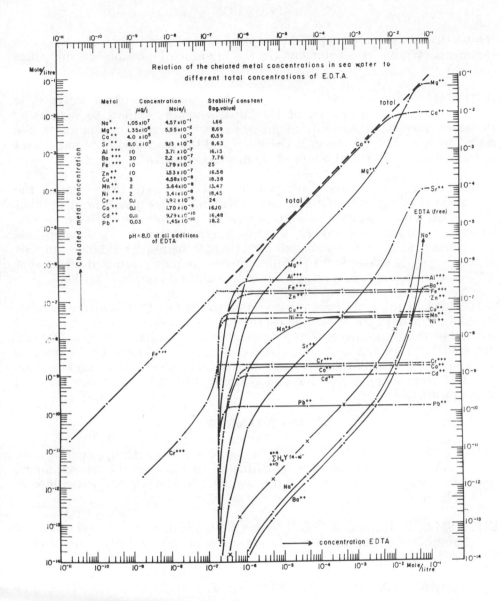

Fig. 3. Relationship of EDTA concentrations to the concentrations of metal-EDTA complexes (MY⁻⁻) in sea water as calculated from the total metal concentrations and stability constants (Y^{4-} = $EDTA^{4-}$). The metal concentrations are taken from Riley and Skirrow (1965) except for Cr^{++} (from R. Fukai, personal communication). The stability constants are from Hodgman (1961) and Flaschka (1964).

DISCUSSION

HAWKINS: I was interested in the sorption of the cobalt-leucine complex on sediments. Would you comment on the amount of possible organic trace element complex?

DUURSMA: The agreement between theory and experiment leaves little argument for the adsorption of the cobalt-leucine complex to sediments. However, very small amounts might have been adsorbed in relation to the main processes of complexing in the water and the adsorption of ionic cobalt to the sediment. The methods used are not too sensitive.

HOOD: Two papers now have pointed up the need to determine the composition of organic matter in sea water. In the first place, I noticed that zinc in all your calculations ends up being very poorly chelated by the known compounds, yet anyone who has worked with zinc in sea water finds that almost all of it is associated with organic forms. The details provide various types of evidence for it. Much of the copper is also tied up in what appears to be an organic form, yet the calculations do not lead us there.

DUURSMA: I think the problem is related to the fact that these are present. We should investigate these things that are remains of living material. I remember from your paper to the Atomic Energy Commission, that this also suggests that materials such as the non-dialyzable zinc might be the remains of living organisms. It would also be nice to know the rates of reactions, the speed of complexing. I have not talked about this but it is certainly involved in the problem.

REFERENCES

DUURSMA, E. K., and C. J. BOSCH. In press. Theoretical, experimental, and field studies concerning diffusion of radioisotopes in sediments and suspended particles of the sea. Part B. Method and experiments. Nethl. J. Sea. Res.

DUURSMA, E. K., and W. SEVENHUYSEN. 1966. Note on chelation and solubility of certain metals in sea water at different pH values. Nethl. J. Sea Res., 3: 96-106.

FLASCHKA, H. A. 1964. EDTA titrations, 2nd ed. Pergamon, London. 144 p.

HODGMAN, C. D. [ed. in chief]. 1961. Handbook of chemistry and physics, 43rd ed. The Chemical Rubber Publ. Co., Ohio. 3513 p.

HOOD, D. W. 1966. The chemistry and analysis of trace metals in sea water. A & M Project 276, Ref. 66-2F. AEC Contract No. AT-(40-1)-2799. 105 p.

MARTELL, A. E., and L. G. SILLÉN. 1964. Stability constants of metal-ion complexes. Chem. Soc. Spec. Pub. No. 17. Burlington House, London. 754 p.

RILEY, J. P., and G. SKIRROW [ed.]. 1965. Chemical oceanography, I. Academic Press, London. 712 p.

THE ENHANCED PRESERVATION OF ORGANIC MATTER IN ANOXIC MARINE ENVIRONMENTS

Francis A. Richards
Department of Oceanography
University of Washington
Seattle, Washington 98105

THE LOCATIONS STUDIED

For some years the author has been concerned with the effects of the decomposition of organic matter on the composition of sea water in marine systems with limited circulation. Specific attention has been given to basins and fiords when the circulatory replacement of oxygen is less than the biological-biochemical oxygen demand, and as a result, all the oxygen is consumed and anoxic conditions arise. Examples of such systems to be cited in this paper are the Black Sea, the Cariaco Trench, Saanich Inlet and Lake Nitinat.

The Black Sea

This is probably the largest and best known anoxic marine environment. It is approximately 2000 m deep and receives small influxes of new sea water through the Bosporus (Richards, 1965a). Oxygen disappears from depths of around 125 m in the centers of the eastern and western gyres in the sea, but the oxygen-sulfide interface deepens around the borders of the gyres. Sulfide concentrations gradually increase to maximum values, at the bottom, of around 300 μM.

The Cariaco Trench

The Cariaco Trench (Richards and Vaccaro, 1956; Richards, 1965a) is a 400 m deep depression in the Continental Shelf of the Caribbean Sea along the Venezuelan Coast. The deepest connection with the rest of the Caribbean is about 140 m, near Farallón Centinela. Oxygen disappears at 300 to 400 m, and maximum sulfide concentrations are around 30 μM at depths near 900 m.

Saanich Inlet

Saanich Inlet is a fiord about 20 km long on Vancouver Island, British Columbia, Canada. Maximum depths are around 240 m near the head of the fiord and it has a limiting sill at about 75 m separating its deep waters from those of Haro Strait. Sulfides develop in the bottom waters in spring and summer, but they are flushed out, apparently each fall, by the influx of water denser than any in the fiord. On occasion, the sulfide-bearing water has been observed at mid-depths, probably shortly after such an influx had displaced the older, sulfide-bearing water upward from the bottom and before mixing, oxidation and advection had destroyed the sulfide-bearing layer. Only 25 to 30 μM sulfide concentrations have been observed.

Lake Nitinat

Lake Nitinat, in spite of its name, is a marine fiord also on Vancouver Island, of dimensions comparable to those of Saanich Inlet, about 20 km long with maximum depths of around 200 m. However, it has a much shallower limiting sill depth, 3 to 4 m, and receives much more freshwater runoff than does Saanich Inlet. Oxygen disappears at about 30 m, and sulfides increase with depth to concentrations near bottom in the greatest depth of around 300 μM — comparable to the concentrations at 2000 m in the Black Sea. On some occasions, the sulfide concentrations near the bottom increase sharply; on the other hand, the influx of new water to the bottom is sometimes suggested by sharp decreases of sulfides near the bottom. It has been estimated that, between June and August, 1966, some 20% of the sulfide-bearing water was removed by advective and diffusive displacement (W. W. Broenkow, personal communication). However, it is probable that the fiord never flushes completely and always has sulfide-bearing water in its deeper parts.

THE EFFECTS

The disappearance of dissolved oxygen and the continued decomposition of organic matter in these systems results in processes and conditions that differ from those in oxygen-bearing environments. Some of these are as follows:

Processes

1. Denitrification, with the reduction of NO_2^- and NO_3^- ions and the formation of free N_2. An intermediate buildup of NO_2^- ions may occur. An estimate of the free nitrogen formed by this process in the Cariaco Trench was reported by Richards and Benson (1961), and the intermediate buildup of NO_2^- in Saanich Inlet has been reported by Richards (1965b). The occurrence of relatively large concentrations of nitrite in the oxygen deficient (although generally not anoxic) intermediate waters of the eastern tropical Pacific Ocean off Central America and off Peru has also been reported (Brandhorst, 1959; Wooster, 1967; Thomas, 1966) and generally attributed to denitrification.

2. Sulfate reduction to hydrogen sulfide.

3. Anaerobic fermentation, with the production of methane. Methane concentrations of about 12 μM have been observed in the Cariaco Trench, about 10 μM in the Black Sea, and up to about 70 μM in Lake Nitinat (Atkinson and Richards, 1967).

4. The accumulation of larger concentrations of the products of organic decomposition than takes place in the open ocean. Some of these products are N_2, PO_4^{3-}, silicate and NH_3. Examples are given by Richards (1965a,b).

5. The solution of metal carbonates as a result of the production of CO_2, according to the equation

$$MeCO_3 + H_2O + CO_2 = Me^{2+} + 2\ HCO_3^-,$$

resulting in increased alkalinities and alkaline earth ion chlorinity ratios.

Conditions

1. Lowered pH values. In Lake Nitinat, the pH decreases with depth to values of about 7.15. Skopintsev (1957) has reported values decreasing from more than 8.3 in the surface water to 7.72 at 2000 m in the Black Sea.

2. Decreased oxidation-reduction potentials. Measured values of oxidation-reduction potentials are of dubious significance, but Skopintsev (1957) reported a pattern of oxidation-reduction potentials in the Black Sea that one would expect to be typical of these environments. The potential is not particularly sensitive to either oxygen or sulfide concentrations as long as appreciable concentrations of either are present. As the oxygen content decreases as the depth increases, the potential gradually drops from surface values around +400 mv and then dramatically decreases in the interface zone in which oxygen disappears and sulfides appear. It then again slowly decreases as the sulfide concentrations increase, to about -200 mv at 2000 m.

3. Toxicity to organisms higher than bacteria. Gross et al. (1963) have described the occurrence of varied sediments in Saanich Inlet. Light and dark layers of diatomaceous material alternate, and C^{14} dating indicates the layers are annual. The chemical cause of the different coloration had not been elucidated, but it is reasonable to attribute it to the alternating oxidizing and reducing conditions, and to attribute the preservation of the layering to the absence of organisms to disturb the sedimentary pattern. Apparently the oxidizing phase does not persist long enough for benthic organisms to invade the bottom and disorganize the sediment.

Anoxic conditions frequently develop in areas of relatively high primary production, but they arise because of the absolute amounts of organic matter showering into them and decomposing there rather than because any critical rate is exceeded, although the rate of addition of organic matter must outbalance the rate of circulatory oxygen replacement.

The decreased oxidation-reduction potentials in these environments might lead one to expect decreased rates of oxidation of organic matter and thus its enhanced preservation. The elimination of higher organisms might also lead one to expect enhanced preservation of organic matter because of the absence of the mechanical and enzymatic breakdown of tissues and organs during feeding and digestion. Bacterial enzymes are potent in breaking down organic matter, but there is evidence that bacterial populations in the water column of anoxic environments are not very dense, although they may be on the bottom.

To evaluate the preservation of organic matter, it would be desirable to know the distribution of soluble and particulate organic matter in the water column and sediment, both quantitatively and qualitatively. A survey of the literature shows that this information is not abundant.

THE SEDIMENTS

There is little question that sediments accumulated under anoxic conditions contain more organic matter than those accumulated under oxidizing conditions. The latter generally contain 1 or 2% organic matter (of which about 50% is carbon), but much higher percentages exist in the sediments of anoxic basins and fiords. Gucluer (1962) found that the surface sediments of Saanich Inlet contained up to 7.21% organic carbon in the part of the inlet that is alternately covered by sulfide-bearing and oxygen-bearing waters, whereas values were 1 to 2% on the sill, over which the water is probably never anoxic and sulfide-bearing. In the Cariaco Trench (Richards and Vaccaro, 1956), the sediments contain up to 4% organic carbon, in contrast to the 0.5 to 1% expected for the nearby open Caribbean Sea. Another example comes from Lake Maracaibo which, although a freshwater lake, receives occasional influxes of sea water from the Gulf of Venezuela (Redfield, 1958). This water stagnates in the deep central part of the lake, where hydrogen sulfide has been observed and an inverse correlation between the oxygen content of near bottom water and the organic content of the sediment is evident. Maximum concentrations of organic carbon of more than 5% are found in the sediments in the south central part of the lake, generally corresponding to the minimum oxygen content (nil or nearly nil) of the water near the bottom.

Richards and Redfield (1954) pointed out another inverse correlation between the oxygen content of the near bottom water and the organic content of the sediments in the northwestern part of the Gulf of Mexico. In this case, maximum quantities of organic carbon and nitrogen were found in the sediments at the depths (350 to 450 m) at which the oxygen minimum zone impinges on the bottom. However, the minimum oxygen concentrations are around 2.8 ml/liter, so this is far from an anoxic condition. The authors tended to attribute the correlation to a decreased supply of oxygen to the sediments, but one wonders why the organic carbon content should respond to oxygen concentrations that probably do not represent particularly low oxidation-reduction potentials and should not eliminate benthic organisms from the bottom. Other mechanisms may be responsible.

THE WATER COLUMN

Some data on the distribution of organic carbon in the water column of the Black Sea are available. Datsko (1951) reported a gradual increase in soluble organic matter with depth accompanied by a gradual decrease in colloidal and suspended organic matter. However, the latter values are suspect because of the analytical methods used. Datsko's data also indicated a gradual decrease in the total organic carbon in the anoxic zone from about 3.4 to 3.1 mg C/liter. However, Skopintsev and Timofeeva (1960) reported that the amounts of organic carbon in the Black Sea decrease with depth from 3.7 mg/liter at 10 m to around 3.0 at the top of the sulfide zone and then to 2.3 mg/liter at 2000 m. They reported a sudden increase in the organic carbon at 200 m, the depth at which oxygen disappears and hydrogen sulfide appears. Other data reported by Skopintsev and Timofeeva (1961) suggest the enrichment of the Black Sea in organic matter. They determined the average carbon content at four stations in the Black Sea to be 3.5 mg/liter at depths of 0 to 200 m, compared with their average value of 1.5 mg/liter for the Atlantic Ocean.

Additional evidence regarding the organic content of the water column is available from total and reactive phosphorus determinations from the Cariaco Trench, Saanich Inlet, and Lake Nitinat. Richards and Vaccaro (1956) reported that the inorganic and total phosphorus content of the Cariaco Trench were not sufficiently different to indicate significant amounts of organically bound phosphorus at any depth, according to the criterion of Ketchum, Corwin and Keen (1955). These observations were corroborated by observations made in the Cariaco Trench in November, 1965, from the Research Vessel THOMAS G. THOMPSON; maximum values of total and of reactive phosphorus were not significantly different from 3 μg-atom/liter.

The amount of organic phosphorus in Saanich Inlet does appear to reach significant values in the anoxic parts of the system, as illustrated by the contrasting conditions at Sheppard Point in Saanich Inlet on September 12 and December 19, 1962 (Table 1). On the earlier date, there was a layer of sulfide-bearing water extending from 110 to 140 m and a corresponding layer of significant values of organic phosphate — values up to 0.83 μg-atom/liter. On the other hand, oxygen was present in the entire water column during the December sampling, and even though the oxygen concentrations were low — significantly lower than the concentrations in the oxygen minimum in the Northwestern Gulf of Mexico cited by Richards and Redfield (1954) — significant concentrations of organic phosphorus were absent.

Several observations of the organic matter in Lake Nitinat have been made, but they do not lead to much clarification of the question. Total and reactive phosphorus concentrations have been observed on several occasions; gravimetric estimates of the amounts of non-volatile residues of petroleum ether and ethyl acetate extracts of soluble organic matter are reported by Adams and Richards (1968); three determinations of total dissolved organic carbon were made by Dr. P. M. Williams (Adams and Richards, 1968); and a series of particulate carbon determinations was carried out by Mr. W. W. Broenkow. For comparative purposes, these have been reduced to equivalent carbon concentrations in Table 2, assuming the organic matter to be 50% carbon and also assuming that 1 atom of phosphorus bound in organic matter represents 106 atoms of carbon similarly bound.

Table 1. Dissolved oxygen, hydrogen sulfide and organic phosphorus at Sheppard Point, Saanich Inlet, on September 12, 1962, when sulfides were present in the water column and on December 19, 1962, when no sulfides were present. The organic phosphorus values are the difference between the total phosphorus and the reactive phosphorus values.

(Concentrations are expressed in terms of μg-atoms/liter.)

Depth (m)	September 12, 1962			December 19, 1962	
	Oxygen	H_2S-S	Organic phosphorus	Oxygen	Organic phosphorus
50	214	0	0.33	378	0.16
60	47	0	0.24	372	0.30
70	19	0	0.22	320	0.19
80	18	0	0.28	223	0.24
90	32	0	0.21	118	0.33
100	29	0	0.30	-	-
110	6	1.4	0.68*	-	-
120	0	18.1	0.76*	-	-
125	-	-	-	10	0.21
130	0	15.2	0.78*	-	-
135	-	-	-	8	0.21
140	0	14.2	0.47	-	-
145	-	-	-	8	0.26
150	5	0	0.53	-	-
155	-	-	-	-	0.14
160	52	0	0.83*	-	-
165	-	-	-	11	0.25
170	77	0	0.35	-	-
175	-	-	-	10	0.31
180	82	0	0.41	-	-
185	-	-	-	7	0.34
187	85	0	0.25	-	-
195	-	-	-	10	0.39
197	94	0	0.36	-	-
205	-	-	-	12	0.34
207	93	0	0.46*	-	-
215	-	-	-	3	0.26
217	100	0	0.29	-	-
225	-	-	-	8	0.53
227	104	0	0.50*	-	-
230	-	-	-	7	0.78*
231	103	0	0.52*	-	-

* The asterisks indicate significant concentrations of organic phosphorus according to the criterion of Ketchum, Corwin and Keen (1955).

Table 2. Various estimates of the organic carbon content of Lake Nitinat water, June, 1967. (Concentrations are in mg/liter, except for particulate carbon values, which are in μg/liter.)

Depth (m)	From organic phosphorus estimates[1] Station 1	2	3	4	Total dissolved organic carbon[2]	Particulate carbon[3]	From non-volatile soluble organic matter[4] Petroleum ether extracted	Ethyl acetate extracted
0	0.79	0.74	1.77	1.08				
4	2.25	3.55	2.40	0.79				
9	0.46	1.06	1.07					
12	2.43	1.41	0.25					
15	3.04	0.61	0.56					
18	1.09*	1.86	1.65					
21	1.07	1.23*	0.70					
24				0.98		149, 164, 179		
25	0.47	0.44	0.27*					
30		0.14		1.31*	1.60		0.22-0.36	
35		0.14		0.06				
40	0.02	0.10	0.90					
45		0.67						
50	0.20	0.65	0.05	0.01		118, 124, 135		
55	0.39	0.20						
60	0.08	0.62	0.67	0.10				
65	0.14	0.45						
70	0.14							
75		0.42		0.56	2.14			
80	0.14	0.72				83, 99, 117	0.53-0.85	0.33
85								
90	0.04	0.74						
95				0.52		53, 65, 86		
100		0.08						
105		0.16						
115		1.28						
125								
130								
135	0.69	0.27						
140				0.61				
150	0.08					50, 55, 61		
160								
175	0.79				1.42		0.56-0.90	0.33
180						48, 68, 82		
190	2.36							
196	1.86							

[1] The total phosphorus value minus the inorganic phosphate value, converted to equivalent carbon values using the atomic ratio C:P=106:1. * The asterisks mark the shallowest sample from sulfide-bearing waters. The underscored values are significant, according to the criterion of Ketchum, Corwin and Keen (1955).

[2] Determined by D. P. M. Williams (Adams and Richards, 1968).

[3] Determined by Mr. W. W. Broenkow. The range and average of four determinations are given.

[4] From Adams and Richards (1968).

The above cited observations do not suggest that there is any spectacular increase in the organic content of the water column accompanying the advent of anoxic conditions. On the contrary, it appears that in the Black Sea there is a decrease in the total organic carbon with depth. The Lake Nitinat data suggest that the minimum organic phosphorus concentrations appear 30 to 40 m below the oxygen-sulfide interface. However, the apparent increases in organic phosphorus in the deep water of Lake Nitinat and in the sulfide-bearing water of Saanich Inlet observed in September, 1962 (Table 1), are not corroborated by either the data on soluble, non-volatile organic matter or the data on total organic carbon in Lake Nitinat. The apparent increase in organic phosphorus in the sulfide-bearing layer of Sheppard Point, Saanich Inlet, and in the deep water of Lake Nitinat seems to be inconsistent with the lowered phosphorus content of the sediments in the central part of Lake Maracaibo reported by Redfield (1958), and no such increase is suggested by the phosphorus data from the Cariaco Trench. The Saanich Inlet and Lake Nitinat data may reflect abnormal phosphorus content of the organic material, or they may simply reflect larger absolute amounts of organic matter near the bottom in Lake Nitinat and in the sulfide-bearing water of Saanich Inlet.

Data for comparing the amounts of organic matter in the water column of anoxic systems with that in otherwise comparable oxygen-bearing systems are lacking. However, numerous data on the soluble and particulate organic matter in the open ocean are available; the papers of Duursma (1965) and of Menzel (1967) and Menzel and Ryther (1968) are good examples. They cite evidence from the southwest Atlantic, the Sargasso Sea, the Pacific off Ecuador, and the North Sea indicating that maximum quantities of particulate organic carbon do not exceed about 0.1 mg/liter in the open ocean. Maximum quantities of soluble organic carbon were found by Duursma to approximate 1.8 mg/liter; at the locations cited by Menzel and by Menzel and Ryther, maximum quantities of soluble organic carbon were on the order of 1.0 mg/liter. The Black Sea data gathered by Skopintsev and Timofeeva (1960) and Datsko (1951) suggest that the total organic carbon content there is of the order of 3 mg/liter, while our data from Saanich Inlet and Lake Nitinat indicate 2 to 2.5 mg of soluble organic carbon per liter and about 0.2 mg/liter of particulate organic carbon in Lake Nitinat.

Thus, the anoxic environments from which we have data appear to have 2 to 3 times the concentrations of both soluble and particulate organic carbon reported by Duursma and Menzel. However, the environments are *not* otherwise comparable and the higher quantities cannot definitely be attributed to enhanced preservation of organic matter under anoxic conditions.

QUALITATIVE DIFFERENCES

There is some evidence that the organic matter in solution in anoxic systems differs qualitatively from that in oxygen-bearing systems. Adams and Richards (1968) report chromatographic evidence that the polarity of compounds extracted from Lake Nitinat water with petroleum ether and ethyl acetate decreased with depth in the anoxic zone, and the elemental composition of the material increased in its ratio of carbon and hydrogen to the other elements (Table 3). Their techniques resulted in the loss of volatile components (the extracts were evaporated under a nitrogen stream), but none the less, qualitative spot tests and thin layer chromatography indicated the presence of the organic sulfhydryl (-SH) group in extracts of the anoxic waters, so it is probable that there are mercaptans in solution in the fiord. The sediments in all these environments contain large quantities of chlorophyll degradation products.

It should be noted that sulfide-bearing sea waters also generally contain relatively large amounts of methane (Atkinson and Richards, 1967), but the methane is apparently produced by anaerobic fermentation, so its presence suggests the decomposition, rather than the preservation, of more complex organic matter.

CONCLUSIONS

1. There is no clear-cut evidence that the preservation of organic matter is enhanced by anoxic conditions in marine environments.

2. The greater quantities of organic matter in the sediments underlying anoxic sea waters may well represent faster rates of sedimentation and accumulation, rather than slower rates of organic decomposition.

3. The relatively large concentrations of organic matter in the waters of the Black Sea and Lake Nitinat may similarly represent different dynamic equilibria among primary production, settling rates and rates of organic decomposition than prevail in the open ocean systems reported by Duursma (1965), Menzel (1967) and Menzel and Ryther (1968).

DISCUSSION

DUURSMA: Have you any evidence of the results Datsko reported for particulate carbon? He determined particulate carbon by precipitation with aluminum hydroxide. He put aluminum chloride in the water and called the precipitate particulate carbon. It looks like he extracted with aluminum hydroxide like other people have with iron hydroxide. Do you have any evidence of whether these values are good?

RICHARDS: No, the only evidence I have is that they seem to be out of line with everything else that I could find. They were so much higher.

DUURSMA: I do not think the methods they used to determine carbon are very good either. The results are high.

RICHARDS: They got appreciably higher soluble carbon values than Skopintsev and Timofeeva.

Table 3. Carbon and hydrogen content of petroleum ether and ethyl acetate extracts of dissolved organic matter from Lake Nitinat, December 1965*.

Depth	Petroleum ether extracts			Ethyl acetate extracts		
	C (%)	H (%)	C+H (%)	C (%)	H (%)	C+H (%)
30	31.6	7.4	38.0			
75	47.3	10.7	58.0	27.1	8.7	35.8
175	63.1	14.1	77.5	48.8	9.8	58.6

* From Adams and Richards (1968).

CHRISTMAN: Did I understand you to say that you had chromatographic evidence of organic sulfhydryl groups in the deep waters? Could you comment on that a little more and maybe on whether this was a major component or minor component?

RICHARDS: I do not think it was a major component. The spots matched up, though, with some known mercaptans. Adams used some spot tests, too.

MORITA: You talked about methane coming from fermentation and yet you said the concentration of microbes was very low. What physiological types were you looking for?

RICHARDS: We never looked for types. I said they were probably low in the water column. We have never done any bacteriology in the systems. I am sorry; I wish we had. You are certainly welcome to come along on any of our cruises and do it.

JONES: André Cobet and I have recovered methane bacteria from the Cariaco Trench. We have not reported it yet.

RICHARDS: From the water column or the sediments?

JONES: From the water column. We have the data on this, we just have not gotten around to publishing it yet.

RICHARDS: We are pretty sure that the methane in Lake Nitinat is formed in the sediments, and diffuses upward. But I don't know about the Cariaco; it is quite a different system.

MENZEL: Does the water have to go truly anoxic before nitrate starts to be removed?

RICHARDS: I cannot say definitely. I am pretty sure that you have to have very low concentrations of dissolved oxygen before nitrogen starts to be released, but the data that I have now are not conclusive. One of my students is working on nitrate reductase activity, and we hope to be able to answer this question.

MORITA: Nitrate reduction can take place in the presence of oxygen in a microbial system.

RICHARDS: What sort of oxygen pressures?

MORITA: I do not remember the data, but I do know that it can take place in the presence of oxygen.

RICHARDS: I have seen some figures from the sewage people and they say they get denitrification at 10% oxygen saturation, but I think this was a bulk oxygen concentration, rather than the concentration in the micro-environment.

ACKNOWLEDGMENTS

Contribution No. 465 from the Department of Oceanography, University of Washington.

Studies of anoxic environments have been carried out at the University of Washington with the support of National Science Foundation Grant GA 644.

The author is indebted to M. L. Healy, W. W. Broenkow, J. D. Cline, R. C. Dugdale, L. K. Atkinson and D. D. Adams for many helpful discussions and for technical assistance.

REFERENCES

ADAMS, D. D., and F. A. RICHARDS. 1968. Dissolved organic matter in an anoxic fiord with special reference to the presence of mercaptans. Deep-Sea Res., *15*: 471-481.

ATKINSON, L. P., and F. A. RICHARDS. 1967. The occurrence and distribution of methane in the marine environment. Deep-Sea Res., *14*: 673-684.

BRANDHORST, W. 1959. Nitrification and denitrification in the eastern tropical North Pacific. J. Cons., *25*: 3-20.

DATSKO, V. G. 1951. Vertical distribution of organic matter in the Black Sea [In Russian]. Dokl. Akad. Nauk SSSR, 77: 1059-1062.

DUURSMA, E. K. 1965. The dissolved organic constituents of sea water, p. 433-475. *In* J. P. Riley and G. Skirrow [ed.], Chemical oceanography. Academic Press, London.

GROSS, M. G., S. M. GUCLUER, J. S. CREAGER, and W. A. DAWSON. 1963. Varved marine sediments in a stagnant fiord. Science, *141*: 918-919.

GUCLUER, S. M. 1962. Recent sediment in Saanich Inlet, British Columbia. M.S. Thesis, Univ. Washington, Seattle. 119 p.

KETCHUM, B. H., N. CORWIN, and D. J. KEEN. 1955. The significance of organic phosphorus determinations in ocean waters. Deep-Sea Res., *2*: 172-181.

MENZEL, D. W. 1967. Particulate organic carbon in the deep sea. Deep-Sea Res., *14*: 229-238.

MENZEL, D. W., and J. H. RYTHER. 1968. Organic carbon and the oxygen minimum in the South Atlantic Ocean. Deep-Sea Res., *15*: 327-337.

REDFIELD, A. C. 1958. Preludes to the entrapment of organic matter in the sediments of Lake Maracaibo. *In* Habitat of oil. Amer. Ass. Petroleum Geol., Tulsa, Okla.

RICHARDS, F. A. 1965a. Anoxic basins and fiords, p. 611-645. *In* J. P. Riley and G. Skirrow [ed.], Chemical oceanography. Academic Press, London.

RICHARDS, F. A. 1965b. Chemical observations in some anoxic, sulfide-bearing basins and fjords, p. 215-243. Proc. 2nd Intern. Water Poll. Res. Conf., Tokyo, 1964.

RICHARDS, F. A., and B. B. BENSON. 1961. Nitrogen/argon and nitrogen isotope ratios in two anaerobic environments, the Cariaco Trench in the Caribbean Sea and Dramsfjord, Norway. Deep-Sea Res., 7: 254-264.

RICHARDS, F. A., and A. C. REDFIELD. 1954. A correlation between the oxygen content of sea water and the organic content of marine sediments. Deep-Sea Res., *1*: 279-281.

RICHARDS, F. A., and R. F. VACCARO. 1956. The Cariaco Trench, an anaerobic basin in the Caribbean Sea. Deep-Sea Res., *3*: 214-228.

SKOPINTSEV, B. A. 1957. The study of redox potential of the Black Sea waters [In Russian]. Gidrokhim. Materialy, *27*: 21-37.

SKOPINTSEV, B. A., and S. N. TIMOFEEVA. 1960. The organic carbon in the waters of the northern part of the Black Sea [In Russian]. Dokl. Akad. Nauk SSSR, *134*: 688-690.

SKOPINTSEV, B. A., and S. N. TIMOFEEVA. 1961. New data on the content of total organic carbon in waters of the Atlantic and Black Sea [In Russian]. Pervichnaya Produktsiya Morei i Vnutr. Vod, *1961*: 60-66.

THOMAS, W. H. 1966. On denitrification in the northeastern tropical Pacific Ocean. Deep-Sea Res., *13*: 1109-1114.

WOOSTER, W. D. 1967. Further observations on the secondary nitrite maximum in the northern equatorial Pacific. J. Mar. Res., *25*: 154-166.

INFLUENCE OF ORGANIC MATTER ON INORGANIC PRECIPITATION

Y. Kitano, N. Kanamori and A. Tokuyama
Water Research Laboratory, Faculty of Science
Nagoya University
Chikusa-ku
Nagoya, Japan

ABSTRACT

Carbonates were precipitated in the laboratory from solutions chemically similar to those in which marine carbonate skeletons are formed. In the parent solution, calcium bicarbonate was varied by adding the chlorides of minor elements, sodium chloride, magnesium chloride and organic compounds in various proportions. Mg poor calcite, aragonite and Mg rich calcite were precipitated. The crystal form and minor element constituents of carbonates prepared in the laboratory were determined and compared with those of marine skeletal materials. The influence of organic substances on crystal form and the distribution of minor elements in marine carbonate skeletons is discussed.

INTRODUCTION

Carbonate sediments are an important geochemical material. These sediments are abundant and widely distributed. They result from the accumulation of carbonate fossils of marine animals. These sediments yield information regarding many important geochemical subjects such as the volume and chemical composition of primeval sea water and changes in the chemical composition of sea water during the past hundred million years (Rubey, 1955, 1964; Kitano, 1968); the role of carbonate sediments in the geochemical balance of chemical elements (Mackenzie and Garrels, 1966; Kramer, 1965; Holland, 1965; Kitano, 1967a); the stable pH value of today's sea water (Hindman, 1943; Weyl, 1961); the activity coefficients of dissolved calcium, carbonate and bicarbonate in sea water determined on the basis of the solubility of calcium carbonate and the chemical meaning of these activity coefficients (Garrels et al., 1961; Garrels and Thompson, 1962; Berner, 1965).

The physico-chemical analysis of carbonates has been fruitful. The paleo-temperature and paleo-salinity of sea water have been determined by analysis of the crystal form of marine carbonates (Lowenstam, 1954; Dodd, 1963, 1966). Data regarding the paleo-chemical composition and paleo-temperature of sea water have come from studies of the concentration of minor elements in marine carbonates (Odum, 1951; Chave, 1954; Pilkey and Hower, 1960; Pilkey and Goodwell, 1963; Lowenstam, 1961, 1963). The paleo-temperature of sea water has also been calculated on the basis of the O^{18}/O^{16} ratio of marine carbonates (Urey et al., 1951; Epstein et al., 1951). The age of carbonate sediments has been determined using C^{14}/C^{12}, Io/U^{234} or Pa^{231}/U^{235} tests of the sediments.

These and related studies involve two areas of investigation: (1) factors controlling the formation of carbonates of the various crystal forms observed in marine biological systems and (2) factors controlling the concentration of minor elements in carbonates of marine biological systems. Either of two research approaches can be used. The first, field observation, involves analysis of the crystal form and minor element distribution of marine carbonate skeletons and of the environmental conditions under which the skeletons were formed. A determination of the relationship among these variables must then be made. The second approach is laboratory study of the factors influencing the formation of carbonates of various crystal forms and the distribution of minor elements.

The present authors have employed the second approach in studies of the factors controlling crystal formation and the distribution of minor elements in carbonate sediments. Carbonates were precipitated from the simplest solutions that closely resemble the environment in which marine carbonate skeletons are formed. Crystal forms and minor element constituents of carbonates precipitated in the laboratory were determined and compared with those of marine skeletal materials.

It was important to use the simplest solution which is chemically similar to the medium in which calcification occurs in marine biological systems. The parent solution had to contain the inorganic materials present in sea water and the organic materials present in the body fluid of calcareous marine organisms. Although the presence of enzymes such as carbonic anhydrase in such a system is also to be considered (Kitano, 1964; Kitano and Hood, 1965), in this case the inorganic and organic materials were added but enzymes were not included in the parent medium.

The rate of carbonate precipitation was controlled by changing the rate of escape of carbon dioxide from the solution mechanically.

Organic materials added to the parent solution in the laboratory were known to be available in the parent medium of the marine biological system and to influence calcification through interaction with calcium or minor elements.

Crystal formation and minor element distribution phenomena which are seldom observed in inorganic systems but are common in marine biological systems were considered to be the result of the presence of organic materials in the parent medium.

An homogeneous precipitation reaction was used for calcium carbonate formation in the laboratory. Calcium carbonate was precipitated from a calcium bicarbonate solution from which carbon dioxide gas escaped into the atmosphere. This reaction was chosen because the calcium bicarbonate solution does not contain any material other than calcium ions, carbonates and water (Kitano, 1962a and b).

This paper reports briefly our experimental results concerning the influence of various organic materials on the form of crystal which forms. The minor element composition of skeletal carbonates is then reported in detail.

CRYSTAL FORM

Field observations

Most sedimentary carbonates are derived from the skeletons of calcareous marine organisms. These skeletons are composed of minerals, Mg poor calcite, Mg rich calcite and aragonite. Magnesium carbonate in skeletal calcites is present as a solid solution between calcite and dolomite (Chave, 1952; Kitano and Furutsu, 1959). Mg rich calcite and aragonite are unstable relative to Mg poor calcite at low temperatures and pressures (Chave et al., 1962; Jansen and Kitano, 1963). Mg rich calcite and Mg poor calcite are completely different crystals although they have the same calcitic lattice configuration.

The carbonate crystal forms in the skeletons of three representative groups of marine calcareous organisms were observed (Fig. 1, Kitano, 1964): (a) organisms which secrete only skeletal parts composed of aragonite through a temperature range; (b) organisms which form calcite through a temperature range. With increasing sea water temperature, the concentration of magnesium carbonate in the calcite increases. The rate of increase in magnesium carbonate content with temperature varies with the phylogenetic level of the organisms. With increasing concentration of magnesium ions in sea water, the magnesium carbonate content of precipitated Mg rich calcite increases (Pilkey and Hower, 1960; Pilkey and Goodwell, 1963; Lowenstam, 1963); (c) organisms which deposit calcite in one portion and aragonite in another portion of their skeletons. With increasing sea water temperature, the proportion of aragonite increases, and the magnesium carbonate content of the calcite portion increases.

Laboratory results

The influence of various inorganic ions and compounds on crystallization of polymorphic forms of calcium carbonate has been reported (Kitano et al., 1962; Kitano and Hood, 1962; Kitano and Kanamori, 1966). The earlier work indicates that considering their concentration in sea water, the inorganic ions likely to influence marine biological systems are Na^+, Mg^{2+}, Cl^-, SO_4^{2-} and HCO_3^- (Fig. 2). The laboratory results indicate that magnesium ions have the greatest influence on crystallization of calcium carbonate and favor precipitation of aragonite (Kitano, 1964). The proportion of aragonite increases with increasing temperature as observed in skeletons (Kitano, 1962b).

Kitano and Hood (1965) reported on the influence of organic materials in a parent solution on the crystalline structure of precipitated carbonate (Fig. 3). Calcium bicarbonate, organic material and magnesium chloride solutions were mixed in various proportions in an Erlenmeyer flask, plugged with cotton and allowed to stand at constant temperature for 2 to 8 weeks. The rate constants in the first order reaction were calculated (Fig. 4).

Laboratory results indicate the organic compounds such as citrate, malate, pyruvate and glycogen form complexes with calcium ions, reduce the

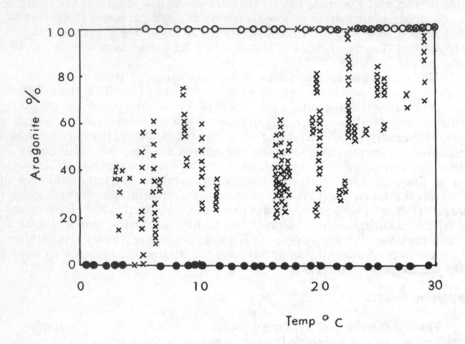

Fig. 1. A plot of per cent aragonite versus environmental temperature in skeletons of marine calcareous organisms.

●: Foraminifera, Sponge, Echinoderms, Asteroid, Ophiursid, Crinoid, Crustacean, Barnacle, Alcyonarian Coral, Pelagic Algae, Brackipod, etc.;

○: Madreporian Coral, Gastropod, Pelecypod, Bryozoa, Benthonic Algae, Annelid, etc.;

X: Serpulidae, Schizoporella, Mytilus, Littorina, Pelecypod, Annelid, Gastropod, Bryozoa, etc.

(Reprinted from Kitano, 1964.)

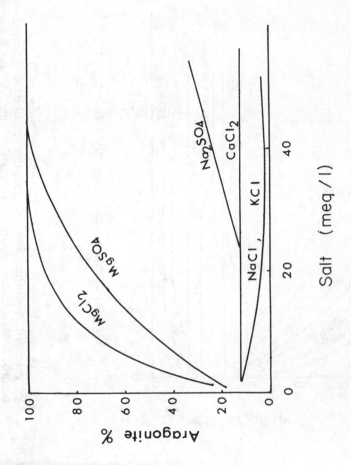

Fig. 2.   Influence of salt in calcium bicarbonate mother solution on the type of calcium carbonate crystal formed (28 ± 3 C).

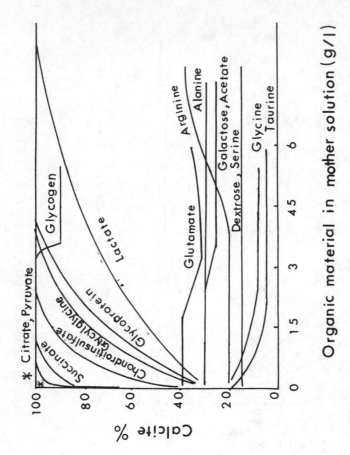

Fig. 3.   Polymorphic composition of calcium carbonate formed from calcium bicarbonate solution containing organic material and magnesium chloride (27 ± 2 C).

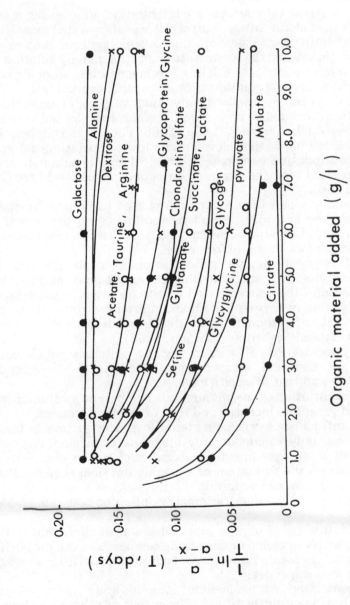

Fig. 4. Rate constant in the reaction: $Ca(HCO_3)_2 \longrightarrow CaCO_3 + CO_2 \uparrow + H_2O$ in presence of specific organic compounds (27 ± 2 C).

rate of carbonate precipitation and favor the formation of the stable forms, calcite, even in the presence of magnesium ions which greatly hinder calcite formation. On the other hand, compounds such as galactose and dextrose have little effect on the rate of carbonate precipitation (Kitano and Hood, 1965). Kitano and Kanamori (1966) showed that sodium citrate or malate favors formation of Mg rich calcite from a calcium bicarbonate solution, probably by complexing calcium ions, reducing the precipitation rate, helping to form a stable calcitic lattice configuration and causing a capture of magnesium in the calcitic lattice. Further, it was shown that increasing the concentration of both magnesium ions and organic material such as citrate and malate and increasing the temperature of the parent solution cause formation of a magnesium richer calcite. The magnesium carbonate content differs with the kind and the concentration of organic compounds.

Mg rich calcite was synthesized only under very high temperature and pressure conditions or under very specific conditions in the absence of organic compounds (Harker and Tuttle, 1955; Glover and Sippel, 1967). However, its synthesis has been achieved under low temperature and pressure conditions by precipitating carbonate from a calcium bicarbonate solution containing magnesium ions and organic compounds mentioned here (Kitano and Kanamori, 1966).

Organic compounds which reduce the rate of carbonate precipitation to a moderate degree have only a moderate influence on the crystal form. Their influences vary. Chondroitin sulfate, succinate and lactate favor calcite formation; taurine favors aragonite formation.

These data suggest that the major factors controlling crystal forms found in marine biological systems are the concentration of magnesium ions in the parent medium, the concentration of certain organic materials which complex calcium ions in a parent medium, the temperature of the parent medium and the rate of carbonate deposition in relation to the presence of enzymes such as carbonic anhydrase (Kitano, 1964).

As the concentration of certain organic materials which complex calcium ions increases and temperature decreases, the proportion of aragonite decreases and that of calcite increases.

As the concentration of magnesium ions in a parent medium increases, the proportion of aragonite increases and that of calcite decreases.

When the influence of organic material is greater or smaller than that of magnesium ions, only calcite or only aragonite is formed, respectively. The formation of a stronger organic material-calcium ion complex in the parent medium causes the formation of a magnesium richer calcite. Further, as temperature and the concentration of magnesium ions in the parent solution increases, the magnesium carbonate content of precipitated Mg rich calcites increases.

When the influence of organic material is almost equivalent to that of magnesium ions, with increasing or decreasing temperature the proportion of calcite decreases or increases respectively and the proportion of aragonite increases or decreases respectively.

The concentration of magnesium ions in body fluids of marine calcareous organisms seems little different from that of other organisms.

If the term "biological species" in the discussion of field observations is exchanged for the term "kind and concentration of organic material," the observed facts are completely in accord with the results of the laboratory experiments.

Only the presence of certain organic materials accomplishes formation of carbonate crystals observed in marine biological systems. This emphasizes the important role of organic material in the formation of crystals found in skeletal carbonates.

MINOR ELEMENT DISTRIBUTION

Field observations

From observed relationships between minor element distribution in calcareous skeletons of marine organisms and the physico-chemical environment in which the skeletons were formed, factors controlling the distribution of minor elements such as magnesium and strontium were considered to be: (a) the mineralogy of calcium carbonate; (b) biological species; (c) the temperature of the sea water in which the calcareous organisms lived; and (d) the concentration of minor elements in sea water in which the skeletons were formed (Chave, 1954; Pilkey and Goodwell, 1963; Lowenstam, 1963). Factors (a) and (b) are related. The influence of factors (a), (c) and (d) on minor element distribution is complex and dependent on the species of marine calcareous organisms involved.

To determine the importance of the factors observed, the distribution of minor elements in the solution and the precipitate formed in the solution had to be known. That is, the distribution coefficients of minor elements between solid and liquid phases had to be measured. To accomplish this, materials which seem to influence the crystallization of carbonate in biological systems were added successively to the calcium bicarbonate solution containing minor elements. The solution was stirred and carbonate precipitated with the escape of carbon dioxide gas from the solution.

During carbonate precipitation, the calcium and minor element dissolved in the filtrate of the solution were determined. The distribution coefficient was calculated by the following equations. If equilibrium is maintained between the liquid and crystalline phases, equation (1) is used to calculate the apparent distribution coefficient K_{Me}^{S}:

$$K_{Me}^{S} = \frac{M_{MeCO_3}^{S}}{M_{CaCO_3}^{S}} \frac{M_{Me}^{L}}{M_{Ca}^{L}} \tag{1}$$

where $M_{MeCO_3}^{S}$, $M_{CaCO_3}^{S}$, M_{Me}^{L} and M_{Ca}^{L} denote the concentrations of minor element and calcium in the crystalline phase and the concentrations of minor element (II) and calcium (III) dissolved in solution.

If equilibrium is maintained only between solution and the surface of the crystalline phase in contact with the solution, according to Doerner and Hoskins (1925) the apparent distribution coefficient K_{Me}^S can be written:

$$K_{Me}^S = \log \left(\frac{M_{Me}^L, \text{initial}}{M_{Me}^L, \text{final}} \right) \bigg/ \log \left(\frac{M_{Ca}^L, \text{initial}}{M_{Ca}^L, \text{final}} \right) \qquad (2)$$

A constant value of K_{Me}^S calculated from equation (1) indicates that complete equilibrium has been established between solution and precipitate. A constant value of K_{Me}^S calculated from equation (2) indicates that equilibrium has been maintained only between the solution and the surface of the precipitate.

The apparent distribution coefficient K_{Me}^S (equation 1) can be written:

$$K_{Me}^S = \frac{M_{MeCO_3}^S}{M_{CaCO_3}^S} \cdot \frac{M_{Ca}^L}{M_{Me}^L}$$

$$= \frac{\lambda_{CaCO_3}^S}{\lambda_{MeCO_3}^S} \cdot \frac{A_{MeCO_3}^S}{A_{CaCO_3}^S} \cdot \frac{\gamma_{Me}^L}{\gamma_{Ca}^L} \cdot \frac{A_{Ca}^L}{A_{Me}^L}$$

$$= \frac{\lambda_{CaCO_3}^S}{\lambda_{MeCO_3}^S} \cdot \frac{\gamma_{Me}^L}{\gamma_{Ca}^L} \cdot \frac{S_{CaCO_3}^o}{S_{MeCO_3}^o} \qquad (3)$$

where $M_{CaCO_3}^S$, $M_{MeCO_3}^S$, M_{Ca}^L and M_{Me}^L respectively denote the concentrations of $CaCO_3$ $MeCO_3$ in the crystalline phase, dissolved calcium and minor element in solution; $\lambda_{CaCO_3}^S$, $\lambda_{MeCO_3}^S$, γ_{Ca}^L and γ_{Me}^L denote the activity coefficients of $CaCO_3$, $MeCO_3$ in the crystalline phase, dissolved calcium and minor element in solution; $A_{CaCO_3}^S$ and $A_{MeCO_3}^S$ denote the activities of $CaCO_3$ and $MeCO_3$ in the crystalline phase; A_{Ca}^L and A_{Me}^L denote the activities of dissolved calcium and minor elements in solution; and $S_{MeCO_3}^o$ and $S_{CaCO_3}^o$ denote the solubility products in distilled water of pure $MeCO_3$ and pure $CaCO_3$, the crystal form of which is similar to that of $MeCO_3$.

The major component in the crystalline phase is $CaCO_3$, and therefore the value of $\lambda_{CaCO_3}^S$ is considered to be one in the present case.

From equation (3), it can be seen that the value of the distribution coefficient is determined by the ratio of the solubility product of pure $MeCO_3$ in distilled water to that of pure $CaCO_3$ in the same crystal form as $MeCO_3$, by the ratio of the activity coefficient of dissolved calcium to that of dissolved minor element in solution and by the activity coefficient of $MeCO_3$ in the carbonate crystal.

Since Mg poor calcite, aragonite and Mg rich calcite are found in the skeletal parts of marine organisms, the three crystals were considered to be in crystalline phase in this experiment (Kitano, 1964). Mg poor calcite was precipitated from calcium bicarbonate solution with a slow precipitation of carbonate or from the calcium bicarbonate solution containing sodium chloride and/or organic material. Aragonite was precipitated from calcium bicarbonate solution with a rapid precipitation of carbonate or from the calcium bicarbonate solution containing magnesium chloride and/or sodium chloride. Mg rich calcite was precipitated from the calcium bicarbonate solution containing magnesium chloride, organic material and/or sodium chloride.

The activity coefficients of minor elements and calcium dissolved in solution were controlled by adding sodium chloride to change the ionic strength of the solution, and by adding organic compounds and/or chloride ions to form ion pairs and/or complexes with minor element and/or calcium ions.

The thirty parent solution systems in which carbonates are formed are shown in Table 1 (Kitano, 1967b).

The distribution coefficients of zinc at 20 ± 1 C in the above thirty systems are shown in Table 2. In all runs the constant values were calculated using equation (2) rather than equation (1) as seen in Fig. 5. The reference numbers in Table 1 are used in Table 2 and in the following discussion of the distribution coefficients of the more significant solution systems.

(1) Simplest solution system. In this solution system, either calcite or aragonite was precipitated by changing the rate of calcium carbonate precipitation. That is, only calcite was formed from 20 liters of solution within two days by stirring the solution moderately, whereas only aragonite was formed from 800 ml of solution within 6 to 8 hours by vigorous stirring.

$$K_{Zn}^{Calcite} = 50 \pm 4, \quad K_{Zn}^{Aragonite} = 2 \pm 0.3 \qquad \text{at } 20 \pm 1 \text{ C}$$

These results are consistent with zinc carbonate's calcitic lattice configuration (see Fig. 5).

Table 1. Solution systems for which the distribution coefficients were calculated.

(In all parent solutions, the concentrations of calcium and zinc were about 40 mg/liter and 2 mg/liter respectively.)

(1) $Ca(HCO_3)_2$ + $ZnCl_2$ $\longrightarrow$ calcite or aragonite

(2) $Ca(HCO_3)_2$ + NaCl + $ZnCl_2$ $\longrightarrow$ calcite or aragonite

(3) $Ca(HCO_3)_2$ + $MgCl_2$ + $ZnCl_2$ $\longrightarrow$ calcite or aragonite

(4) $Ca(HCO_3)_2$ + NaCl + $MgCl_2$ + $ZnCl_2$ $\longrightarrow$ aragonite

(5) $Ca(HCO_3)_2$ + Na·citrate + $ZnCl_2$ $\longrightarrow$ calcite or aragonite

(6) $Ca(HCO_3)_2$ + NaCl + Na·citrate + $ZnCl_2$ $\longrightarrow$ calcite

(7) $Ca(HCO_3)_2$ + $MgCl_2$ + Na·citrate + $ZnCl_2$ $\longrightarrow$ Mg rich calcite or aragonite

(8) $Ca(HCO_3)_2$ + NaCl + $MgCl_2$ + Na·citrate + $ZnCl_2$ $\longrightarrow$ Mg rich calcite

(9) $Ca(HCO_3)_2$ + Na·acetate + $ZnCl_2$ $\longrightarrow$ calcite

(10) $Ca(HCO_3)_2$ + Na·malate + $ZnCl_2$ $\longrightarrow$ calcite

(11) $Ca(HCO_3)_2$ + $MgCl_2$ + Na·malate + $ZnCl_2$ $\longrightarrow$ Mg rich calcite

(12) $Ca(HCO_3)_2$ + Na·pyruvate + $ZnCl_2$ $\longrightarrow$ calcite

(13) $Ca(HCO_3)_2$ + $MgCl_2$ + Na·pyruvate + $ZnCl_2$ $\longrightarrow$ Mg rich calcite or aragonite

(14) $Ca(HCO_3)_2$ + Na·succinate + $ZnCl_2$ $\longrightarrow$ calcite or aragonite

(15) $Ca(HCO_3)_2$ + Na·lactate + $ZnCl_2$ $\longrightarrow$ calcite or aragonite

(16) $Ca(HCO_3)_2$ + galactose + $ZnCl_2$ $\longrightarrow$ calcite or aragonite

(17) $Ca(HCO_3)_2$ + dextrose + $MgCl_2$ + $ZnCl_2$ $\longrightarrow$ aragonite

(18) $Ca(HCO_3)_2$ + glycogen + $ZnCl_2$ $\longrightarrow$ calcite or aragonite

(19) $Ca(HCO_3)_2$ + glycine + $ZnCl_2$ $\longrightarrow$ calcite or aragonite

(20) $Ca(HCO_3)_2$ + $MgCl_2$ + glycine + $ZnCl_2$ $\longrightarrow$ aragonite

(21) $Ca(HCO_3)_2$ + serine + $ZnCl_2$ $\longrightarrow$ calcite or aragonite

(22) $Ca(HCO_3)_2$ + alanine + $ZnCl_2$ $\longrightarrow$ calcite or aragonite

(23) $Ca(HCO_3)_2$ + $MgCl_2$ + alanine + $ZnCl_2$ $\longrightarrow$ aragonite

(24) $Ca(HCO_3)_2$ + Na·glutamate + $ZnCl_2$ $\longrightarrow$ calcite or aragonite

(25) $Ca(HCO_3)_2$ + $MgCl_2$ + Na·glutamate + $ZnCl_2$ $\longrightarrow$ aragonite

(26) $Ca(HCO_3)_2$ + arginine + $ZnCl_2$ $\longrightarrow$ calcite or aragonite

(27) $Ca(HCO_3)_2$ + $MgCl_2$ + arginine + $ZnCl_2$ $\longrightarrow$ aragonite

(28) $Ca(HCO_3)_2$ + taurine + $ZnCl_2$ $\longrightarrow$ calcite or aragonite

(29) $Ca(HCO_3)_2$ + glycylglycine + $ZnCl_2$ $\longrightarrow$ calcite or aragonite

(30) $Ca(HCO_3)_2$ + Na·chondroitin sulfate + $ZnCl_2$ $\longrightarrow$ calcite or aragonite

Table 2. Values of the distribution coefficient of zinc measured in the solution systems shown in Table 1. (Equation numbers in this table correspond to those in Table 1.)

(1) $K_{Zn}^{C} = 50 \pm 4$; $K_{Zn}^{A} = 2 \pm 0.3$

(2) $K_{Zn}^{C} = 25 \pm 2$ (Cl⁻: 1 g/liter); 8.5 ± 0.5 (Cl⁻: 13.5 g/liter);
    5 ± 0.3 (Cl⁻: 18 g/liter)

(3) $K_{Zn}^{A} = 3.3 \pm 0.2$ (Mg²⁺: 1.2 g/liter); 10 ± 1 (Mg²⁺: 1.75 g/liter);
    26 ± 2 (Mg²⁺: 2.26 g/liter)

(4) $K_{Zn}^{A} = 3.1 \pm 0.2$ (Cl⁻: 1 g/liter, Mg²⁺: 0.2 - 1.3 g/liter);
    12 ± 1 (Cl⁻: 10 g/liter, Mg²⁺: 0.2 - 0.6 g/liter);
    2.2 ± 0.2 (Cl⁻: 10 g/liter, Mg²⁺: 1.3 g/liter);
    10 ± 2 (Cl⁻: 19 g/liter, Mg²⁺: 0.6 g/liter);
    3 ± 0.3 (Cl⁻: 19 g/liter, Mg²⁺: 1.3 g/liter)

(5) $K_{Zn}^{C} = 39 \pm 1$ (citrate: 0.1 - 0.2 g/liter);
    18 ± 1 (citrate: 1 - 1.5 g/liter)

(6) $K_{Zn}^{C} = 23 \pm 3$ (combination of Cl⁻: 1 - 19 g/liter and citrate:
    0.2 - 1.5 g/liter)

(7) $K_{Zn}^{Mg\ rich\ calcite} = 29 \pm 2$ (citrate: 0.5 g/liter, Mg²⁺: 0.3 g/liter);
    5.0 ± 0.5 (citrate: 0.5 g/liter, Mg²⁺: 1.9 g/liter);
    14 ± 1 (citrate: 1 g/liter, Mg²⁺: 0.3 g/liter);
    2.1 ± 0.2 (citrate: 1 g/liter, Mg²⁺: 1.9 g/liter);
    17 ± 1 (citrate: 1.5 g/liter, Mg²⁺: 0.3 g/liter);
    1.5 ± 0.2 (citrate: 1.5 g/liter, Mg²⁺: 1.9 g/liter);

(8) $K_{Zn}^{Mg\ rich\ calcite} = 4.5 \pm 0.3$ (citrate: 0.1 g/liter)
    2.0 ± 0.2 (citrate: 1 g/liter)
    1.0 ± 0.2 (citrate: 1.5 g/liter)

All solutions contain NaCl (Cl⁻: 19 g/liter) and MgCl₂
                         (Mg²⁺: 1.3 g/liter).

(9) $K_{Zn}^{C} = 26 \pm 2$ (acetate: 0.1 g/liter); 22 ± 2 (acetate: 1.5 g/liter)

(10) $K_{Zn}^{C} = 50 \pm 4$ (malate: 1 - 2 g/liter); 25 ± 1 (malate: 3 g/liter)

(11) $K_{Zn}^{Mg\ rich\ calcite} = 0.7 \pm 0.3$ (malate: 0.5 g/liter);
    1.0 ± 0.2 (malate: 1 g/liter);
    1.0 ± 0.2 (malate: 2 g/liter)

All solutions contain MgCl₂ (Mg²⁺: 1.3 g/liter).

(12) $K_{Zn}^{Mg\ rich\ calcite} = 0.8 \pm 0.3$ (pyruvate: 0.3 g/liter, Mg²⁺: 1.3 g/liter);
    3.5 ± 0.2 (pyruvate: 0.5 g/liter, Mg²⁺: 1.3 g/liter);
    3.0 ± 0.3 (pyruvate: 1 g/liter, Mg²⁺: 1.3 g/liter)

(13) $K_{Zn}^{C} = 40 \pm 4$ (succinate: 1 g/liter)

(14) $K_{Zn}^{A} = 2.0 \pm 0.2$ (lactate: 1 - 2 g/liter)

(15) $K_{Zn}^{C} = 21 \pm 2$ (galactose: 0.1 g/liter);
    $K_{Zn}^{A} = 1.0 \pm 0.2$ (galactose: 3 - 5 g/liter)

(16) $K_{Zn}^{A} = 3.3 \pm 0.2$ (dextrose: 1 - 2 g/liter, Mg²⁺: 1.3 g/liter)

(17) $K_{Zn}^{C} = 12 \pm 1$ (glycogen: 0.3 g/liter);
    $K_{Zn}^{A} = 2.0 \pm 0.2$ (glycogen: 1 g/liter)

(18) $K_{Zn}^{A} = 1.5 \pm 0.2$ (glycine: 0.1 g/liter);
    0.6 ± 0.2 (glycine: 0.5 g/liter);
    0.3 ± 0.2 (glycine: 1 g/liter)

(19) $K_{Zn}^{A} = 1.7 \pm 0.2$ (glycine: 0.1 g/liter, Mg²⁺: 1.3 g/liter);
    0.55 ± 0.2 (glycine: 0.5 g/liter, Mg²⁺: 1.3 g/liter);
    0.30 ± 0.2 (glycine: 1 g/liter, Mg²⁺: 1.3 g/liter)

(20) $K_{Zn}^{A} = 1.5$ ± 0.2 (serine: 0.2 g/liter);
    0.53 ± 0.2 (serine: 0.4 g/liter);
    0.20 ± 0.1 (serine: 1 g/liter)

(21) $K_{Zn}^{A} = 1.9 \pm 0.2$ (alanine: 0.2 g/liter);
    1.0 ± 0.2 (alanine: 0.5 g/liter);
    0.7 ± 0.2 (alanine: 1 g/liter)

(22) $K_{Zn}^{A} = 2.2 \pm 0.3$ (alanine: 0.5 g/liter, Mg²⁺: 1.3 g/liter)

(23) $K_{Zn}^{A} = 2.3 \pm 0.3$ (glutamate: 0.2 g/liter);
    1.5 ± 0.2 (glutamate: 0.5 g/liter);
    1.0 ± 0.2 (glutamate: 1 g/liter)

(24) $K_{Zn}^{A} = 2.8 \pm 0.3$ (glutamate: 0.5 g/liter, Mg²⁺: 1.3 g/liter)
    1.8 ± 0.2 (glutamate: 1 g/liter, Mg²⁺: 1.3 g/liter)

(25) $K_{Zn}^{A} = 1.7 \pm 0.3$ (arginine: 0.2 - 1.0 g/liter)

(26) $K_{Zn}^{A} = 3.0 \pm 0.3$ (arginine: 0.3 g/liter, Mg²⁺: 1.3 g/liter);
    0.9 ± 0.2 (arginine: 0.75 - 1.0 g/liter, Mg²⁺: 1.3 g/liter)

(27) $K_{Zn}^{C} = 13 \pm 1$ (taurine: 0.5 g/liter);
    $K_{Zn}^{A} = 1.6 \pm 0.2$ (taurine: 3 g/liter)

(28) $K_{Zn}^{A} = 2.3 \pm 0.3$ (glycylglycine: 0.2 g/liter);
    1.5 ± 0.2 (glycylglycine: 0.5 g/liter)

(29) $K_{Zn}^{C} = 8 \pm 1$ (chondroitin sulfate: 1 g/liter)

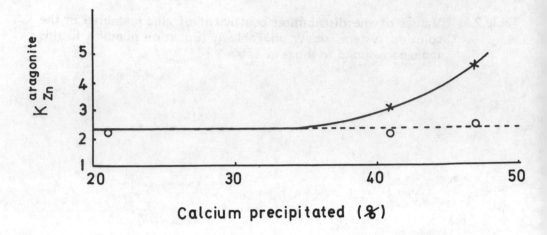

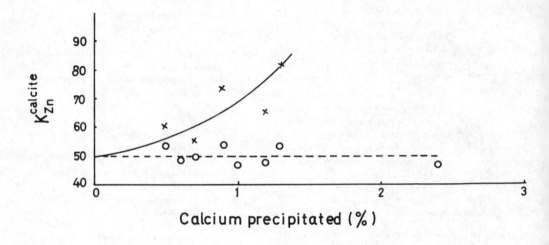

X   calculated from equation (1)

o   calculated from equation (2)

Fig. 5.   Values of the distribution coefficients $K_{Zn}^{aragonite}$ and $K_{Zn}^{calcite}$ plotted against the per cent calcium precipitated in $Ca(HCO_3)_2$ —— $ZnCl_2$ runs $(20 \pm 1\ C)$.

When the value of $\gamma_{Me}^{L}/\gamma_{Ca}^{L}$ is one, $\lambda_{MeCO_3}^{S}$ is 0.6, according to equation (3), because $\lambda_{CaCO_3}^{S}$ is one, $S_{CaCO_3}^{o}/S_{MeCO_3}^{o}$ is 30 and $K_{Zn}^{Calcite}$ in this system is 50. If $\gamma_{Me}^{L}/\gamma_{Ca}^{L}$ is 0.6 in this system, $\lambda_{MeCO_3}^{S}$ must be unity. It is not yet known whether $\gamma_{Me}^{L}/\gamma_{Ca}^{L}$ is one or near 0.6.

If no complex or ion pair forms in a parent solution, the distribution coefficient of zinc between calcite and solution (thermodynamic distribution coefficient) must be 30.

(2) The body fluid of marine calcareous organisms always contains sodium chloride. Zinc ions form complexes and ion pairs with chloride ions in solution, whereas calcium ions do not:

$$Zn^{2+} + Cl^- \rightleftharpoons ZnCl^+$$

$$ZnCl + Cl^- \rightleftharpoons ZnCl_2^0$$

$$ZnCl_2^0 + Cl^- \rightleftharpoons ZnCl_3^-$$

$$ZnCl_3^- + Cl^- \rightleftharpoons ZnCl_4^{2-} \tag{4}$$

$$\frac{M_{ZnCl^+}^{L}}{M_{Zn^{2+}}^{L} \cdot M_{Cl^-}^{L}} = 10^{0.72}$$

$$\frac{M_{ZnCl_2^0}^{L}}{M_{ZnCl^+}^{L} \cdot M_{Cl^-}^{L}} = 10^{-0.23}$$

$$\frac{M_{ZnCl_3^-}^{L}}{M_{ZnCl_2^0}^{L} \cdot M_{Cl^-}^{L}} = 10^{-0.68}$$

$$\frac{M_{ZnCl_4^{2-}}^{L}}{M_{ZnCl_3^-}^{L} \cdot M_{Cl^-}^{L}} = 10^{0.37} \tag{5}$$

where $M_{Zn^{2+}}^L$, $M_{Cl^-}^L$, $M_{ZnCl^+}^L$, $M_{ZnCl_2^0}^L$, $M_{ZnCl_3^-}^L$, and $M_{ZnCl_4^{2-}}^L$ denote the molar concentrations of Zn^{2+}, Cl^-, $ZnCl^+$, $ZnCl_2^0$, $ZnCl_3^-$ and $ZnCl_4^{2-}$ in solution respectively.

As the concentration of chloride ions in solution increases, the activity coefficient of zinc in solution decreases and the value of the apparent distribution coefficient of zinc must decrease. In this solution system, calcite crystals are formed. The values of $K_{Zn}^{Calcite}$ are plotted against the concentrations of chloride ions in solution in Fig. 6 and the results are consistent with predicted values.

Using the stability constants in equation (5), the concentrations of zinc ions ($M_{Zn^{2+}}^L$) and Zn^{2+}-Cl^- complexes ($\alpha \cdot M_{Zn^{2+}}^L$) are calculated.

$$M_{Zn}^L = (1 + \alpha)M_{Zn^{2+}}^L \tag{6}$$

$$\alpha = 10^{0.72} \cdot M_{Cl^-}^L + 10^{0.49} \cdot (M_{Cl^-}^L)^2 + 10^{-0.19} \cdot$$

$$(M_{Cl^-}^L)^3 + 10^{0.18} \cdot (M_{Cl^-}^L)^4 \tag{7}$$

Since the concentration of chloride ions in solution is very large compared with that of zinc in solution the molar concentration of chloride ions added to the solution is used as $M_{Cl^-}^L$ for the calculation of γ.

The apparent distribution coefficient can be written:

$$K_{Zn}^C = \frac{1}{1 + \gamma} \cdot K_{Zn}^{0,C} = \frac{1}{1 + \gamma} \cdot \frac{S_{CaCO_3}^0 \text{(Calcite)}}{S_{ZnCO_3}^0} \cdot$$

$$\frac{\lambda_{CaCO_3}^S}{\lambda_{ZnCO_3}^S} \cdot \frac{\gamma_{Zn^{2+}}^L}{\gamma_{Ca^{2+}}^L} \tag{8}$$

where $M_{Zn^{2+}}^L$ and M_{Zn}^L are the molar concentrations of zinc ions and total dissolved zinc; $\gamma_{Zn^{2+}}^L$ and $\gamma_{Ca^{2+}}^L$ are the activity coefficients of zinc ions and calcium ions; and $K_{Zn}^{0,C}$ is the thermodynamic distribution coefficient.

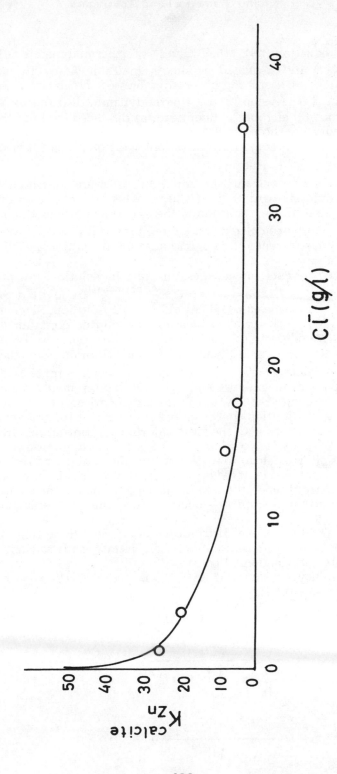

Fig. 6. Variation of the distribution coefficient $K_{Zn}^{calcite}$ with the Cl concentration in $Ca(HCO_3)_2$ —— NaCl —— $ZnCl_2$ runs (20 C).

From equation (8), the values of thermodynamic distribution coefficient $K_{Zn}^{0,C}$ are calculated as shown in Table 3, by the use of the calculated values of α and the observed values of the apparent distribution coefficient K_{Zn}^{C}. The value of the thermodynamic distribution coefficient should be about 30 at room temperature, as discussed in (1) of this section. The calculated value shown in Table 3 is approximately 30 even though the concentration of chloride ions in the parent solution is high. It is known that the value of $\lambda_{ZnCO_3}^{S}$ is near one.

The stability constants in equation (5) were measured only in a solution of ionic strength 0.69 ($HClO_4$). When more exact values of the constants suitable for each solution in the experiment are used, a more exact value of $K_{Zn}^{0,C}$ can be calculated and a more precise discussion could be made of the activity coefficients of calcium and zinc in solution and of $ZnCO_3$ in crystalline phase.

(3) The presence of magnesium ions in solution favors aragonite formation. In Fig. 7, the values of $K_{Zn}^{Aragonite}$ are plotted against the concentrations of magnesium and chloride ions in solution. Since magnesium chloride is added to the calcium bicarbonate solution containing zinc ions, zinc-chloride complexes and ion pairs form in solution. However with increasing concentrations of magnesium and chloride ions the value of $K_{Zn}^{Aragonite}$ increases (Fig. 7). This strange effect is probably due to the peculiar behavior of magnesium ions. The mechanism involved and the state of $ZnCO_3$ in aragonite remain unsolved. A comparison of Fig. 6 and Fig. 7 shows that the distribution coefficient of zinc is larger for aragonite than for calcite in some solutions with the same chloride concentration, although zinc carbonate occurs only in the calcitic lattice crystal configuration.

This result is analogous to the strontium content of the calcite and aragonite portions of the *Mytilus* skeleton shown in Fig. 8 (Dodd, 1965). There is more strontium carbonate in the calcite than in the aragonite layer, although strontium carbonate occurs only in the aragonite crystal configuration.

(5) The value of the distribution coefficient is a function of the difference in stability constants between citrate and calcium ions and between citrate and zinc ions (Fig. 9).

The stability constants of $ZnC_6H_5O_7^-$ and $CaC_6H_5O_7^-$ were reported (Sillèn and Martell, 1964):

$$\frac{M_{ZnC_6H_5O_7^-}^{L}}{M_{Zn^{2+}}^{L} \cdot M_{C_6H_5O_7^{3-}}^{L}} = 10^{4.71} \qquad (9)$$

$$\frac{M_{CaC_6H_5O_7^-}^{L}}{M_{Ca^{2+}}^{L} \cdot M_{C_6H_5O_7^{3-}}^{L}} = 10^{3.22} \qquad (10)$$

Table 3. $Ca(HCO_3)_2 + NaCl + ZnCl_2 \longrightarrow$ calcite.

Cl^- (g/liter)	Ionic strength	Experimentally measured value K_{Zn}^C	α	Calculated value $K_{Zn}^{0,C}$	$\lambda_{ZnCO_3}^S$
1	0.068	25	0.15	29	1
3	0.12	20	0.46	30	1
13.5	0.42	8.5	2.5	30	1
18	0.55	5	3.6	23	1.2
35.5	1.53	4	10.5	46	0.7

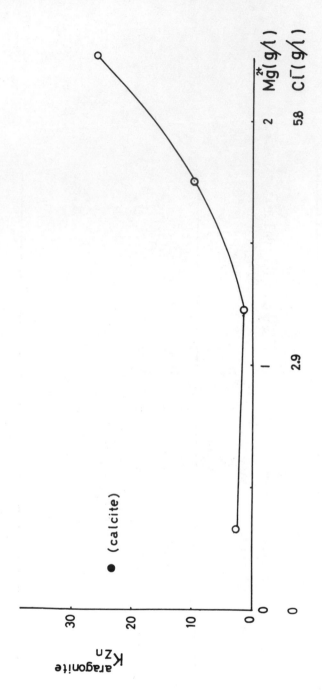

Fig. 7. Variation of the distribution coefficient $K_{Zn}^{aragonite}$ with Mg^{2+} or Cl^{-} concentration in $Ca(HCO_3)_2$ — $MgCl_2$ — $ZnCl_2$ runs (20 C).

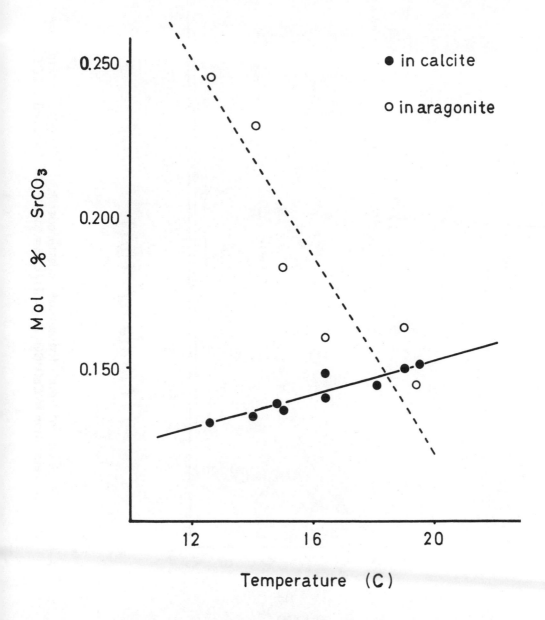

Fig. 8.   SrCO$_3$ content of the calcite outer prismatic layer and aragonite
nacreous layer of *Mytilus*.

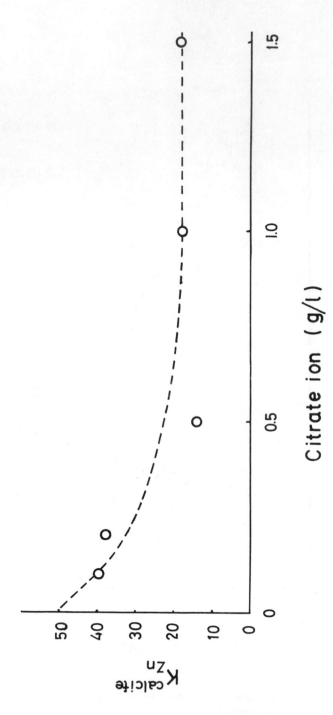

Fig. 9. Variation of the distribution coefficient $K_{Zn}^{calcite}$ with citrate ion concentration in $Ca(HCO_3)_2$ — Na-Citrate — $ZnCl_2$ runs (20 ± 1 C).

where $M^L_{Zn^{2+}}$, $M^L_{C_6H_5O_7^{3-}}$, $M^L_{ZnC_6H_5O_7^-}$, $M^L_{Ca^{2+}}$ and $M^L_{CaC_6H_5O_7^-}$ denote the molar concentrations of Zn^{2+} $C_6H_5O_7^{3-}$, $ZnC_6H_5O_7^-$, Ca^{2+} and $CaC_6H_5O_7^-$ in solution.

The concentration of zinc dissolved in solution, M^L_{Zn}, is written:

$$M^L_{Zn} = M^L_{Zn^{2+}} + M^L_{ZnC_6H_5O_7^-} = M^L_{Zn^{2+}} \cdot (1 + \alpha) \qquad (11)$$

where

$$\alpha = M^L_{C_6H_5O_7^{3-}} \times 10^{4.71} \qquad (12)$$

The concentration of calcium dissolved in solution, M^L_{Ca}, is written:

$$M^L_{Ca} = M^L_{Ca^{2+}} + M^L_{CaC_6H_5O_7^-} = M^L_{Ca^{2+}} \cdot (1 + \beta) \qquad (13)$$

where

$$\beta = M^L_{C_6H_5O_7^-} \times 10^{3.22} \qquad (14)$$

The pH of the solution changes from 7.8 to 8.5 during carbonate precipitation. The dissociation constants of citric acid are:

$$K_1 = 8.7 \times 10^{-4}, \qquad K_2 = 1.8 \times 10^{-5}, \qquad K_3 = 4.0 \times 10^{-6}.$$

The molar concentration of citrate in solution $(M^L_{C_6H_5O_7^{3-}}, T)$ is written:

$$M^L_{C_6H_5O_7^{3-}, T} = M^L_{C_6H_5O_7^{3-}} + M^L_{ZnC_6H_5O_7^-} + M^L_{CaC_6H_5O_7^-} \qquad (15)$$

α and β are calculated from equations (9) to (15).

The apparent distribution coefficient K^C_{Zn} is written:

$$K_{Zn}^C = \frac{1+\beta}{1+\alpha} \cdot K_{Zn}^{0,C} = \frac{1+\beta}{1+\alpha} \cdot \frac{S_{CaCO_3}^0}{S_{ZnCO_3}^0} \cdot \frac{\lambda_{CaCO_3}^S}{\lambda_{ZnCO_3}^S} \cdot \frac{\gamma_{Zn^{2+}}^L}{\gamma_{Ca^{2+}}^L} \tag{16}$$

Given the values of M_{Ca}^L, M_{Zn}^L and $M_{C_6H_5O_7^{3-}}^L$, $_T$, the values of α and β can be calculated from equations (9) to (15).

To compute α and β, the authors first calculated the ratios $M_{Zn^{2+}}^L$: $M_{ZnC_6H_5O_7^-}^L$ and $M_{Ca^{2+}}^L$: $M_{CaC_6H_5O_7^-}^L$ for each value of $M_{C_6HO_7^{3-}}^L$, and then calculated the value of $M_{C_6H_5O_7^{3-}}^L$, $_T$ in the solution (Table 4).

From Table 4 the values of α and β in the solution in question can easily be calculated. $K_{Zn}^{0,C}$ and $\lambda_{ZnCO_3}^S$ can be obtained from equation (16), as shown in Table 5.

The resulting values of $K_{Zn}^{0,C}$ are surprising. They are large in comparison with the values of 30 to 50 in systems (1) and (2). The values of $\lambda_{ZnCO_3}^S$ are likewise unexpected.

The formation of $Ca(C_6H_5O_7)_2^{4-}$ reported by Sillèn and Martell (1964) must not be neglected in this calculation.

$$\frac{M_{Ca(C_6H_5O_7)_2^{4-}}^L}{M_{Ca^{2+}}^L \cdot (M_{C_6H_5O_7^{3-}}^L)^2} = 10^{8.02} \tag{17}$$

$$M_{C_6H_5O_7^{3-}}^L, _T = M_{C_6H_5O_7^{3-}}^L + M_{ZnC_6H_5O_7^-}^L + M_{CaC_6H_5O_7^-}^L +$$

$$2M_{Ca(C_6H_5O_7)_2^{4-}}^L \tag{18}$$

$$M_{Ca}^L = M_{Ca^{2+}}^L + M_{CaC_6H_5O_7^-}^L + M_{Ca(C_6H_5O_7)_2^{4-}}^L = M_{Ca^{2+}}^L \cdot (1+\beta) \tag{19}$$

Table 4. Ratios of the concentrations of free ions to complexes and the concentration of citrate ions and total citrate in solution.

$M^L_{C_6H_5O_7^{3-}}$	ratio $M^L_{Zn^{2+}}:M^L_{ZnC_6H_5O_7^-}$		ratio $M^L_{Ca^{2+}}:M^L_{CaC_6H_5O_7^-}$		$M^L_{C_6H_5O_7^{3-},T}$
1.0×10^{-5}	1	0.512	1	0.0166	0.018×10^{-2}
3.0×10^{-5}	1	1.54	1	0.0497	0.051×10^{-2}
3.1×10^{-5}	1	1.59	1	0.0514	0.052×10^{-2}
5.0×10^{-5}	1	2.56	1	0.0829	0.082×10^{-2}
6.8×10^{-5}	1	3.48	1	0.112	0.100×10^{-2}
7.0×10^{-5}	1	3.59	1	0.116	0.111×10^{-2}
1.9×10^{-4}	1	9.7	1	0.315	0.260×10^{-2}
3.0×10^{-4}	1	15	1	0.497	0.335×10^{-2}
5.3×10^{-4}	1	27	1	0.879	0.52×10^{-2}
6.0×10^{-4}	1	31	1	0.995	0.560×10^{-2}
1.1×10^{-3}	1	56.4	1	1.82	0.755×10^{-2}
1.18×10^{-3}	1	60.5	1	1.96	0.780×10^{-2}
1.2×10^{-3}	1	61.5	1	1.99	0.785×10^{-2}
2.0×10^{-3}	1	102	1	3.32	0.968×10^{-2}

Table 5. Calculation of $K_{Zn}^{0,C}$ in the system, $Ca(HCO_3)_2$ + Na-citrate + $ZnCl_2 \longrightarrow$ calcite.

(Amounts of Ca and Zn added are 10^{-2} and 3×10^{-5} M respectively.)

Citrate added (g/liter)	(M)	Experimental value K_{Zn}^C	Calculated value				
			α	β	$\dfrac{1+\beta}{1+\alpha}$	$K_{Zn}^{0,C}$	$\lambda_{ZnCO_3}^S$
0.1	5.2×10^{-4}	40	1.6	0.05	0.40	100	0.033
0.2	1.0×10^{-3}	38	3.5	0.11	0.248	150	0.019
0.5	2.6×10^{-3}	14	9.7	0.32	0.123	110	0.026
1.0	5.2×10^{-3}	18	27	0.88	0.067	270	0.011
1.5	7.8×10^{-3}	19	60	2.0	0.049	390	0.007

$$\beta = M_{C_6H_5O_7^{3-}}^{L} \times 10^{3.22} + (M_{C_6H_5O_7^{3-}}^{L})^2 \times 10^{8.02} \qquad (20)$$

From equations (9), (10), (17) and (18), the ratio $M_{Zn^{2+}}^{L}$: $M_{ZnC_6H_5O_7^{-}}^{L}$ and $M_{Ca^{2+}}^{L} : M_{CaC_6H_5O_7^{-}}^{L} : M_{Ca(C_6H_5O_7)_2^{4-}}^{L}$ and $M_{C_6H_5O_7^{3-}}^{L}$, $_T$ are calculated for any value of $M_{C_6H_5O_7^{3-}}^{L}$ (Table 6).

From Table 6, by using equations (19) and (20), α and β can be computed very easily when M_{Ca}^{L} and M_{Zn}^{L} are 10^{-2} and 3×10^{-5} M/liter respectively. $K_{Zn}^{0,C}$ and $\lambda_{ZnCO_3}^{S}$ are calculated according to equation (16) (Table 7). $S_{CaCO_3}^{0}/S_{ZnCO_3}^{0}$ is 30 and $\lambda_{CaCO_3}^{S}$ and $\gamma_{Zn^{2+}}^{L}/\gamma_{Ca^{2+}}^{L}$ are considered to be one in equation (16).

The calculated values of $K_{Zn}^{0,C}$ and $\lambda_{ZnCO_3}^{S}$ in Table 7 seem reasonable, though the values in Table 5 do not.

Although the formation of $Zn(C_6H_5O_7)_2^{4-}$ is possible, the complex formation would not have a significant effect on this calculation. However, the exact stability constants of $Ca^{2+} - C_6H_5O_7^{3-}$ and $Zn^{2+} - C_6H_5O_7^{3-}$ for this series of experiments should be determined.

(6) In this system, the solution contains chloride and citrate ions which form complexes with zinc ions. The value of the distribution coefficient is shown in Fig. 10, which indicates that the influence of the zinc-citrate complex is so strong that the influence of chloride ions as shown in (2) is negligible.

(7) Mg rich calcite is formed in $Ca(HCO_3)_2$-minor element -$MgCl_2$-$NaCl$-$Na_3(C_6H_5O_7)$ solution systems. The value of $K_{Zn}^{Mg\ rich\ calcite}$ are presented in Fig. 11.

From the results above, several conclusions can be drawn. In the calcium bicarbonate solution containing no ions other than zinc ions, the distribution coefficient for calcite is larger than that for aragonite. However, in calcium bicarbonate solutions containing sodium chloride, magnesium chloride and sodium citrate in various proportions, the distribution coefficient of zinc for calcite ranges between 1 and 20 and for aragonite, between 0 and 4, depending on the concentration of the salts. The three compounds are found in the body fluid of marine calcareous organisms. In general, the value for calcite is larger than that for aragonite. However, sometimes there is no difference.

The distribution coefficient of zinc between sea water and skeletal calcite ranges from 1 to 20, whereas that between sea water and skeletal

Table 6. Ratios of the concentration of free ions to complexes and of citrate ions and total citrate in solution.

$M^L_{C_6H_5O_7^{3-}}$	ratio $M^L_{Zn^{2+}}:M^L_{ZnC_6H_5O_7^-}$		ratio $M^L_{Ca^{2+}}:M^L_{CaC_6H_5O_7^-}:M^L_{Ca(C_6H_5O_7)_2^{4-}}$			$M^L_{C_6H_5O_7^{3-},T}$
1.26×10^{-5}	1	0.646	1	0.021	0.016	0.051×10^{-2}
1.3×10^{-5}	1	0.667	1	0.021	0.017	0.053×10^{-2}
1.5×10^{-5}	1	0.769	1	0.024	0.023	0.068×10^{-2}
1.9×10^{-5}	1	0.974	1	0.031	0.038	0.100×10^{-2}
1.95×10^{-5}	1	1.00	1	0.032	0.040	0.106×10^{-2}
2.0×10^{-5}	1	1.02	1	0.033	0.042	0.110×10^{-2}
3.46×10^{-5}	1	1.77	1	0.057	0.125	0.26×10^{-2}
3.5×10^{-5}	1	1.79	1	0.058	0.128	0.265×10^{-2}
3.6×10^{-5}	1	1.84	1	0.060	0.135	0.280×10^{-2}
5.5×10^{-5}	1	2.82	1	0.091	0.316	0.51×10^{-2}
5.55×10^{-5}	1	2.84	1	0.092	0.322	0.52×10^{-2}
6.0×10^{-5}	1	3.07	1	0.100	0.377	0.58×10^{-2}
7.5×10^{-5}	1	3.84	1	0.124	0.589	0.766×10^{-2}
7.6×10^{-5}	1	3.89	1	0.126	0.605	0.78×10^{-2}

Table 7. Calculation of $K_{Zn}^{0,C}$ in the system $Ca(HCO_3)_2$ + Na-citrate + $ZnCl_2 \longrightarrow$ calcite.

(Amounts of Ca and Zn added are 10^{-2} and 3×10^{-5} M respectively.)

Citrate added (g/liter)		Experimental value K_{Zn}^C	Calculated value				
			α	β	$\dfrac{1+\beta}{1+\alpha}$	$K_{Zn}^{0,C}$	$\lambda_{ZnCO_3}^S$
0.1	5.2×10^{-4}	40	0.646	0.037	0.630	63	0.48
0.2	1.0×10^{-3}	38	0.974	0.069	0.541	70	0.42
0.5	2.6×10^{-3}	14	1.77	0.182	0.426	33	0.93
1.0	5.2×10^{-3}	18	2.84	0.414	0.368	50	0.61
1.5	7.8×10^{-3}	19	3.89	0.731	0.354	53	0.58

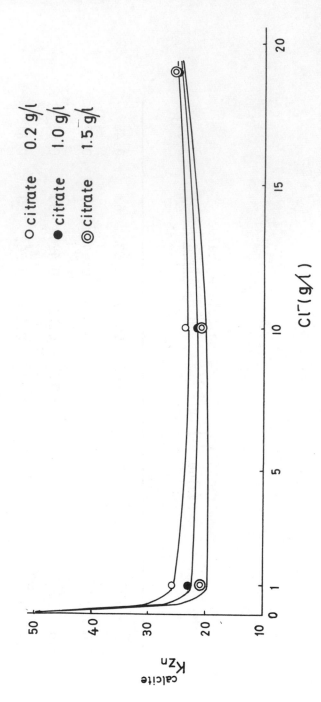

Fig. 10. Variation of the distribution coefficient $K_{Zn}^{calcite}$ with Cl concentration in $Ca(HCO_3)_2$ — Na·citrate — NaCl — $ZnCl_2$ runs (20 ± 1 C).

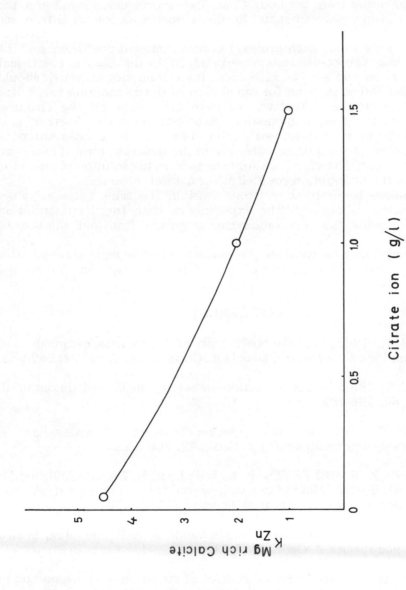

Fig. 11. Variation of the distribution coefficient $K_{Zn}^{Mg\ rich\ calcite}$ with citrate ion concentration in $Ca(HCO_3)_2$ — Na·citrate — $MgCl_2$ — NaCl — $ZnCl_2$ runs (20 ± 1 C).

aragonite ranges from 0 to 4. Sometimes there is no difference in the distribution coefficient of zinc for skeletal or sedimentary calcite and aragonite.

It should be noted that skeletal carbonate is not formed directly from sea water but rather from the body fluid. Two processes are involved in the precipitation of skeletal carbonate. In one, elements are captured from sea water and enter the body fluid. In the second, elements are precipitated as carbonate in body fluid. Each process has an enrichment coefficient and the product of these two coefficients corresponds to the distribution coefficient between sea water and skeletal carbonate. Body fluid, not sea water, should be used as the parent solution for calculation of the distribution coefficient for skeletal carbonates. However, we have little data on the chemical composition of body fluids of marine calcareous organisms. Further, it is known that there is a clear relationship between the concentration of strontium and magnesium in sea water and in the skeletons formed in the sea water environment. Therefore, sea water is used as the solution phase in the calculation of the distribution coefficient for natural carbonates.

The values for natural skeletons exist in the same range as values measured in the laboratory. The experimental data for the distribution coefficients indicate that the values change greatly from one solution to another.

It is important to consider the interaction of organic material with calcium and zinc in discussions of the distribution of zinc in natural carbonates.

REFERENCES

BERNER, R. A. 1965. Activity coefficients of bicarbonate, carbonate, and calcium ions in sea water. Geochim. Cosmochim. Acta, *29*: 947-965.

CHAVE, K. E. 1952. A solid solution between calcite and dolomite. J. Geol., *60*: 190-192.

CHAVE, K. E. 1954. Aspects of biogeochemistry of magnesium. I. Calcareous marine organisms. J. Geol., *62*: 266-283.

CHAVE, K. E., K. S. DEFFEYES, P. K. WEYL, R. M. CARRELES, and M. E. THOMPSON. 1962. Observations on the solubility of skeletal carbonates in aqueous solutions. Science, *137*: 33-34.

DODD, J. R. 1963. Paleoecological implications of shell mineralogy in two Pelecypod species. J. Geol., *71*: 1-11.

DODD, J. R. 1965. Environmental control of strontium and magnesium in *Mytilus*. Geochim. Cosmochim. Acta, *29*: 385-398.

DODD, J. R. 1966. The influence of salinity on mollusk shell mineralogy: a discussion. J. Geol., *74*: 85-89.

DOERNER, H. A., and W. M. HOSKINS. 1925. Coprecipitation of radium and barium sulfates. J. Amer. Chem. Soc., 47: 662-675.

EPSTEIN, S., R. BUCHSBAUM, H. A. LOWENSTAM, and H. C. UREY. 1951. Carbonate water isotopic temperature scale. Geol. Soc. Amer. Bull., 62: 417-425.

GARRELS, R. M., and M. E. THOMPSON. 1962. A chemical model for sea water at 25 C and one atmosphere total pressure. Amer. J. Sci., 260: 57-66.

GARRELS, R. M., M. E. THOMPSON, and R. SIEVER. 1961. Control of carbonate solubility by carbonate complexes. Amer. J. Sci., 259: 24-45.

GLOVER, E. D., and R. F. SIPPEL. 1967. Synthesis of magnesium calcites. Geochim. Cosmochim. Acta, 31: 603-613.

HARKER, R. I., and O. F. TUTTLE. 1955. Studies in the system $CaO-MgO-CO_2$. II. Limits of solid solution along the binary join, $CaCO_3$-$MgCO_3$. Amer. J. Sci., 253: 274-282.

HINDMAN, J. C. 1943. Properties of the system $CaCO_3$-CO_2-H_2O in sea water and sodium chloride solutions. Ph.D. Thesis, Univ. California, Los Angeles.

HOLLAND, H. D. 1965. The history of ocean water and its effect on the chemistry of the atmosphere. Nat. Acad. Sci., Proc., 53: 1173-1183.

JANSEN, J. F., and Y. KITANO. 1963. The resistance of recent marine carbonate sediments to solution. J. Oceanogr. Soc. Japan, 18: 42-53.

KITANO, Y. 1962a. Behavior of various inorganic ions in the process of calcium carbonate separation from bicarbonate solution. Chem. Soc. Japan Bull., 35: 1973-1980.

KITANO, Y. 1962b. A study of polymorphic formation of calcium carbonate in thermal spring with emphasis on the temperature. Chem. Soc. Japan Bull., 35: 1980-1985.

KITANO, Y. 1964. On factors influencing the polymorphic crystallization of calcium carbonate found in marine biological systems, p. 305-319. In Recent researches in the fields of hydrosphere, atmosphere and nuclear geochemistry. Maruzen Co. Ltd., Tokyo, Japan.

KITANO, Y. 1967a. Chemistry of sea water and shell materials. Kagaku, 37: 9-15.

KITANO, Y. 1967b. Paleo-chemical composition and paleotemperature of sea water. Kagaku, *37*: 366-372.

KITANO, Y. 1968. Evolution of chemical composition of sea water. Kagaku (Iwanami Co. Ltd., Tokyo, Japan), *38*: 224-229.

KITANO, Y., and T. FURUTSU. 1959. The state of a small amount of magnesium contained in calcareous shells. Chem. Soc. Japan Bull., *33*: 1-4.

KITANO, Y., and D. W. HOOD. 1962. Calcium carbonate crystal forms formed from sea water by inorganic processes. J. Oceanogr. Soc. Japan, *18*: 35-39.

KITANO, Y., and D. W. HOOD. 1965. Influence of organic matter on the polymorphic crystallization of calcium carbonate. Geochim. Cosmochim. Acta, *29*: 29-41.

KITANO, Y., and N. KANAMORI. 1966. Synthesis of magnesian calcite at low temperatures and pressures. Geochim. J., *1*: 1-10.

KITANO, Y., K. PARK, and D. W. HOOD. 1962. Pure aragonite synthesis. J. Geophys. Res., *67*: 4873-4874.

KRAMER, J. R. 1965. History of sea water. Constant temperature-pressure equilibrium models compared to liquid inclusion analysis. Geochim. Cosmochim. Acta, *29*: 912-945.

LOWENSTAM, H. A. 1954. Factors affecting the aragonite:calcite ratios in carbonate secreting marine organisms. J. Geol., *62*: 284-322.

LOWENSTAM, H. A. 1961. Mineralogy, O^{18}/O^{16} ratios, and strontium and magnesium contents of recent and fossil brachiopods and their bearing on the history of the oceans. J. Geol., *69*: 241-260.

LOWENSTAM, H. A. 1963. Biologic problems relating to the composition and diagenesis of sediments, p. 137-195. *In* T. W. Donnelly [ed.], The earth sciences. Univ. Chicago Press.

MACKENZIE, F. T., and R. M. GARRELS. 1966. Chemical mass balance between rivers and oceans. Amer. J. Sci., *264*: 507-525.

ODUM, H. T. 1951. The stability of the world strontium cycle. Science, *114*: 407-411.

PILKEY, O. H., and H. G. GOODWELL. 1963. Trace elements in recent mollusk shells. Limnol. Oceanogr., *8*: 137-148.

PILKEY, O. H., and J. HOWER. 1960. The effect of environment on the concentration of skeletal magnesium and strontium in *Dendraster*. J. Geol., *68*: 203-216.

RUBEY, W. W. 1955. Development of the hydrosphere and atmosphere, with special reference to probable composition of the early atmosphere, p. 631-650. *In* A. Poldervaat [ed.] Crust of the earth. Geol. Soc. Amer. Bull. Spec. Paper No. 62.

RUBEY, W. W. 1964. Geologic history of sea water, p. 1-63. *In* The origin and evolution of atmosphere and oceans. Wiley and Sons, New York.

SILLÉN, L. G., and A. E. MARTELL. 1964. Stability constants of metal-ion complexes. The Chemical Society, Burlington House, London.

UREY, H. C., H. A. LOWENSTAM, S. EPSTEIN, and C. R. McKINNEY. 1951. Measurement of paleotemperatures and temperatures of the Upper Cretaceous of England, Denmark, and the southeastern United States. Geol. Soc. Amer. Bull., *62*: 399-416.

WEYL, P. K. 1961. The carbonate saturometer. J. Geol., *69*: 32-44.

GENERAL DISCUSSION AFTER SESSION IV

MORGAN: This is a response to a comment made by Dr. Hood. If you considered all of the amino acids in sea water to be at some sort of a reasonable distribution and calculated the sum of the equilibrium constants, I think you would come rather close to the observed results. Admittedly the equilibrium constants are not very large for copper and zinc and most of the amino acids. The problem is we do not know about the existence of relatively special ligands. For example, cardamine has great affinity for iron because of stearic considerations, and a very low affinity for calcium and most of the bivalent ions. When ferric iron and a molecule like cardamine occur in the same system, the cardamine completely dominates the situation. This would lead me to believe that your observations on zinc and copper suggest that there is not a special ligand which really goes after the iron, for example, but that there is a distribution of ligands with a range of affinities for zinc, copper and nickel.

RICHARDS: I might comment on zinc. We have done some work with anodic stripping voltametry, and most zinc in the open ocean seems to be in an inorganic form available to the electrode once you reduce the pH to a value of about 5. We do this by bubbling carbon dioxide through the solution. On the other hand, in the Columbia River plume, we found that zinc was not available to the electrode until we had done something else to it to destroy an organic complex, but I think most of the zinc that we observed in the open ocean was inorganic, probably a zinc carbonate ion.

HOOD: I have not followed the work on anodic stripping. There is quite a lot of it going on. As I recall, when sea water has passed through a 10 mμ filter, then through 3 to 5 mμ Viskine tubing (a very small range in pore size) you get from 10 to 50% non-dialyzable zinc depending on the depth. When this is oxidized with persulphuric acid, the zinc is extractable with diethyldithio carbamate. This method is used for determining whether it is ionic or non-ionic. Also, there is quite a bit of evidence that some of the zinc will not stick to ion exchange resins; it passes through. I think a combination of methods will pin this down more, and anodic stripping certainly is one of the powerful tools available. We will probably find that there are some high molecular weight compounds in sea water that complex some of the elements very tenaciously. We have recently obtained a zinc complex from Sephadex resin techniques. We are now trying to characterize these materials.

RICHARDS: The source of the water is also a factor.

DUURSMA: Dr. Hood, are the zinc non-dialyzable compounds equally distributed in the sea? As I recall, in the deep sea zinc is more dialyzable.

HOOD: Right. Actually, there are two areas, at least in the Gulf of Mexico, that are rich, the surface and 1000 m, strangely enough. And this is true not only for zinc but for copper. Manganese is not often found in non-dialyzable fractions, which I think would be expected.

I think there is a matter that someone brought up; this matter of copper extracted by chloroform. This particular compound does not seem to be chelated at all, but some kind of an organo-metalic. This may also be true of zinc. I do not think chelates are going to answer the whole question.

DUURSMA: Perhaps a question will point up the importance of investigating chelates. Is it sufficient to know the stability constants, or are the biologists more interested in position, velocities and rates? All these things are related to uptake by organisms. If organisms can give off, for example, zinc quite quickly, then it does not matter if the zinc is chelated or not.

PARSONS: Galen Jones had some evidence that heavy metals in sea water poison terrestrial bacteria, but that this effect is not observed in the presence of a chelating agent. To answer Dr. Duursma's question with an example, then, it would seem that what the biologist would want to know is whether heavy metal chelation is a reasonable explanation for the removal of toxic factors in sea water; that is, can the chemist put some numbers on the degree of chelation of heavy metals in natural waters?

RICHARDS: Dr. Menzel, you and Dr. Ryther raised the possibility that a lag is induced in primary productivity in freshly upwelled water because free trace metals are somehow bound and no longer toxic to the organisms. Wasn't this your thesis?

MENZEL: I can tell you very briefly what will happen if you bring up deep water and seed it with surface phytoplankton. Ordinarily in about five days you will start to see signs of growth. Whereas, if you put in a little bit of EDTA (I cannot remember the concentrations), growth will start in about one day.

RICHARDS: I think this is the sort of thing biologists want to know from the chemists.

MORGAN: I think Dr. Duursma's point was very good. If you ask a question about not only the stability, to use a thermodynamic term, but the lability of the complexes, I think that question is very pertinent, because formation of the chelate keeps the ion in solution. If in addition it can exchange rapidly with the free form of the metal ion, the ion is available to do some business. If a very robust complex forms, one which will not exchange freely, the effects on a biological system will be different.

DUURSMA: Yes, but some groups, for example, zinc-EDTA complexes, exchange quite rapidly, but this is not always true for another element. It does not work with manganese, for example. This might also be related to the oxidation state, but I imagine that for normal compounds in the sea velocity might be a problem.

SESSION V.   RECENT DEVELOPMENT - INVITED SHORT PAPERS

LOW MOLECULAR WEIGHT HYDROCARBONS AND CARBON MONOXIDE IN SEA WATER

V. J. Linnenbom and J. W. Swinnerton
Naval Research Laboratory
Code 8330
Washington, D.C. 20390

ABSTRACT

This presentation covers some of our recent work on trace amounts of dissolved gases in sea water. After a review of our work on hydrocarbons, our more recent measurements of carbon monoxide in sea water will be described.

HYDROCARBONS IN SEA WATER

The work on the distribution of low molecular weight hydrocarbons in sea water started about two years ago with the development of an analytical technique based on gas chromatography. For hydrocarbons in the C_1 to C_4 region, this technique has a sensitivity of about 10^{-8} ml/liter sea water. In absolute terms, this is about 10^{-12} moles of gas (Swinnerton and Linnenbom, 1967a). This sensitivity, achieved through the use of a flame-ionization detector rather than the thermal conductivity detector used for fixed gases, has enabled us to show for the first time the presence of gaseous hydrocarbons other than methane in sea water (Swinnerton and Linnenbom, 1967b).

Briefly, the technique involves first stripping the dissolved hydrocarbons from the sea water by purging with helium, then concentrating them in cold traps containing appropriate adsorbents. The trapped gases are subsequently released by warming the adsorbents, and swept into the chromatograph by a second stream of helium carrier gas. With this technique, sample size is not restricted and very dilute solutions may be analyzed. Two cold traps at -80 C in series are used. In the first, activated alumina traps all hydrocarbons except methane. In the second, activated charcoal traps methane. When the stripping is complete, the traps are isolated by closing a valve and the temperature is raised to approximately 90 C. Helium carrier gas then strips each adsorbent in turn of the adsorbed gases, and carries these gases into the chromatograph for further separation and analysis.

Our work thus far has been largely exploratory; we are trying to get an idea of the distribution of C_1 to C_4 compounds and at the same time are evaluating our methods for shipboard use. Several trends appear evident at this time.

1. Surface concentrations appear to be pretty much the same in different areas. Methane has about the value one would expect on the basis of its partial pressure in the atmosphere. For the higher C_2 to C_4 hydrocarbons, partial pressure data in the atmosphere are not available, and

it is not possible at this time to predict whether equilibrium between dissolved and atmospheric gases exists.

2. In the upper layer (0 to 200 m) we have found pronounced concentration peaks, with the olefins generally being higher in concentration than their saturated homologues. This non-homogeneous distribution suggests the existence of processes occurring at rates faster than physical mixing rates. The fact that plankton distributions in the upper layer also show pronounced peaks suggests a possible correlation between the hydrocarbon distribution and biological processes. This is one of the directions in which we are working.

3. In oxygenated waters concentrations generally tend to decrease with depth, but in anoxic areas the situation is reversed, with methane increasing 3 to 4 orders of magnitude and ethane approximately 2 orders. Unsaturated compounds, however, show no such increase. This suggests that the mechanism of hydrocarbon production in anoxic waters is different from that in the oxygenated upper layer. It is known that methane is produced by the anaerobic decomposition of organic matter. Whether higher hydrocarbons are also produced during this process has never been unambiguously determined.

This difference between oxygenated and anoxic waters with respect to hydrocarbon production is clearly shown by data in Fig. 1 through 3. Fig. 1, for example, shows that the ethylene peaks in the upper, highly oxygenated waters of the Atlantic are much more pronounced than those for ethane. Conversely, there is a pronounced increase in ethane concentration with depth in the Black Sea, beginning at the level where the oxygen concentration approaches zero. Although not shown, this increase is even more striking in the case of methane. In all areas there is in general a greater concentration of unsaturates than of the corresponding saturates except in the deeper anoxic layers of the Black Sea. The behavior of methane in anoxic waters is illustrated in Fig. 2, based on samples from the Cariaco Trench. In the upper oxygenated zone, concentration peaks of methane are observed at 50 and 90 m. Beginning at about 300 m, the depth at which dissolved oxygen decreases to zero, the methane concentration begins to increase and continues increasing to the bottom. Similar data by Atkinson and Richards (1967) in the anoxic zone are also plotted in Fig. 2 to illustrate the general agreement as to methane distribution with depth. Fig. 3 shows the distribution of the C_2 and C_3 compounds in the Cariaco Trench. In these samples, ethane and ethylene were not separated analytically, and the plotted points (circles) represent total C_2 concentrations. In the upper zone, the points represent predominately ethylene; at greater depths where oxygen is depleted, the increase in concentration is due primarily to ethane. A noticeable increase in propane concentration with depth is also evident. This increase is probably due to decomposition of organic materials, although this has not yet been demonstrated.

In summing up the situation for low molecular weight hydrocarbons, the following general areas need further investigation.

1. The relation between atmospheric partial pressures and the concentrations of hydrocarbons in the upper layers needs further investigation.

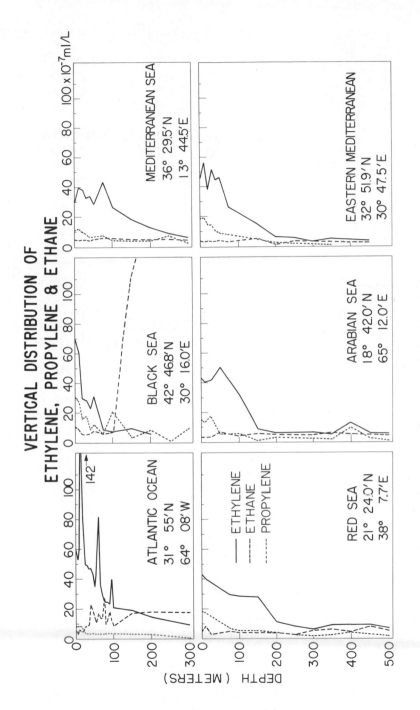

Fig. 1. Vertical distribution in the upper layer of ethylene, propylene and ethane.
——— ethylene; — — ethane; - - - propylene

-457-

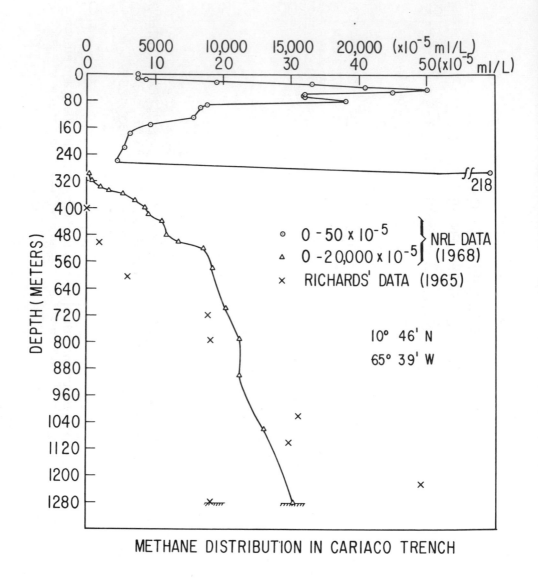

Fig. 2.   Vertical distribution of methane in the Cariaco Trench.

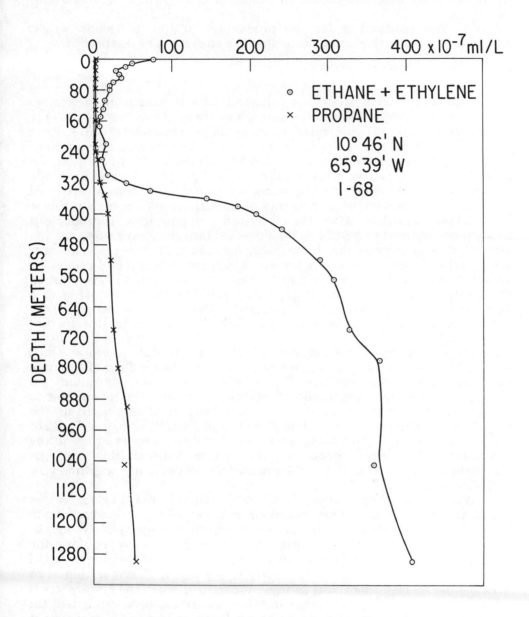

Fig. 3.   Vertical distribution of C_2 (ethane plus ethylene) and C_3 (propane) hydrocarbons in the Cariaco Trench.

2. The concentration peaks which appear in the vertical profiles of the upper layers are probably related to biological activity, but this point must be clarified.

3. The mechanism for the production of low molecular weight hydrocarbons other than methane in anoxic waters must be established.

CARBON MONOXIDE IN SEA WATER

Our most recent work has concerned the measurement of carbon monoxide in sea water. After a few simple modifications we were able to use our existing analytical equipment to make these measurements. Fig. 4 is a schematic diagram of the apparatus being used. The samples are purged as usual with helium in a stripping chamber (not shown in this figure), and the gases are then trapped in the two cold traps. A slight modification was made in the second cold trap by using as the adsorbent a mixture of activated charcoal and molecular sieve. This trap quantitatively retains both methane and carbon monoxide. After the prescribed stripping time, the sample is isolated and warmed to 90 C. It is then injected into the chromatograph. The sample proceeds through the chromatographic column, in this case molecular sieve, and then passes through a furnace which contains a nickel catalyst in an atmosphere of hydrogen at 300 C. Under these conditions, the carbon monoxide is reduced to methane, which can then be measured with a flame-ionization detector. This technique, therefore, has a sensitivity equivalent to that for hydrocarbons, that is, 10^{-12} moles of gas (Swinnerton et al., 1968).

In June of 1968, we participated in an oceanographic cruise which originated in Washington, D. C., and terminated in Puerto Rico. This cruise had two purposes. One was to evaluate the flame-ionization gas chromatographic equipment under shipboard conditions; the second was to obtain measurements of carbon monoxide and methane both in the atmosphere and surface waters during the transit from Washington, D. C., to Puerto Rico. Prior to this time, samples for analysis were returned to the laboratory. The work done on this cruise showed that the gas chromatograph, in particular the flame-ionization detector, performs very satisfactorily on board ship.

From the data collected on atmospheric and surface water concentrations of both carbon monoxide and methane we hoped to obtain information on the direction of transport across the air-sea interface: that is, whether these gases are generated in the water and escape into the atmosphere, or whether as a result of relatively high atmospheric partial pressures, the gases go into solution in the sea water. This question as to whether the sea might be acting as a sink for waste gases in the atmosphere is an important one with long range implications. It has been estimated, for example, that carbon monoxide is being produced by man-made processes at a rate approaching 200 million tons per year; the residence time of this major pollutant in the atmosphere is not well known and it is possible that appreciable amounts are being absorbed into the ocean. Junge (1963) estimates that the average atmospheric concentration of methane on a

F & M MODEL 700 GAS CHROMATOGRAPH

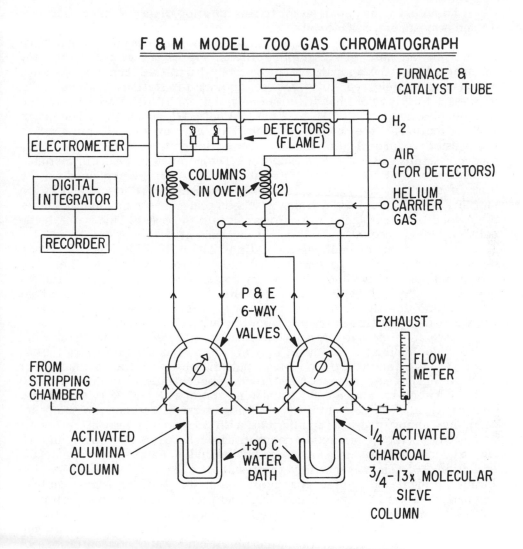

Fig. 4.   Schematic flow diagram for carbon monoxide analysis.

world-wide basis is between 1.2 and 1.5 ppm. However, carbon monoxide concentrations vary widely as the result of both natural and man-made processes, and best estimates (outside of contaminated urban areas) generally range between 0.01 and 0.20 ppm.

To obtain some data relevant to this question of gas exchange between sea and atmosphere, surface water samples were collected in one-liter bottles, and air samples were collected approximately three inches above the surface by drawing air into glass sampling flasks. Fig. 5 shows the results for methane. Along the abscissa are successively numbered sampling stations, with approximately ten miles between points for stations 1 through 22. Stations 1 to 9 are Potomac River samples, stations 10 to 15 are Chesapeake Bay samples, and stations 16 to 29 are Atlantic Ocean samples. The ocean samples begin at the mouth of the Bay and extend 60 miles on a southeasterly course. The methane concentration in the surface waters tends to decrease downriver from Washington. The anomalous peaks in methane concentration observed in the water at station 16 can be explained on the basis of tides and the James River influence. Sample 16 was taken in the morning during a slack tide, which had been preceded by an ebb tide; under these conditions, the James River flows out into the ocean. This water, being polluted, could account for the rise in methane at both stations 16 and 17. The concentrations of methane for stations 24 to 29, while they appear to be zero on the graph, have values of from 3 to 4 x 10^{-5} ml/liter. The concentrations of methane in the air after station 3 tend to remain remarkably constant, with an average value of 1.24 ± 0.03 ppm; the high values found for the first three stations (in the Potomac River) are very likely a result of methane escaping from the surface waters.

Carbon monoxide presents an entirely different picture from that observed for methane. In Fig. 6, it is apparent that the concentrations in water do not follow the consistent pattern observed for methane. For example, an increase in carbon monoxide concentration by a factor of 20 occurs between stations 8 and 21. Between stations 18 and 23 (well out into the ocean), a sharp concentration peak is observed; methane, on the other hand, has almost reached equilibrium with the atmosphere in this area. Atmospheric carbon monoxide concentrations between stations 1 and 15 tend to decrease as the urban areas are left behind. An abrupt increase occurs at station 16; this was possibly the result of a change in wind direction during the night and the fact that considerable ship traffic was noticeable in this particular area during the sampling operation. The lowest concentration in the air samples, 75 ppb, was observed at station 28.

At several points in Fig. 6, there appears to be a possible cause and effect relationship between the atmospheric and water concentrations of carbon monoxide (e.g., stations 18 to 22). In an attempt to determine whether such a correlation might exist, and to obtain further information on the direction of gas transport across the air-sea interface for both carbon monoxide and methane, a ratio W/T of measured to theoretical concentrations in the water was determined for each of the stations. The theoretical concentration T is the amount of gas which would be present in the water if the only source were the atmosphere. It was calculated by

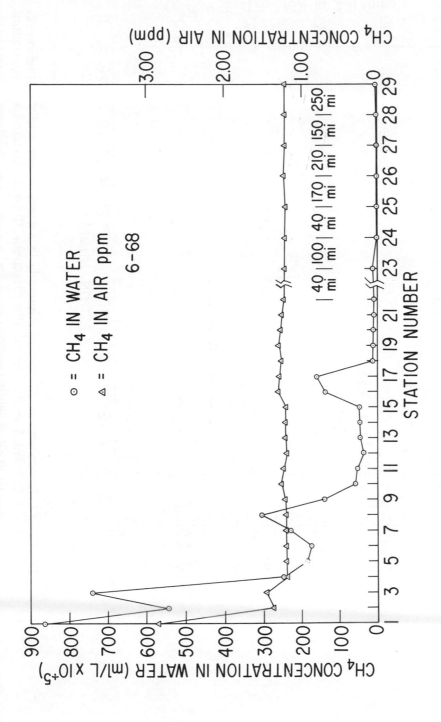

Fig. 5.   Concentration of methane in surface waters and the atmosphere. Stations 1 to 9, Potomac River; stations 10 to 15, Chesapeake Bay; stations 16 to 29, Atlantic Ocean.

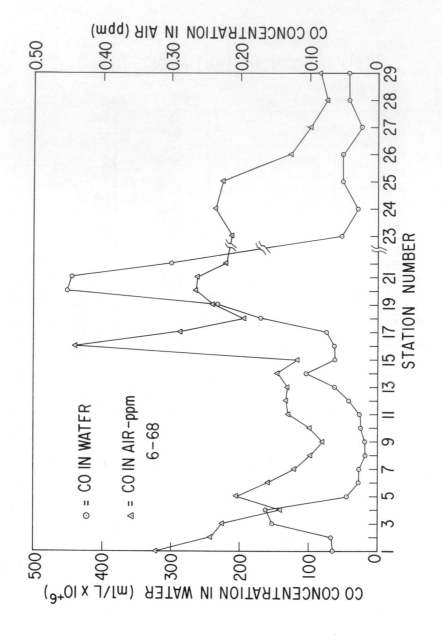

Fig. 6.   Concentration of carbon monoxide in surface waters and the atmosphere. Stations 1 to 9, Potomac River; stations 10 to 15, Chesapeake Bay; stations 16 to 29, Atlantic Ocean.

multiplying the measured atmospheric partial pressures by the appropriate solubility coefficient. The solubility coefficients used for methane are from Atkinson and Richards (1967); those for carbon monoxide are from Douglas (1967). These calculated ratios are shown in Fig. 7. At stations 1 to 9 (Potomac River) high values for the methane ratios are noted, indicating probable transport of gas from the water to the atmosphere. However, as the open ocean is reached, the values approach 1 (see stations 24 to 29). This is the value expected if equilibrium conditions exist between the partial pressure of atmospheric methane and the concentration in the surface water. The highest W/T values for carbon monoxide approach 90 and occur at station numbers 20 and 21 (in the open ocean). A W/T value of 1 for carbon monoxide was not observed for any of the samples collected during this cruise, the lowest value being about 7.

These results suggest that the ocean, bay and river may themselves be a source of carbon monoxide, with the transport of gas being from the water to the atmosphere. It is known that various algae, green plants and some species of siphonopores produce carbon monoxide. Whether their population density is sufficiently high to contribute to the carbon monoxide concentration observed in the water at stations 20 and 21 is not known at this time. Unfortunately, no water samples were collected during this cruise for biological analysis. Therefore, we can only speculate as to the source of carbon monoxide observed in the water. It would appear that the concentrations of carbon monoxide found in the water are not caused by man-made pollution, contrary to what seems to be the case for methane since the highest values found for dissolved carbon monoxide were observed in the open ocean. Rather than acting as a sink for atmospheric carbon monoxide, the sea appears to be a source. The mechanisms responsible for the production of carbon monoxide in the water remain to be determined.

REFERENCES

ATKINSON, L. P., and F. A. RICHARDS. 1967. The occurrence and distribution of methane in the marine environment. Deep-Sea Res., *14*: 673-684.

DOUGLAS, E. 1967. Carbon monoxide solubilities in sea water. J. Phys. Chem., *71*: 1931-1933.

JUNGE, C. E. 1963. Air chemistry and radioactivity. Academic Press, New York.

SWINNERTON, J. W., and V. J. LINNENBOM. 1967a. Determination of the C_1 to C_4 hydrocarbons in sea water by gas chromatography. J. Gas Chromatogr., *5*: 570-573.

SWINNERTON, J. W., and V. J. LINNENBOM. 1967b. Gaseous hydrocarbons in sea water: determination. Science, *156*: 1119-1120.

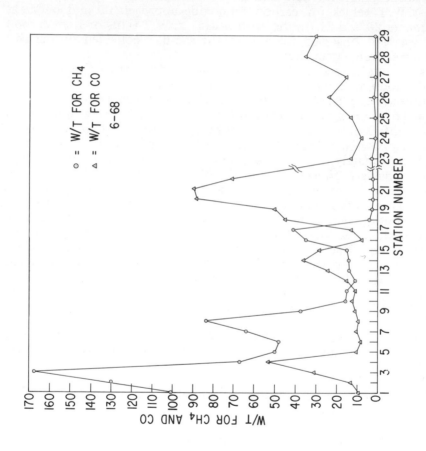

Fig. 7. Variations in the ratio of measured to calculated concentrations in surface waters. W = measured concentration, T = calculated concentration assuming atmosphere as sole source. Stations 1 to 9, Potomac River; stations 10 to 15, Chesapeake Bay; stations 16 to 29, Atlantic Ocean.

SWINNERTON, J. W., V. J. LINNENBOM, and C.H. CHEEK. 1968. A sensitive gas chromatographic method for determining carbon monoxide in sea water. Limnol. Oceanogr., *13*: 193-195.

ORGANIC CHEMISTRY OF NATURAL SEA SURFACE FILMS

W. D. Garrett
Chemical Oceanography Branch
Naval Research Laboratory
Washington, D.C. 20390

BACKGROUND

The chemical composition and physical effects of adsorbed monomolecular films at the air/sea interface have been active subjects of study in recent years. The most pronounced surface effect of these one-molecule-thick layers is the damping of the capillary wave spectrum (wavelengths less than 1.7 cm). When the adsorbed surface molecules are compressed into an immobile film, the resulting ripple-free zone produces a light reflectance anomaly known commonly as a sea slick (Garrett, 1967a). These surface films are truly mono-molecular since only the polar molecules directly attached to the air/sea interface can reduce its surface free energy and alter its physical properties. Furthermore, film pressures measured in natural sea slicks are almost always less than the collapse pressures of lipid or protein monolayers. Thus, sea surface films are not usually compressed by convergent forces to the point where they are forced into a multilayered structure.

Surface-active organic substances reach the air/sea interface through a number of transport modes (Fig. 1). In quiescent water, when vertical mass transport does not operate, the film accumulation rate is controlled by the slow process of molecular diffusion. Much more rapid transport is provided by thermal circulation cells which not only carry material to the surface, but also generate surface convergences necessary to increase film pressure and alter surface properties. Film forming material is transported by rising bubbles whose gas/water interfaces adsorb surface-active materials on their journey to the surface. Organic substances are also transported vertically by upwellings, buoyant organisms and organic particulate matter.

The life cycle of surface-active material (Fig. 1) reveals the large number of dispersive forces which act upon the adsorbed monomolecular film. Low molecular weight and water soluble compounds are lost from the surface by dissolution and evaporation. Other substances are returned to the sea by bacteriological attack (ZoBell, 1963; Pilpel, 1968), adsorption onto nonbuoyant particles and the physical action of waves and breaking water. In addition, constituents of the surface are forced back into the sea by sinking water beneath wind-driven streaks of surface film (Kraus, 1967). Chemically unsaturated components are readily attacked by ultraviolet radiation. This photochemical oxidation ultimately breaks the unsaturated molecules into smaller, more soluble fragments (Timmons, 1962). In addition to evaporation, organic film material is carried into the marine atmosphere by wind-generated spray or by fragments of bursting bubbles (Blanchard, 1964). Nature's compound attack upon the sea surface prevents the ocean from becoming wholly slick covered and partially destroys and

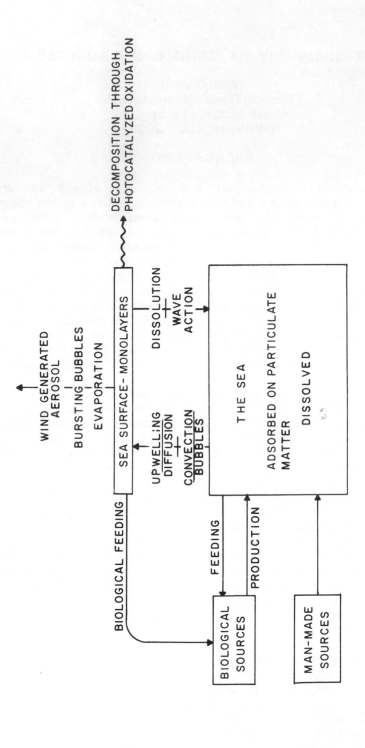

Fig. 1.   Cycle of surface-active organic compounds in the ocean.

disperses the vast quantities of oil contamination from bilge pumping, petroleum spills and coastal oil-drilling operations.

SEA SURFACE COMPOSITION

Any polar organic compound will adsorb for a period of time when it contacts a phase boundary. At the sea surface polar molecules adsorb with their hydrophilic functional groups attached to the water and their hydrophobic segments oriented away from the sea. It is necessary to determine which of the many classes of compounds common to the ocean will adsorb preferentially and possess the greatest lifetime under the dynamic conditions which prevail at a wave-covered sea surface. Williams (1967) sampled the upper few tenths of a millimeter of the sea and found increased surface concentrations of dissolved and particulate organic carbon, nitrogen and phosphorous. Concentration gradients were found between surface samples and subsurface water at all stations whether a visible slick was present or not. Similar results were reported by Garrett (1967b) who found lipid material in a wide range of surface samples regardless of the sea surface conditions. Thus, it can be concluded that surface-active organic material exists at the sea surface at all locations providing a chemical potential for the formation of slicks. In biologically rich coastal regions, where the concentrations are greatest and dispersive conditions the least active, convergent forces often compress or concentrate the surface molecules into coherent films capable of damping capillary waves to produce visible surface scars.

The data of Williams (1967) suggest that lipids, proteins, phosphorous-containing compounds and possibly carbohydrates are available at the sea surface to contribute to film formation. However, based upon the previous discussion of forces operating upon a surface film, it is likely that the most important and durable family of compounds at the air/water interface would be the lipids of high molecular weight. For example, a fatty acid or glyceride fatty ester would be highly polar and water insoluble. Consequently, these molecules would possess a strong tendency to adsorb preferentially, displace other less active species and endure longer at the sea surface. According to Jarvis et al. (1967), the working of a coherent surface film by the contractions and dilations of the surface due to passing waves progressively excludes the more soluble and less permanent molecules. Thus, the fatty acids, alcohols and esters are the principal modifiers of the sea surface, especially under conditions which perturb the developed film. Proteinaceous substances which have denatured to a water-insoluble configuration may also constitute a part of the effective surface modifying film.

An example of fatty acid and fatty alcohol distributions in two related samples appears in Table 1. Sample A was collected by the screen technique (Garrett, 1965) which removes the upper 0.15 mm of the sea, while B was a bucket sample taken from the same station. The lipid material was concentrated, extracted and analyzed by gas chromatography by a previously described procedure (Garrett, 1967b). These two samples were collected in the Atlantic Ocean, 19 miles south of Block Island, Rhode

Table 1.   Fatty acids and alcohols obtained from sea samples.

Alcohols and fatty acids (Carbons:double bonds)	Relative quantities* A	B
11:0	-	0.5
12:0	-	-
Dodecanol	12.5	54.5
14:0	16.5	2.5
14:1	-	-
	4.0	1.0
15:0	-	-
16:0	26.0	14.5
16:1	-	2.5
Hexadecanol	-	0.5
17:0	6.0	1.0
	11.0	-
18:0	11.0	10.0
18:1	4.5	3.5
18:2	1.0	2.5
18:3	3.0	1.5
19:0	-	-
20:0	2.0	1.5
	2.5	3.0
22:0	-	-
Average carbon chain length	16.0	14.8

*Per cent of total peak area occupied by a particular chromatographic peak. Values calculated to nearest 0.5%.

Island. At the time of sampling, the sea had been calm for several hours and was 75% slick covered. The collected chloroform-soluble constituents were spread onto a hydrophil balance for the measurement of their force-area characteristics on a clean artificial sea water surface. The force exerted by the two dimensional layer was recorded as a function of film area covered per unit weight of material (Fig. 2). A force-area curve was also plotted for oleic acid, a fatty acid common to the sea surface which spreads completely into a film of monomolecular dimensions.

By comparison with the oleic acid data, surface sample A behaved much like a pure surface-active compound giving a spread film with 74% area coverage of that of the pure fatty acid at 19 dynes/cm film pressure. On the other hand, bucket sample B from the same location yielded a film several molecules thick which was partly soluble and difficult to reproduce. Film B occupied only 26% of the area per mg of that of oleic acid indicating that many of its constituents did not contribute to surface effects. This sample contained nonpolar and/or soluble substances displaced from the surface by the more surface-active molecules as the film was compressed. The fatty acid and alcohol spectra (Table 1) reveal a high variability in the specific organic compounds in the sea. While the general chemical classes are found in most areas of the ocean, great variability may occur due to localized events, one of which is the presence of a phase boundary where selective adsorption occurs. Larger amounts of dodecanol were found in the bucket sample accounting for its shorter average carbon chain length. These analytical data are consistent with the sampling conditions and the force-area measurements. That is, the screen-collected surface sample contained molecules which were less soluble, had longer carbon chains and were more permanent residents of the sea surface. The subsurface water, on the other hand, contained compounds having shorter carbon chains, less surface activity and greater solubility.

Although the sea is a complex mixture of many classes of biologically produced chemicals, selective adsorption at the air/water interface may result in an enrichment of the more polar, water insoluble species. This has been substantiated not only by analytical results, but also by capillary wave damping studies (Garrett, 1967a) and measurements of single-bubble lifetimes at a sea water surface (Garrett, 1967c). These physical effects of natural films were shown to be characteristic of incompressible water insoluble monolayers of lipids or possibly proteins.

DISCUSSIONS

MENZEL. Do you have any feeling at all for what percentage of ocean slicks are man-made? What I am asking essentially is, are there not some tags you can use to distinguish between a natural and a man-made slick?

GARRETT: Most man-made slicks contain a high degree of petroleum. This is not a monomolecular film. You usually see interference colors in oil slicks which may be several thousand Ångstroms thick, rather than the thirty Ångstrom thickness of a molecule such as oleic acid standing on end. Did you want a comment about the distribution of the sea slicks themselves?

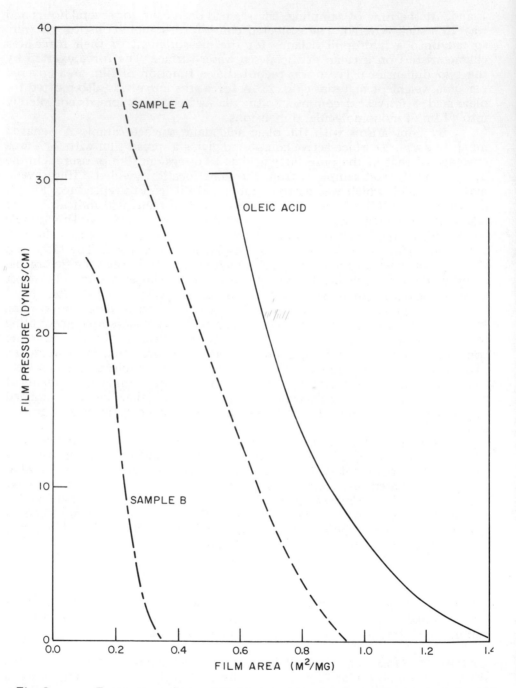

Fig. 2. Force-area plots of lipid extracts of sea samples and oleic acid.

MENZEL: The reason I am asking is that I went on a rather long trip this spring and, while twiddling my thumbs on deck when there was nothing else to do, I was watching for slicks. I never saw any, except in a shipping lane.

GARRETT: The open ocean is usually rough enough so that sea slicks are very rare. Consequently I think that this study is mainly of interest in coastal regions and in areas that are biologically rich. The slicks that you saw in shipping lanes are definitely pollution, and I think if you collected them, you would find a high concentration of petroleum hydrocarbons.

PARSONS: Is not the natural slick heavily modified by bacteria floating at the surface as well? I am thinking of the Carlucci and Williams paper about bacteria aggregating on bubbles at the sea surface (Carlucci and Williams, 1965).

GARRETT: Yes, I imagine it is a very complex picture. The bacteria are eating on the slick and in turn producing organic surface active materials of their own.

CHAVE: In your fatty acid analyses, you showed these differences from the surface down. What sort of differences do you get with two samples of the same surface water?

GARRETT: In other words, what is the repeatability? It is quite good. There are a lot of data I did not show, depth profiles, for example. These profiles were taken at 10 m intervals in an area that was well mixed. Some of these fatty acid spectra are hardly distinguishable, one from another. I just showed the interesting ones which indicate large fatty acid differences due to localized events occurring at sea.

ROSEN: I would like to know more about that screen sampler. I never heard of this. How quantitative is it? How does it work?

GARRETT: I do not know if you could call it quantitative or not, it is just a device for taking a very thin slice of the ocean surface. It has been tested in a tank at the laboratory with an artificial monolayer, and each bite that it takes removes an amount of monolayer equivalent to the open space between the wires. The wires themselves do not remove surface film once they have become hydrophobic through the adsorption of polar organic material.

WILLIAMS: I would like to mention something in answer to Dr. Menzel. We have used this screen in the North and South Pacific. In most cases there was not any indication of a slick of any type, and yet in every case there was a concentration of organic matter of 5 to 10 orders of magnitude over that of water about 5 to 10 cm below. Whether these were monolayers or stacked up multilayers I do not know. This occurs even in the presence of white caps. It is not necessarily associated with anything you can see.

GARRETT: That is right. There is material, but it is too dilute to cause a surface effect known as a sea slick. When the material becomes sufficiently concentrated and the molecules get shoved close enough together so that they begin to act like an immobile sheet at the water surface, hydrodynamically this is the way it is described; then it starts interfering with the propagation of the capillary waves and the formation of new ones.

MALCOLM: How does the composition of the sea slick compare to the highly ordered structure of the sea foam that you see on the shore or the coastline?

GARRETT: I have never analyzed sea foam, but sea foam results from a very fancy collection job done by Nature, when a long fetch of wind has swept the sea surface. Usually these foams are stabilized, I understand, by almost dust-like particulate matter. This is part of the stabilizing mechanism. I do not know too much about this, but I think the analysis of such a foam would come fairly close to that of the sea surface. Also, I think it would be fairly high in protein material, a good foam stabilizer. Since the foam has been generated by a sweeping of the surface by the wind, these foams usually appear in fairly stormy weather.

SIEBURTH: We have used Garrett's sampler to enumerate the bacteria in the upper few hundred microns (Sieburth, 1965). In the Pacific Ocean, we found an average of eight organisms/ml at ten meters, while at the sea surface it would go up to 10,000/ml. This slick material averaged 2000/ml. This is unusual for open ocean bacterial counts and indicated a lot of organic matter at the surface.

REFERENCES

BLANCHARD, D. C. 1964. Sea-to-air transport of surface active material. Science, *146*: 396-397.

GARRETT, W. D. 1965. Collection of slick-forming materials from the sea surface. Limnol. Oceanogr., *10*: 602-605.

GARRETT, W. D. 1967a. Damping of capillary wave at the air sea interface by oceanic surface-active material. J. Mar. Res., *25*: 279-291.

GARRETT, W. D. 1967b. The organic chemical composition of the ocean surface. Deep-Sea Res., *14*: 221-227.

GARRETT, W. D. 1967c. Stabilization of air bubbles at the air sea interface by surface-active material. Deep-Sea Res., *14*: 661-672.

JARVIS, N. L., W. D. GARRETT, M. A. SCHEIMAN, and C. O. TIMMONS. 1967. Surface chemical characterization of surface-active material in sea water. Limnol. Oceanogr., *12*: 88-97.

KRAUS, E. B. 1967. Organized convection in the ocean resulting from slicks and wave radiation stress. Phys. Fluids, *10*: S294-S297, (Suppl.).

PILPEL, N. 1968. The natural fats of oil on the sea. Endeavour, *100*: 11-13.

TIMMONS, C. O. 1962. Stability of plankton oil films to artificial sunlight. U.S. Nav. Res. Lab. Rep. No. 5774. 8 p.

WILLIAMS, P. M. 1967. Sea surface chemistry: organic carbon and organic and inorganic nitrogen and phosphorus in surface films and subsurface waters. Deep-Sea Res., *14*: 791-800.

ZOBELL, C. E. 1963. The occurrence, effects and fate of oil polluting the sea. Int. J. Air. Water Poll., 7: 173-193.

CONDITIONAL STABILITY CONSTANTS OF A NORTH CAROLINA SOIL FULVIC ACID WITH Co^{2+} AND Fe^{3+} [1]

R. L. Malcolm, E. A. Jenne and P. W. McKinley
U.S. Geological Survey
Federal Center
Denver, Colorado 80225

ABSTRACT

Fulvic acid-Co^{2+} conditional stability constants are 2.7, 4.0 and 6.6 at pH 3.0, 4.5 and 6.0, respectively. Conditional constants for fulvic acid-Fe^{3+} complexes are 4.5, 5.4 and 5.6 at pH 3.0, 4.5 and 6.0, respectively. These values were obtained using the resin-exchange method of Schubert (1948) which involves radio-tracer techniques. The conditional stability constants are believed to be more indicative of F.A.-ionic relationships in natural soil and water environments than the thermodynamic constants. The thermodynamic stability constants for the complexes studied can be calculated by correcting the conditional constants for competitive complex formation with the Cl^- ligand, hydrolysis of ionic species, protonation of the organic ligand, and activity coefficients of the reacting species.

INTRODUCTION

Complexes of organic materials with dissolved metals are abundant in natural waters. The specificity of dissolved and particulate organics for the various metals affects both the transport properties and the availability of these metal ions for organic and inorganic reactions. Since the fulvic and humic acids formed in soils are believed to be a major source of both the dissolved and particulate organic matter of streams, fulvic acid-metal and humic acid-metal stability constants are useful tools in the interpretation of observed concentrations of metals in natural waters.

The ability of natural organic material to complex metal ions is commonly expressed on a weight-weight basis because of the difficulty of characterizing the molecular weight of natural organic matter separates. However, the weight-weight basis is relatively noninformative as to specific affinities and stabilities of the organic matter and resulting complexes.

A recent development, the accurate and rapid determination of the molecular weight of soluble natural organics, facilitates the calculations of organic matter-metal conditional stability constants. Stability constants quantify the affinity of the ligand (organic matter) for specific ions on a strictly chemical basis. Schnitzer and Skinner (1966, 1967) reported on the conditional stability constants of Co^{2+}, Fe^{2+} and other divalent species with fulvic acid from a Canadian podzol. This paper reports initial results from studies of conditional stability constants for Co^{2+} and Fe^{3+} with fulvic acid from a North Carolina podzol.

[1] Published with approval of the Director, U.S. Geological Survey

CONDITIONAL STABILITY CONSTANTS (Ringbom, 1963)

Strictly speaking, stability constants are thermodynamic quantities based on activities rather than concentrations of the reacting species. In instances when the activity of certain species is not known or cannot be determined, concentrations are used rather than activities, and the resulting constant is called an apparent or concentration stability constant. The magnitude of these constants is a function of ionic strength. Additional complications are involved in stability constant evaluation when the reactants participate in side reactions in addition to the reaction of interest. In this study, for example, hydrolysis of the metal ion, protonation of the organic ligand and complexation of metal ions with the competing Cl^- ligand must be considered. Stability constants uncorrected for such competing side reactions are called conditional stability constants.

METHODS

The soil sample from which the fulvic acid was extracted was taken from a podzol Bh horizon in Brunswick County, North Carolina, along the inland waterway approximately one mile from the ocean. The bulk organic matter was extracted with 0.1 N NaOH under nitrogen using a soil:solution ratio of 1:10. Purification of the organic material was accomplished by centrifugation, pressure filtration, dialysis and resin exchange. Humic-fulvic acid separation was accomplished at pH 1.0. After purification, the organic material was freeze-dried.

The conditional stability constants were determined by Schubert's (1948) resin-exchange method at pH 3.0, 4.5 and 6.0 utilizing the relationships

$$\log \left| (\frac{\lambda o}{\lambda})\text{-1} \right| = \log_{10} K + x \log_{10} F.A.$$

$$\lambda o = \frac{\alpha o}{(100 - \alpha o)} \frac{V}{g}$$

where λo = the distribution constant when F.A. (fulvic acid) is absent; λ = distribution constant in the presence of F.A.; $\log_{10} K$ = $\log_{10}$ stability constant; x = the molar ratio or the number of moles of F.A. combining with one mole of metal; F.A. = concentration of fulvic acid in moles per liter; αo = per cent of total metal bound to exchange resin; 100 - αo = per cent of total metal remaining in solution; V = volume of solution; and g = weight of exchange resin. The molar ratio x was obtained from the slope of the plot of $(\lambda o/\lambda)$-1 versus F.A. concentration in moles per liter. The experimental procedure described by Schnitzer and Skinner (1966) was used with the exception that all experiments were scaled down to a volume of 10.0 ml and 0.2 g of exchange resin. The concentrations of Fe^{3+} and Co^{2+} were 0.05 $\mu g/ml$ and 10.0 $\mu g/ml$, respectively. The supporting electrolyte for maintainence of a constant ionic strength was 1 F KCl. Both Co^{2+} and Fe^{3+}

concentrations were determined by radiometric techniques for duplicate 1.0 ml solution aliquots after resin equilibration. The average molecular weight of fulvic acid, determined to be 585 g/mole by vapor pressure osmometry, made possible molarity calculations for F.A. solutions.

RESULTS AND DISCUSSION

Conditional stability constant calculations are illustrated by Schnitzer and Skinner (1966, 1967). The values for F.A.-Co^{2+} complexes increase linearly with increasing pH from 2.7 at pH 3.0 to 4.0 at pH 4.5 and to 6.6 at pH 6.0. These values are higher than those reported by Schnitzer and Skinner (1967) who obtained values of 2.2 at pH 3.5 and 3.7 at pH 5.0, but both sets of data show the great dependence of F.A.-Co^{2+} conditional stability constants on pH.

The conditional stability constants for F.A.-Fe^{3+} complexes are 4.5, 5.4 and 5.6 for pH 3.0, 4.5 and 6.0, respectively. These values are higher than those for Co^{2+} at pH 3.0 and 4.5, but lower than Co^{2+} values at pH 6.0. The F.A.-Fe^{3+} conditional stability constants exhibit little pH dependence. There are no published conditional stability constants for Fe^{3+} with which to compare these data other than the values for Fe^{2+} constants determined by Schnitzer and Skinner (1966), 5.1 at pH 3.5 and 5.8 at pH 5.0.

The molar ratios for Co^{2+} increase with increasing pH from 1.1 at pH 3.0 to 1.8 at pH 6.0. Thus, at pH 3.0 and 4.5, Co^{2+} and fulvic acid react in approximately equal molar quantities, whereas at pH 6.0, nearly two moles of F.A. react with one mole of Co^{2+}. The molar ratios for Fe^{3+} show little pH dependence, increasing slightly from 1.1 at pH 3.0 to 1.2 at pH 4.5 and then decreasing to 1.1 at pH 6.0. At all three pH values, the Fe^{3+} and fulvic acid react in approximately equal molar quantities.

The relative consistency of F.A.-Fe^{3+} molar ratios with pH and the increasingly higher F.A.-Co^{2+} molar ratios with increasing pH are intriguing. The molar ratios might be expected to decrease with increasing pH due to an increase in negative charge (or pH dependent charge) of the fulvic acid. As more reactive groups become ionized, the amount of metal ion complexed per mole of fulvic acid might be expected to increase. Apparently the weak acid sites, those nonionized at pH 3.0, have very little affinity for the metals in question. The hydrolysis of Fe^{3+} is undoubtedly an important factor in determining molar ratios, and can be evaluated when the thermodynamic stability constant is calculated.

Although it is desirable to establish thermodynamic stability constants for F.A. metal complexes, conditional constants are especially useful to the organic geochemist, because they evaluate the reaction of interest in competition with all possible side reactions which the ligand, the metal ion and the resulting complex undergo in a given environment. For example, competing side reactions in the complexation of Fe^{3+} by fulvic acid in Nature and in this study are hydrolysis of Fe^{3+}, competition of the Cl^- and fulvic acid ligands for Fe^{3+}, and protonation of the organic ligand. Even if the true stability constant were known for F.A.-Fe^{3+} complexes, it would be necessary to calculate a conditional constant which could then be applied to the natural environment. In this instance the conditional constant would be much smaller than the true constant; therefore, if one used the true constant rather than the conditional constant, one could over-estimate the importance of fulvic acid in the tie-up or complexation of Fe^{3+} in relation to other reactions or mechanisms in the natural environment.

Conditional stability constants were determined directly in this study in order (1) to appraise the importance of F.A.-Fe and F.A.-Co complexes in a natural stream or soil environment and (2) to provide a basis for subsequent calculation of true stability constants of F.A.-Fe and F.A.-Co complexes. The experimental results suggest that fulvic acid forms relatively stable complexes with Co and Fe ions, especially at pH 4 to 6. Thus fulvic acid is probably an important scavenger of these ions in the natural environment and would be important in the physico-chemical transformations, transport and distribution of these ions. When the stability constants for Fe and Co ions with clay minerals, sesquioxides and other ionic scavengers and ligands in the natural environment are determined, the precise role of fulvic acid as a specific ion scavenger can be determined.

It is desirable to determine the thermodynamic stability constant for fulvic acid with given metal ions so that a conditional constant can be calculated for any given chemical environment. The thermodynamic constant for fulvic acid and a given metal ion is constant or truly a constant, but there is an infinity of conditional stability constants because there is an infinite variety of chemical conditions in natural waters containing fulvic acid and the metal ions. The thermodynamic constant is a base from which any conditional constant may be calculated, but it is sometimes difficult if not impossible to calculate one conditional constant from another conditional constant.

The appropriate corrections in the F.A.-Co^{2+} and F.A.-Fe^{3+} conditional constants necessary for calculations of the respective true thermodynamic constants are now being considered and evaluated. The corrections include competitive complex formation with the Cl^- ligand, competitive complex formation with the OH^- ligand (hydrolysis of Fe species), protonation of the organic ligand, and activity coefficients for the reacting species. After these corrections the thermodynamic constants for F.A.-Co^{2+} and F.A.-Fe^{3+} complexes are expected to be much larger than the conditional constants.

DISCUSSION

MORGAN: I want to make an observation I think Dr. Duursma would probably agree with about Dr. Malcolm's data. First, I think the equilibrium constant for the functional groups on your organic material is probably on the order of 10^{13} and 10^{14} after you have corrected for the fact that the acid material is binding protons at the pH of your experiment. In other words, the alpha coefficients for hydrogen ion binding are on the order of, I would guess, 10^7 to 10^8, if you assign reasonable pK's to the acidity groups. Your constants for ferric iron at this acidity are really much higher than, I think, you are prepared to believe. Also you must correct these data for the hydrolysis of the ferric iron, and that would correspond to log alpha coefficients on the order of 10^2 to 10^3, even at the pH's with which you work. So your constants really are large, not small, compared to, say, the ferrous iron constants, because there will be a relatively smaller hydrolysis correction in any event. I have not seen Schnitzer's data on the ferrous iron. But the other point is that it is not, in general, true that the higher oxidation state of an element always has a larger stability constant.

MALCOLM: I appreciate your comments. The experimental design was such that the iron was mixed with the organic at low pH and then the pH was adjusted after all the ingredients were in the system. Secondly, a blank with each set without fulvic acid indicated that 80% of the iron was on the resin and not in solution even at pH 6.0. Thus most of the iron was in an ionic form attracted to the resin and not as the completely hydrolyzed $Fe(OH)_3$ uncharged species. I do not know the ratio of variously charged species, but it can be calculated. Essentially, the organic material that is associated with the iron in this system hopefully would prevent hydrolysis as the pH is increased if this is a very stable complex.

MORGAN: Not if your constant is considered an equilibrium constant. Then you are talking about a system which satisfies the demands of equilibrium.

ACKNOWLEDGMENTS

The molecular weight determination was made by S.I.M. Skinner and M. Schnitzer of the Soils Research Institute of the Canadian Department of Agriculture.

REFERENCES

RINGBOM, A. 1963. Complexation in analytical chemistry. Interscience, New York, entire.

SCHNITZER, M., and S. I. M. SKINNER. 1966. Organic-metallic interactions in soils: 6. Stability constants of Cu^{++}-, Fe^{++}-, and Zn^{++}-fulvic acid complexes. Soil Sci., *102*: 361-365.

SCHNITZER, M., and S. I. M. SKINNER. 1967. Organo-metallic interactions in soils: 7. Stability constants of Pb^{++}-, Ni^{++}-, Mn^{++}-, Co^{++}-, Ca^{++}-, and Mg^{++}-fulvic acid complexes. Soil Sci., *103*: 247-252.

SCHUBERT, J. 1948. Use of ion exchangers for the determination of physical-chemical properties of substances, particular radiotracers. J. Phys. Coll. Chem., *52*: 340-350.

TRANSITION METAL BINDING BY LARGE MOLECULES IN HIGH LATITUDE WATERS

Robert J. Barsdate
Institute of Marine Science
University of Alaska
College, Alaska 99701

INTRODUCTION

A fairly convincing argument has been established for the presence of nonionic but filterable zinc and copper in sea water. However, as Morgan (1968) has pointed out, this is based largely on observations that a portion of the metals found do not behave as predicted by the known inorganic chemistry of the metals in question. Carritt (1964) observed that a substantial portion of the zinc from productive inshore waters is unreactive to concentration by a diathizime technique. Slowey (1966) and Slowey, Jeffrey, and Hood (1967) found that fractions of the trace metals manganese, copper and zinc from ocean water are retained in dialysis bags when exhaustively dialyzed against tridistilled water. This material is not extractable with ordinary chelating reagents, which react with the divalent forms of these elements, but is readily extractable when oxidized with persulfuric acid prior to the extraction process. In addition it was observed that extraction with chelating agents responsive to the divalent elements gives significantly lower results for copper and zinc in sea water than are obtained by the same extraction procedures after oxidation of the water with persulfuric acid. Little is known of the origin, character or residence time in the sea of these metal-containing entities; moreover, their biological and geochemical significance is largely undefined.

In fresh water environments the colored organic substances, which for convenience I will term humic acids, undoubtedly play an important role in transition metal complexation. Through the work of Christman (1970) and others, the rather complicated chemical structure of these materials is being clarified. The carboxyl and hydroxyl functional groups of these polyaromatic ligands offer many binding sites for metal ions. Whether the associations formed between many of the transition elements (for example, copper) and these organic acids should be called dissolved complexes is somewhat problematical, as the reaction products of these substances, at least when formed at high concentrations, can be exceedingly insoluble. Although I know of very little experimental evidence bearing directly upon this, I expect that we at least in part are dealing with metal-containing organic colloids, stabilized perhaps by the chemical interactions between the hydroxyl groups of the colloidal particles and the water. Stumm (1967) speculates that the chelation of ferric iron by humic acids may result in a colloidal dispersion rather than true solution in the environmental pH range. On the other hand, Christman (1970), who has been working with iron-containing humic materials, has not observed the presence of size classes larger than the organic molecules. Thus the question is not resolved.

In the initial complexation work in this laboratory a lake for study was chosen specifically on the basis of its rich dissolved organic materials. Gel filtration was used to obtain fractions of organic materials containing substantial amounts of copper and lead and simultaneously to determine the molecular weight of the organic materials involved. After concentration by vacuum evaporation and fractionation by starch gel filtration the total and free ionic metals were determined by anodic stripping voltametry. The molarity of the organic materials was estimated from the molecular weight and the amount of dissolved organic carbon recovered. From this work we calculated an apparent stability constant for lead on the order of 10^{20} (Barsdate and Matson, 1966) and established that colored organic acids are involved in the association with the trace metals (Barsdate, 1967).

The techniques used in this early work were necessarily quite laborious and somewhat unsuited to routine application. To develop a rapid assay for the detection and quantification of metal binding substances in natural waters and in various experimental media, a number of dialytic and electrodialytic techniques were investigated. The dialytic method having the greatest promise, and subsequently being employed in the work described below, also is readily adaptable to the use of radioisotopes, which greatly reduces the number of quantitative analytical determinations necessary in this type of study.

METHODS

This technique consists of adding distilled water to two dialysis bags, which then are suspended in the common medium of lake water. An appropriate radionuclide is added to one of the dialysis bags and the system is allowed to equilibrate. When the concentration of the added tracer is equal in each of the two dialysis sacs, it can be assumed that thermodynamic activity of the metal under study is the same in both sacs and that this equilibration has been achieved by exchange with the central compartment which separates the two sacs. A higher concentration of radionuclide activity in the lake water then indicates that substances in the lake water are associating with the radionuclides to provide sufficiently stable entities to resist dialysis.

Experiments also were conducted in which the lake water was placed in the two dialysis bags, using distilled water as the common medium. When this is done, the radioisotope is added to one of the lake water compartments, and after the equilibration period the radioactivities of the two lake water compartments are similar but not always identical. The disparities so far observed have not been large, and the results of the experiments done in this manner are in agreement with those in which the radionuclides have been added to the distilled water compartments.

Equilibrations were done in 25 x 150 mm culture tubes. The apparatus is shown schematically in Fig. 1. Two dialysis sacs with internal volumes of 11 ml were made up of 28 mm Visking tubing and suspended in a 22 ml volume in each of the culture tubes. Agitation was provided by bubbling a purified, water-saturated gas through these tubes. It was observed

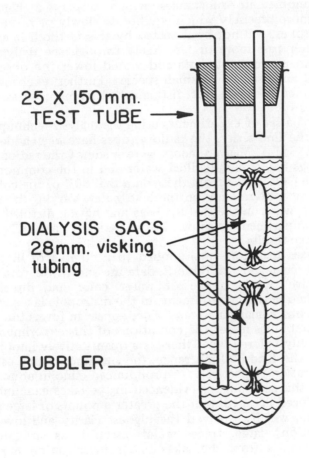

25 X 150mm.
TEST TUBE →

DIALYSIS SACS
28mm. visking
tubing

BUBBLER

Fig. 1.   Schematic diagram of dialysis apparatus.

that the shortest equilibration times were obtained with unrestricted gas inlet tubes which supplied large gas bubbles. Air usually was used as the gas but water-pumped nitrogen was used for some samples containing much ferrous iron.

RESULTS

Perhaps it would be in order to note what this technique will not measure. Organometallic substances which display a high degree of covalency, or more precisely which equilibrate slowly or not at all with the added radioisotopes, will not be detected by this method. In addition those complexes which pass more or less freely through the dialysis membrane would appear in all compartments and would lower the observed ratio of radioactivity of large species to small species. Further, exchangeable metals associated with colloids are not distinguished from those associated with dissolved species.

Results of a set of experiments using the dialysis technique are shown in Table 1. In the first series, the radioisotopes have been added to distilled water in dialysis sac A. Measurements were made of the radioactivity in the two dialysis bags containing distilled water and in the common medium of lake water, tube C. It is seen from these data that 80% of the cobalt and 68% of the manganese were retained in the lake water. Varying the technique by placing the lake water in the dialysis bags and having distilled water in the intermediate compartment as shown in the Series II data of Table 1 did not change greatly the results.

The dialysis technique was applied to a number of Interior Alaskan lakes of diverse character. In Table 2, data are shown for four lakes which are representative of the range of water color and dissolved organic components found in this environment. In the distrophic lakes well over 50% of the tracers, cobalt, manganese and zinc, appear in forms too large to pass through the membranes under the conditions of this experiment. It is quite clear that in highly colored lakes there is a quantitatively important pool of trace metals in the 2 to 500 mμ range, the size limits being established by dialysis and filtration respectively. A pronounced cline in abundance of the material within this size range is evidenced in the lakes examined here. The more highly colored lakes contain the greater amounts of large associations. In Harding Lake, which displayed the highest clarity and lowest dissolved iron concentration, large trace metal associations are quantitatively negligible. In samples from the lakes under investigation here the metal binding substances, after suitable manipulation of pH, are extractable in polar solvents, and the dried extracts retain their metal binding properties after re-solution. From this I am inclined to believe that we are observing complexation or association with highly dispersed organic colloids rather than inorganic colloid phenomena such as sorption or ferric hydroxide.

Morgan (1968) has pointed out that there is an order of magnitude difference in the amount of dissolved organic substances between fresh water and marine environments. Stumm (1967) notes that the major cations compete with transition metals for available binding sites. It follows that the

Table 1. Distribution of radionuclides between distilled water and lake water upon dialysis. In each experiment the total volume in the two dialysis sacs (A and B) is equal to the volume of solution in tube C. R is the ratio of final radioactivity in the lake water to that in the distilled water.

Series*	Initial activity			Final activity				
	Sac A	Sac B	Tube C	A	B	A+B	C	R
% Co^{60}								
I	100	0	0	10	10	20	80	4.0
II	100	0	0	45	35	80	20	4.0
% Mn^{54}								
I	100	0	0	17	15	32	68	2.1
II	100	0	0	37	34	71	29	2.4

* I: Distilled water in sacs; lake water in tube.

II: Lake water in sacs; distilled water in tube.

Table 2. Relative activity of nuclides in lake waters after dialysis against equal volumes of distilled water.

Lake	Co^{60}	Mn^{54}	Zn^{65}	Water color (ppm Pt.)
Ace	4.0	2.4	5.8	750
Smith	2.5	2.3	2.8	370
Birch	1.5	1.2	1.4	160
Harding	1.0	1.0	1.1	16

presence of less organic material and a higher salt concentration are factors unfavorable for transition metal complexation in the marine environment.

Assays for complexation were made during the Bering Sea cruise of the University of Alaska's R/V ACONA in June, 1968. In addition to cobalt, manganese and zinc isotopes, Cu^{64} and Pb^{210} were also employed. Samples were taken from Unimak Pass, where water from the Gulf of Alaska is moving into the Bering, and from a station a short distance to the northeast in the Bering in an area of high primary productivity associated with the upwelling and mixing along the passes between the Aleutians. The results (Table 3) indicate that very little was present in the way of the large exchangeable complexes detected by this technique. In a sample taken from the dock at the Seward small boat harbor, presumably a somewhat polluted area, approximately 60% of the exchangeable copper was in the form of large complexes. Results of this preliminary work suggest that in at least some marine environments, complexation of the type detected by this method may be quantitatively unimportant.

ACKNOWLEDGMENTS

Contribution No. 43 from the Institute of Marine Science, University of Alaska.

This work was supported by U.S. Atomic Energy Commission Contract AT(04-3)310 PA4, and NSF Grant GB 8274.

REFERENCES

BARSDATE, R. J. 1967. Pathways of trace elements in Arctic lake ecosystems. Unpublished manuscript. Progress Rep. AT(04-3)-310 PA 4, 1965-1966. Inst. Mar. Sci., Univ. Alaska.

BARSDATE, R. J., and W. R. MATSON. 1966. Trace metals in Arctic and Subarctic lakes with reference to the organic complexes of metals. *In* B. Aberg and F. Hungate [ed.], Radioecological concentration processes. Pergamon Press, Oxford.

CARRITT, D. E. 1964. Personal communication cited in A. Siegel. 1967. A new approach to the concentration of trace organics in seawater, p. 235-256. *In* T. A. Olson and F. J. Burgess [ed.], Pollution and marine ecology. Interscience, New York.

CHRISTMAN, R. F. 1970. Chemical structures of color producing organic substances in water. *In* D. W. Hood [ed.], Proc. Symp. Organic matter in natural waters. Inst. Mar. Sci., Univ. Alaska, Occa. Pub. No. 1, this volume.

MORGAN, J. 1968. Metal organic complexes. Paper presented at Symp. Organic matter in natural waters. Inst. Mar. Sci., Univ. Alaska. Sept. 2-4, 1968.

Table 3. Relative activity of nuclides in marine waters after dialysis against distilled water. Samples taken on the Bering Sea Cruise of the R/V ACONA, June, 1968.

Station	Location	Co^{60}	Cu^{64}	Mn^{54}	Pb^{210}	Zn^{65}
066/2310	Unimak Pass, 5 m	1.0	1.0	1.0	1.2	1.0
066/2310	Unimak Pass, 25 m (near bottom)	0.9	1.0	1.0	1.1	1.1
066/2326	SE Bering Sea, 5 m	1.0	0.9	1.1	1.5	1.2
066/2326	SE Bering Sea, 250 m (near bottom)	1.0	1.0	1.0	1.2	1.1
066/NN	Small boat harbor Seward, Alaska, 0 m	-	2.5	-	-	-

SLOWEY, J. F., L. M. JEFFREY, and D. W. HOOD. 1967. Evidence for organic complexed copper in sea water. Nature, *214*: 377-378.

STUMM, W. 1967. Metal ions in aqueous solution, p. 520-560. *In* S. D. Faust and J. B. Hunter [ed.], Principles and applications of water chemistry. John Wiley and Sons, New York.

INTERACTIONS BETWEEN ORGANISMS AND DISSOLVED ORGANIC SUBSTANCES IN THE SEA. CHEMICAL ATTRACTION OF THE STARFISH *ASTERIAS VULGARIS* TO OYSTERS

K. J. Whittle and M. Blumer
Woods Hole Oceanographic Institution
Woods Hole, Massachusetts 02543

ABSTRACT

Behavior patterns of aquatic animals such as food finding, avoidance of injury, choosing of a habitat or host, social communication, migration or recognition of territory and sexual behavior may be controlled by chemical cues.

The chemical basis of the food finding behavior of the starfish *Asterias vulgaris* has been investigated. Under controlled conditions in a flow tank this starfish can sense intact oysters (*Crassostrea virginica*) upstream at distances of at least 120 cm.

The starfish orient positively to aqueous extracts of oyster tissue at concentrations in the parts per billion range. Molecular size fractionation of the extract by gel filtration indicates that the active components have a low molecular weight, below a few hundred. The attractive factors are resistant to boiling and prolonged acid hydrolysis.

INTRODUCTION

At this symposium much attention has been focused on the distribution, levels and origins of dissolved organic materials in the ocean, the types and classes of compounds present and the utilization of some of these compounds by marine organisms. This paper is concerned with the specific role of extremely dilute dissolved organic compounds in the control of animal behavior patterns. Such patterns are an integral part of the animal's life history.

All organisms are sensitive to chemical changes in the environment. In the animal kingdom, evolutionary progression can be correlated well with greater differentiation of the chemical sense. Thus, in the aquatic environment chemosensitivity is a general property of the body surface in the Protozoa and Porifera, while Elasmobranch and Teleost fishes have well developed olfactory pits and specialized olfactory epithelia (Hasler, 1957; Nicol, 1967).

It is becoming increasingly obvious that many aspects of behavior of marine organisms are elicited or controlled, partly or wholly, by specific chemical cues. Interaction with the chemosensory tissues occurs at low concentration. Such specific control of behavior emphasizes the importance of chemical cues in providing aquatic organisms with an appreciation of their surroundings. The behavior patterns, for which chemical cues have been suggested, are summarized with examples in Table 1. Additional information can be found in reviews by Hasler (1966), Pfeiffer (1963), Davenport (1955) and Kohn (1961), and the references to Table 1.

Table 1.   **Examples of behavior patterns controlled by chemical cues.**

SECURING FOOD

        Shark, Gilbert (1966). Mud snail, Carr (1967).
        Sea lamprey, Kleerekoper and Morgensen (1963).
        Tuna, Tester et al. (1955). Eel, Hashimoto et al. (1968).

AVOIDING INJURY, ESCAPING FROM ENEMIES

        Fish schooling, Hemmings (1966), Steven (1959).
        Alarm substances, Von Frisch (1938), Pfeiffer (1963).
        Escape reactions, Kohn (1961), Pfeiffer (1963).

CHOOSING A HABITAT OR HOST

        Larvae settlement, Crisp (1964), Gray (1966).
        Commensalism, Davenport et al. (1960), Wear (1966).
        Other relationships, Davenport (1955).

SOCIAL COMMUNICATION

        Jewelfish, Kuhme (1963).
        Yellow bullhead, Todd et al. (1967).

MIGRATION, RECOGNITION OF TERRITORY

        Migration of elvers, Creutzberg (1959).
        Home-stream migration of salmon, Hasler (1956).
        Stream recognition, Hasler (1966).

SEXUAL BEHAVIOR

        Excitation to mating in: American lobster, Hughes and
        Matthiessen (1962); *Portunus*, Ryan (1966); some members
        of the Brachyura and Anomura, Knudsen (1964).

Kleerekoper and Mogensen (1963) reported that the sea lamprey responds to specific amines in trout scent at concentrations of 2 parts in 10^8, and Lenhoff (1968) has recently provided much evidence supporting the view that glutathione in concentrations as low as 3 parts in 10^8 evokes the feeding response in hydra and other coelenterates. In 1938, Von Frisch described the alarm reaction of minnows, since described for other cyprinoids, and found that the fish react to extracts of minnow skin. *Phoxinus laevis* responds to skin extract at a concentration equivalent to 2 parts skin in 10^8 (Schutz, 1956). Both Crisp (1964) and Gray (1966) have shown that the larvae of various sand dwellers are attracted to the substrate by bacterial products on the sand grains. The parent jewelfish is said to recognize its brood by chemical signals (Kuhme, 1963). The chemical basis of the recognition of the home stream by returning salmon has been intensively investigated and much of the work has been described by Hasler (1966). Hughes and Matthiessen (1962) have shown that the male lobster shows a positive chemotaxis to the freshly moulted female.

In the many examples of chemotaxis that have been described in the literature, compounds such as amino acids, proteins, peptides, fatty acids, sialic acids, amines, aromatics and other substances of small molecular weight have been implicated, but instances in which a specific substance has been shown to be wholly responsible for a chemotactic response are few. However, the specificity and sensitivity of the chemosensory tissues of aquatic organisms has been amply demonstrated by experiments in which an animal was conditioned to respond to a specific chemical. Thus, the minnow was taught to respond to quinine hydrochloride at a concentration as low as 15 parts in 10^9 (Glaser, 1966), and Teichmann (1957) showed that the eel recognizes β-phenylethyl alcohol at concentrations as low as $1:2.857 \times 10^{-18}$. In fact, Teichmann calculated that at this concentration the eel's perception of the alcohol is of the order of molecules.

A number of species of starfish prey almost exclusively on shellfish. This report deals with an investigation of the chemosensory basis of food finding by starfish. The results of previous workers in this field have led to somewhat contradictory conclusions, and although a number of authors had stressed that an olfactory or chemical sense was involved, no specialized organs were described (reviewed by Feder and Christensen, 1966).

METHODS AND RESULTS

In preliminary experiments using a flow tank, the attraction of the starfish, *Asterias vulgaris*, to shellfish such as sand clams, mussels, quahogs and oysters, was compared. *A. vulgaris* appeared to show a preference for oysters (*Crassostrea virginica*) even though they had not encountered oysters previously. The starfish could be attracted to intact oysters upstream from them at distances of at least 120 cm. They moved toward their prey at speeds of 20 to 30 cm/min. The response to whole oysters could also be induced either by an aqueous homogenate of oyster tissue or by the supernatant solution from centrifugation of the homogenate at 35,000 x *g*.

Method of assay

To assay the potency of various extracts of oyster tissue a Plexiglas testing tank (Fig. 1) was constructed. Local sea water piped into the aquarium and maintained at 15 to 20 C passes through a coarse mesh stainless steel filter which removes small animals, detritus, etc. and enters across the width of the testing tank. The flow rate is controlled at about 2 liters/min.

For the comparative assay of different samples, each test solution is prepared by dilution of an equivalent aliquot of sample to 250 ml with filtered sea water. To estimate the threshold of response to a particular sample, the required dilutions are made with filtered sea water and a 250 ml sample is used for assay. Test solutions are introduced at about 1 ml/min with the constant flow device labeled X in Fig. 1. This terminates in 22 gauge hypodermic tubing. A concentration gradient of the test material is formed along the longitudinal axis of the tank between positions Y and Z (Fig. 1), and water with no stimulus added flows on either side.

The individual response of 36 starfish is observed for each test solution. The animals are introduced one at a time into the middle of the tank at position Z (Fig. 1) and their subsequent movement is noted. The base of the testing tank is divided into twelve equal areas and the position of the animals after five minutes is noted as well as the number of direct approaches to Y. The potency of the test solutions is compared with control experiments without stimulus on the basis of percentage response (i.e., the percentage of animals which directly approach Y), and a simple chi square distribution (giving probabilities of random distribution) as shown in Table 2. These experiments may be monitored with a movie camera operated at two frames per minute.

Tissue fractionation

Mild conditions were chosen for the fractionation and concentration of the attractive component(s) of oyster tissue (Fig. 2). The soft tissues from a single oyster are homogenized with ice-cold distilled water for 1 min in a Waring Blender. The homogenate is centrifuged and the supernatant is extracted with an equal volume of chloroform. Phase separation is assisted by centrifugation and results in three fractions: the aqueous phase which is subsequently freed from chloroform in vacuum, the organic phase which contains lipids and a white interfacial layer of proteolipid. The aqueous phase is centrifuged at 35,000 x g to yield the "final supernatant."

At each stage of the separation, the fractions are tested for their potency in attracting starfish. Table 2 shows the results of assays taken at various stages in the preparation of a final supernatant. The percentage response and the relative probabilities of random distribution demonstrate that the active component(s) remain in the aqueous phase throughout the separation. Thus, the final supernatant which contains about 3 mg solids/ml is a potent attractant; boiling for 15 min did not destroy the activity.

The chemical sensitivity of the starfish is demonstrated by the potency of various dilutions of the final supernatant. Thus, the activity of a

Fig. 1.   In this Plexiglas testing tank test samples are introduced into the sea water stream through the constant flow device X and enter the testing area at Y. A concentration gradient of test solution occurs along Y-Z.

Table 2. Attractiveness to starfish of samples taken during the fractionation of oyster tissue.

Sample for assay	% response of 36 starfish	x^2	Probability of randomness
Control	3	6.7	0.35
35,000 x *g* supernatant (dilution 1:5)	69	35.7	<0.001
Lipids	5	3.3	0.74
Aqueous phase (dilution 1:5)	72	42.7	<0.001
Final supernatant (dilution 1:50)	61	35.7	<0.001
Final supernatant (dilution 1:500)	30	34.3	<0.001
Final supernatant (dilution 1:5000)	5	2.0	0.85

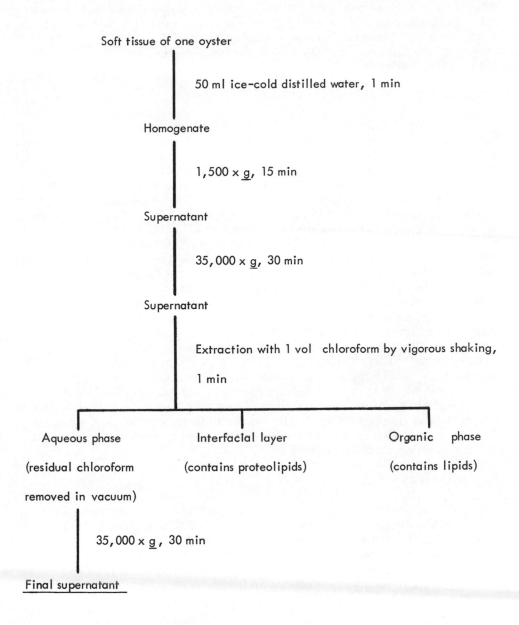

Soft tissue of one oyster

      50 ml ice-cold distilled water, 1 min

Homogenate

      1,500 x g, 15 min

Supernatant

      35,000 x g, 30 min

Supernatant

      Extraction with 1 vol chloroform by vigorous shaking,

      1 min

Aqueous phase   Interfacial layer   Organic phase

(residual chloroform   (contains proteolipids)   (contains lipids)

removed in vacuum)

      35,000 x g, 30 min

Final supernatant

Fig. 2.   **Scheme for the preparation of oyster tissue extracts.**

1:5000 dilution of final supernatant does not differ very much from that of a control, but a 1:500 dilution has significant activity. With the further dilution (x 800) of the test solution in the sea water stream before issuing into the testing area at Y (Fig. 1), it was calculated that the starfish are responding to oyster extract at a concentration of 8 parts solids in 10^9. However, the true concentration of the active component(s) in the sea water surrounding a starfish at Z is probably considerably lower.

Gel filtration

Further fractionation of the final supernatant on the basis of molecular size is achieved by gel chromatography. Dextran gels are used, and the effluent from the chromatography columns is monitored at 230 mμ, and with ninhydrin reagent which gives a colored product with α-amino acids, free or combined. A crude separation of 15 ml final supernatant is achieved on a G-25 Sephadex column (column volume, 192 ml; exclusion volume, 80 ml; eluant, distilled water); 5 ml fractions are collected. The chromatogram shows large peaks at the exclusion volume (peak 1) and at an elution volume of 150 ml (peak 2). A fraction (1/3) of the material from each of these peaks is assayed along with controls consisting of the final supernatant (5 ml) before chromatography, and response under conditions of no applied stimulus. The results indicate that peak 2 produces the same response (58%) as the final supernatant before chromatography.

The remaining material (2/3) of peak 2 is concentrated by rotary evaporation under vacuum and then is rechromatographed on a G-10 Sephadex column (column volume, 95 ml; exclusion volume, 40 ml; eluant, distilled water). The chromatogram features peaks at elution volumes of 60 ml (peak X, which also corresponds with a maximum in the ninhydrin profile), 80 ml (peak Y) and 100 ml (peak Z). Samples (1/2) of the material from each of these peaks and of all the remaining chromatographic fractions are assayed as described above. The results indicate that peak X produces a 61% response. This compares to the 58% response for the sample before chromatography on G-10 Sephadex.

Acid hydrolysis

The material from peak X of a duplicate G-10 chromatogram is hydrolyzed with 6N hydrochloric acid in a sealed tube under nitrogen for 20 hours at 105 C. After adjustment of the pH to 7.5 with sodium hydroxide followed by filtration, the hydrolysate is assayed for its activity, taking an aliquot for comparison with the unhydrolyzed sample. The response of the starfish to the hydrolysate is 58% compared to 61% for the unhydrolyzed sample.

Amino acid analysis

Thin layer chromatography indicates the presence of a number of components, including free amino acids, in both the hydrolyzed and the unhydrolyzed samples. Automated amino acid analysis shows similar patterns for both samples. This suggests that little or no peptide material is present in the original peak X. Synthetic mixtures of the amino acids found by the analysis were assayed. Although some activity was present the amino acid mixture could not account for the intensity of response obtained with the hydrolyzed and unhydrolyzed materials from peak X.

Thus, it would appear that the attractive compound(s) present in peak X has a low molecular weight, probably below 300, since it is eluted from the column together with the amino acids. It is stable to boiling and to acid hydrolysis. Further studies on the identification of the active component(s) are being conducted.

CONCLUSIONS

The starfish, *Asterias vulgaris*, has been shown to orient positively to a fairly specific, soluble and stable low molecular weight material or materials present in oyster tissue. This invertebrate responds to concentrations in the parts per billion range. The compound(s) may be the normal stimulus responsible for eliciting the food finding behavior of *A. vulgaris* in the natural environment. This again demonstrates that chemical cues can initiate or control behavior patterns essential to the animals involved. The great specificity and sensitivity of the chemosensory tissues of marine organisms has a number of implications.

There is some evidence that straight chain hydrocarbons may cause reversible or irreversible inhibition of the primary chemoreceptors of insects (Steinhardt et al., 1966). The injury to the chemoreceptors resembles hydrocarbon narcosis of nerve. This raises the question whether petroleum and/or other pollutants may — in addition to their gross toxicity — interfere on a much more subtle scale with the life processes of aquatic organisms. Damage to the chemosensory tissues, whether temporary or permanent, might lead to alterations in behavorial patterns and to consequent changes in ecology. We hope to test this assumption in the near future on starfish and other marine organisms. The response to a specific attractant will be checked in the presence of pollutants. In this respect, it is interesting that Radtke and Turner (1967) noted that erratic spawning of migrating bass (*Roccus saxatilis*) occurred at high concentrations of total dissolved solids in the San Joaquin River.

Continued and intensive investigation of chemotactic responses in a wide variety of marine organisms is necessary to provide the background knowledge for eventual identification of the specific compounds involved. In turn, this offers the attractive possibility of using such natural products in well defined areas, in low concentration and without fear of polluting the waters, for the chemical control of marine organisms — the attraction and localization of some and the discouragement or repulsion of others such as predators and noxious animals. Fine control of certain aspects of the life cycles of organisms, such as the settling of selected larvae and the inducement of mating and spawning, can be envisaged. Chemical controls of this nature may assist in better utilization of marine resources.

This investigation of the attractiveness of oyster extracts may lead to a new method of bioassay; the animal is sensitive to a specific compound(s) and shows a much faster response than, e.g., cultures of microorganisms. It may be possible to select organisms for the assay of many specific biochemicals in the sea, quickly and without much pretreatment of the sample.

Although much has been written, our knowledge of the mechanism of chemoreception is very scant. However, the apparent specificity of chemotactic responses seems to reflect a molecular specificity of the chemosensitive tissues. This may provide a useful tool in the investigation of the mechanism of chemoreception.

DISCUSSION

SIEBURTH: I found your work very interesting, but I was troubled by the fact that you were mincing up the whole oyster. The whole animal, pardon the use of the word, exudes. It is going to be an exudate which is going to attract, not the tissue itself. Have you tried fecal pellets or pseudofeces to see whether these will attract the starfish? I wonder whether you are looking for something too complicated. I wonder if you have tried ammonia, something as simple as ammonia may be the attractant in the tissues.

WHITTLE: The attraction of starfish to an homogenate appears to mimic the effect obtained with the whole organism. The advantage in using such an homogenate of the whole soft tissue is that it provides readily and easily a good yield of the attractive fraction. If we have such a good concentration of active material it might be less difficult to isolate the compound(s) involved. If it is possible to identify a substance(s) in this extract, one then has to go back and test the water surrounding the animals and see whether the same substance(s) is there.

SIEBURTH: You have not answered my question. Have you tried pseudofeces or feces? These materials contain proteinaceous mucus from the animal.

WHITTLE: No, I have not tested the feces, but I do not rule out the possibility of metabolites of low molecular weight as the attractants.

SIEBURTH: It might be interesting to try feces, pseudofeces and ammonia.

WHITTLE: In similar experiments with other chemotactic responses that are described in the literature, initial tissue extracts are very active. A definite response can be shown. In the isolation procedure or the manner in which the extract is fractionated, the activity of the fraction tends to be lost relative to the original activity. In the experiments just described, testing of the amino acids shows that there certainly is a response at concentrations of certain amino acids of about 2 parts in 10^4, a relatively high concentration, but it certainly is not the whole story. A number of reports claim that concentrations of amino acids of about 1 in 10^4 have been identified as attractants. To consider that kind of concentration as an attractant means that the animal is responding to a substance which is present in a concentration two orders of magnitude higher than the total dissolved organic matter in the sea assuming a figure for dissolved organics as 0.5 to 5 mg/liter. So one has to think in terms of concentrations of 10^6 or less for these attractants.

NORRIS: What oyster is this?

WHITTLE: This is *Crassostrea virginica*.

ACKNOWLEDGMENTS

Our thanks are extended to Mr. Jeremy Sass, who helped to collect the starfish.

We are also grateful to Dr. Egon Degens for providing the amino acid analyses.

Contribution No. 2221 from the Woods Hole Oceanographic Institution. This work was supported by the Office of Naval Research (N00014-66-CO-241), the National Science Foundation (GA539,GA1625), and by the American Petroleum Institute (85A).

REFERENCES

CARR, W. E. S. 1967. Chemoreception in the mud snail *Nassarius obsoletus*. I. Properties of stimulatory substances extracted from shrimp. Biol. Bull., *133*: 90-105.

CREUTZBERG, F. 1959. Discrimination between ebb and flood tide by migrating elvers (*Anguilla vulgaris* Turt.) by means of olfactory perception. Nature, *184*: 1961-1962.

CRISP, D. J. 1964. Surface chemistry, a factor in the settlement of marine invertebrate larvae. Bot. Gothobergensia, *3*: 51-64.

DAVENPORT, D. 1955. Specificity and behavior in symbioses. Quart. Rev. Biol., *30*: 29-46.

DAVENPORT, D., G. CAMOUGIS, and J. F. HICKOK. 1960. Analyses of the behavior of commensals in host factor. I. A hesioned polychaete and a pinnotherid crab. Anim. Behav., *8*: 209-218.

FEDER, H., and A. M. CHRISTENSEN. 1966. Aspects of asteroid biology, p. 87-127. *In* R. A. Boolootian [ed.], Physiology of echinodermata. Interscience, New York.

GILBERT, P. W. 1966. Feeding and attack patterns of sharks. Proc. 11th Pacific Sci. Congr., 7, No. 32.

GLASER, D. 1966. Untersuchungen über die absoluten Geschmacksschwellen von Fischen. Z. Verg. Physiol., 52: 1-25.

GRAY, J. S. 1966. The attractive factory of intertidal sands to *Protodrilus symbioticus*. J. Mar. Biol. Ass. U.K., 46: 627-645.

HASHIMOTO, Y., S. KONOSU, N. FUSETANI, and T. NOSE. 1968. Attractants for eels in extracts of short-necked clam. I. Survey of constituents eliciting feeding behavior by the omission test. Bull. Jap. Soc. Sci. Fish., 34: 78-83.

HASLER, A. D. 1957. Olfactory and gustatory senses of fishes, p. 187-209. *In* M. E. Brown [ed.], Physiology of fishes, vol. 2. Academic Press, New York.

HASLER, A. D. 1966. Stream phase of salmon homing, p. 13-58. *In* A. D. Hasler [ed.], Underwater guideposts, homing of salmon. Univ. Wisconsin Press, Madison.

HEMMINGS, C. C. 1966. Olfaction and vision in fish schooling. J. Exp. Biol., 45: 449-464.

HUGHES, J. T., and G. C. MATTHIESSEN. 1962. Observations on the biology of the American lobster, *Homarus americanus*. Limnol. Oceanogr., 7: 414-421.

KLEEREKOPER, H., and J. MORGENSEN. 1963. Role of olfaction in the orientation of *Petromyzon marinus*. I. Response to single amine in prey body odor. Physiol. Zool., 36: 347-360.

KNUDSEN, J. 1964. Observations of the reproductive cycles and ecology of the common Brachyura and crab-like Anomura of Puget Sound, Washington. Pacific Sci., 18: 3-33.

KOHN, A. J. 1961. Chemoreception in gastropod molluscs. Amer. Zool., 1: 291-308.

KUHME, W. 1963. Chemisch ausgelöste Bruptflege — und Schwarmreaktionen bei *Hemichromis bimaculatus* (Pisces). Z. Tierphysiol., 20: 688-704.

LENHOFF, H. M. 1968. Behavior, hormones and hydra. Science, 161: 434-442.

NICOL, J. A. C. 1967. Sensory organs and reception, p. 348-355. *In* J. A. C. Nicol [ed.], The biology of marine animals, 2nd ed. John Wiley and Sons, Inc., New York.

PFEIFFER, W. 1963. Alarm substances. Experientia, *19*: 113-168.

RADTKE, L. D., and J. L. TURNER. 1967. High concentration of total dissolved solids block spawning migration of striped bass, *Roccus saxatilis* in the San Joaquin River, California. Trans. Amer. Fish. Soc., *96*: 405-407.

RYAN, E. P. 1966. Pheromone: evidence in a decapod crustacean. Science, *151*: 340-341.

SCHUTZ, F. 1956. Untersuchungen über die Schreckreaktion bei Fischen. Z. Vergl. Physiol., *38*: 84-135.

STEINHARDT, R. A., H. MORITA, and E. S. HODGSON. 1966. Mode of action of straight chain hydrocarbons on primary chemoreceptors of the blowfly, *Phormia regina*. J. Cell. Physiol., *67*: 53-62.

STEVEN, D. M. 1959. Studies on the shoaling behavior of fish. I. Responsens of two species to changes of illumination and to olfactory stimuli. J. Exp. Biol., *36*: 261-280.

TEICHMANN, H. 1957. Das Riechvermögen des Aales (*Anguilla anguilla*, L.). Naturwissenschaften, *44*: 242.

TESTER, A. L., P. M. VAN WELL, and J. J. NAUGHTON. 1955. Reaction of tuna to stimuli. I. Response of tuna to chemical stimuli. Spec. Sci. Rep. U.S. Fish Wildl. Serv., No. 130, part 1.

TODD, J. H., J. ATEMA, and J. E. BARDACH. 1967. Chemical communication in social behavior of a fish, the yellow bullhead (*Ictalurus natalis*). Science, *158*: 672-673.

VON FRISCH, K. 1938. Zur Psychologie des Fisch-Schwarmes. Naturwissenschaften, *26*: 601-606.

WEAR, R. G. 1966. Commensalism: polychaete and bivalve. Biol. Bull., *130*: 141-149.

MICRODETERMINATION OF URONIC ACIDS AND RELATED COMPOUNDS IN THE MARINE ENVIRONMENT

P. M. Williams and J. S. Craigie[1]
Institute of Marine Resources
University of California, San Diego
P. O. Box 109
La Jolla, California 92037

ABSTRACT

A determination of uronic acids on the microgram level has been developed by modification of the classical acidic decarboxylation procedure of Lefèvre and Tollens. Using this method, the presence of uronic acids or related compounds has been established in five species of phytoplankters and in the particulate organic detritus in the sea.

INTRODUCTION

A fully satisfactory method for the quantitative determination of uronic acids and their polymers has not yet been developed. Existing methods are based upon direct titrimetry, colorimetry or decarboxylation under specified conditions. The first is useful only for purified compounds. The second depends upon the reaction of a suitable phenol with furfurals derived from uronic acids by a reaction which is in itself not quantitative (for a comparative study of some colorimetric procedures see Anderson and Garbutt, 1963b). Colorimetry is further complicated by a serious interference from other carbohydrates, a difficulty which is only partially alleviated by the introduction of multichromatic spectrophotometric readings. The third method is based upon the classic work of Lefèvre and Tollens (1907) who observed the rapid and quantitative release of CO_2 when uronic acids, their lactones or polymers were heated in 12% hydrochloric acid. This reaction has been extensively used for the determination of uronic acids and their polymers in soils and seaweeds and is generally accepted as the most accurate existing method.

The mechanism of this reaction has been studied by Anderson and Garbutt (1961, 1963a) and by Huber and Deuel (1951). The overall reaction has been formulated as:

$$C_6H_{10}O_7 \xrightarrow[130\ C]{12\%\ HCl} C_5H_4O_2 + CO_2 + 3\,H_2O$$

(hexuronic acid)   (furfural)

[1] On sabbatical leave from the National Research Council of Canada, Atlantic Regional Laboratory, Halifax, Nova Scotia, Canada

However, the yield of furfural is always less than theoretical at the reaction time which gives one mole of CO_2. The decarboxylation has been proposed by Anderson and Garbutt (1963) to proceed via a S_E^2 mechanism, where the first order rate constants are of the order of 10^{-4} to 10^{-6} sec^{-1} depending upon the particular uronic acid under investigation.

The difficulty of establishing the specificity of the decarboxylation method is its chief weakness. Tracey (1948) examined fifty biologically important compounds for interference in the decarboxylation. Only a few substances released 1% or more of their weight as CO_2 under conditions which quantitatively liberated CO_2 from uronic acids (hexuronic acids liberate 23% w/w CO_2). The most important of these interfering substances are urea and ascorbic acid. A large excess of carbohydrate interferes with the determination but by a study of the rates of CO_2 release from the sample, as little as 1% of hexuronic acid in glucose may be measured. Additional limitations of the decarboxylation method, as it is usually employed, reside in the complicated apparatus, the gas collection train, and the fact that the CO_2 has been determined by gravimetric analysis, titrimetry or by the Van Slyke method. For these reasons replicate analyses are difficult and microanalysis has been almost impossible.

EXPERIMENTAL PROCEDURES

A modification of the Lefèvre and Tollens method involves conducting the decarboxylation under nitrogen in sealed ampuls and measuring the CO_2 with an infrared analyzer. A method using an infrared spectrophotometer to detect CO_2 after decarboxylation has been reported by Anderson (1959) and Anderson, Garbutt and Zaidi (1963), but is limited to milligram quantities of uronic acids.

General

To a ten ml glass ampul, previously heated to 500 C to free it of organic matter, is added a 2.5 cm diameter Whatman CF/C glass-fiber filter pad (heated to 450 C to free it of organic matter) upon which a suitable amount of phytoplankton cells or particulate organic detritus has been deposited by filtration. The pore size of this filter is nominally 2 μ. The ampul is then charged with 5 ml of 12% w/w HCl (3.3N) and degassed for 6 min by bubbling with organic carbon-free, CO_2-free nitrogen gas. This removes all inorganic carbonates. The ampul is then sealed under nitrogen (see Menzel and Vaccaro, 1964) and heated in a constant temperature oven at 130 C for the desired time. After cooling the ampul is connected to a gas train. The ampul is broken, and the CO_2 is entrained in N_2 and swept through a magnesium perchlorate trap to remove water, and the quantity of CO_2 is measured by a Beckman model 15-A non-dispersive infrared gas analyzer. The integrated peak area is a direct measure of the CO_2 liberated from the sample. Standardization is effected by use of appropriate amounts of sodium glucuronate solutions and blank corrections (《0.02 μg CO_2) are made for pads and reagents. The method is sensitive to ± 0.2 μg of CO_2 (one sigma) which is equivalent to 1.2 μg of hexuronic acid. The optimum concentration range is 10 to 100 μg of hexuronic acid per sample, and the optimum heating period at 130 C is 4 to 8 hr. This latter period is established by kinetic studies.

Phytoplankters

Individual phytoplankters were grown in enriched sea water medium (SWM-1, McLachlan, 1964), illuminated in continuous light and harvested during the log phase of growth. The cells were gently filtered onto the glass-fiber filters, washed with fresh sea water and transferred into the glass ampuls. Cell counts were made with a Coulter Counter (model A).

Particulate organic detritus

A volume of 1 to 10 liters of sea water, depending upon the amount of particulate matter, is filtered through a glass-fiber filter and the filter introduced into the 10 ml ampul.

Total carbon determinations are made on separate aliquots of the cell suspension or sea water by filtration onto the glass-fiber filters. The filters are transferred into 10 ml ampuls and charged with 200 mg of potassium persulphate, 0.5 ml of 3% phosphoric acid and 5 ml of organic carbon-free double distilled water. The ampul is then degassed with N_2, sealed and autoclaved at 130 C for 1 hr. The resultant CO_2 is detected with the infrared analyzer.

RESULTS AND DISCUSSION

The type of kinetic data obtained from representative samples of phytoplankton and particulate detritus is depicted in Fig. 1. The points are mean values of triplicate samples. Essentially all the CO_2 derived from the uronic acids has been obtained after 4 hr heating while decarboxylation of the other carbohydrates in the phytoplankters and particulate matter slowly liberates CO_2 at a much diminished rate. Extrapolation of this latter section of the curve to zero time gives a measure of the uronic acids present. In the case of particulate detritus, the curve levels off after 8 to 10 hr when evolution of CO_2 stops, while in the case of phytoplankters, containing excess carbohydrate, decarboxylation continues up to 16 hr.

The results for 6 species of phytoplankters represent the maximum amount of polyuronides present in these organisms (Table 1). These values are expressed as "hexuronic acid carbon," a value taken as 6 times the amount of CO_2-carbon released during decarboxylation. The amounts of CO_2 liberated from dextrin, agar and casein over a 16 hr period are included in Table 1 for comparison. The total carbohydrate in *Skeletonema costatum* and *Syracosphaera carterae* found by Parsons, Stephens and Strickland (1961) was 21 and 18% respectively on a dry weight basis (equivalent to 8.4 and 7.2% carbon). The above authors also detected the presence of hexuronic acids in these same two plankters, as determined by paper

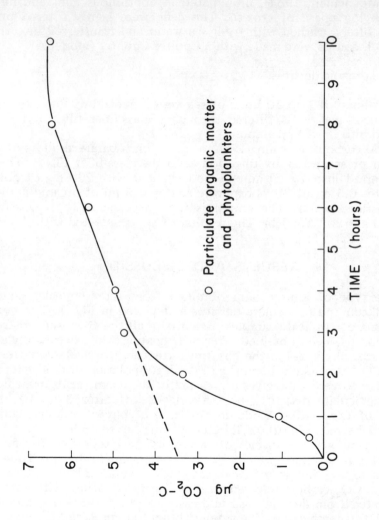

Fig. 1. Representative rate curves for the decarboxylation of phytoplankters and particulate organic matter.

○ Particulate organic matter and phytoplankters

TIME (hours)

μg CO₂-C

Table 1. Carbon dioxide evolved by various phytoplankters, casein, dextrin and agar after 16 hours in 12% HCl at 130 C.

Sample	Total C (μg/10^6 cells)	Decarboxylated C (μg/10^6 cells)	Carbon (% of total C)	Maximum value of "hexuronic acid" C as % of total C
Coccolithus huxleyi BT-6	6.6	0.040	0.61	3.6
Coccolithus sp. F-S	8.0	0.067	0.84	5.0
Syracosphaera sp. 181	159.0	0.88	0.55	3.2
S. carteri	76.0	0.46	0.61	3.7
S. elongata	372.0	3.50	0.94	5.7
Skeletonema costatum	6.6	0.042	0.64	3.8
Dextrin	98.4*	1.05	1.07	-
Casein	110.0*	0.17	0.15	-
Agar	82.4*	1.25	1.49	-

* Total carbon (μg) of purified compound.

chromatography of the acid hydrolysis product of the algal cells. Acid hydrolysis partially destroys hexuronic acids and their polymers, hence quantitation is not possible under these conditions. Evidently, uronic acids or related compounds may comprise up to 50% of the carbohydrate in *S. costatum* and *S. carterae*.

The particulate organic detritus contains 11 to 46% "hexuronic acid carbon," substantially more than the phytoplankters (Table 2). This may arise from an accumulation of polyuronides derived from sessile seaweeds or it may represent more refractory cell-wall material, rich in polyuronides, which then accumulates in the marine detritus. Galacturonic and glucuronic acids have been reported by Ernst (1967) as comprising up to 1.5% of the polysaccharides of deep-sea marine sediments (corresponding to $1.4 \times 10^{-3}\%$ of the total dry weight of sediment). These uronic acids may be an incorporation of particulate detrital polyuronides in the sediments.

The presence of hexuronic acids in the dissolved organic matter of the sea has not been reported. The kinetics of the decarboxylation of urea, dehydroascorbic acid and sodium glucuronate in sea water are shown in Fig. 2. These compounds were added at the level of 50 μg/liter to sea water freed of organic matter by high energy ultraviolet oxidation (Armstrong, Williams and Strickland, 1966). Urea has been qualitatively shown to be present in sea water taken from the northeast Pacific Ocean (Degens, Reuter and Shaw, 1964) and dehydroascorbic acid was detected by Wangersky (1952) in coastal waters of the Gulf of Mexico. These two compounds, if present in appreciable amounts, would mask the presence of uronic acids in sea water.

Fig. 3 provides data from some preliminary rate studies on the decarboxylation of surface and deep sea water. Ten ml of filtered sea water plus 7 ml of concd HCl in a 20 ml ampul are treated by the above techniques. The amount of CO_2-carbon formed after 8 hr at 130 C for a series of surface and deep samples varied from 3 to 12% of the total dissolved organic carbon. This indicates 18 to 72% of the total dissolved carbon is "hexuronic acids." However, blank determinations are erratic and these results can only be regarded as evidence for the presence of organic matter in sea water which will decarboxylate under these experimental conditions.

The ultimate identification of the compounds present in phytoplankters, particulate detritus and dissolved organic matter is the only real proof of their existence. However, the relative specificity of this acid hydrolysis is strong indirect evidence of hexuronic acid type compounds (including urea and dehydroascorbic acid) in the marine environment.

ACKNOWLEDGMENTS

The technical assistance of Mrs. Sharon Davidor is gratefully acknowledged.

This project was supported by U.S. Atomic Energy Commission Contract AT(11-1) GEN 10, P.A. 20.

Table 2. Carbon dioxide evolved from particulate organic matter in 12% HCl at 130 C.

Sample	Reaction time (hr)	Total C (µg/liter)	Decarboxylated C (µg/liter)	Carbon (% of total C)	Maximum value of "hexuronic acid" C as % of total C
SIO Pier	16	208	5.5	2.7	16.2
SIO Pier	16	54.5	4.2	7.6	45.6
150 miles offshore	6	48.0	3.7	7.7	46.2
SIO Pier	8	319	6.5	2.0	12.0
SIO Pier	8	422	8.0	1.9	11.4

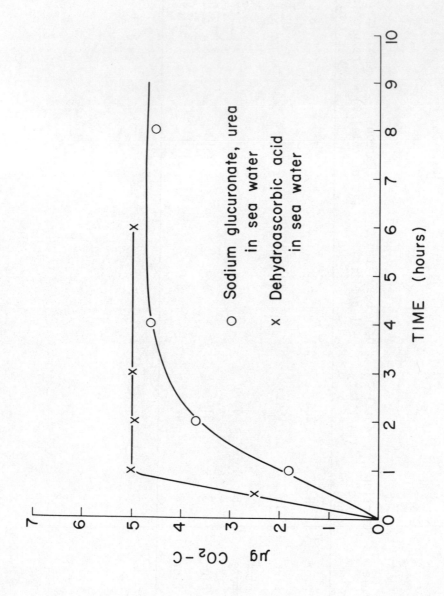

Fig. 2.   Rate curves for the decarboxylation of urea, dehydroascorbic acid and sodium glucuronate in sea water.

○   Sodium glucuronate, urea in sea water

×   Dehydroascorbic acid in sea water

TIME (hours)

μg CO₂-C

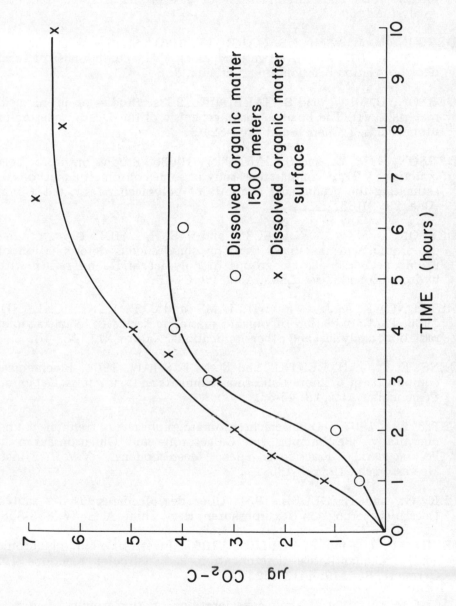

Fig. 3.   Rate curves for the decarboxylation of dissolved organic matter in sea water.

O   Dissolved organic matter
      1500 meters

x   Dissolved organic matter
      surface

TIME (hours)

μg CO₂-C

REFERENCES

ANDERSON, D. M. W. 1959. Applications of infra-red spectroscopy: the identification and determination of gas-chromatographic fractions. Analyst, *84*: 50-56.

ANDERSON, D. M. W., and S. GARBUTT. 1961. Studies on uronic acid materials. III. An investigation, using ^{14}C compounds of acid decarboxylation reaction-times. Atlanta, *8*: 605-611.

ANDERSON, D. M. W., and S. GARBUTT. 1963a. Studies on uronic acid materials. VII. The kinetics and mechanism of the decarboxylation of uronic acids. J. Chem. Soc., 3204-3210.

ANDERSON, D. M. W., and S. GARBUTT. 1963b. Studies on uronic acid materials. VIII. A comparative study of some colorimetric methods of estimating the uronic acid contents of polysaccharides. Anal. Chim. Acta, *29*: 31-38.

ANDERSON, D. M. W., S. GARBUTT, and S. S. H. ZAIDI. 1963. Studies on uronic acid materials. IX. The simultaneous determination of uronic acid and alkoxyl groups in polysaccharides by reflux with hydroiodic acid. Anal. Chim. Acta, *29*: 39-45.

ARMSTRONG, F. A. J., P. M. WILLIAMS, and J. D. H. STRICKLAND. 1966. Photo-oxidation of organic matter in seawater by ultra-violet radiation, analytical and other applications. Nature, *211*: 481-483.

DEGENS, E. T., J. H. REUTER, and K. N. F. SHAW. 1964. Biochemical compounds in offshore California sediments and sea waters. Geochim. Cosmochim. Acta, *28*: 45-66.

ERNST, W. 1967. Dünnschichtchromatographische Trennung und quantitative Bestimmung von Galacturon- und Glucuronsäuren in Polysaccharid Fractionen des Meeresbodens. Veröff. Inst. Meeresforsch., *10*: 183-185.

HUBER, G., and H. DEUEL. 1951. Über der Mechanismus der säuren Decarboxylierung von Hexuronsäuren. Helv. Chim. Acta, *34*: 853-858.

LEFÈVRE, K. U., and B. TOLLENS. 1907. Investigation of glucuronic acid, its quantitative determination and its color reactions [In German]. Ber., *40*: 4513-4523.

McLACHLAN, J. 1964. Some considerations on the growth of marine algae in artificial medium. Can. J. Microbiol., *10*: 769-782.

MENZEL, D. W., and R. F. VACCARO. 1964. The measurement of dissolved organic and particulate carbon in seawater. Limnol. Oceangr., *9*: 138-142.

PARSONS, T. R., K. STEPHENS, and J. D. H. STRICKLAND. 1961. On the chemical composition of eleven species of marine phytoplankton. J. Fish. Res. Bd. Canada, *18*: 1001-1016.

TRACEY, M. V. 1948. A manometric method for the estimation of milligram quantities of uronic acids. Biochem. J., *43*: 185-189.

WANGERSKY, P. J. 1952. Isolation of ascorbic acid and rhamnosides from seawater. Science, *115*: 685.

GLYCOLLIC ACID UPTAKE BY PLANKTONIC BACTERIA

Richard T. Wright
Department of Biology
Gordon College
Wenham, Massachusetts 01984

ABSTRACT

Glycollic acid, an important algal excretory product, is a potential energy source for aquatic bacteria. Using C^{14}-labeled glycollate, uptake by the natural planktonic microorganisms has been measured in a lake in eastern Massachusetts. Uptake of glycollate during the summer is highest in the epilimnion and decreases sharply with increasing depth and lower temperatures. This pattern suggests a correlation with algal photosynthesis and experiments indicate that uptake and production of glycollate are in the same order of magnitude. Glycollate uptake compares with that of glucose and acetate, suggesting that glycollate is as important as these two compounds in nourishing the epilimnetic bacteria. Bacteria able to grow on glycollate can be readily isolated from lake water and exhibit the same uptake pattern seen in natural waters. It is suggested that bacterial uptake of glycollate prevents that substrate from accumulating and later serving as an energy source for heterotrophic growth of algae.

INTRODUCTION

Glycollic acid is commonly lost (or excreted) by a large number of algae under culture conditions (Fogg, 1966) and in natural waters (Watt, 1966). Although the reason for this loss of energy is still obscure, the ecological consequences of glycollate excretion may be great for other organisms in the plankton. In fact, glycollic acid may be the single most important energy source for those aquatic microorganisms deriving their nutrition from organic solutes.

Several processes must be evaluated to determine the trophic importance of glycollic acid or any other organic solute. There must be some means of measuring the rate of production of the compound, its concentration and the rate at which the compound is removed by natural plankton or other factors. More specific information may be sought concerning the identity and the importance of the algae producing it and the microorganisms using it for energy.

A few measurements of the production rate of glycollic acid are now available (Watt, 1966) and there have been a few determinations of natural concentrations (see Fogg, 1966), but nothing is known of the magnitude of uptake by microorganisms or the identity of forms capable of accomplishing this uptake. This report presents some results of investigations to date in a study of the trophic role of glycollic acid in natural waters.

METHODS

Field work is being conducted on Gravel Pond, a lake with an area of 17.8 hectares and a maximum depth of 17 m, used by the town of Manchester, Mass., as a water supply. The lake is slightly eutrophic, is fed by ground water sources, has a neutral pH, low color (average, 5 platinum-cobalt units) and low specific conductance (average, 72 micromhos/cm).

Methods used to measure uptake of glycollic acid by planktonic microorganisms are basically those of Wright and Hobbie (1966). Varying concentrations of glycollate-1-C^{14} were added in duplicate to bottles containing natural water, normally covering low (up to 200 μg/liter) but sometimes also high (1 to 4 mg/liter) concentration ranges of glycollate. Samples were incubated at natural temperatures and filtered through 0.45μ membrane filters to stop the uptake. The dried filters were counted in a Baird-Atomic Model 732 Automatic Counting Assembly. To correct for adsorption on filters and on detritus, blanks were prepared for each concentration by fixing a sample with Lugol's acetic acid immediately after introduction of the labeled glycollate. Filtration and counting followed and the blank counts were then subtracted from the appropriate samples to give a corrected value.

The raw data were analyzed with equations derived in Wright and Hobbie (1965, 1966), based on the kinetics of active transport. Data yielded by this technique are the parameters maximum velocity (V), a figure combining a transport constant and the natural substrate concentration ($K_t + S_n$), and the apparent turnover time for the natural substrate at the natural level of uptake (T_t). Loss of counts through respiration of labeled substrate during the incubation time represents a possible source of error in the measurement technique. This probably causes V to indicate something between maximum velocity of uptake and the lower value of maximum velocity of incorporation of substrate.

Kinetics yielding these parameters apply when uptake is accomplished by a mechanism capable of carrying specific molecules across living membranes. The permease systems described for bacteria (Kepes, 1963) are an example of such a mechanism. Since uptake is dependent on membrane sites for delivery of the compound inside the cell, the uptake velocity does not increase directly with increasing substrate concentration. Instead it approaches a maximum value which applies when all the membrane sites are saturated with substrate. This is the kinetic parameter V measured for natural samples, which is useful for evaluating uptake potential of a planktonic population. The actual uptake velocity is some fraction of V and can be determined only when the natural substrate concentration is known and a respiration correction can be made. The concentration range over which uptake is responsive to substrate increase is indicated by the transport constant K_t, by definition the concentration at which uptake is half of maximum velocity. One basic limitation of the kinetic approach to natural waters is that the natural substrate concentration (S_n) must be determined independently. However, the value ($K_t + S_n$) is useful in that it sets an upper limit on both K_t and S_n, neither of which is easily determined independently.

RESULTS

Uptake of glycollate by natural plankton of Gravel Pond has been measured for a range of depths and at various times of the year. The data obtained by adding low concentrations of glycollate usually show a straight line when plotted according to the inverse plot in which saturation kinetics give a straight line (Wright and Hobbie, 1965). Fig. 1 shows two measurement results, a "good" one (A) and a "bad" one (B). Two possible reasons for poor results that have received some attention in similar measurements of glucose and acetate are the presence of large populations of algae (Wright and Hobbie, 1966) and a lack of adaptation for uptake because of a shortage of substrate (Vaccaro and Jannasch, 1967). Fortunately, most measurements have given data that can be reasonably fitted to the kinetic scheme.

For summer conditions in the epilimnion, V usually ranges between 5 and 10 x 10^{-4} mg glycollate liter^{-1} hr^{-1}, $(K_t + S_n)$ from 0.05 to 0.20 mg glycollate/liter, and T_t from 60 to 200 hr. Determining this uptake ability at any given depth does not necessarily mean that the microorganisms (presumably bacteria) are getting their nourishment from glycollate. The system for glycollate uptake may be present even though the bacteria are using other substrates for energy. The values for maximum velocity and $(K_t + S_n)$ do show that given a source of glycollate, the bacteria are capable of taking it in from low concentrations.

The data in Table 1 are from a study of depth distribution of the uptake parameters for August 9 and 11, 1967. Samples from 13 and 16 m, incubated at 8 C, showed no measurable uptake above the blanks, which were much higher than usual. The depth pattern indicates that uptake is highest in the epilimnion and diminishes with increasing depth through the metalimnion and into the hypolimnion, with somewhat uncertain results closer to the bottom.

Watt (1966) was unable to show this kind of uptake in Lake Windermere, but he was working in a concentration range of 1 to 11 mg/liter of glycollate. He reported that uptake was directly proportional to substrate concentration, apparently due to diffusion. There was no difference in uptake between samples incubated in the light or the dark. With similarly high concentrations, diffusion-like uptake can also be demonstrated for Gravel Pond (Fig. 2A). When the concentration range is reduced by two orders of magnitude, however, uptake shows saturation kinetics (Fig. 2B). This points out the necessity of working at the lowest possible concentrations of added substrate, to approach as closely as possible the basic conditions of a tracer experiment. The problem of these two kinds of uptake is discussed in detail in Wright and Hobbie (1966), where evidence is presented indicating that the diffusion-like uptake is due to the algae and the uptake showing saturation kinetics may be traced to the bacteria.

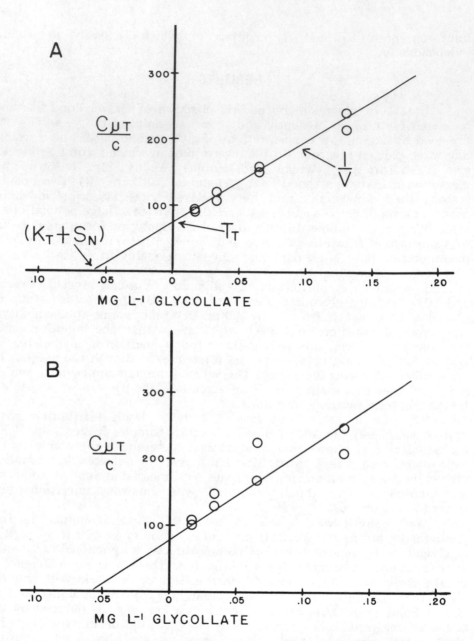

Fig. 1.   Uptake of glycollate at two depths in Gravel Pond, August 11, 1967.
Symbols used in ordinate units as follows: C, counts per minute (CPM) of
1 microcurie in counting system used; μ, fraction of a microcurie added to
sample; t, incubation time; c, CPM of sample filter in counting system. Fig.
1A from 3 m depth; V = 8.1 x 10^{-4} mg/liter/hr, $(K_t + S_n)$ = 0.060, T_t = 75
hr. Fig. 1B from 1 m depth.

Table 1. Kinetic parameters of glycollate uptake in Gravel Pond, August 9 and 11, 1967.

Depth (m)	Temp (C)	Uptake - V max. (10^{-4} mg liter^{-1} hr^{-1})	$K_t + S_n$ (mg/liter)	T_t (hr)
surface	25	8.3	0.10	110
1	24	8.1	0.06	75
3	24	8.1	0.06	75
5	17	1.8	0.06	350
7	14	0.8	0.05	600
10	9	0.4	0.05	1300
13	8	below limits of measurement		
16	8	below limits of measurement		

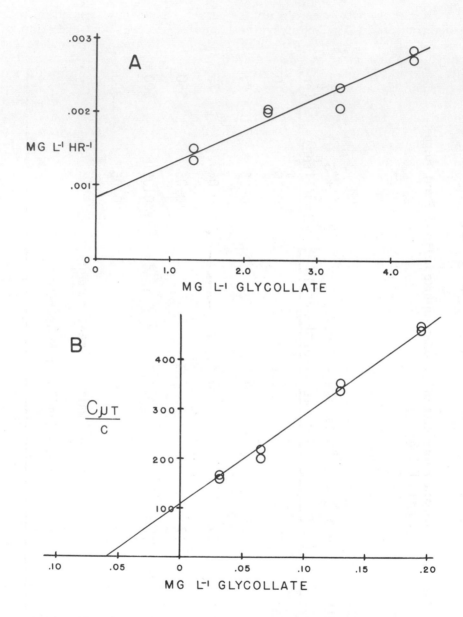

Fig. 2.   Uptake of glycollate over two concentration ranges, from 1 m in Gravel
            Pond, Aug. 30, 1967. A: uptake velocity plotted against substrate
            concentration in the high range. B: uptake in the low concentration range,
            plotted according to kinetic scheme where saturation kinetics show
            linearity.

The depth distribution of uptake certainly suggests a correlation with the distribution of algal photosynthesis and, therefore, algal excretion of glycollate. To investigate this possibility, algal production of particulate and excreted organic matter was measured in the field (using methods presented by Watt, 1966), and uptake of glycollate by the same sample water was measured in the laboratory. Table 2 shows these results for the five depths tested, with glycollate uptake given as glycollate-carbon for direct comparison with photosynthetic fixation. All rates are extrapolated to a 24-hr day. The values for excreted carbon are not precise because of low counts, but are useful in placing excretion rate in an order of magnitude. Two significant points emerge from this experiment. First, the general profile of particulate production agrees with that for glycollate V. Second, glycollate V and the rate of production of excreted organic carbon are within the same order of magnitude.

A breakdown of the compounds making up the excreted matter was not performed in this study. The only data available for fractionation of the excreted product are those of Watt (1966), who found glycollate to be 10, 13 and 92% of the total in three different samples. Even with the potentially great variability in glycollate production indicated by Watt's work, the above data suggest that the microorganisms are present with an uptake mechanism functioning in the same order of magnitude, a situation strongly suggesting a steady state where production and uptake are balanced.

Another important question is the uptake of glycollate relative to other organic solutes. Glucose, acetate, galactose and fructose have been the subject of previous uptake kinetic studies in fresh water (Wright and Hobbie, 1966; Allen, 1967; Wetzel, 1967). The general finding has been that uptake of bacterial glucose and acetate due to bacteria is occurring and may be measured at all depths, all seasons and in a variety of fresh water situations. Uptake of galactose and fructose was much lower (Wetzel, 1967), apparently indicating that those compounds are less important than glucose and acetate to natural bacteria. To assess the relative importance of glycollate, acetate and glucose a direct comparison of uptake of the three compounds was made over three days, July 31 to Aug. 2, 1968. Lake conditions remained similar during this period of time.

The results are given in Table 3 and the V values are plotted against depth in Fig. 3. Several points are noteworthy. First, the $(K_t + S_n)$ values for glycollate are at least an order of magnitude greater than those for glucose and acetate. This means much higher natural concentrations of glycollate, or a higher transport constant or perhaps a combination of both. Turnover times are also higher by an order of magnitude, a phenomenon difficult to interpret at this time. Second, glycollate V follows acetate more closely than glucose in magnitude. This may be due to a population of bacteria having a general ability to metabolize organic acids and specific uptake mechanisms for a number of them. All 16 bacterial isolates from Gravel Pond growing in liquid culture on glycollate are capable of growing on acetate. Third, at depths below 10 m and approaching the bottom, both glucose and acetate increase in V, whereas glycollate uptake falls below the limits of detection. A similar pattern of increase toward the lake bottom was found in other lakes

Table 2. A comparison of rates of glycollate uptake with rates of particulate and dissolved photosynthetic carbon fixation, August 16, 1967.

Depth (m)	Particulate fixation (μg C liter^{-1} day^{-1})	Dissolved fixation (μg C liter^{-1} day^{-1})	Uptake $-$ V max. (μg C liter^{-1} day^{-1})
surface	134	7.8	6.7
1	120	11	5.3
3	82.3	2.5	5.8
5	24.8	2.4	1.5
7	6.7	3.2	0.67

Table 3. A comparison of uptake kinetic parameters for glycollate, acetate and glucose in Gravel Pond, July 31 to August 2, 1968.

Depth (m)	Temp (C)	Substrate	Uptake $-$ V max. (10^{-4} mg/liter^{-1} hr^{-1})	$K_t + S_n$ (mg/liter)	T_t (hr)
surface	25	glycollate	7.8	0.070	90
		acetate	9.0	0.007	7
		glucose	2.8	0.005	18
1	25	glycollate	7.8	0.070	90
		acetate	9.0	0.007	7
		glucose	2.8	0.005	18
3	25	glycollate	10.0	0.200	200
		acetate	8.8	0.010	12
		glucose	2.1	0.006	30
5	19.5	glycollate	2.2	0.080	370
		acetate	2.5	0.008	30
		glucose	1.3	0.005	35
7	13	glycollate	1.0	0.040	370
		acetate	1.4	0.005	40
		glucose	0.65	0.004	45
10	7	glycollate	0.73	0.060	900
		acetate	0.81	0.005	60
		glucose	0.31	0.004	140
13	7	glycollate	-	-	-
		acetate	1.1	0.004	30
		glucose	0.50	0.004	90
16	7	glycollate	-	-	-
		acetate	3.7	0.008	20
		glucose	1.3	0.005	35

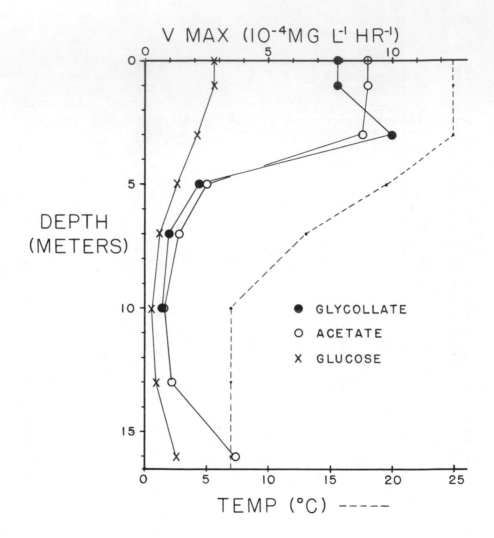

Fig. 3.   A comparison of the depth distribution of V for glycollate, acetate and glucose in Gravel Pond, July 31 to Aug. 2, 1968.

for glucose and acetate (Wright and Hobbie, 1966; Wetzel, 1967) and may be the result of accumulation of particulate matter from upper waters and also proximity to the bottom; both of these conditions favor the increase of bacterial activity as a result of increased surfaces and nutritive organic matter. If, as assumed, the source of glycollate is the photosynthesizing algae, then there should be very little glycollate present in water shut off from circulation and effective light for several months. The absence of detectable glycollate uptake below 10 m agrees with this assumption.

Interpretation of these and other results rests firmly on the hypothesis that uptake being measured is due to the planktonic bacteria. The arguments used by Wright and Hobbie (1966) to support this hypothesis for glucose and acetate uptake are applicable here. One additional point for glycollate is the apparent inability of all algae so far tested to grow heterotrophically on glycollate (e.g., Droop and McGill, 1966). It is hard to imagine that forms not able to use a substrate would possess specific mechanisms for its uptake. However, the question of photoassimilation and photorespiration of glycollate by algae must be clarified before any final analysis may be made. The results reported in this paper are from experiments carried out in the dark or very dim light, ruling out any significant interference from these sources.

I have found that bacteria using glycollate for energy are readily isolated from lake waters, and I am presently studying the uptake and growth characteristics of more than 20 such isolates. Further, uptake by cultured bacteria exhibits the same kind of transport kinetics found in natural waters. Fig. 4 shows uptake of glycollate by a dilute suspension of isolate G-7 after extensive washing and a starvation period. Note that the transport constant K_t falls in the same concentration range as the natural ($K_t + S_n$) values. Other work, to be published elsewhere, shows inhibition of glycollate uptake by competing compounds to follow a similar pattern in the bacterial cultures and in the natural water. For example, acetate shows effects resembling non-competitive inhibition — seriously reducing V but not affecting K_t. Lactate appears to compete almost equally for uptake with glycollate, its effects being to greatly increase the apparent K_t value while having little effect on maximum velocity.

Additional work in progress is designed to provide information on the identity and relative counts of glycollate bacteria. The results of one promising method are shown in Fig. 5. For each of the depths a volume of 0.5 ml diluted to 10 ml is filtered through a Millipore Field Monitor, and the filters are incubated on agar containing a dilute mineral medium, 100 mg/liter of sodium glycollate and a known quantity of glycollate-1-C^{14}. After five days of incubation visible colonies are counted; then the filters are air-dried and placed in contact with x-ray films for five more days. The concentrated dots resulting from exposure to dried colonies containing C^{14} obtained from the labeled glycollate in the medium can then be counted on the developed film. Colony counts obtained in this way have gone as high as 950/ml from epilimnetic water and are always 75% or more of the total visible colonies appearing on the filter.

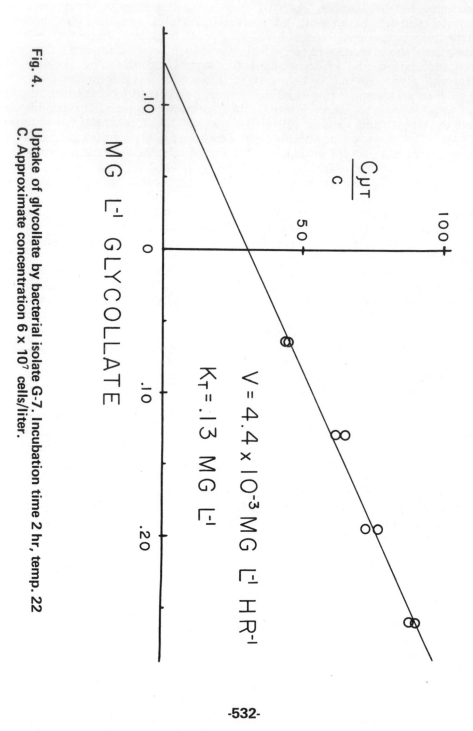

$\dfrac{C_{\mu T}}{c}$

100

50

MG L⁻¹ GLYCOLLATE

$V = 4.4 \times 10^{-3} \, MG \, L^{-1} \, HR^{-1}$

$K_T = .13 \, MG \, L^{-1}$

.10   0   .10   .20

Fig. 4. Uptake of glycollate by bacterial isolate G-7. Incubation time 2 hr, temp. 22
C. Approximate concentration 6 x 10⁷ cells/liter.

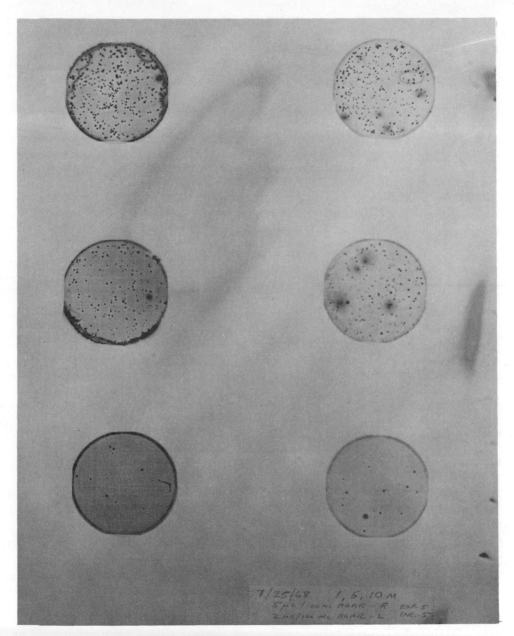

Fig. 5.   X-ray of filters incubated on glycollate agar containing glycollate-1-C-14. Left side series on agar containing 5 μcuries per 100 ml, right side series with 2 μcuries per 100 ml. Top, 1 m; middle, 5 m; bottom, 10 m. All samples represent colonies developing from a 0.5 ml volume. Incubation time on agar, 5 days. Exposure to x-ray, 5 days.

CONCLUSIONS

It is certainly no surprise to find bacterial populations capable of taking up glycollic acid in natural waters. This finding is another element in the overall picture of energy relationships involving the dissolved organic matter. The magnitude of uptake seems to be very close to the magnitude of production, though more definitive work is needed. The depth pattern also follows the pattern of photosynthesis, which confirms the basic idea that the algae are nourishing bacteria through their loss of glycollate. Comparison of glycollate uptake with that of glucose and acetate indicates that the bacteria are at least as active in taking up glycollate and, therefore, it must be an important energy source for them. Based on what is known so far, it seems reasonable to conclude that the bacteria are using any glycollate excreted by the phytoplankton algae and are thereby keeping it from accumulating in the water. This appears to rule out glycollate as an excretory product which might later be used by algae for heterotrophic growth when photosynthesis is impossible (Fogg, 1963; Rodhe, 1955). On the other hand, glycollate excreted by algae and then taken up by bacteria represents an important phase in the energy flow in aquatic ecosystems, as predicted by Fogg (1963).

DISCUSSION

DUURSMA: Tolbert and Zill (1956, 1957) felt that glycollate is very strongly related to respiration and photosynthesis due to the fact that with the transport of anions in the cells there should be an equilibrium, otherwise you would have potentials. They hypothesized that the glycollate makes the equilibrium. If there is more bicarbonate in a cell, glycollate should go out; if there is less, glycollate should go in. They did these experiments with *Chlorella*. Are these hypotheses or theories confirmed by you?

WRIGHT: I have not worked on the algal end of it at all. I cannot say what is happening inside of the algae to make them produce glycollate. As far as I know, this is an open question. I do not think anyone knows exactly why so much glycollate does appear in the liquid medium, but if there is an equilibrium here it certainly is not going to favor the algae because you have a sink with the bacteria utilizing the excretions.

DUURSMA: But it is stated that this is the reason why glycollate is taken up.

WRIGHT: I do not know what the reason is; I do not think there is general agreement on that.

JANNASCH: Do you have any idea how much of the substrate is oxidized in your experiments, that is, how much is respired and given off as CO_2? And secondly, have you identified your bacterial isolates?

WRIGHT: No, I do not know how much is respired. Respiration certainly occurs to some extent and this means that the V_{max} that we have is probably a conservative estimate of how much they take up. They are probably taking up even more than is indicated by the V_{max}.

JANNASCH: How much more?

WRIGHT: I do not know. Hobbie (Hobbie and Crawford, 1969) has some figures that indicate that respiration ranges from maybe 20 to 50%. We have tentatively identified a number of the isolates. Many of them seem to be Pseudomonads. As to the species, I do not really know. I doubt that too many of them have been described; there seems to be a large number of different kinds. Many are pigmented, by the way, pink and yellow forms.

BREZONIK: How widespread is the ability of algae to produce and use glycolic acid? All the work I have seen, except for Hellebust's (Hellebust, 1965), was on *Chlorella*, a common laboratory algae, but not necessarily representative of algae in the environment.

WRIGHT: Hellebust has shown that quite a number of marine algae produce it. This may not be the major excretory product but just about everywhere it has been looked for, it has shown up in cultures and in the very little work that has been done on natural waters by Watt.

ACKNOWLEDGMENTS

This work is supported by National Science Foundation grants GB-5135 and GB-7741.

REFERENCES

ALLEN, L. 1967. Acetate utilization by heterotrophic bacteria in a pond. J. Hungarian Hydrol. Soc. (Hidrológiai Közlöny), *47*: 295-297.

DROOP, M. R., and S. McGILL. 1966. The carbon nutrition of some algae: the inability to utilize glycolic acid for growth. J. Mar. Biol. Ass. U.K., *46*: 679-684.

FOGG, G. E. 1963. The role of algae in organic production in aquatic environments. Br. Phycol. Bull., *2*: 195-205.

FOGG, G. E. 1966. The extracellular products of algae. Oceanogr. Mar. Biol. Annu. Rev., *4*: 195-212.

KEPES, A. 1963. Permeases: identification and mechanism, p. 38-48. *In* N. E. Gibbons [ed.], Recent progress in microbiology. 8th Intern. Congr. Microbiol., Montreal, 1962. Univ. Toronto Press, Toronto.

RODHE, W. 1955. Can plankton production proceed during winter darkness in subarctic lakes? Verh. Intern. Ver. Limnol., *12*: 117-122.

VACARRO, R. F., and H. W. JANNASCH. 1967. Variations in uptake kinetics for glucose by natural populations in sea water. Limnol. Oceanogr., *12*: 540-542.

WATT, W. D. 1966. Release of dissolved organic material from the cells of phytoplankton populations. Roy. Soc. Br., Proc., B.*164*: 521-551.

WETZEL, R. G. 1967. Dissolved organic compounds and their utilization in two marl lakes. J. Hungarian Hydrol. Soc. (Hydrológicai Közlöny), *47*: 298-703.

WRIGHT, R. T., and J. E. HOBBIE. 1965. The uptake of organic solutes in lake water. Limnol. Oceanogr., *10*: 22-28.

WRIGHT, R. T., and J. E. HOBBIE. 1966. The use of glucose and acetate by bacteria and algae in aquatic ecosystems. Ecology, *47*: 447-464.

SOME FACTORS INFLUENCING KINETIC CONSTANTS FOR MICROBIAL GROWTH IN DILUTE SOLUTION

D. K. Button
Institute of Marine Science
University of Alaska
College, Alaska 99701

A growing microorganism reproducing in dilute aqueous environments such as our natural water systems is faced with the problems of recognizing and concentrating desired nutrients, preventing the concomitant entry of chemical species not required and retaining desired components within itself. This is successfully accomplished by simple diffusion accompanied by a set of transport systems, each capable of recognizing a required species and carrying it across the cell wall to a site of chemical modification so that the nutrient cannot move back by the same path. The nutrient molecules a species of microorganism can recognize are genetic parameters and some transport systems can be produced or omitted in response to the chemical environment. These systems are sufficiently enzyme-like to behave in a similar kinetic fashion and can be described with maximum velocities, apparent Michaelis constants and inhibition constants. These kinetic constants are a measure of effective collision frequency at the site of the growth rate limiting step as compared with the growth rate when that step is saturated.

The rate limiting step for a microorganism grown in dilute solution can therefore be nutrient diffusion through the aqueous environment to the cell surface, transport of recognized nutrients through the cell surface into the organism or a subsequent slow step in the conversion of the nutrient into useful biochemical forms. The kinetics of each step except the first can be affected by the external environment of the organism. The following observations describe how growth velocity can be affected by nutrient concentration, mixing, temperature, pH and heavy metal concentration.

Growth velocity is normally an increasing function of limiting substrate concentrations. This can be hyperbolic, linear or logistic depending on the rate limiting mechanism. The bottom curve of Fig. 1 shows how the growth velocity of a yeast cell *Cryptococcus albidus* varies with the vitamin thiamine at the cell surface. The curve is computed from the Michaelis-Menton equation, the variation in cell yield with growth rate, the variation in organism size with growth rate and the apparent Michaelis constant for growth experimentally determined and reported elsewhere (Button, 1969). The upper curve is based on a computation of the concentration of thiamine required in the bulk of the medium to supply thiamine at the cell surface at the required rate assuming no mixing and Flickian diffusion. A convenient equation presented by Borkowski and Johnson (1967) for this purpose is presented below. As one can see, the effective concentration at the cell surface is about half that in the bulk of the medium in an unmixed system. Normal growth rates of yeast, bacteria and algae are indicated to provide a reference scale. These data would

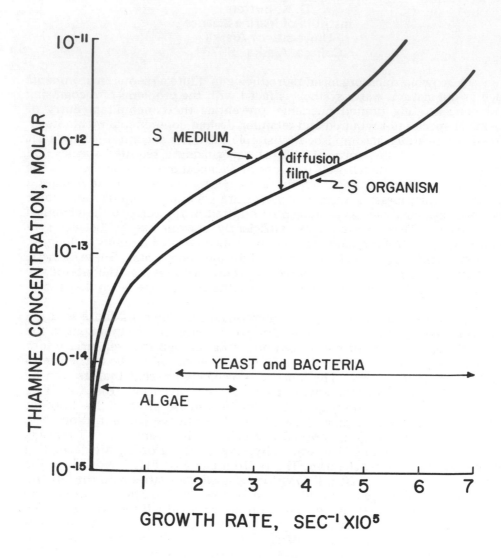

Fig. 1.   The lower curve represents the thiamine concentration at the surface of the organism, *Cryptococcus albidus*, computed from the Michaelis Menton equation, K_s 4.4 x 10^{-13} M, and the changes in cell volume and yield with growth rate. The upper curve represents the thickness of the diffusion film in a non-mixed solution computed from equation 1.

indicate that in this case of vitamin limited growth, diffusion to the cell surface is the growth rate limiting step. If that is the case, the thiamine utilization rate is a function of mixing. We found this to be the case experimentally (Button, 1969).

Fig. 2 shows how the stagnant film thickness would vary with growth rate if a concentration of nutrient equivalent to its apparent Michaelis constant were provided in the nutrient medium. Curves shown were obtained as described by Borkowski and Johnson (1967). Using the experimentally determined Michaelis constant for thiamine limited growth of 4×10^{-13} M (center line) as the concentration at the cell surface, the film thickness at usual growth rates of $5 \times 10^5 \sec^{-1}$ is about one micron, which is within the normal range of stagnant film thicknesses. The upper and lower lines represent how the film thickness would vary if the apparent Michaelis constant were either ten times larger or ten times smaller than its actual value. The divergence suggests the existence of a rational relationship between the Michaelis constant for a substrate and the amount of substrate required by a microorganism. This was first noticed in tabulations of published Michaelis constant data. The resulting relationship is about what one would expect on the basis of molecular collision frequency in the *Salmonella typhimurium* system at published concentrations of sulfate binding enzyme (Dreyfuss, 1964) and assumed values of sulfate flux. The same relationship can be obtained from the *C. albidus*-thiamine system by substituting the film thickness at half the maximum growth rate of 5.4×10^{-4} cm, obtained from Fig. 2, into the general equation for relating diffusion limited nutrient concentration drops presented by Borkowski and Johnson (1967).

$$ Cf - Cs = \frac{0.1 \, r^2 \, \mu \, (1-1/x)}{D\lambda} \tag{1} $$

where Cf and Cs are concentrations of nutrient in the bulk of the medium and at the cell surface; μ is the growth rate; x is the distance from the cell center to the outside of the film in units of r, the cell radius; D is the diffusivity of the nutrient in the medium; and λ is the yield of cell mass from nutrient provided. If the experimental values of these constants for the *C. albidus*-thiamine system are substituted into equation (1) the following relationship is obtained:

$$ \lambda = \frac{1}{7 \times 10^7 \, K_s} \tag{2} $$

A logarithmic plot of this equation is shown in Fig. 3. Notice that the experimental values of Wright and Hobbie (1965) and Borkowski and Johnson (1967) for acetate and oxygen, respectively, fall near this line, although the yield constants are a factor of 10^6 lower than the thiamine data used to formulate the relationship.

Growth velocities of microorganisms when the rate limiting step is substrate saturated follow the Arrhenius equation as shown in Fig. 4. Pena (1955) suggested a similar relationship to temperature. Our values of K_s for

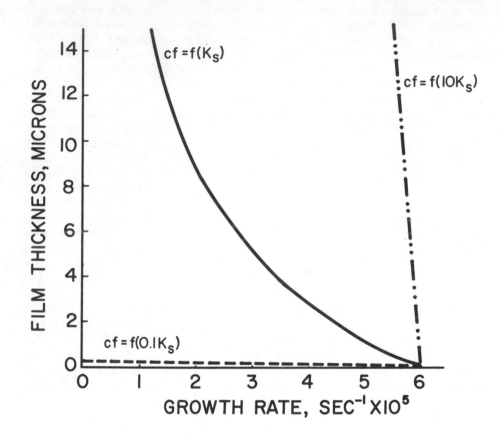

Fig. 2.   The center curve (solid line) represents the maximum diffusion film thickness that will allow the indicated growth rates with the concentration in the bulk of the unmixed medium equivalent to the Michaelis constant for thiamine in the thiamine requiring *Cryptococcus albidus* system. The darkened lines show the same maximum film thicknesses when the bulk medium is raised or lowered by a factor of ten.

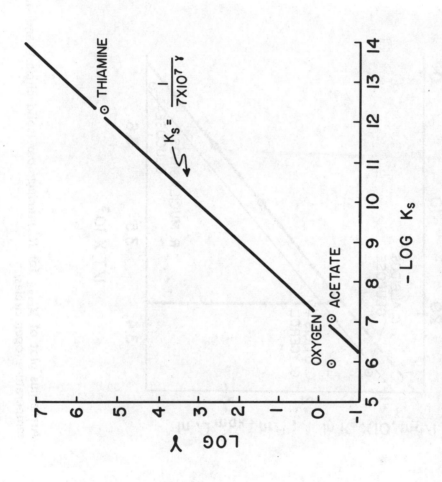

Fig. 3. Fit of experimental K_s data to equation 5. Points to the left of the line represent departure from diffusion limited systems.

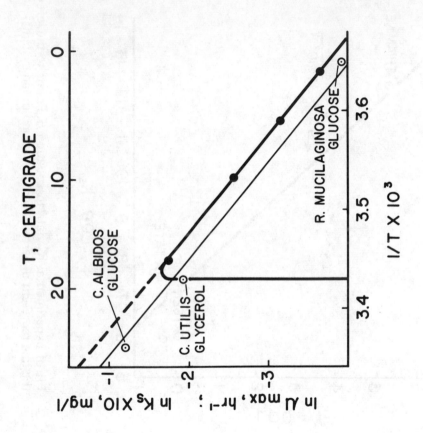

Fig. 4. Arrhenius plot of V_{max} for *R. mucilaginosa* (solid circles), and ʊ, K_s vs. temperature (open circles).

glucose at 1.6 C are shown along with the value of K_S for glucose at 25 C with *C. albidus* and Pena's value for glycerol using *C. utilis* at 15 C. The values for these yeast K_S data increase with temperature in the same way as the maximum velocity of growth. Thus if

$$\mu_{max} = A\,e^{-E_a/RT} \tag{3}$$

then

$$K_S = A'\,e^{-E_a/RT} \tag{4}$$

and from (1)

$$A'\,e^{-E_a/RT} = \frac{1}{7 \times 10^7 \lambda} \tag{5}$$

Where growth rate is limited at the cell surface by nutrient transport the system can be likened to substrate competition for passage through a matrix of doors. These doors at the cell surface are chemical in nature and subject to closing (chemical modification) by inhibitory components of the medium.

Table 1 shows the maximum growth rate of *C. utilis* after extended growth at steady state in continuous culture. Population was regulated by flow rate at a low value so that the population remained at μ_{max}. The rates observed were different from the corresponding batch growth rates and much slower after the first three days. Notice that the rate responds to glycerol concentration in a different way at pH 4 than at pH 6, indicating a Michaelis constant of a higher order of magnitude at pH 6. This difference between batch and continuous culture data also occurred with *C. albidus* and *Rhodotorula glutinis* and is under current consideration. The data show that long term substrate limited growth at low population can respond to concentration in a different way than short term substrate uptake.

Fig. 5 shows the response of *R. glutinis*, a marine pink yeast, to copper. The yeast was selected because it grows well in continuous culture with no added chelates or buffers and only substrate quantities of phosphate (Button, 1969). Under these conditions the rate of growth was sharply reduced, about 70%, by the addition of copper to a final concentration of 10^{-6} M. The copper content of the continuous culture reactor decayed at the rate shown and the population approached its original value of 1.5×10^8 cells/liter. Succeeding additions of heavy metals had progressively less effect on the growth rate. However, the steady state population was reduced to about 1×10^8 cells/liter as shown. This indicates a higher heavy metal tolerance at the expense of a less efficient transport system which lowers the total standing crop at a given level of nutrients.

In summary, mixing, temperature, nutrient concentration and inhibitor concentration all affect the efficiency and rate at which microbial processes occur and effects can be described in a rational manner.

Table 1. The maximum growth rate of *C. utilis* after extended growth at steady state in continuous culture.

Glycerol (mg/liter)	pH	μ_{max} (hr^{-1})
5	4.0	0.425
1000	4.0	0.425
5	6.2	0.024
1000	6.2	0.144

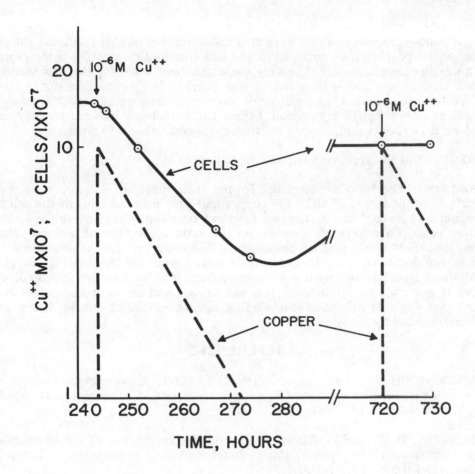

Fig. 5.   Effect of first and second addition of 10^{-6} M Cu^{++} added to the reactor of a steady state continuous culture of a marine yeast (pink 1) growth at 0.092/hr.

DISCUSSION

BELSER: Dr. Button, Dr. Jones reported alterations in cellular morphology with the emergence of resistants. Have you observed a similar phenomenon in these kinds of studies?

BUTTON: This is recent work. We have developed a theory of this over the past couple of years and this was experiment number one. If I had had things organized properly, we could have had size distribution profiles throughout this copper perturbation. The only yeast that will work for this has turned out to be tiny and it was below our current facility for measuring size distribution. We have the facility for answering your question but I do not have an answer for your question. I think the probability of what you say, or of what Dr. Jones said, happening, though, is certainly quite great.

JONES: Did the yeast concentrate the metals at all?

BUTTON: The ratio between the copper concentrations and cell mass was 10^6; in other words, if all of the copper had gone into the mass of the cell it would be one part in 10^6 copper. I do not have data, but I cannot see how they could do otherwise. One has on the surface the type of material that has ligands of the type that binds things like heavy metals. As you know, if you do not have a really clean system and you try inoculating, as Dr. Jannasch pointed out, with a small inoculum, it is hard to get things going, but if you use a large inoculum, it is not so hard and this is probably because the cell surfaces are good complexing agents which, of course, has been demonstrated by many people.

REFERENCES

BORKOWSKI, J. D., and M. J. JOHNSON. 1967. Experimental evaluation of liquid film resistance in oxygen transport to microbial cells. Appl. Microbiol., *15*: 1483-1488.

BUTTON, D. K. 1969. Effect of clay on the availability of dilute organic nutrients to steady-state heterotrophic populations. Limnol. Oceanogr., *14*: 95-100.

BUTTON, D. K. 1969. Thiamine limited steady state growth of the yeast *Cryptococcus albidus*. J. Gen. Microbiol., *57*: 777.

DREYFUSS, J. 1964. Characterization of a sulfate and thiosulfate-transporting system in *Salmonella typhimurium*. J. Biol Chem., *239*: 2292-2297.

PENA, C. E. 1955. The influence of temperature on the growth of *T. utilis*. M.S. Thesis, Univ. Wisconsin. Univ. Microfilms, Ann Arbor, Michigan.

WRIGHT, R. T., and HOBBIE, J. E. 1965. The uptake of organic solutes in lake water. Limnol. Oceanogr., *10*: 22-28.

CAROTENOIDS OF THE CRINOID *FLOROMETRA SERRETISSIMA*

Richard A. Nevé and Guy A. Howard
Central Washington State College
Ellensburg, Washington 98926

ABSTRACT

Pigments of *Florometra serretissima* were column chromatographed and then characterized by their visible and infrared absorption spectra, partition ratio between hexane and 95% methanol, and behavior on thin layer chromatograms when mixed with known pigments. Echinenone, canthaxanthin and astaxanthin were present in the largest amounts. Small amounts of β-carotene, zeaxanthin, xanthophyll and an unidentified carotenoid pigment were also present.

INTRODUCTION

The purpose of the study was to separate and identify the pigments of *Florometra serretissima*, a marine Echinoderm found in the San Juan archipelago. No attempt was made to determine any physiological functions of the pigments. This is the first reported study of the pigmentation of this species know to us.

Crinoids, commonly called Sea Lilies or Feather Stars, are stalked or stalkless pentamerous Pelmatozoa with pinnulated branched or unbranched arms containing extensions of the food grooves, coelom, and nervous, water-vascular and reproductive systems (Hyman, 1955). Other than the recorded colors, knowledge of the chemical nature of the pigments of these animals is incomplete (Fox, 1953).

Studies of *Antedon petasus* (Lomberg, 1932) and *Antedon bifida* (Dimelow, 1958) have shown carotenoids to be the main components of the pigments responsible for their color. β-carotene, astaxanthin, esterified astaxanthin, xanthophyll and some hydroxynaphaquinones were reported in the latter study. Sutherland and Wells (1959) reported hydroxyanthraquinones to be the main pigments of *Comatulina pectinata*.

METHODS AND RESULTS

F. serretissima was collected by dredging in about 120 feet of water in Satellite Channel northeast of Sydney off the east coast of Vancouver Island, British Columbia, Canada. The pigments were extracted from the whole animal with 95% ethanol, transferred to petroleum ether (bp 30 to 60 C) by water saturation of the ethanol, concentrated under vacuum and stored at -4 C under nitrogen in the dark until used.

Esterified pigments in the petroleum ether extract were saponified with 12% methanolic potassium hydroxide according to the method of Karrer and Jucker (1950). After saponification, the pigments were divided into hypophasic and epiphasic fractions by partition between petroleum ether and methanol. Those pigments in the hypophase were extracted with diethyl ether. Both the hypophasic and epiphasic extracts were then dried over anhydrous sodium sulfate and concentrated.

The individual pigments were separated on solid-liquid columns of chromatographic grade neutral alumina, 80 to 200 mesh (Merck and Co., Inc., Rahway, N. J.). The glass columns used (24 cm x 2 cm) were packed by gravity using constant flowing petroleum ether as a solvent. The crude pigment extract was placed on the column and eluted step-wise with petroleum ether (bp 30 to 60 C) containing increasing 10% increments of diethyl ether, followed by ethanol, and finally, ethanol plus 5% acetic acid. The eluted pigments were collected in 2 to 5 ml fractions and their visible and infrared absorption spectra were determined by scanning with a Beckman DB spectrophotometer and with a Perkin-Elmer model 137B Infrared Spectrophotometer with pigments neat (Fig. 1). The appropriate fractions were combined, resulting in six to eight main fractions. The purity of each fraction was determined by thin layer chromatography using prepared silica gel sheets (Eastman Chromagram Sheets, K301-R-silica gel, Distillation Products Industries, Division Eastman Kodak Co., Rochester, N. Y.). These chromatograms were developed with 3:1 hexane:ethyl acetate (Griffiths, 1966) (Fig. 2).

Table 1 summarizes the results obtained in this study. The various fractions are listed in the order in which they were eluted. The partition coefficients were determined by the method of Petracek and Zechmeister (1956) using hexane and 95% methanol. The relative amount of each pigment present is given as a percentage of the total pigment. This figure is based on the extinction coefficient at λ_{max}; however, the quantities are only approximate, as no allowance was made for the difference in molar extinction values.

The visible absorption spectrum of fraction I (Table 1) is very similar in shape to that of β-carotene with corresponding maxima in carbon disulfide and petroleum ether as reported by Goodwin (1954). When partitioned the pigment showed a ratio of 100:0 which is the figure reported for β-carotene (Petracek and Zechmeister, 1956). In the Carr-Price test, with antimony trichloride in chloroform (Carr and Price, 1926), fraction I gave a blue solution with an absorption maximum at 590 mμ which is typical of β-carotene (Euler et al., 1932). The infrared spectrum of fraction I is identical to that reported for β-carotene (Lunde and Zechmeister, 1955) (Fig. 3). The identity of fraction I with β-carotene was further established by thin layer chromatography of fraction I mixed with β-carotene of known purity (Griffiths, 1966) on two different adsorbents. In no case did the pigments separate.

Only a trace amount of fraction II (Table 1) was obtained. It was shown to be a slightly slower moving pigment than either fraction I or known β-carotene. A larger quantity of pigment is needed for further identification.

Fraction III (Table 1) has properties which identify it as echinenone (4-keto-β-carotene) (Ganguly et al., 1956). The visible absorption spectrum has only one asymmetric peak in carbon disulfide, petroleum ether or

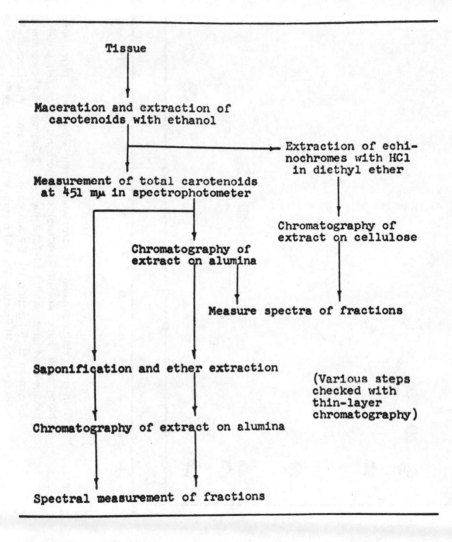

Fig. 1.   Outline of methods of separation and measurement of pigments in *Florometra serretissima*.

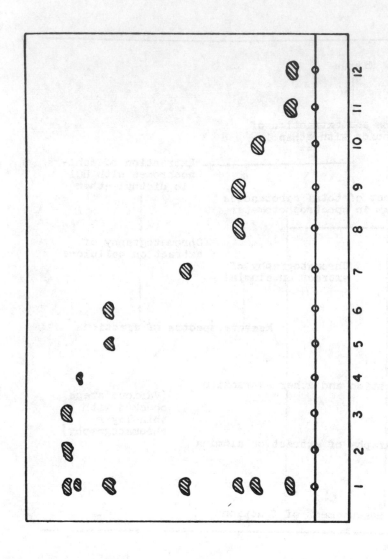

Fig. 2. Thin-layer chromatogram of carotenoids from *Florometra serretissima* along with some known carotenoids. Adsorbent: silica gel; solvent: hexane-ethyl acetate, 3:1. 1-Total pigment, 2-Fraction I, 3-β-carotene, 4-Fraction II, 5-Fraction III, 6-echinenone, 7-Fraction IV, 8-Fraction V, 9-zeaxanthin, 10-Fraction VI, 11-Fraction VII, 12 astacene.

Table 1. Carotenoids of *Florometra serretissma**.

| Fraction | Relative abundance (approximate) (%) | Ethyl ether in petroleum ether required for elution (%) | Absorption maxima | | | | Partition coefficient (hexane: 95% methanol) | Probable identity |
			Carbon di-sulfide	Petroleum ether	Ethanol	Chloroform		
I	3	0	520,486 ~450**	483,453 ~425	-	-	100:0	β-carotene
II	trace	1-2	-	-	-	-	-	?
III	46	25	490	460	-	475	94:6	echinenone
IV	31	100	500	463	-	-	50:50	canthaxanthin
V	5	ethanol	515,480 ~450	-	483,450 ~420	-	10:90	zeaxanthin
VI	3	ethanol	510,480 ~446	475,448 ~420	-	-	13:87	xanthophyll
VII	12	ethanol, 5% acetic acid	502	-	-	-	2:98	astaxanthin

*. The pigments are listed in the order in which they were eluted from an (S-L) alumina column.

** ~ indicates a shoulder or inflection.

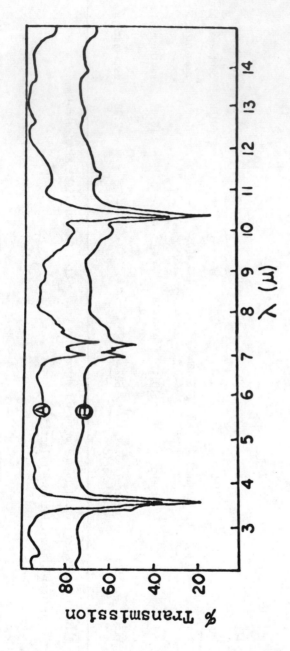

Fig. 3. Infrared spectra of carotenoid fraction I (A) and β-carotene (B).

chloroform. Infrared spectra of fraction III and known echinenone (7) are identical (Fig. 4). Thin layer chromatography of known echinenone mixed with fraction III on two different adsorbents failed to show any separation of the pigments. When partitioned, fraction III gave a ratio of 94:6 which is in close agreement with the 93:7 reported for echinenone (Petracek and Zechmeister, 1956).

Visible absorption spectra of fraction IV (Table 1) in carbon disulfide and in petroleum ether showed single, broad peaks with maxima identical to those reported for canthaxanthin (4,4'-diketo-β-carotene) (Lee, 1966). Partition of fraction IV between hexane and 95% methanol gave a ratio of 50:50. This is the figure reported for canthaxanthin (Petracek and Zechmeister, 1956).

Fractions V and VI (Table 1) were eluted together from the first alumina column using 100% ethanol. Separation could not be effected on a second alumina column. The two fractions were separated with solid-liquid columns packed in the same manner as above, but with silica gel, 140 mesh (chromatographic grade, J. T. Baker Chemical Co., Phillipsburg, N. J.) and cellulose (Whatman Cellulose Powder CF 11, Van Waters and Rogers, Inc., Seattle, Wash.) (2:1, by volume) as the absorbent. Passing each of the fractions (V and VI) through a second silica gel-cellulose column purified the separated pigments.

The visible absorption spectra of fraction V in carbon disulfide and petroleum ether are similar to those of zeaxanthin (3,3'-dihydroxy-β-carotene) (Griffiths, 1966). When subjected to partition the pigment showed a ratio of 10:90 which agrees with the 11:89 reported for zeaxanthin (Petracek and Zechmeister, 1956). The infrared spectrum of fraction V is identical to that reported for zeaxanthin (Strain et al., 1961) (Fig. 5). In the Carr-Price test fraction V gave a blue solution with an absorption maximum at 590 mμ, the reported value for zeaxanthin (Euler et al., 1932). Thin layer chromatography of fraction V mixed with known zeaxanthin (Griffiths, 1966) on two different adsorbents showed no separation of the pigments.

Fraction VI (Table 1) gave visible absorption maxima in carbon disulfide and in petroleum ether similar to those of (lutein) xanthophyll (3,3'-dihydroxy-β-carotene) (Hausser and Smakula, 1934). Partition between hexane and 95% methanol gave a ratio of 13:87 which agrees with the reported 12:88 for xanthophyll (Petracek and Zechmeister, 1956). The Carr-Price test on fraction VI gave a blue solution with an absorption maximum of 585 mμ which agrees with the 586 mμ reported for xanthophyll (Euler et al., 1932). The infrared spectrum of fraction VI is identical to that reported for (lutein) xanthophyll (Strain et al., 1961) (Fig. 6).

Fraction VII (Table 1) was eluted from the first alumina column with 5% acetic acid in ethanol; this is a characteristic property of astaxanthin (3,3'-dihydroxy-4,4'-diketo-β-carotene). The acetic acid-ethanol solution of this fraction was diluted with an equal volume of water and the pigment was extracted with diethyl ether. This extract was then concentrated and identified as described. The visible absorption spectrum in carbon disulfide is

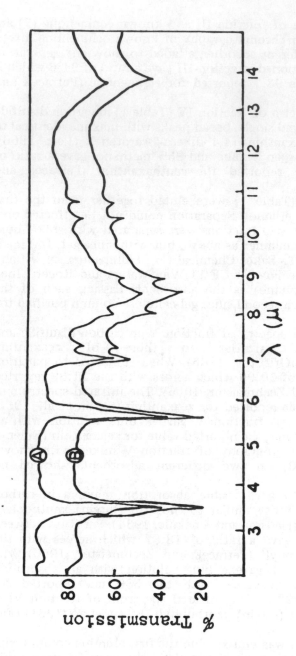

Fig. 4.　Infrared spectra of carotenoid fraction III (A) and known echinenone (B).

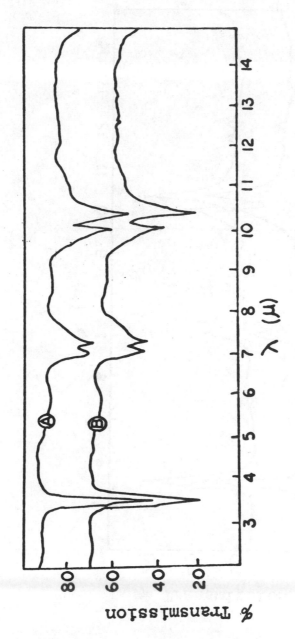

Fig. 5.   Infrared spectra of carotenoid fraction V (A) and zeaxanthin (B).

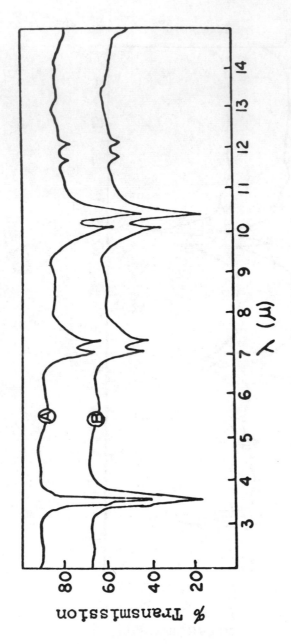

Fig. 6. Infrared spectra of carotenoid fraction VI (A) and xanthophyll (B).

similar in shape to that of astaxanthin and has a corresponding maximum (Goodwin and Srisukh, 1949). Thin layer chromatography of fraction VII (after saponification) mixed with authentic astacene on two different adsorbents did not separate the pigments. Astaxanthin is the natural pigment, for astacene does not occur in Nature. Astacene is formed from astaxanthin by saponification (Goodwin and Srisukh, 1949). This conversion was shown to take place with fraction VII. The infrared spectrum of this fraction (after saponification) is identical to that of known astacene (Fig. 7).

CONCLUSIONS

It is not surprising that these various fractions were found together, since β-carotene is reported to be the precursor of echinenone, canthaxanthin (Davies et al., 1965), and astaxanthin (Goodwin and Srisukh, 1949). The following reaction sequence has been elucidated: β-carotene $\rightarrow$ echinenone $\rightarrow$ canthaxanthin $\rightarrow$ astaxanthin (Thomen and Wackernagel, 1964), although the exact mechanisms for these steps have not been worked out. Xanthophyll in crinoids has been found by others (Lonnberg and Hellstrom, 1931). Dimelow (1958) reported the presence of xanthophyll with β-carotene and astaxanthin in the same crinoid.

This work represents the first reported isolation of canthaxanthin from an echinoderm, although it has been found in a crustacean (Krinsky, 1964).

ACKNOWLEDGMENTS

This work was supported in part by a grant from the Research Corporation.

This research report was submitted in partial fulfillment of requirements for the degree of Master of Science by Guy A. Howard.

We thank Robert L. Fernald, Director, University of Washington Laboratories, Friday Harbor, Washington, for use of facilities; Mary Griffiths, Zoology Department, University of Washington, for advice and contributions of known pigments; Robert D. Gaines and Richard W. Hasbrouck, Chemistry Department, Central Washington State College, for many helpful suggestions; and Phillip von Phul for help at the start of this study.

REFERENCES

CARR, F. H., and E. A. PRICE. 1926. Color reactions attributed to Vitamin A. Biochem. J., *20*: 497-501.

DAVIES, B. H., W. J. HUS, and C. O. CHINCHESTER. 1965. The metabolism of carotenoids in the brine shrimp (*Artemia salina*). Biochem. J., *94*: 26.

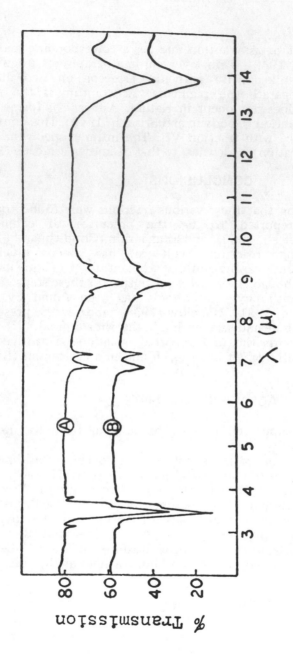

Fig. 7.   Infrared spectra of carotenoid fraction VII (A) (after saponification) and known astacene (B).

DIMELOW, E. J. 1958. Pigments present in arms and pinnules of the crinoid *Antedon bifida* (Pennant). Nature, *182*: 812.

EULER, H. VAN, P. KARRER, and E. KLUSSMANN. 1932. Spectrometrische Messungen an Carotenoiden. Helv. Chim. Acta, *15*: 502-507.

FOX, D. L. 1963. Animal biochromes and structural colors. Cambridge Univ. Press, London. 278 p.

GANGULY, J., N. I. KRINSKY, and J. H. PINCKARD. 1956. Isolation and nature of echinenone. A provitamin A. Arch. Biochem. Biophys., *60*: 345-351.

GOODWIN, T. W. 1954. Carotenoids: their comparative biochemistry. Chemical Publ., New York. 356 p.

GOODWIN, T. W., and S. SRISUKH. 1949. The biochemistry of locusts. I. Carotenoids of the integument. Biochem. J., *45*: 263-268.

GRIFFITHS, M. 1966. The carotenoids of the eggs and embryos of the sea urchin *Strongylocentrotus purpuratus*. Devel. Biol., *13*: 296-309.

HAUSSER, K. W., and A. SMAKULA. 1935. Absorption of light and the double bond. III. Investigation in the furane series. Z. Phyzik. Chem., *B29*, 378-383.

HYMAN, L. H. 1955. The invertebrates: Echinodermata, IV. McGraw-Hill, New York. 763 p.

KARRER, P., and E. JUCKER. 1950. Carotenoids. Elsevier, New York. 384 p. Translated and revised by E. A. Braude.

KRINSKY, N. I. 1965. The carotenoids of the brine shrimp *Artemia salina*. Comp. Biochem. Physiol., *16*: 181-187.

LEE, W. L. 1966. Pigmentation of the marine isopod *Idotea montereyensis*. Comp. Biochem. Physiol., *18*: 17-36.

LONNBERG, E. 1931. Untersuchungen über das Vorkommen Carotenoider Stoffe bei Marinen Evertebraten. Ark. Zool., *22A*(14): 1-49.

LONNBERG, E. 1932. Zur Kenntnis der Carotenoide bei Marinen Evertebraten. Ark. Zool., *23*(4): 1-74.

LUNDE, K., and L. ZECHMEISTER. 1955. Infrared spectra and cis-trans configurations of some carotenoid pigments. J. Amer. Chem. Soc., 77: 1647-1653.

PETRACEK, F. J., and L. ZECHMEISTER. 1956. Determination of partition coefficients of carotenoids as a tool in pigment analysis. Anal. Chem., *28*: 1484-1485.

STRAIN, H. H., M. R. THOMAS, and J. J. KATZ. 1961. Spectrum of eschscholtzxanthin and other carotenoid pigments. J. Org. Chem., *26*: 5061-5064.

SUTHERLAND, M. D., and J. W. WELLS. 1959. Anthraquinone pigments from the crinoid *Comatula pectinata*. Chem. Ind., *37*: 291-292.

THOMEN, H., and H. WACKERNAGEL. 1964. Zum Vorkommen von Keto-Carotenoiden in Crustaceen. Naturwissen, *51*: 87-88.

WHAT YOU DON'T KNOW CAN HURT YOU: ORGANIC COLLOIDS AND NATURAL WATERS[1]

Irving A. Breger
U. S. Department of the Interior
Geological Survey
Washington, D. C. 20242

ABSTRACT

Most studies of organic substances in natural waters and associated sediments are concerned with the isolation and identification of relatively simple compounds. Complex compounds of high molecular weight, which may account for as much as 90% of the total organic matter, are being neglected because they are so difficult to characterize.

The complex material consists of high polymers which must have colloidal properties. Interactions among these substances may lead to phenomena such as syneresis, coprecipitation, adsorption, flocculation or protection, and may result in unusual associations of compounds. As a result, the simple compounds found in natural waters may, to an appreciable extent, represent merely the residua from such colloidal interactions. Without some knowledge and consideration of the colloidal phenomena that may take place, therefore, explanations for the occurrences of dissolved compounds should be viewed with skepticism.

INTRODUCTION

Development of sophisticated analytical tools, such as gas-liquid, paper and thin-layer chromatography, and mass and infrared spectroscopy, has made it possible to detect and identify traces of many types of organic compounds in aquatic environments. As a result, we now have an extensive catalogue of information regarding the occurrence and distribution of hydrocarbons, fatty acids, carbohydrates and other compounds in natural waters.

Little is known about the organic polymers in natural waters. Of particular interest is a study conducted by Lamar and Goerlitz (1966) of the organic acids in the colored waters of streams from California, Washington and Hawaii. It was noted that about 90% of the acids they recovered were too complex to be identified by gas-liquid chromatography and that infrared analysis gave them only the most generalized structural information. Extrapolation of their results suggests that only about 10% of the organic matter in waters is amenable to analysis by these techniques and that 90% of the material is generally neglected.

Compounds of low molecular weight should remain in true solution, whereas those of high molecular weight would be expected to be in colloidal suspension or to precipitate to become part of the sediment. We can only

---

[1] Publication authorized by the Director, U.S. Geological Survey

speculate on the contribution of such organic detritus to the sediments at the bottom of a large body of water. Some pertinent information was accumulated by Trask (1953), who conducted a survey of the sediments of the western part of the Gulf of Mexico. The area studied does not appear to be unique, yet the sediments were reported to contain about 1% by weight of complex organic matter. Obviously, these compounds represent a large proportion of the organic matter that occurs in aquatic environments.

In view of the limited information regarding complex organic substances in natural waters, I should like to resort to the application of Woodward's Law (1968), namely, that a theory is better than its explanation. In effect, the unfortunate absence of facts compels me to discuss the nature and importance of complex organic substances rather broadly and hypothetically. Nevertheless, it is hoped that some of the ideas discussed in this paper will provoke consideration of the problem.

SOURCES OF COMPLEX ORGANIC MATTER

Marine environment

Only recently have we begun to appreciate the fact that various sources contribute complex organic matter to the marine environment. Realization has been a result of studies of the disseminated organic complexes in sea water; of those marine products, such as coorongite, which separate from the sea water; of the complex substances of recent marine sediment; and of the complex materials that occur in ancient marine sediments and are known by the general term "kerogen." The previously ignored but significant contribution of terrestrially derived organic material to the marine environment must now also be considered.

As already noted, information regarding the nature and concentration of organic complexes in sea water is extremely sparse and, to a great extent, speculative. Parsons and Strickland (1962) found an average of 49.5 μg/liter of particulate carbon in temperate waters of the North Pacific Ocean between 500 and 3000 m. Less than 1% of this matter consisted of lipids, the remainder having a high nitrogen content indicative of protein. Riley, van Hemert and Wangersky (1965) suggest that some dissolved organic matter may be adsorbed by particulate material to maintain the equilibrium of nutrients used by organisms. If this is the case, several reasonable suggestions can be made regarding the organic particulate matter in such a marine environment. First, it appears from the low C:N ratio that adsorbed material, if adsorption occurs, is of the same general compositon as the particulate matter, that is, proteinaceous. Second, the absence of lipids may indicate that these compounds, which appear to be quite resistant to biochemical degradation, may be in solution in the free state or as salts, or may have disappeared by interaction to form complexes of high molecular weight that subsequently sank to the bottom sediment. This observation suggests that an equilibrium exists with respect to proteins in which the particulate matter is being produced and re-utilized. Lipids and the complex products derived from lipids would, on the contrary, not be re-utilized and, if not in solution, would precipitate.

I am not aware of any significant studies of complex organic substances in shore-line waters. The discharges of certain rivers are known to carry enormous quantities of terrestrially derived humic substances into the sea, and there must be considerable contributions of the same material on a smaller scale all along shore lines. Most of our knowledge regarding such materials in near-shore environments comes, however, not primarily from the study of recent sediments, but rather from the study of ancient shales.

Of particular importance in this field is the work conducted by Stadnikoff (1930). He concluded that the organic constituents of certain shales were partly derived from terrestrial humic substances that were transformation products of lignin, and partly from aquatic detritus generated from lipids. Although this dual source of the organic constituents of shales was recognized by Stadnikoff about forty years ago, most work reported in the literature since then has still concentrated on an effort to find a single source of the organic matter in marine shales.

Breger and Brown (1962, 1963), in a study of the kerogen of the Chattanooga and Pierre Shales, concluded that complex terrestrial organic substances can be distributed over enormous areas in marine basins. Since it can mingle and co-precipitate with high molecular weight organic substances derived from the marine source, it is no wonder that the organic material found in near-shore marine environments should have highly variable composition and structure. Consideration of the likely composition of complex organic compounds from terrestrial and marine sources has provided a technique for discriminating between the deep and near-shore environments in which ancient sediments are deposited (Breger and Brown, 1963).

Lacustrine environment

The complex organic substances that occur in lakes and ponds are perhaps subject to even more variations in composition than are those that occur in marine environments. The organic debris of lakes is derived from algal and planktonic growths supplemented by more or less humic material derived from neighboring grasses and plants, and by wind-blown material, such as spores. All such substances are eventually whipped into a stew which is ultimately transformed into kerogen. Because of the infinite variety of possible combinations of progenitor substances, the term kerogen describes the composition of the product only in a very broad sense. To illustrate this point, we need only consider the variable composition of the shale of the Green River Formation and its accompanying secondarily derived complexes, such as gilsonite, wurtzilite, elaterite and similar substances.

Rivers and streams

The complex organic matter carried by rivers and streams depends primarily on the regions they drain. Being for the most part aerated environments, less stable organic matter is bound to be lost by either microbiological attack or oxidative degradation. As a result, only the most stable organic residues should be discharged by a river into a marine environment. In actuality, the river is constantly picking up dissolved and particulate suspended matter, so it may well be transporting original as well as partly transformed organic substances. As an example, it would not be surprising to find a river carrying relatively fresh lignin and cellulose from newly fallen debris, as well as a series of degradation products derived from these substances where they have been exposed to biochemical decomposition over extended periods of time.

NATURE OF COMPLEX ORGANIC SUBSTANCES

The origin of stable complex terrestrial organic substances, generally called humic substances, is controversial. Accepting the ready degradation of cellulose by many varieties of microorganisms, and a high degree of stability for lignin and its simple degradation products, Fischer and Schrader (1922), Stadnikoff (1930), and many others have concluded that lignin is primarily responsible for the origin of most complex terrestrial organic substances of geological interest. Manskaya and Drozdova (1964) have supported the concept that humic material is not wholly derived from lignin but, rather, may result from an interaction between the sugars and amino acids that are eliminated by the hydrolysis of carbohydrates and proteins. This theory appears to have had its roots in the search for a source of the nitrogen found in humic substances. Although such a reaction may occur in Nature, the reactants would very likely be rapidly destroyed microbiologically and be denied the opportunity to interact. Besides, the humic substances are not always found associated with the alkaline environment conducive to such a reaction. In contrast, chemical and spectroscopic evidence points very clearly to a mother-daugher relationship between lignin and humic substances. As with many problems in organic geochemistry, there is little likelihood that a definitive experimental solution to this problem will be found. The solution will depend on the accumulation of evidence pointing in a particular direction, and its interpretation will in part be based on both experience and intuition.

The origin of organic complexes from strictly aquatic sources, fresh water, brackish or marine, presents a different problem. These substances tend to have relatively high hydrogen contents and are generally unlike terrestrial humic substances. Stadnikoff (1930) suggests, and presents chemical data to support his suggestion, that the aquatic complexes are formed from polymerized unsaturated lipids. As described by Stadnikoff, these substances, when derived from algal lipids, are mono- and polycyclic carboxylic acids and oxygenated compounds. Other, less important, organic complexes appear to be derived from terpenes.

VISIBLE MANIFESTATIONS OF COMPLEX ORGANIC MATTER

The term "complex", which has been used to describe the compounds under consideration, is synonymous with "high molecular weight." The compounds might, therefore, be expected to have colloidal dimensions and to undergo many of the phenomena attributed to colloidal substances. Many such substances are well known to have, or to have at one time had, gelatinous, rubbery or other clearly defined colloidal properties. As colloidal substances, moreover, these substances are subject to the action of, as well as interaction with, water under natural conditions.

A number of organic colloids, as we may designate such substances, occur in sufficient quantity and concentration to warrant special consideration. One of these substances is coorongite, and another is balkhashite; other related substances of prime interest that at one time had colloidal properties have contributed to the composition of boghead coals, alginites, cannel coals and a host of other exotic materials.

Coorongite

This material occurs in a lagoon along the coast of South Australia. Known since 1864, the coorongite is thought to be a product of a blue-green alga that was named *Elaeophyton coorongiana* by R. Thiessen (1925). These algae live in colonies and it has been reported that at the end of winter a green scum collects on the surface of the lagoon and is driven toward shore where it rapidly dries to form lamellae of dark-brown, rubber-like material. According to Stadnikoff (1930), this material has formed by the transformation of lipids along two paths. One process involves an oxidative polymerization not unlike that which drying oils undergo. The product of this reaction is an elastic, saponifiable substance insoluble in most organic solvents. The second path, along which lipids are transformed under anaerobic conditions, is thought by Stadnikoff to lead to the production of ketones, hydrocarbons and other substances that are unsaponifiable but soluble in organic solvents. Obviously, if these are the processes involved, one or the other, or both under certain conditions, can take place at various stages in the development of coorongite and result in products of varying composition and properties.

Balkhashite

This brown, elastic, rubber-like substance is found on the shores of Lake Balkhash in Western Siberia. It appears to be derived from the oil-bearing green alga, *Botryococcus braunii* K., which lives in a swampy and somewhat saline arm of the lake (Ala-Kul Lake). Studies have indicated that, as in the case of coorongite, the balkhashite is in part a product derived from the aerobic polymerization of unsaturated lipids.

Sapropelite

Sapropelite, like coorongite, balkhashite and similar substances, appears to be a polymer derived from aquatic lipids. The major difference between the coorongite and sapropelitic substances is, however, that the latter are of widespread occurrence and probably account for much of the complex organic constituents found in many recent sediments. In the light of Stadnikoff's suggestion that polymerizates of this nature require an aerobic environment for formation, it is likely that such substances also account for a good share of the complex organic matter found in sea water.

INVISIBLE MANIFESTATIONS OF COMPLEX ORGANIC MATTER IN THE MARINE ENVIRONMENT

Assuming much of the high molecular weight organic matter derived from the sea to have a composition basically related to polymerized fatty acids, it becomes possible to speculate on the significance of the material on the marine environment. Thus, we may ask ourselves, what effect can such material have on simpler compounds dissolved in the sea? As already noted, the large molecules must have colloidal properties and we cannot ignore the interaction between the compounds and the aqueous medium and all its constituents in which they are suspended.

If the substances are polymerized lipids, they probably consist of complex ring and non-ring structures to which oxygenated groups are attached. Carboxyl groups are known to be present, and there is also evidence for the presence of carbonyl groups. These substances have many of the properties of colloidal electrolytes and are frequently subject to swelling. Although retention of water is a result of weak Van der Waal's forces, the amount of water retained may be phenomenal and lead to a fifty- to one-hundred-fold increase in volume. On a volumetric basis, therefore, the complex organic compounds in the sea may actually be even more important, especially as scavengers, than would be presumed on the basis of weight percentage. Moreover, as is well known, an electrically charged colloidal particle may interact with another oppositely charged colloidal particle resulting in the flocculation of both or, under special circumstances, in the protection of one. Such reactions result in either removal of the flocculate to the sediment, or in an apparent change in the composition of each colloid as well as of the organic constituents in the water. In either case, such reactions of colloids must be considered in evaluating the quantity and nature of complex organic substances in, especially, marine and lacustrine environments.

Possible examples of such interactions are the associations of humic acids with sugars, amino acids or other complex organic bases that have been noted by several workers and discussed by Degens and Reuter (1964). Such combinations of compounds are rather surprising and may reflect colloidal phenomena between unlike substances that have led to flocculation of the humic acids. Once flocculation has occurred, reactions between the precipitated substances may further complicate the problem. It is pertinent to note, however, that the possibility of such colloidal phenomena has been ignored in efforts to explain such associations of compounds.

Complex acidic compounds may also behave as ion exchange resins capable of acting as scavengers for certain cations in the natural environment. Among the most likely candidates for the formation of organo-metallic complexes are some of the heavier elements, among which are copper, vanadium, nickel and cobalt. The behaviour of iron is anomalous;

this element may be reduced to the ferrous state by the organic matter, may be hydrolyzed and precipitated as ferric hydroxide before it reacts with organic matter, or may enter into an equilibrium in which these and other reactions are involved. Hem (1960) describes reactions of ferrous iron with tannic acid, a substance similar to humic substances of terrestrial origin. Organic complexes of aquatic origin are more highly hydrogenated and contain less oxygen than tannic acid and are, therefore, better reducing agents than either humic or tannic acid. Which reactions will occur depends upon redox potential, pH, temperature and, to a degree, on the type of organic matter.

Although copper forms some of the most stable organo-metallic complexes known, the absence of appreciable concentrations of copper in marine sediments attests to rapid removal of the element from streams at or near the shoreline. In all likelihood, it is precipitated as an extremely insoluble copper sulfide. Manganese, on the contrary, forms weak complexes, in spite of which we cannot help but wonder if such complexes may not have played an important role in the formation of the well-known but little understood marine manganese nodules. For instance, may not manganese, derived from some submarine source, have been precipitated from solution as gelatinous, colloidal complexes which then underwent syneresis? The chloride ion is particularly effective in promoting syneresis, which is essentially the opposite of swelling. Thus, we may conceive of a gelatinous mass containing manganese and other constituents being precipitated from sea water and then undergoing the equivalent of dehydration while still in contact with the water.

A number of years ago we reported a similar phenomenon in which organic solvents failed to extract any appreciable quantity of organic material from a recent marine sediment. Only after initial extensive extraction with water did the organic solvents affect the sediment, dissolving an amazingly large quantity of soluble material (Whitehead and Breger, 1950). It is our impression that solution and removal of salt from the sediment led to peptization of the organic matter, making it more readily available to the organic extracting solution. Failure to recognize the importance of pre-extraction of recent sediments with water has led us to question the results of a number of studies published since our work was carried out.

Marine organic matter precipitates because the material is inedible (a biochemical reason), because it becomes too heavy to remain in suspension (a physical reason) or because it may precipitate with inorganic substances. On deposition, the precipitate may be transposed from an oxidizing zone to a reducing zone at which point the material enters a different environment where other reactions may occur. Time is an important factor in colloidal phenomena and more than sufficient time is available for these reactions. If proteins were co-precipitated with polymerized lipids, organisms and enzymatically catalyzed reactions could destroy the proteins, and the hydrogen sulfide and nitrogen compounds thus formed might then react with the still unsaturated lipid-derived material. This is one explanation of the introduction of nitrogen and sulfur into organic sediments.

Such a sequence of events could alter the association of the organic components in a natural aqueous medium and lead to the formation of secondary compounds not directly derived from biological processes. As a hypothetical example, a protein and a partially polymerized lipid might co-precipitate. The protein and original lipid, both of which were biologically produced, might then undergo further biological degradation, the hydrogen sulfide from the protein reacting with the unsaturated lipid to produce a secondary compound. These secondary compounds could be found in either the water or the sediment or both; examples might be hydrocarbons, carboxyl- or hydroxyl-containing compounds, or even nitrogenous or sulfur-bearing compounds.

Where such reactions occur in the sediment, we must consider the possibility that the gelatinous organic matter may unmix, or undergo coacervation. The resultant simpler secondary compounds could separate into a new colloidal phase.

Assuming the validity of Stadnikoff's suggestions regarding the polymerization of unsaturated lipids in oxygenated waters, we must consider the possible formation of a semi-permeable membrane as a film enclosing a micelle of as yet unpolymerized lipids. A classic situation is then at hand for a Donnan Equilibrium in which concentration of a particular ion could occur. Such a phenomenon, based primarily on the colloidal properties of a substance, could easily be misinterpreted to represent primary concentration of the ion by a biological mechanism, or the formation of a secondary organo-metallic complex.

The naturally occurring clay-organic complex has long been a subject for speculation, and even today we are not really certain whether this is an adsorptive process based on the colloidal properties of the clay, or whether a chemical bond exists. Regardless, the importance of the association cannot be underestimated in terms of the possible preservative effect of the clay on the organic matter. The work by Kroepelin (1963), who reported that amino acids associated with clays can be heated as high as 500 C without decomposition, should be cited in this context.

These few examples of colloidal phenomena related to organic matter in natural waters suggest effects which are being ignored. It is disturbing to think that the various organic compounds isolated from natural waters may actually represent residua, whose quantitative interrelationships may be nonrepresentative because of differential subtractions by various colloidal mechanisms. Similarly, associations of nitrogen compounds with the organic complexes or sediments may also be nonrepresentative of the starting materials, and may only reflect the effects of secondary colloidal associations. I suggest, then, that the study of organic compounds in natural waters be coordinated with a similar study of associated sediments, and that more attention be given to colloidal phenomena.

It is not difficult to see why such work has been pretty much neglected. Not only is the organic matter difficult to characterize, but it is also subject to continuing chemical reaction, dehydration, aging and other phenomena which may be either reversible or irreversible. Avoidance of such work, because of its difficulty, cannot be severely criticized. To paraphrase a well-known quotation, blame them not, for they know what they do not do.

The study of colloidal phenomena that occur in natural waters may lead to more rational solutions to problems concerned with the accumulation and degradation of complex organic residues, as well as to problems related to the accumulation or nonaccumulation of certain elements. On a practical basis, there is even the possibility that certain polluted streams might best be treated by the addition of organic substances capable of tying up and removing contaminants as a consequence of colloidal phenomena. As long as the principles of colloid chemistry are ignored, however, I feel that the significance of much of the analytical data being accumulated with respect to organic matter in natural waters must be examined with much skepticism.

DISCUSSION

BLUMER: You were comparing the polymerization of the drying oils with the possible fate of unsaturates in the sea. These reactions have to be bimolecular. In the drying oils they are easily accomplished. At the great dilution of sea water, this is more difficult. There are other reactions competing with polymerization. The first step is the oxidation of the double bonds. Then, if there is another molecule nearby, polymerization occurs. If not, the chain may break at the double bond. The question is one of rates. We are convinced that much of the smell of sea water comes from fragmentation products, i.e., aldehydes and ketones. Do you have a feeling for the relative rates of the polymerization and breakdown under typical marine conditions?

BREGER: I cannot argue with your comment on this. All I can say is that the amounts of these highly unsaturated oils or fats or acids that do occur in certain environments are phenomenal. I have some information on the Sargasso Sea; there are some areas such as the ones I mentioned in the lakes and lagoons where the quantities are very large. I believe if you go into the menhaden problem with fish (I would call it menhaden, I do not know what others call it) thousands and thousands of tons are concentrated under these conditions. Obviously there are going to be other areas where what you say may very well be true, namely that they are just not concentrated in sufficient quantities to have any particular effect. Maybe it is there that we will find something entirely different, but I do maintain that whether you are dealing with drying oils or working with something else, most of these high molecular weight complexes do have colloidal dimensions and collodial properties, and they cannot be ignored.

BLUMER: Another comment I would like to make concerns your suggestion of the very great variability of the marine polymers. My comment is more a matter of definition. If you analyze crude oil fractions of increasing molecular weight, you find at low molecular weight large amounts of saturates and aromatics, whereas at higher molecular weights there are fewer saturates. In the end, everything is aromatic, simply because your analysis defines any large molecule which contains a single aromatic ring as an aromatic compound or, as another example, we have found that the porphyrin pigments in many rocks are polymerized into very large molecules. If you define anything that has a porphyrin absorption spectrum as a porphyrin, this means that these sediments consist of nearly 100% porphyrin. In a similar sense, I believe that the large molecules in sea water, by definition, are very similar, because they contain protein fragments, carboxyl groups, keto groups, straight-chain and aromatic rings, etc. Are they really as different as you have suggested?

BREGER: I think so. I had hoped you would not get into this problem. I think this is outside the realm of what we are talking about here. In this sense, the data represent a product of the discussion. In other words, the organic material has presumably been deposited and worked over and has been transformed by some unknown mechanism or mechanisms into crude oil. So I would rather we would not discuss that at all. I do not think that it bears on the subject at hand.

But, as for what you say regarding the similarity of all the molecules, my answer to that is, in my opinion, no. I think that certain major portions of the material are degraded rather rapidly and disappear or almost disappear, or are converted into new products which now have to be taken into account. I do not think they are all the same. I think that we have quite a spectrum of different types of substances, and that we can consider each individual, unless they adhere to some sort of association. If you have a protein protecting the lipid, a polymerized lipid, and this precipitates as a unit and is isolated and analyzed, someone is going to say that here we have a protein-lipid compound, or complex, when in actuality, proper treatment may easily break this down into the component protein and lipid, which really has nothing to do with the metabolite under the natural conditions, except that one associates with the other. This is the thing that bothers me.

CHRISTMAN: I would like to say, in connection with your reference to colloids that, classically at least, with the Gelbstoff-type materials in natural waters, this was the first type of thing that was suspected. For those of us that have labored in this area, I think it is safe to say that it has not been proven that they are colloidal. At least if a colloid is as a colloid does, and you do not insist on a specific size, no one has proved that they are colloidal.

BREGER: They may not be. I have never worked with Gelbstoff; I do not know. But you may be perfectly right in saying that they are relatively low molecular weight compounds with sufficient functional groups so that they go into complete solution.

CHRISTMAN: I do not think that it can simply be said that because the molecular weight is such and such, as we have heard this week, it is therefore colloidal. They are certainly right on the border line.

BREGER: You see, I put a disclaimer on that, which you had not noted. I said if they are of sufficient molecular weight with a sufficient number of functional groups they may not be colloidal. In other words, you may have a function there which brings them into true solution in spite of their size. I am not sure of this. It is very hard to tell when you get to the borderline. I have checked on this over a period of months, and you cannot state a true definition of what is and what is not colloidal. The general definition is based solely on the size factor. Fortunately, however, in the case of many of the things that we are dealing with in Nature, we are dealing with linear colloids and they are colloidal because they are of that size in at least one dimension. By definition they have to be accepted as being colloidal.

REFERENCES

BREGER, I. A., and A. BROWN. 1962. Kerogen in the Chattanooga shale. Science, *137*: 221-224.

BREGER, I. A., and A. BROWN. 1963. Distribution and types of organic matter in a barred marine basin. New York Acad. Sci., Trans. Ser. II, *25*: 741-755.

DEGENS, E. T., and J. H. REUTER. 1964. Analytical techniques in the field of organic geochemistry, p. 390-391. *In* U. Colombo and G. D. Hobson [ed.], Advances in organic geochemistry. Pergamon, London.

FISCHER, F., and H. SCHRADER. 1922. Entstehung und chemische Struktur der Kohle. Girardet. Essen.

HEM, J. D. 1960. Complexes of ferrous iron with tannic acid. U.S. Geol. Surv. Water-Supply Paper 1459-D: 75-94.

KROEPELIN, H. 1963. Amino acids in Posidonian shales and their behaviour when heated. Fortschr. Geol. Rheinland Westfalen, *10*: 293-294.

LAMAR, W. L., and D. F. GOERLITZ. 1966. Organic acids in naturally colored surface waters. U. S. Geol. Surv. Water-Supply Paper 1817-A. 17 p.

MANSKAYA, S. M., and T. V. DROZDOVA. 1964. Geochemistry of organic substances. Moscow. Translated and edited by L. Shapiro and I. A. Breger, 1968, Pergamon, Oxford.

PARSONS, T. R., and J. D. H. STRICKLAND. 1962. Organic detritus. Science, *136*: 313-314.

RILEY, G. A., D. VAN HEMERT, and P. J. WANGERSKY. 1965. Organic aggregates in surface and deep waters of the Sargasso Sea. Limnol. Oceanogr., *10*: 354-363.

STADNIKOFF, G. 1930. The origin of coal and oil. Enke, Stuttgart.

THIESSEN, R. 1925. Origin of the boghead coals. U. S. Geol. Surv. Prof. Paper 132-K: 121-137.

TRASK, P. D. 1953. Chemical studies of sediments of the western Gulf of Mexico, Part II of the sediments of the western Gulf of Mexico. Mass. Inst. Technol. and Woods Hole Oceanogr. Inst. Paper *12*(4): 49-120.

WHITEHEAD, W. L., and I. A. BREGER. 1950. The origin of petroleum: effects of low-temperature pyrolysis on the organic extract of a recent marine sediment. Science, *111*: 335-337.

WOODWARD, H. P. 1968. Cited in R. L. Bates, The geological column. Geotimes, *13*(6): 46.

MASTER BIBLIOGRAPHY

ABELSON, P. H., and T. C. HOERING. 1961. Carbon isotope fractionation in formation of amino acids by photosynthetic organisms. Proc. Nat. Acad. Sci., *47*: 623-632.

ACKMAN, R. G., and J. C. SIPOS. 1965. Isolation of the saturated fatty acids of some marine lipids with particular reference to normal odd-numbered fatty acids and branched chain acids. Comp. Biochem. Physiol., *15*: 445-456.

ADAM, N. K. 1937. Rapid method for determining the lowering of tension of exposed water surfaces, with some observations on the surface tension of the sea and of inland waters. Roy. Soc., Proc., B.*122*: 134-139.

ADAMS, D. D. 1966. Dissolved organic matter in Lake Nitinat, an anoxic fjord. M.S. Thesis, Univ. Washington. 46 p.

ADAMS, D. D., and F. A. RICHARDS. 1968. Dissolved organic matter in an anoxic fiord with special reference to the presence of mercaptans. Deep-Sea Res., *15*: 471-481.

ADAMS, J. A., and J. H. STEELE. 1966. Shipboard experiments on the feeding of *Calanus finmarchicus* (Gunnerus), p. 19-35. *In* H. Barnes [ed.], Some contemporary studies in marine science. Allen and Unwin Ltd., London.

ALBRIGHT, L. J. 1966. The effect of temperature and hydrostatic pressure on deamination of L-serine by *Vibrio marinus*, an obligate psychrophile. M.S. Thesis, Oregon State Univ., Corvallis.

ALEXANDER, J., and E. CORCORAN. 1961. A further report on the separation of dissolved organic material from sea water. Personal communication.

ALLEN, L. 1967. Acetate utilization by heterotrophic bacteria in a pond. J. Hungarian Hydrol. Soc. (Hidrológiai Közlöny), *47*: 295-297.

ALLEN, M. B. 1956. Excretion of organic compounds by *Chlamydomonas*. Arch. Mikrobiol., *24*: 163-168.

AMES, G. F. 1964. Uptake of amino acids by *Salmonella typhimurium*. Arch. Biochem. Biophys., *104*: 1-18.

ANDERSON, D. M. W. 1959. Applications of infra-red spectroscopy: the identification and determination of gas-chromatographic fractions. Analyst, *84*: 50-56.

ANDERSON, D. M. W., and S. GARBUTT. 1961. Studies on uronic acid materials. III. An investigation, using ^{14}C compounds of acid decarboxylation reaction-times. Atlanta, *8*: 605-611.

ANDERSON, D. M. W., and S. GARBUTT. 1963a. Studies on uronic acid materials. VII. The kinetics and mechanism of the decarboxylation of uronic acids. J. Chem. Soc.: 3204-3210.

ANDERSON, D. M. W., and S. GARBUTT. 1963b. Studies on uronic acid materials. VIII. A comparative study of some colorimetric methods of estimating the uronic acid contents of polysaccharides. Anal. Chim. Acta, *29*: 31-38.

ANDERSON, D. M. W., S. GARBUTT, and S. S. H. ZAIDI. 1963. Studies on uronic acid materials. IX. The simultaneous determination of uronic acid and alkoxyl groups in polysaccharides by reflux with hydroiodic acid. Anal. Chim. Acta, *29*: 39-45.

ANDERSON, W. W., and J. W. GEHRINGER. 1958. Physical oceanographic biological and chemical data. South Atlantic Coast of the United States. M/V THEODORE N. GILL Cruise 6 and 8. Spec. Sci. Rep. - Fisheries. No. 265: 1-99; 303: 1-227.

ANN, W. D., E. L. HIRST, and D. J. MANNERS. 1965. The constitution of laminarin. V. The location of 1,6-glucosidic linkages. J. Chem. Soc.: 885-893.

ANTIA, A. L., and C. T. LEE. 1963. Studies on the determination and differential analysis of dissolved carbohydrate in sea water. Fish. Res. Bd. Canada. (Manuscript Rep. Ser. 168.)

ANTIA, N. J., C. D. McALLISTER, T. R. PARSONS, K. STEPHENS, and J. D. H. STRICKLAND. 1963. Further measurements of primary production using a large-volume plastic sphere. Limnol. Oceanogr., *8*: 166-183.

ARMSTRONG, F. A. J., and G. T. BOALCH. 1960. Volatile organic matter in algal culture media and sea water. Nature, *185*: 761-762.

ARMSTRONG, F. A. J., and G. T. BOALCH. 1961. The ultra-violet absorption of sea water. J. Mar. Biol. Ass. U.K., *41*: 591-597.

ARMSTRONG, F. A. J., P. M. WILLIAMS, and J. D. H. STRICKLAND. 1966. Photo-oxidation of organic matter in seawater by ultra-violet radiation, analytical and other applications. Nature, *211*: 481-483.

ASPINALL, G. O. 1957. Simplified periodate oxidation. Chem. Ind., 1216.

ATKINSON, L. P., and F. A. RICHARDS. 1967. The occurrence and distribution of methane in the marine environment. Deep-Sea Res., *14*: 673-684.

AWAPARA, J. 1962. Free amino acids in invertebrates: a comparative study of their distribution and metabolism, p.158-175. *In* J. T. Holden [ed.], Amino acid pools. Elsevier, Amsterdam.

BADER, R. G., D. W. HOOD, and J. B. SMITH. 1960. Recovery of dissolved organic matter in seawater and organic sorption by particulate material. Geochim. Cosmochim. Acta, *19*: 236-243.

BAKER, R. A. 1965. Microchemical contaminants by freeze concentration and gas chromatography. J. Water Poll. Cont. Fed., *37*: 1164.

BAKER, R. A., and B. A. MALO. 1967. Water quality characterization — trace organics. Proc. Amer. Soc. Civil. Eng., *SA6*: 41-54.

BALDWIN, E. 1947. Dynamics aspect of biochemistry. Cambridge Univ. Press, New York.

BARBER, R. T. 1966. Interaction of bubbles and bacteria in the formation of organic aggregates in seawater. Nature, *211*: 257-258.

BARBER, R. T. 1967. The distribution of dissolved organic carbon in the Peru current system of the Pacific Ocean. Ph.D. Thesis, Stanford Univ., Palo Alto. 132 p.

BARBER, R. T. 1968. Dissolved organic carbon from deep waters resists microbial oxidation. Nature, *220*: 274-275.

BARBER, R. T., and J. H. RYTHER. 1969. Organic chelators: factors affecting primary production in the Cromwell Current Upwelling. J. Exp. Mar. Biol. Ecol., *3*: 191-199.

BARRY, V. C., D. T. DILLON, B. HAWKINS, and P. O'COLLA. 1950. The xylan of *Rhodymenia palmata*. Nature, *166*: 788.

BARSDATE, R. J. Unpublished manuscript. Pathways of trace elements in Arctic lake ecosystems. Progress Rep. AT(04-3)-310 PA 4, 1965-1966. Inst. Mar. Sci., Univ. Alaska.

BARSDATE, R. J., and W. R. MATSON. 1966. Trace metals in Arctic and Subarctic lakes with reference to the organic complexes of metals. *In* B. Aberg and F. Hungate [ed.], Radioecological concentration processes. Pergamon Press, Oxford.

BASSETTE, R., S. OZERIS, and C. H. WHITNAH. 1962. Gas chromatographic analysis of head space gas of dilute aqueous solution. Anal. Chem., *34*: 1540-1543.

BAYLOR, E. R., and W. H. SUTCLIFFE, Jr. 1963. Dissolved organic matter in sea water as a source of particulate food. Limnol. Oceanogr., *8*: 369-371.

BEATTIE, A., E. L. HIRST, and E. PERCIVAL. 1961. Studies on the metabolism of the Chrysophyceae. Comparative structural investigations on leucosin (Chrysolaminarin) separated from diatoms and laminarin from the brown algae. Biochem. J., *79*: 531-537.

BEERS, J. R., and G. L. STEWART. 1967. Microzooplankton in the euphotic zone at five locations across the California current. J. Fish. Res. Bd. Canada, *24*: 2053-2068.

BELSER, W. L. 1963. Bioassay of trace substances, p. 220-231. *In* M. N. Hill [ed.], The sea, v. 2. Interscience, New York.

BENTLEY, J. A. 1960. Plant hormones in marine phytoplankton, zooplankton and sea water. J. Mar. Biol. Ass. U.K., *39*: 433-444.

BERG, W., A. JOHNELS, B. SJOSTRAND, and T. WESTERMARK. 1966. Mercury content in feathers of Swedish birds from the past 100 years. Oikos, *17*: 71-83.

BERNARD, F. 1963. Vitesse de chute en mèr des amas palmelloides de *Cyclococcolithus*. Ses consequence pour le cycle vital des mèrs chaudes. Pelagos, *1*: 5-34.

BERNARD, F. 1964. La nanoplancton en zone aphotique des mèrs chaudes. Pelagos, *2*: 1-32.

BERNARD, F., and J. LECAL. 1960. Plancton unicellulaire recolté dans l'ocean Indien par le *Charot* (1950) et le *Norsel* (1955-56). Bull. Intern. Oceanogr., Monaco., *1166*: 1-59.

BERNER, R. A. 1965. Activity coefficients of bicarbonate, carbonate, and calcium ions in sea water. Geochim. Cosmochim. Acta, *29*: 947-965.

BERNER, R. A. 1966. Chemical diagenesis of some modern carbonate sediments. Amer. J. Sci., *264*: 1-36.

BIDWELL, R. G. S. 1967. Photosynthesis and metabolism in marine algae. VII. Products of photosynthesis in fronds of *Fucus vesiculosus* and their use in respiration. Can. J. Bot., *45*: 1557-1565.

BIDWELL, R. G. S., and N. R. GHOSH. 1962. Photosynthesis and metabolism in marine algae. IV. The fate of C^{14}-mannitol in *Fucus vesiculosus*. Can. J. Bot., *40*: 803-811.

BIGELEISEN, J. 1958. The significance of the product and sum rules to isotopic fractionating processes, p. 121-157. *In* J. Kisttemaker, J. Bigeleisen and A. O. C. Nier [ed.], Proc. Int. Symp. Isotope separation. Interscience, New York.

BIGELEISEN, J., and M. MAYER. 1947. Calculation of equilibrium constants for isotopic exchange reactions. J. Chem. Phys., *15*: 261.

BIGELEISEN, J., and M. WOLFSBERG. 1958. Theoretical and experimental aspects of isotope effects in chemical kinetics, p. 15-77. *In* I. Prigogine [ed.], Advances in chemical physics. Interscience, New York.

BINNS, R., and A. J. PETERSON. 1969. Nitrogen excretion by the spiny lobster *Jasus edwardsi* (Hutton): the role of the antennal gland. Biol. Bull., *136*: 147-153.

BIRGE, E. A., and C. JUDAY. 1934. Particulate and dissolved organic matter in inland lakes. Ecol. Monogr., *4*(4): 440-474.

BLANCHARD, D. C. 1964. Sea-to-air transport of surface active material. Science, *146*: 396-397.

BLINKS, L. R. 1955. Photosynthesis and productivity of littoral marine algae. J. Mar. Res., *14*: 363-373.

BLUMER, M. 1965. Contamination of a laboratory building by air filters. Contamination Control, *4*: 13-14, Sept.

BLUMER, M. 1967. Hydrocarbons in digestive tract and liver of a basking shark. Science, *156*: 390-391.

BLUMER, M. 1970. Dissolved organic compounds in sea water. *In* D. W. Hood [ed.], Proc. Symp. Organic matter in natural waters. Occa. Pub. No. 1, Inst. Mar. Sci., Univ. Alaska.

BLUMER, M., M. M. MULLIN, and D. W. THOMAS. 1963. Pristane in zooplankton. Science, *140*: 974.

BLUMER, M., M. M. MULLIN, and D. W. THOMAS. 1964. Pristane in the marine environment. Helgoländ. Wiss. Meeresunters., *10*: 187-201.

BLUMER, M., and W. D. SNYDER. 1965. Isoprenoid hydrocarbons in recent sediments: presence of pristane and probable absence of phytane. Science, *150*: 1588-1589.

BOGDANOV, Y. A. 1965. Suspended organic matter in the Pacific. Okeanologiya, 5: 77-85.

BORKOWSKI, J. D., and M. J. JOHNSON. 1967. Experimental evaluation of liquid film resistance in oxygen transport to microbial cells. Appl. Microbiol., 15: 1483-1488.

BORNEFF, J., and R. FISCHER. 1961. Cancerogene Substanze in Wasser und Boden. Arch. Hyg. Bakteriol., 145: 241.

BORNEFF, J., and R. FISCHER. 1962. Cancerogene Substanzen in Wasser und Boden. Arch. Hyg. Bakteriol., 146: 183.

BOYLE, H. W., R. H. BURTTSCHELL, and A. A. ROSEN. 1966. Infrared identification of chlorinated insecticides in tissues of poisoned fish, p. 207-218. In Organic pesticides in the environment. Adv. Chem. Ser. No. 60.

BRAMLETTE, M. N. 1961. Pelagic sediments, p. 345-366. In M. Sears [ed.], Oceanography. Amer. Ass. Adv. Sci. Pub. 67.

BRANDHORST, W. 1959. Nitrification and denitrification in the eastern tropical North Pacific. J. Cons., 25: 3-20.

BRAUS, H., F. M. MIDDLETON, and G. WALTON. 1951. Organic chemical compounds in raw and filtered surface waters. Anal. Chem., 23: 1160-1164.

BREGER, I. A. 1963. Organic geochemistry. Pergamon, New York.

BREGER, I. A., and A. BROWN. 1962. Kerogen in the Chattanooga shale. Science, 137: 221-224.

BREGER, I. A., and A. BROWN. 1963. Distribution and types of organic matter in a barred marine basin. New York Acad. Sci., Trans. Ser. II, 25: 741-755.

BRITTEN, R. J., and F. T. McCLURE. 1962. The amino acid pool in Escherichia coli. Bact. Rev., 26: 294-335.

BROCK, T. D., and G. MOO-PENN. 1962. An amino acid transport system in Streptococcus faecium. Arch. Biochem. Biophys., 98: 183-190.

BUBNOV, V. A. 1966. The distribution pattern of minimum oxygen concentrations in the Atlantic [In Russian]. Okeanologiya, Akad. Nauk SSSR, 6: 240-250. Translated into English: Oceanology, 6: 193-201.

BUBNOV, V. A. 1967. Some regularities in the formation of the oxygen minimum layer in the North Atlantic [In Russian, English abstract]. Okeanologiya, Akad. Nauk SSSR, 7: 997-1004.

BUCH, K., and S. D. GRIPENBERG. 1932. Ueber den Einfluss des Wasserdruckes auf pH und das Kohlensauerqleichqewicht in grösseren Meerestiefen. J. Cons., 7: 233-245.

BUNCH, R. L., and E. F. BARTH, Jr. 1958. Serological detection of fermentation wastes. Nature, *182*: 1680.

BUNCH, R. L., and M. B. ETTINGER. 1966. A field countercurrent extractor for water pollutants, p. 93-97. *In* Proc. 20th Purdue Ind. Waste Conf., Eng. Ext. Ser. No. 118.

BURTTSCHELL, R. H., A. A. ROSEN, J. G. WELLS, and E. S. YUNGHANS. 1957. Characterization of organic contaminants of ground waters. Presented at 131st Nat. Meeting of Amer. Chem. Soc., Miami.

BUSCH, P. L., and W. STUMM. 1968. Chemical interactions in the aggregation of bacteria. Bioflocculation in waste treatment. Environ. Sci. Technol., 2: 49-53.

BUTTON, D. K. 1969. Effect of clay on the availability of dilute organic nutrients to steady-state heterotrophic populations. Limnol. Oceanogr., *14*: 95-100.

BUTTON, D. K. 1969. Thiamine limited steady state growth of the yeast *Cryptococcus albidus*. J. Gen. Microbiol., *57*: 777.

CAHN, R. D. 1967. Detergents in membrane filters. Science, *155*: 195-196.

CALDER, J. A., and P. L. PARKER. 1968. Stable carbon isotope ratios as indices of petrochemical pollution of aquatic systems. Environ. Sci. Technol., 2: 535-539.

CARLUCCI, A. F., and P. M. WILLIAMS. 1965. Concentration of bacteria from seawater by bubble scavenging. J. Cons., *30*: 28-33.

CARR, F. H., and E. A. PRICE. 1926. Color reactions attributed to Vitamin A. Biochem. J., *20*: 497-501.

CARR, W. E. S. 1967. Chemoreception in the mud snail *Nassarius obsoletus*. I. Properties of stimulatory substances extracted from shrimp. Biol. Bull., *133*: 90-105.

CARRITT, D. E. 1964. Personal communication cited in A. Siegel. 1967. A new approach to the concentration of trace organics in seawater, p. 235-256. *In* T. A. Olson and F. J. Burgess [ed.], Pollution and marine ecology. Interscience, New York.

CHAPMAN, G., and A. G. TAYLOR. 1968. Uptake of organic solutes by *Nereis virens*. Nature, *217*: 763-764.

CHAVE, K. E. 1952. A solid solution between calcite and dolomite. J. Geol., *60*: 190-192.

CHAVE, K. E. 1954. Aspects of biogeochemistry of magnesium. I. Calcareous marine organisms. J. Geol., *62*: 266-283.

CHAVE, K. E. 1965. $CaCO_3$: association of organic matter in surface sea water. Science, *148*: 1723-1724.

CHAVE, K. E., K. S. DEFFEYES, P. K. WEYL, R. M. CARRELES, and M. E. THOMPSON. 1962. Observations on the solubility of skeletal carbonates in aqueous solutions. Science, *137*: 33-34.

CHAVE, K. E., and R. F. SCHMALZ. 1966. Carbonate-sea water interactions. Geochim. Cosmochim. Acta, *30*: 1037-1048.

CHAVE, K. E., and E. SUESS. 1967. Suspended minerals in sea water. N. Y. Acad. Sci., Trans., *29*: 991-1000.

CHRISTENSEN, H. N. 1962. Biological transport. Benjamin, New York. 133 p.

CHRISTENSEN, H. N. 1966. Methods for distinguishing amino acid transport systems of a given cell or tissue. Fed. Proc., *25*: 850-853.

CHRISTMAN, R. F. 1970. Chemical structures of color producing organic substances in water. *In* D. W. Hood [ed.], Proc. Symp. Organic matter in natural waters. Inst. Mar. Sci., Univ. Alaska, Occa. Pub. No. 1.

CHRISTMAN, R. F., and M. GHASSEMI. 1966. Chemical nature of organic color in water. Amer. Water Works Ass., *58*: 723-741.

CHRISTMAN, R. F., and R. T. OGLESBY. In press. Chapter 18. The microbiological degradation of lignin and the formation of humus. *In* K. V. Sarkanen and C. H. Ludwig [ed.], Lignins, chemistry and utilization. Interscience, New York.

CLARK, G. L., and H. R. JAMES. 1939. Laboratory analysis of the selective absorption of light by sea water. J. Opt. Soc. Amer., *29*: 43-55.

CLARK, R. C., Jr., and M. BLUMER. 1967. Distribution of n-paraffins in marine organisms and sediment. Limnol. Oceanogr., *12*: 79-87.

CLOUD, P. E. 1962. Environment of $CaCO_3$ deposition west of Andros Island, Bahamas. U.S. Geol. Surv. Prof. Paper 350. 138 p.

COBET, A. B. 1968. The effect of nickel ions on *Arthrobacter marinus*, a new species. Ph.D. Thesis, Univ. New Hampshire, Durham. 212 p.

COHEN, G. N., and H. V. RICKENBERG. 1956. Concentration specifiqué réversible des amino acids chez *Escherichia coli*. Annu. Inst. Pasteur, *91*: 693-720.

COLLIER, A., S. M. RAY, A. M. MAGNITZKY, and J. O. BILL. 1953. Effect of dissolved organic substances on oysters. U.S. Dept. Int., Fish. Wild. Fish. Bull., *84*: 167-185.

CONOVER, J. T., and J. McN. SIEBURTH. 1964. Effect of *Sargassum* distribution on its epibiota and antibacterial activity. Bot. Mar., *6*: 147-157.

CONOVER, R. J. 1966a. Assimilation of organic matter by zooplankton. Limnol. Oceanogr., *11*: 338-345.

CONOVER, R. J. 1966b. Factors affecting the assimilation of organic matter by zooplankton and the question of superfluous feeding. Limnol. Oceanogr., *11*: 346-354.

COOMBS, J., P. J. HALICKI, O. HOLM-HANSEN, and B. E. VOLCANI. 1967. Changes in concentration of nucleoside triphosphates in silicon-starvation synchrony of *Navicula pelliculosa* (Bréb.) Hilse, Exp. Cell Res., *47*: 315-328.

COOPER, W. J., and M. BLUMER. 1968. Linear, *iso* and *anteiso* fatty acids in recent sediments of the North Atlantic. Deep-Sea Res., *15*: 535-540.

CORCORAN, E. F., J. F. CORWIN, and D. B. SEBA. 1967. Gas chromatographic analysis of chlorodane by head gas. J. Amer. Water Works Ass., *59*: 752.

CORNER, E. D. S., and B. S. NEWELL. 1967. On the nutrition and metabolism of zooplankton. IV. The forms of nitrogen excreted by *Calanus*. J. Mar. Biol. Ass. U.K., *47*: 113-120.

CORWIN, J. F. 1960. The separation of dissolved organic materials from sea water. Report to the Charles Kettering Foundation. (Unpublished.)

CORWIN, J. F. 1970. Volatile organic materials in sea water. *In* D. W. Hood [ed.], Proc. Symp. Organic matter in natural waters. Occa. Pub. No. 1, Inst. Mar. Sci., Univ. Alaska.

CRAIG, H. 1953. The geochemistry of the stable carbon isotopes. Geochim. Cosmochim. Acta, *3*: 53-92.

CRAIG, H. 1957. Isotopic standards for carbon and oxygen and correction factors for mass-spectrometric analysis of carbon dioxide. Geochim. Cosmochim. Acta, *12*: 139-149.

CRAIGIE, J. S., and J. McLACHLAN. 1964. Excretion of colored ultraviolet absorbing substances by marine algae. Can. J. Bot., *42*: 23-33.

CREAC'H, P. V. 1955. Sur la presence des acides citriques et maliques dans les eaux marines littorales. C. R. Acad. Sci., Paris, *240*: 2551-2553.

CREUTZBERG, F. 1959. Discrimination between ebb and flood tide by migrating elvers (*Anguilla vulgaris* Turt.) by means of olfactory perception. Nature, *184*: 1961-1962.

CRISP, D. J. 1964. Surface chemistry, a factor in the settlement of marine invertebrate larvae. Bot. Gothobergensia, *3*: 51-64.

CUSHING, D. H. 1958. The effect of grazing in reducing primary production: a review. Rapp. Cons. Explor. Mer, *144*: 149-154.

CUSHING, D. H. 1964. The work of grazing in the sea, p. 207-225. *In* D. J. Crisp [ed.], Grazing in terrestrial and marine environments. Blackwells, Oxford.

DAL PONT, G., and B. NEWELL. 1963. Suspended organic matter in the Tasman Sea. Aust. J. Mar. Freshwater Res., *14*: 155-165.

DATSKO, V. G. 1951. Vertical distribution of organic matter in the Black Sea [In Russian]. Dokl. Akad. Nauk SSSR, *77*: 1059-1062.

DAVENPORT, D. 1955. Specificity and behavior in symbioses. Quart. Rev. Biol., *30*: 29-46.

DAVENPORT, D., G. CAMOUGIS, and J. F. HICKOK. 1960. Analyses of the behavior of commensals in host factor. I. A hesioned polychaete and a pinnotherid crab. Anim. Behav., *8*: 209-218.

DAVIES, B. H., W. J. HUS, and C. O. CHINCHESTER. 1965. The metabolism of carotenoids in the brine shrimp (*Artemia salina*). Biochem. J., *94*: 26.

DEGENS, E. T. In press. Biogeochemistry of stable carbon isotopes. *In* G. Eglinton and M. Murphy [ed.], Organic geochemistry: methods and results. Springer-Verlag, Inc., New York.

DEGENS, E. T. 1967. Diagenesis of organic matter, p. 343-390. *In* G. Larsen and G. V. Chilingar [ed.], Diagenesis in sediments. Elsevier, Amsterdam-London-New York.

DEGENS, E. T., M. BEHRENDT, B. GOTTHARDT, and E. RAPPMANN. 1968. Metabolic fractionation of carbon isotopes in marine plankton. II. Data on samples collected off the coasts of Peru and Ecuador. Deep-Sea Res., *15*: 11-20.

DEGENS, E. T., and J. M. HUNT. 1968. Data on the distribution of stable isotopes and amino acids in Indian Ocean sediments. Woods Hole Oceanogr. Inst. Tech. Rep. Ref. No. 68-4. 49 p.

DEGENS, E. T., and J. MATHEJA. 1967. Molecular mechanisms on interactions between oxygen co-ordinated metal polyhedra and biochemical compounds. Woods Hole Oceanogr. Inst. Tech. Rep. Ref. No. 67-57. 312 p.

DEGENS, E. T., and J. H. REUTER. 1964. Analytical techniques in the field of organic geochemistry, p. 390-391. *In* U. Colombo and G. D. Hobson [ed.], Advances in organic geochemistry. Pergamon, London.

DEGENS, E. T., J. H. REUTER, and K. N. F. SHAW. 1964. Biochemical compounds in offshore sediments and sea waters. Geochim. Cosmochim. Acta, *28*: 45-65.

DEGENS, E. T., H. L. SAUNDERS, and R. R. HESSLER. Unpublished manuscript. Amino acid distribution in recent sediments of the Gay Head - Bermuda and Walvis Bay transects.

DEGENS, E. T., D. W. SPENCER, and R. H. PARKER. 1967. Paleobiochemistry of molluscan shell proteins. Comp. Biochem. Physiol., *20*: 553-579.

DELANEY, A. C., Mrs. A. C. DELANEY, D. W. PARKIN, J. J. GRIFFIN, E. D. GOLDBERG, and B. E. F. REIMANN. 1967. Airborne dust collected at Barbados. Geochim. Cosmochim. Acta, *31*: 885-909.

DELAUNAY, H. 1931. L'excrétion azotée des Invertébrés. Biol. Rev., *6*: 265-301.

DELAUNAY, H. 1934. Le métabolisme de l'ammoniague d'aprés les recherches relative aux Invertébrés. Annu. Physiol. Physiochim. Biol., *10*: 695-729.

DEUSER, W. G., and E. T. DEGENS. 1967. Carbon isotope fractionation in the system CO_2 (gas)-CO_2 (aq)-HCO_3^- (aq). Nature, *215*: 1033-1035.

DEUSER, W. G., E. T. DEGENS, and R. R. L. GUILLARD. 1968. Carbon isotope relationships between plankton and sea water. Geochim. Cosmochim. Acta, *32*: 657-660.

DIMELOW, E. J. 1958. Pigments present in arms and pinnules of the crinoid *Antedon bifida* (Pennant). Nature, *182*: 812.

DODD, J. R. 1963. Paleoecological implications of shell mineralogy in two Pelecypod species. J. Geol., *71*: 1-11.

DODD, J. R. 1965. Environmental control of strontium and magnesium in *Mytilus*. Geochim. Cosmochim. Acta, *29*: 385-398.

DODD, J. R. 1966. The influence of salinity on mollusk shell mineralogy: a discussion. J. Geol., *74*: 85-89.

DOERNER, H. A., and W. M. HOSKINS. 1925. Coprecipitation of radium and barium sulfates. J. Amer. Chem. Soc., *47*: 662-675.

DOUGLAS, E. 1967. Carbon monoxide solubilities in sea water. J. Phys. Chem., *71*: 1931-1933.

DREW, G. H. 1914. On the precipitation of calcium carbonate in the sea by marine denitrifying bacteria, and on the action of denitrifying bacteria in tropical and temperate seas. Papers from Tortugas Lab., Carnegie Inst. Wash., *51*: 7-45.

DREYFUSS, J. 1964. Characterization of a sulfate and thiosulfate-transporting system in *Salmonella typhimurium*. J. Biol. Chem., *239*: 2292-2297.

DROOP, M. R. 1957. Auxotrophy and organic compounds in the nutrition of marine phytoplankton. J. Gen. Microbiol., *16*: 286-293.

DROOP, M. R. 1961. *Haematococcus pluvialis* and its allies. III. Organic nutrition. Rev. Algo., *4*: 247-259.

DROOP, M. R., and S. McGILL. 1966. The carbon nutrition of some algae: the inability to utilize glycolic acid for growth. J. Mar. Biol. Ass. U.K., *46*: 679-684.

DUGOID, J. P. 1951. The demonstration of bacterial capsules and slime. J. Pathol. Bacteriol., *63*: 673-685.

DUURSMA, E. K. 1960. Dissolved organic carbon, nitrogen, and phosphorus in the sea. Ph.D. Thesis, J. B. Wolters, Groningen. 147 p.

DUURSMA, E. K. 1961. Dissolved organic carbon, nitrogen, and phosphorus in the sea. Nethl. J. Sea Res., *1*: 1-148.

DUURSMA, E. K. 1963. The production of dissolved organic matter in the sea, as related to the primary production of organic matter. Nethl. J. Sea Res., *2*: 85-94.

DUURSMA, E. K. 1965. The dissolved organic constituents of seawater, p. 433-475. *In* J. P. Riley and G. Skirrow [ed.], Chemical oceanography. Academic Press, New York-London.

DUURSMA, E. K., and C. J. BOSCH. In press. Theoretical, experimental, and field studies concerning diffusion of radioisotopes in sediments and suspended particles of the sea. Part B. Method and experiments. Nethl. J. Sea. Res.

DUURSMA, E. K., and W. SEVENHUYSEN. 1966. Note on chelation and solubility of certain metals in sea water at different pH values. Nethl. J. Sea Res., *3*: 96-106.

DWYER, F. P., and D. P. MELLOR. 1964. Chelating agents and metal chelates. Academic Press, New York. 530 p.

EMERY, K. O. 1960. The sea off Southern California: A modern habitat of petroleum. Wiley, New York. 366 p.

EMMANUEL, C. F. 1957. The composition of octopus renal fluid. II. A chromatographic examination of the constituents. Z. Vergl. Physiol., *39*: 477-482.

EPPLEY, R. W., R. W. HOLMES, and J. D. H. STRICKLAND. 1967. Sinking rates of marine phytoplankton measured with a fluorometer. J. Exp. Mar. Biol. Ecol., *1*: 191-208.

EPPLEY, R. W., and P. R. SLOAN. 1965. Carbon balance experiments with marine phytoplankton. J. Fish. Res. Bd. Canada, *22*: 1083-1097.

EPSTEIN, S., R. BUCHSBAUM, H. A. LOWENSTAM, and H. C. UREY. 1951. Carbonate water isotopic temperature scale. Geol. Soc. Amer. Bull., *62*: 417-425.

ERNST, W. 1967. Dünnschichtchromatographische Trennung und quantitative Bestimmung von Galacturon- und Glucuronsäuren in Polysaccharid Fractionen des Meeresbodens. Veröff Inst. Meeresforsch., *10*: 183-185.

EULER, H. VAN, P. KARRER, and E. KLUSSMANN. 1932. Spectrometrische Messungen an Carotenoiden. Helv. Chim. Acta, *15*: 502-507.

FARKAS, T., and S. HERODEK. 1964. The effect of envionmental temperature on the fatty acid composition of Crustacean plankton. J. Lipid Res., 5: 369-373.

FEDER, H., and A. M. CHRISTENSEN. 1966. Aspects of asteroid biology, p. 87-127. In R. A. Boolootian [ed.], Physiology of echinodermata. Interscience, New York.

FERGUSON, J. C. 1964. Nutrient transport in starfish. II. Uptake of nutrients by isolated organics. Biol. Bull., 126: 391-406.

FERGUSON, J. C. 1967. Utilization of dissolved exogenous nutrients by the starfishes, Asterias forbesi and Henricia sanguinolenta. Biol. Bull., 132: 161-173.

FISCHER, F., and H. SCHRADER. 1922. Entstehung und chemische Struktur der Kohle. Girardet. Essen.

FLASCHKA, H. A. 1964. EDTA titrations. 2nd ed. Pergamon Press, London. 144 p.

FLEMING, M., E. L. HIRST, and D. J. MANNERS. 1966. The constitution of laminarin. VI. The fine structure of soluble laminarin, p. 255-260. In E. G. Young and J. L. McLachlan [ed.], Proc. Fifth Int. Seaweed Symp., Halifax, Canada.

FLEMING, R. H. 1940. The composition of plankton and units for reporting population and production. Proc. 6th Pacific Sci. Congr., Pacific Sci. Ass., Vancouver, 1939, 3: 535-540.

FLORKIN, M. 1966. Nitrogen metabolism, p. 309-351. In K. M. Wilbur and C. M. Yonge [ed.], Physiology of mollusca, v. 2. Academic Press, New York.

FOGG, G. E. 1952. The production of extracellular nitrogenous substances by a blue-green alga. Roy. Soc. (London), Proc., B. 139: 372-397.

FOGG, G. E. 1962. Extracellular products, p. 475-489. In R. A. Lewin [ed.], Physiology and biochemistry of algae. Academic Press, New York.

FOGG, G. E. 1963. The role of algae in organic production in aquatic environments. Br. Phycol. Bull., 2: 195-205.

FOGG, G. E. 1966. The extracellular products of algae. Oceanogr. Mar. Biol. Annu. Rev., 4: 195-212.

FOGG, G. E., C. NALAWAJKO, and W. D. WATT. 1965. Extracellular products of photosynthesis by phytoplankton. Mem. Ist. Ital. Idrobiol., 18 (Suppl.): 165-174.

FOGG, G. E., and D. F. WESTLAKE. 1955. The importance of extracellular products of algae in fresh water. Verh. Int. Ver. Limnol., *12*: 219-232.

FORD, C. W., and E. PERCIVAL. 1965. The carbohydrate of *Phaeodactylum tricornutum*. I. Preliminary examination of the organism, and characterization of low molecular weight material and of a glucan. J. Chem. Soc., 7035-7042.

FOURNIER, R. O. 1966. North Atlantic deep-sea fertility. Science, *153*: 1250-1252.

FOWDEN, L. 1954. A comparison of the composition of some algal protein. Ann. Bot., *18*: 257-266.

FOX, D. L. 1963. Animal biochromes and structural colors. Cambridge Univ. Press, London. 278 p.

GANGULY, J., N. I. KRINSKY, and J. H. PINCKARD. 1956. Isolation and nature of echinenone. A provitamin A. Arch. Biochem. Biophys., *60*: 345-351.

GARRELS, R. M., and M. E. THOMPSON. 1962. A chemical model for sea water at 25C and one atmosphere total pressure. Amer. J. Sci., *260*: 57-66.

GARRELS, R. M., M. E. THOMPSON, and R. SIEVER. 1961. Control of carbonate solubility by carbonate complexes. Amer. J. Sci., *259*: 24-45.

GARRETT, W. D. 1965. Collection of slick-forming materials from the sea surface. Limnol. Oceanogr., *10*: 602-605.

GARRETT, W. D. 1967a. Damping of capillary wave at the air sea interface by oceanic surface-active material. J. Mar. Res., *25*: 279-291.

GARRETT, W. D. 1967b. The organic chemical composition of the ocean surface. Deep-Sea Res., *14*: 221-227.

GARRETT, W. D. 1967c. Stabilization of air bubbles at the air sea interface by surface-active material. Deep-Sea Res., *14*: 661-672.

GAULD, D. J. 1951. The grazing rate of planktonic copepods. J. Mar. Biol. Ass. U.K., *29*: 695-706.

GELPI, E., and J. ORO. 1968. Gas chromatographic-mass spectrometric analysis of isoprenoid hydrocarbons and fatty acids in shark liver products. J. Amer. Oil Chem. Soc., *45*: 144-147.

GERBER, N. N. 1968. Geosmin, from microorganisms, is *trans*-1, 10-dimethyl-*trans*-9-decalol. Tetrahedron Letters, *25*: 2971.

GILBERT, P. W. 1966. Feeding and attack patterns of sharks. Proc. 11th Pacific Sci. Congr., 7, No. 32.

GJESSING, E. T. 1965. Use of sephadex gel for the estimation of molecular weight of humic substances in natural water. Nature, *208*: 1091-1092.

GLASER, D. 1966. Untersuchungen über die absoluten Geschmacksschwellen von Fischen. Z. Verg. Physiol., *52*: 1-25.

GLOVER, E. D., and R. F. SIPPEL. 1967. Synthesis of magnesium calcites. Geochim. Cosmochim. Acta, *31*: 603-613.

GOLDBERG, E. D. 1963. Geochronology with Pb-210, p. 121-131. *In* Radioactive dating. Int. At. Energy Agency, Vienna.

GOODWIN, T. W. 1954. Carotenoids: their comparative biochemistry. Chemical Pub., New York. 356 p.

GOODWIN, T. W., and S. SRISUKH. 1949. The biochemistry of locusts. I. Carotenoids of the integument. Biochem. J., *45*: 263-268.

GRAY, J. S. 1966. The attractive factory of intertidal sands to *Protodrilus symbioticus*. J. Mar. Biol. Ass. U.K., *46*: 627-645.

GREENFIELD, L. J. 1963. Metabolism and concentration of calcium and magnesium and precipitation of calcium carbonate by a marine bacterium. Ann. N. Y. Acad. Sci., *109*: 23-45.

GRIFFITHS, M. 1966. The carotenoids of the eggs and embryos of the sea urchin *Strongylocentrotus purpuratus*. Devel. Biol., *13*: 296-309.

GROSS, M. G., S. M. GUCLUER, J. S. CREAGER, and W. A. DAWSON. 1963. Varved marine sediments in a stagnant fiord. Science, *141*: 918-919.

GUCLUER, S. M. 1962. Recent sediment in Saanich Inlet, British Columbia. M.S. Thesis, Univ. Washington, Seattle. 119 p.

GUILLARD, R. R. L. 1963. Organic sources of nitrogen for marine centric diatoms, p. 93-104. *In* C. H. Oppenheimer [ed.], Symp. Marine microbiology. C. Thomas, Springfield, Ill.

GUILLARD, R. R. L., and J. H. RYTHER. 1962. Studies of marine planktonic diatoms. I. *Cyclotella nana* Hustedt, and *Detunola confervacea* (Cleve) Gran. Can. J. Microbiol., *8*: 229-239.

GUILLARD, R. R. L., and P. J. WANGERSKY. 1958. The production of extracellular carbohydrates by some marine flagellates. Limnol. Oceanogr., *3*: 449-454.

HAGEN, P. D., D. J. KUSHNER, and N. E. GIBBONS. 1964. Temperature induced death and lysis in a psychrophilic bacterium. Can. J. Microbiol., *10*: 813-823.

HAIGHT, J. J., and R. Y. MORITA. 1966. Some physiological differences of *Vibrio marinus* grown at environmental and optimal temperatures. Limnol. Oceanogr., *11*: 470-474.

HAIGHT, R. D., and R. Y. MORITA. 1966. Thermally induced leakage from *Vibrio marinus*, an obligately psychrophilic bacterium. J. Bacteriol., *92*: 418-423.

HAMILTON, P. B. 1965. Amino acids on hands. Nature, *205*: 284-285.

HAMILTON, R. D., and K. E. AUSTIN. 1967. Assay of relative heterotrophic potential in the sea: the use of specifically labeled glucose. Can. J. Microbiol., *13*: 1165-1173.

HAMILTON, R. D., and O. HOLM-HANSEN. 1967. Adenosine triphosphate content of marine bacteria. Limnol. Oceanogr., *12*: 319-324.

HAMILTON, R. D., O. HOLM-HANSEN, and J. D. H. STRICKLAND. 1968. Notes on the occurrence of living microscopic organisms in deep water. Deep-Sea Res., *15*: 651-656.

HAMILTON, R. D., K. M. MORGAN, and J. D. H. STRICKLAND. 1966. The glucose uptake kinetics of some marine bacteria. Can. J. Microbiol., *12*: 995-1003.

HANDA, N. 1966. Distribution of dissolved carbohydrate in the Indian Ocean. J. Oceanogr. Soc. Japan, *22*(2): 16-22.

HANDA, N. 1967a. The distribution of the dissolved and the particulate carbohydrates in the Kuroshio and its adjacent areas. J. Oceanogr. Soc. Japan, *23*(3): 1-9.

HANDA, N. 1967b. Identification of carbohydrates in marine particulate matters and their vertical distribution. Rec. Oceanogr. Works Japan, *9*(1): 65-73.

HANDA, N., and K. NISIZAWA. 1961. Structural investigation of a laminarin isolated from *Eisenia bicyclis*. Nature, *192*: 1078-1079.

HARDER, W., and H. VELDKAMP. 1966. Observations on marine obligately psychrophilic bacteria, p. 390. *In* 9th Int. Congr. Microbiol. (Abstr.).

HARKER, R. I., and O. F. TUTTLE. 1955. Studies in the system CaO-MgO-CO$_2$. II. Limits of solid solution along the binary join, CaCO$_3$-MgCO$_3$. Amer. J. Sci., *253*: 274-282.

HARRISON, F. M., and A. W. MARTIN. 1965. Excretion in the cephalopod, *Octopus dofleini*. J. Exp. Biol., *42*: 71-98.

HARVEY, H. W. 1937. Note on selective feeding by *Calanus*. J. Mar. Biol. Ass. U.K., *22*: 97-100.

HARVEY, H. W., L. H. N. COOPER, M. V. LEBOUR, and F. W. RUSSELL. 1935. Plankton production and its control. J. Mar. Biol. Ass. U. K., *20*: 407-442.

HASHIMOTO, Y., S. KONOSU, N. FUSETANI, and T. NOSE. 1968. Attractants for eels in extracts of short-necked clam. I. Survey of constituents eliciting feeding behavior by the omission test. Jap. Soc. Sci. Fish. Bull., *34*: 78-83.

HASLER, A. D. 1957. Olfactory and gustatory senses of fishes, p. 187-209. *In* M. E. Brown [ed.], Physiology of fishes, v. 2. Academic Press, New York.

HASLER, A. D. 1966. Stream phase of salmon homing, p. 13-58. *In* A. D. Hasler [ed.], Underwater guideposts, homing of salmon. Univ. Wisconsin Press, Madison.

HAUSSER, K. W., and A. SMAKULA. 1935. Absorption of light and the double bond. III. Investigation in the furane series. Z. Phyzik. Chem., *B29*, 378-383.

HAY, G. W., B. A. LEWIS, and F. SMITH. 1965. Determination of the average length of polysaccharides by periodate oxidation, reduction and analysis of the derived polyalcohol, p. 377-380. *In* R. L. Whistler [ed.], Methods in carbohydrate chemistry. Academic Press, New York.

HAYWARD, J. 1965. Studies on the growth of *Phaeodactylum tricornutum* (Bohlin). I. The effect of certain organic nitrogeneous substances on growth. Physiol. Plant., *18*: 201-207.

HELLEBUST, J. A. 1965. Excretion of some organic compounds by marine phytoplankton. Limnol. Oceanogr., *10*: 192-206.

HELLEBUST, J. A. 1967. Excretion of organic compounds by cultured and natural populations of marine phytoplankton, p. 361-366. *In* G. H. Lauff [ed.], Estuaries. Amer. Ass. Adv. Sci. Pub. 83.

HELLEBUST, J. A. 1967. Excretion of organic compounds by marine phytoplankton. Limnol. Oceanogr., *10*: 192-206.

HELLEBUST, J. A., and R. G. S. BIDWELL. 1963. Protein turnover in wheat and snapdragon leaves. Can. J. Bot., *41*: 969-983.

HELLEBUST, J. A., and R. R. L. GUILLARD. 1967. Uptake specificity for organic substances by the marine diatom *Melosira nummuloides*. J. Phycol., *3*: 132-136.

HELLEBUST, J. A., and J. TERBORGH. 1967. Effects of environmental conditions on the rate of photosynthesis and some photosynthetic enzymes in *Dunaliella tertiolecta* Butcher. Limnol. Oceanogr., *12*: 559-567.

HEM, J. D. 1960. Complexes of ferrous iron with tannic acid. U.S. Geol. Surv. Water-Supply Paper 1459-D: 75-94.

HEMMINGS, C. C. 1966. Olfaction and vision in fish schooling. J. Exp. Biol., *45*: 449-464.

HERBERT, D. 1958. Some principles of continuous culture. 7th Int. Congr. Microbiol. Symp., Stockholm: 381-396.

HERBERT, D., R. ELSWORTH, and R. C. TELLING. 1956. The continuous culture of bacteria: a theoretical and experimental study. J. Gen. Microbiol., *14*: 601-622.

HERLINVEAUX, R. H. 1962. Oceanography of Saanich Inlet on Vancouver Island, British Columbia. J. Fish. Res. Bd. Canada, *19*: 1-37.

HINDMAN, J. C. 1943. Properties of the system $CaCO_3$-CO_2-H_2O in sea water and sodium chloride solutions. Ph.D. Thesis, Univ. California, Los Angeles.

HIRSCH, J., and E. H. AHRENS, Jr. 1958. Separation of complex lipid mixtures by the use of silicic acid chromatography. J. Biol. Chem., *233*: 311-320.

HOAK, R. D. 1962. Recovery and identification of organics in water. Intern. J. Water Poll., *6*: 521.

HOBBIE, J. E., and C. C. CRAWFORD. 1969. Respiration corrections for bacterial uptake of dissolved organic compounds in natural waters. Limnol. Oceanogr., *14*: 528-532.

HOBBIE, J. E., C. C. CRAWFORD, and K. L. WEBB. 1968. Amino acid flux in an estuary. Science, *159*: 1463-1464.

HOBBIE, J. E., and R. T. WRIGHT. 1965. Bioassay with bacterial uptake kinetics: glucose in fresh water. Limnol. Oceanogr., *10*: 471-474.

HOBBIE, J. E., and R. T. WRIGHT. 1965. Competition between planktonic bacteria and algae for organic solutes. Mem. 1st Ital. Idrobiol., *18*(Suppl.): 175-185.

HOBBIE, J. E., and R. T. WRIGHT. 1968. A new method for the study of bacteria in lakes. Mitt. Int. Ver. Limnol., *14*: 64-71.

HOBSON, L. A. 1967. The seasonal and vertical distribution of suspended particulate matter in an area of the northeast Pacific Ocean. Limnol. Oceanogr., *12*: 642-649.

HODGMAN, C. D. [ed. in chief]. 1961. Handbook of chemistry and physics. 43rd ed. The Chemical Rubber Publ. Co., Ohio. 3513 p.

HOERING, T. C. 1960. The biogeochemistry of the stable isotopes of carbon. Carnegie Institution of Washington Year Book, *59*: 158-165.

HOERING, T. C. 1967. The organic geochemistry of precambrian rocks, p. 87-111. *In* P. H. Abelson [ed.], Researches in geochemistry, v. 2. Wiley, New York.

HOLLAND, H. D. 1965. The history of ocean water and its effect on the chemistry of the atmoshere. Nat. Acad. Sci., Proc., *53*: 1173-1183.

HOLM-HANSEN, O., and C. R. BOOTH. 1966. The measurement of adenosine triphosphate in the ocean and its ecological significance. Limnol. Oceanogr., *11*: 510-519.

HOLM-HANSEN, O., J. COOMBS, B. E. VOLCANI, and P. M. WILLIAMS. 1967. Quantitative micro-determination of lipid carbon in microorganisms. Anal. Biochem., *19*: 561-568.

HOLM-HANSEN, O., J. D. H. STRICKLAND, and P. M. WILLIAMS. 1966. A detailed analysis of biologically important substances in a profile off southern California. Limnol. Oceanogr., *11*: 548-561.

HOLM-HANSEN, O., W. H. SUTCLIFFE, Jr., and J. SHARP. 1968. Measurement of deoxyribonucleic acid in the ocean and its ecological significance. Limnol. Oceanogr., *13*: 507-514.

HOOD, D. W. 1963. Chemical oceanography, p. 129-155. *In* H. Barnes [ed.], Oceanogr. Mar. Biol. Annu. Rev., v. 1. Allen and Unwin, Ltd., London.

HOOD, D. W. 1966. The chemistry and analysis of trace metals in sea water. A & M Project 276, Ref. 66-2F. AEC Contract No. AT-(40-1)-2799. 105 p.

HUBER, G., and H. DEUEL. 1951. Über der Mechanismus der sauren Decarboxylierung von Hexuronsauren. Helv. Chim. Acta, *34*: 853-858.

HUEPER, W. C., and C. C. RUCHHOFT. 1954. Carcinogenic studies of adsorbates of industrially polluted raw and finished water supplies. Arch. Ind. Hyg. Occup. Med., *9*: 488.

HUGHES, J. T., and G. C. MATHIESSEN. 1962. Observations on the biology of the American lobster, *Homarus americanus*. Limnol. Oceanogr., 7: 414-421.

HUTCHINSON, G. E. 1957. A treatise on limnology, v. 1. Wiley, New York. 1087 p.

HYMAN, L. H. 1955. The invertebrates: Echinodermata, IV. McGraw-Hill, New York. 763 p.

INGRAHAM, J. L. 1962. Temperature relationships, p. 265-296. *In* I. C. Gunsalus and R. Y. Stanier [ed.], The bacteria, v. 4. Academic Press, New York and London.

IRIKI, Y., T. SUZUKI, T. MIWA, and K. NISIZAWA. 1960. Xylan from siphonaceous green algae. Nature, *187*: 82.

IRUKAYAMA, K. 1966. The pollution of Minamata Bay and Minamata disease. Adv. Water Poll. Res., *3*: 153-180.

JANNASCH, H. W. 1965. Starter populations as determined under steady state conditions. Biotech. Bioeng., 7: 279-283.

JANNASCH, H. W. 1965. Continuous culture in microbiol ecology. Lab. Practice, *14* (83 Special Article): 1162-1167.

JANNASCH, H. W. 1967. Enrichments of aquatic bacteria in continuous culture. Arch. Mikrobiol., *59*: 165-173.

JANNASCH, H. W. 1967. Growth of marine bacteria at limiting concentrations of organic carbon in sea water. Limnol. Oceanogr., *12*: 264-271.

JANNASCH, H. W., and G. E. JONES. 1959. Bacterial populations in sea water as determined by different methods of enumeration. Limnol. Oceanogr., *4*: 128-139.

JANSEN, J. F., and Y. KITANO. 1963. The resistance of recent marine carbonate sediments to solution. J. Oceanogr. Soc. Japan, *18*: 42-53.

JARVIS, N. L., W. D. GARRETT, M. A. SCHEIMAN, and C. O. TIMMONS. 1967. Surface chemical characterization of surface-active material in sea water. Limnol. Oceanogr., *12*: 88-97.

JEFFREY, L. M. 1966. Lipids in sea water. J. Amer. Oil Chem. Soc., *43*(4): 211-214.

JEFFREY, L. M. 1970. Lipids of marine waters. *In* D. W. Hood [ed.], Proc. Symp. Organic matter in natural waters. Occa. Pub. No. 1, Inst. Mar. Sci., Univ. Alaska.

JEFFREY, L. M., and D. W. HOOD. 1958. Organic matter in sea water; an evaluation of various methods for isolation. J. Mar. Res., *17*: 247-271.

JEFFREY, L. M., B. F. PASBY, B. STEVENSON, and D. W. HOOD. 1963. Lipids of ocean water. Advances in organic geochemistry. Proc. Int. Mtg., Milan, 1962.

JERLOV, N. G. 1959. Maxima in the vertical distribution of particles in the sea. Deep-Sea Res., *5*: 173-184.

JOHANNES, R. E. 1963. Uptake and release of phosphorus by representatives of a coastal marine ecosystem. Ph.D. Thesis, University of Hawaii, (Diss. Abstr., *24*: 3812).

JOHANNES, R. E. 1964a. Uptake and release of phosphorus by a benthic marine amphipod. Limnol. Oceanogr., *9*: 235-242.

JOHANNES, R. E. 1964b. Phosphorus excretion and body size in marine animals: microzooplankton and nutrient regeneration. Science, *146*: 923-924.

JOHANNES, R. E., S. J. COWARD, and K. L. WEBB. 1969. Are dissolved amino acids an energy source for marine invertebrates? Comp. Biochem. Physiol., *29*: 283-288.

JOHANNES, R. E., and M. SATOMI. 1967. Measuring organic matter retained by aquatic invertebrates. J. Fish. Res. Bd. Canada, *24*: 2467-2471.

JOHANNES, R. E., and K. L. WEBB. 1965. Release of dissolved amino acids by marine zooplankton. Science, *150*: 76-77.

JOHNSTON, R. 1955. Biologically active organic substances in the sea. J. Mar. Biol. Ass. U.K., *34*: 185-195.

JOHNSTON, R. 1963. Sea water, the natural medium of phytoplankton. I. General features. J. Mar. Biol. Ass. U.K., *43*: 427-456.

JOHNSTON, R. 1964. Sea water, the natural medium of phytoplankton. II. Trace metals and chelation, and general discussion. J. Mar. Biol. Ass. U.K., *44*: 87-109.

JONES, G. E. 1963. Suppression of bacterial growth by sea water, p. 572-579. *In* C. H. Oppenheimer [ed.], Symp. Marine microbiology. C. Thomas, Springfield, Ill.

JONES, G. E. 1964. Effect of chelating agents on the growth of *Escherichia coli* in sea water. J. Bact., *87*: 483-499.

JONES, G. E. 1965. The living economy of the sea. Bull. At. Sci., p. 13-17.

JONES, G. E. 1967. Growth of *Escherichia coli* in heat- and copper-treated synthetic sea water. Limnol. Oceanogr., *12*: 167-172.

JORGENSEN, C. B. 1966. Biology of suspension feeding. Pergamon, London. 357 p.

JUNGE, C. E. 1963. Air chemistry and radioactivity. Academic Press, New York. 382 p.

KALLE, K. 1937. Meereskundliche chemische Untersuchen mit Hilfe des Zeisschen Pulfrich Photometers. Ann. Hydrogr. Berl., *65*: 276-282.

KALLE, K. 1966. The problem of the Gelbstoff in the sea. Oceanogr. Mar. Biol. Annu. Rev., *4*: 91-104.

KANEDA, TOSHI. 1967. Fatty acids in the genus *Bacillus*. I. Iso- and anteiso fatty acids as characteristic constituents of lipids in 10 species. J. Bact., *93*: 894-903.

KANWISHER, J. 1957. Freezing and drying in intertidal algae. Biol. Bull., *113*: 275-285.

KANWISCHER, J. 1966. Photosynthesis and respiration in some seaweeds, p. 407-420. *In* H. Barnes [ed.], Some contemporary studies in marine science. Allen and Unwin Ltd., London.

KARRER, P., and E. JUCKER. 1950. Carotenoids. Elsevier, New York. 384 p. Translated and revised by E. A. Braude.

KATES, M. 1964. Bacterial lipids, p. 17-90. *In* R. Paoletti and D. Kritchevsky [ed.], Advances in lipid research, v. 2. Academic Press, New York.

KEELING, C. 1961. A mechanism for cyclic enrichment of carbon-12 by terrestrial plants. Geochim. Cosmochim. Acta, *24*: 299-313.

KENIS, P. R., and R. Y. MORITA. 1968. Thermally induced leakage of cellular material and viability in *Vibrio marinus* a psychrophilic marine bacterium. Can. J. Microbiol., *14*: 1239-1244.

KEPES, A. 1963. Permeases: identification and mechanisms, p. 38-48. *In* N. E. Gibbons [ed.], Recent progress in microbiology. 8th Int. Congr. Microbiol., Montreal, 1962. Univ. Toronto Press, Toronto.

KEPES, A., and G. COHEN. 1962. Permeation, p. 179-221. *In* I. C. Gunsalus and R. Y. Stanier [ed.], The bacteria, v. 4. Academic Press, New York.

KEPNER, R. E., H. MAARSE, and J. STRATING. 1964. Gas chromatographic head space techniques for the quantitative determination of volatile components in multicomponent aqueous solutions. Anal. Chem., *36*: 77-82.

KETCHUM, B. H., N. CORWIN, and D. J. KEEN. 1955. The significance of organic phosphorus determinations in ocean waters. Deep-Sea Res., *2*: 172-181.

KHAILOV, K. M. 1963. Some unknown organic substances in sea water. Dokl. Akad. Nauk SSSR (Transl.), *147*: 1355-1357.

KHAILOV, K. M. 1965. Dynamic marine biochemistry—development prospects. Oceanology, *5*(1): 1-9.

KHAILOV, K. M., and Z. P. BURLAKOVA. 1969. Release of dissolved organic matter by marine seaweeds and distribution of their total organic production to inshore communities. Limnol. Oceanogr., *14*: 521-527.

KHAILOV, K. M., and Z. Z. FINENKO. In press. Organic macromolecular compounds dissolved in seawater and their inclusion into food chains. Proc. Symp. Marine food chains, Arhus, Denmark, 1968.

KIMBALL, J. R., Jr., E. F. CORCORAN, and E. J. F. WOOD. 1963. Chlorophyll-containing microorganisms in the euphotic zone of the oceans. Bull. Mar. Sci. Gulf Caribbean, *13*: 574-577.

KITANO, Y. 1962a. Behavior of various inorganic ions in the process of calcium carbonate separation from bicarbonate solution. Chem. Soc. Japan Bull., *35*: 1973-1980.

KITANO, Y. 1962b. A study of polymorphic formation of calcium carbonate in thermal spring with emphasis on the temperature. Chem. Soc. Japan Bull., *35*: 1980-1985.

KITANO, Y. 1964. On factors influencing the polymorphic crystallization of calcium carbonate found in marine biological systems, p. 305-319. *In* Recent researches in the field of hydrosphere, atmosphere and nuclear geochemistry. Maruzen Co. Ltd., Tokyo, Japan.

KITANO, Y. 1967a. Chemistry of sea water and shell materials. Kagaku, *37*: 9-15.

KITANO, Y. 1967b. Paleo-chemical composition and paleotemperature of sea water. Kagaku, *37*: 366-372.

KITANO, Y. 1968. Evolution of chemical composition of sea water. Kagaku (Iwanami Co. Ltd., Tokyo, Japan), *38*: 224-229.

KITANO, Y., and T. FURUTSU. 1959. The state of a small amount of magnesium contained in calcareous shells. Chem. Soc. Japan Bull., *33*: 1-4.

KITANO, Y., and D. W. HOOD. 1962. Calcium carbonate crystal forms formed from sea water by inorganic processes. J. Oceanogr. Soc. Japan, *18*: 35-39.

KITANO, Y., and D. W. HOOD. 1965. Influence of organic matter on the polymorphic crystallization of calcium carbonate. Geochim. Cosmochim. Acta, *29*: 29-41.

KITANO, Y., and N. KANAMORI. 1966. Synthesis of magnesian calcite at low temperatures and pressures. Geochim. J., *1*: 1-10.

KITANO, Y., K. PARK, and D. W. HOOD. 1962. Pure aragonite synthesis. J. Geophys. Res., *67*: 4873-4874.

KLEEREKOPER, H., and J. MORGENSEN. 1963. Role of olfaction in the orientation of *Petromyzon marinus*. I. Response to single amine in prey body odor. Physiol. Zool., *36*: 347-360.

KNUDSEN, J. 1964. Observations of the reproductive cycles and ecology of the common Brachyura and crab-like Anomura of Puget Sound, Washington. Pacific Sci., *18*: 3-33.

KOHN, A. J. 1961. Chemoreception in gastropod molluscs. Amer. Zool., *1*: 291-308.

KOYAMA, T. 1962. Organic compounds in seawater. J. Oceanogr. Soc. Japan, 20th Anniv. Vol: 563-576.

KOYAMA, T., and T. G. THOMPSON. 1959. Organic acids in sea water, p. 925-926. *In* Preprints Int. Oceanogr. Congr.

KRAMER, J. R. 1965. History of sea water. Constant temperature-pressure equilibrium models compared to liquid inclusion analysis. Geochim. Cosmochim. Acta, *29*: 912-945.

KRAUS, E. B. 1967. Organized convection in the ocean resulting from slicks and wave radiation stress. Phys. Fluids, *10*: S294-S297, (Suppl.).

KRAUSE, H. R. 1961. Einige Bemerkungen über den postmortalen Abbau von Süsswasser — Zooplankton unter laboratoriums — und Freiland Bedingungen. Arch. Hydrobiol., *57*: 539-543.

KRAUSE, H. R. 1962. Investigation of the decomposition of organic matter in natural waters. FAO Fish. Biol. Rep. No. 34. 19 p.

KRAUSE, H. R., L. MOCHEL, and M. STEGMANN. 1961. Organische Sauren als geloste Intermediarprodukte des postmortalen Abbaues von Süsswasser — Zooplankton. Naturwissenschaften, *48*: 434-435.

KRINSKY, N. I. 1965. The carotenoids of the brine shrimp *Artemia salina*. Comp. Biochem. Physiol., *16*: 181-187.

KRISS, A. E. 1963. Marine microbiology (deep-sea). Translation by J. M. Shewan and Z. Kabata. Oliver and Boyd, London. 536 p.

KROEPELIN, H. 1963. Amino acids in Posidonian shales and their behaviour when heated. Fortschr. Geo. Rheinland Westfalen, *10*: 293-294.

KROGH, A. 1930. Über die Bedentung von gelösten organischen Substanzen bei der Ernahrung von Wassertieren. Z. Vergl. Physiol., *12*: 668-681.

KROGH, A. 1931. Dissolved substances as food of aquatic organisms. Biol. Rev., *6*: 412-444.

KUHME, W. 1963. Chemisch ausgelöste Bruptflege- und Schwarmreaktionen bei *Hemichromis bimaculatus* (Pisces). Z. Tierphysiol., *20*: 688-704.

LAMAR, W. L., and D. F. GOERLITZ. 1966. Organic acids in naturally colored surface waters. U. S. Geol. Surv. Water-Supply Paper 1817-A. 17 p.

LAND, L. S. 1967. Diagenesis of skeletal carbonates. J. Sed. Petr., *37*: 914-930.

LANGRIDGE, P., and R. Y. MORITA. 1966. Thermolability of malic dehydrogenase from the obligate psychrophile, *Vibrio marinus*. J. Bacteriol., *92*: 418-423.

LEBOY, P. S., S. G. CLINE, and R. L. CONNER. 1964. Phosphate, purines, and pyrimidines as excretory products of *Tetrahymena*. J. Protozool., *11*: 217-222.

LEE, W. L. 1966. Pigmentation of the marine isopod *Idotea montereyensis*. Comp. Biochem. Physiol., *18*: 17-36.

LEFÈVRE, K. U., and B. TOLLENS. 1907. Investigation of glucuronic acid, its quantitative determination and its color reactions [In German]. Ber., *40*: 4513-4523.

LEIFSON, E. 1930. A method of staining bacterial flagella and capsules together with a study of the origin of flagella. J. Bact., *20*: 203-211.

LENHOFF, H. M. 1968. Behavior, hormones and hydra. Science, *161*: 434-442.

LENNÉ, H.-U. 1954. Röntgenographische Strukturuntersuchungen hexagonaler Einschlussverbindungen des Thioharnstoffs. Acta Cryst., *7*: 1-15.

LEO, R. F., and P. L. PARKER. 1966. Branched chain fatty acids in sediments. Science, *152*: 649-650.

LEWIN, J. C. 1963. Heterotrophy in marine diatoms, p. 229-235. *In* C. H. Oppenheimer [ed.], Symp. Marine microbiology. C. Thomas, Springfield, Ill.

LEWIN, J. C., R. A. LEWIN, and D. E. PHILPOTT. 1958. Observation of *Phaeodactylum tricornutum*. J. Gen. Microbiol., *18*: 418-426.

LEWIS, F., and W. R. TAYLOR. 1921. Notes from the Woods Hole Laboratory. Rhodora, *23*: 249-256.

LEWIS, G. J., and N. W. RAKESTRAW. 1955. Carbohydrate in sea water. J. Mar. Res., *14*: 253-258.

LEWIS, J. B. 1967. Nitrogeneous excretion in the tropical sea urchin *Diadema antillarum* Philippi. Biol. Bull., *132*: 34-37.

LINDBERG, B. 1953. Low molecular carbohydrates in algae. I. Investigation of *Fucus vesiculosus*. Acta. Chem. Scand., *7*: 1119-1122.

LITTLE, C., and B. L. GUPTA. 1968. Pogonophora: uptake of dissolved nutrients. Nature, *218*: 873-874.

LONNBERG, E. 1931. Untersuchungen über das Vorkommen Carotenoider Stoffe bei Marinen Evertebraten. Ark. Zool., *22A*(14): 1-49.

LONNBERG, E. 1932. Zur Kenntnis der Carotenoide bei Marinen Evertebraten. Ark. Zool., *23*(4): 1-74.

LOVE, J., and E. PERCIVAL. 1964. The polysaccharides of the green seaweed *Codium fragile*. III. A β-1,4-linked mannan. J. Chem. Soc., 3345-3351.

LOWENSTAM, H. A. 1954. Factors affecting the aragonite:calcite ratios in carbonate secreting marine organisms. J. Geol., *62*: 284-322.

LOWENSTAM, H. A. 1961. Mineralogy, O^{18}/O^{16} ratios, and strontium and magnesium contents of recent and fossil brachiopods and their bearing on the history of the oceans. J. Geol., *69*: 241-260.

LOWENSTAM, H. A. 1963. Biologic problems relating to the composition and diagenesis of sediments, p. 137-195. *In* T. W. Donnelly [ed.], The earth sciences. Univ. Chicago Press.

LUCAS, C. E. 1955. External metabolites in the sea. Deep-Sea Res. (Mar. Biol. Oceanogr. Suppl.), *3*: 139-148.

LUCAS, C. E. 1961. Interrelationships between aquatic organisms mediated by external metabolites, p. 499-518. *In* M. Sears [ed.], Oceanography. Amer. Ass. Adv. Sci., Pub. 67.

LUCAS, C. E. 1961. On the significance of external metabolites in ecology, p. 190-206. *In* F. C. Milthrope [ed.], Mechanisms in biological control. Symp. Soc. Exp. Biol., *15*. Academic Press, New York.

LUMBY, J. R., and A. R. FOLKARD. 1956. Variation in the surface tension of sea water in situ. Inst. Oceanogr. Bull., Monaco, *53*(1080): 1-19.

LUNDE, K., and L. ZECHMEISTER. 1955. Infrared spectra and cis-trans configurations of some carotenoid pigments. J. Amer. Chem. Soc., *77*: 1647-1653.

LYMAN, J. 1959. Chemical considerations in physical and chemical properties of sea water. Nat. Acad. Sci., Nat. Res. Council, Pub. *600*: 87-97.

LYMAN, J., and R. H. FLEMING. 1940. Composition of sea water. J. Mar. Res., *3*: 134-146.

LYSYJ, I. 1970. Instrumental techniques for the identification of pollutants. *In* D. W. Hood [ed.], Proc. Symp. Organic matter in natural waters. Occa. Pub. No. 1, Inst. Mar. Sci., Univ. Alaska.

LYSYJ, I., and K. H. NELSON. 1968. Pyrographic method for the analysis of organics in aqueous solution. Anal. Chem., *40*: 1365-1367.

MacFADYEN, A. 1964. Energy flow in ecosystems and its exploitation by grazing, p. 3-20. *In* D. J. Crisp [ed.], Grazing in terrestrial and marine environments. Blackwells, Oxford.

MacINTYRE, W. G., and R. F. PLATFORD. 1964. Dissolved $CaCO_3$ in the Labrador Sea. J. Fish. Res. Bd. Canada, *21*: 1475-1480.

MACKENZIE, F. T., and R. M. GARRELS. 1966. Chemical mass balance between rivers and oceans. Amer. J. Sci., *264*: 507-525.

MACKIE, I. M., and E. PERCIVAL. 1959. The constitution of xylan from the green seaweed *Caulerpa filiformis*. J. Chem. Soc., 1151-1156.

MALCOLM, N. L. 1968. Synthesis of protein and ribonucleic acid in a psychrophilic at normal and restrictive growth temperatures. J. Bacteriol., *95*: 1388-1399.

MANSKAYA, S. M., and T. V. DROZDOVA. 1964. Geochemistry of organic substances. Moscow. Translated and edited by L. Shapiro and I. A. Breger, 1968, Pergamon, Oxford.

MARGALEFF, R. 1946. Contribution al conocimiento del genero *Platymonas*. Collect. Bot., I(1), *8*: 95-105.

MARKER, A. F. H. 1965. Extracellular carbohydrate liberation in the flagellates *Isochrysis galbana* and *Prymnesium parvum*. J. Mar. Biol., Ass. U.K., *45*: 755-772.

MARR, G. A., E. H. NILSON, and D. J. CLARK. 1963. The maintenance of *Escherichia coli*, p. 536-548. *In* C. Lamanna [ed.], Endogenous metabolism with special reference to bacteria. Annu. New York Acad. Sci., *102*.

MARSHALL, S. M., and A. P. ORR. 1955. The biology of a marine copepod, *Calanus finmarchicus* (Gunnerus). Oliver and Boyd, Edinburgh. 188 p.

MARSHALL, S. M., and A. P. ORR. 1956. On the biology of *Calanus finmarchicus*. IX. Feeding and digestion in the young stages. J. Mar. Biol. Ass. U.K., *35*: 587-604.

MARSHALL, S. M., and A. P. ORR. 1958. On the biology of *Calanus finmarchicus*. X. Seasonal changes in oxygen consumption. J. Mar. Biol. Ass. U.K., *37*: 459-472.

MARTELL, A. E., and L. G. SILLÈN. 1964. Stability constants of metal-ion complexes. Chem. Soc. Spec. Pub. No. 17. Burlington House, London. 754 p.

MARTIN, J. P. 1967. Down to earth. 15th Annu. Fac. Res. Lect. April 12, 1967. Riverside, Calif.

MARTIN, J. P., S. J. RICHARDS, and K. HAIDER. 1967. Properties and decomposition and binding action in soil of humic acid synthesized by *Epicoccum nigrum*. Soil Sci. Amer., Proc., *31*: 657-662.

MATHEMEIER, P. F. 1966. Thermal inactivation studies on some enzymes from *Vibrio marinus*, an obligately psychrophilic marine bacterium. Ph.D. Thesis, Oregon State Univ., Corvallis.

MATTHEWS, W. S., and L. L. SMITH. 1968. Sterol metabolism. III. Sterols of marine waters. Lipids, *3*: 239-246.

MAUTNER, H. G. 1954. The chemistry of brown algae. Econ. Bot., *8*: 174-192.

McALLISTER, C. D., T. R. PARSONS, and J. D. H. STRICKLAND. 1960. Primary productivity and fertility at Station "P" in the North East Pacific Ocean. J. Cons., *25*: 240-259.

McGLAUGHLIN, J. J. A., and P. A. ZAHL. 1959. Axenic zooxanthellae from various invertebrate hosts. Annu. N.Y. Acad. Sci., *77*: 55-72.

McKEE, H. S. 1962. Nitrogen metabolism in plants. Clarendon Press, Oxford. 728 p.

McLACHLAN, J. 1964. Some considerations on the growth of marine algae in artificial medium. Can. J. Microbiol., *10*: 769-782.

McLACHLAN, J., and J. S. CRAIGIE. 1964. Algal inhibition by yellow ultraviolet-absorbing substances from *Fucus vesiculosus*. Can. J. Bot., *42*: 287-292.

McWHINNIE, M. A., and R. JOHANNECK. 1966. Utilization of inorganic and organic carbon compounds by Antarctic zooplankton. Antarctic J.U.S., *1*: 210.

MENZEL, D. W. 1964. Distribution of dissolved organic carbon in the western Indian Ocean. Deep-Sea Res., *11*: 757-765.

MENZEL, D. W. 1966. Bubbling of sea water and the production of organic particles: a re-evaluation. Deep-Sea Res., *13*: 963-966.

MENZEL, D. W. 1967. Particulate organic carbon in the deep sea. Deep-Sea Res., *14*: 229-238.

MENZEL, D. W., and J. J. GOERING. 1966. The distribution of organic detritus in the ocean. Limnol. Oceanogr., *11*: 333-337.

MENZEL, D. W., and J. H. RYTHER. 1961. Zooplankton in the Sargasso Sea off Bermuda and its relation to organic production. J. Cons., *26*: 250-258.

MENZEL, D. W., and J. H. RYTHER. 1968. Organic carbon and the oxygen minimum in the South Atlantic Ocean. Deep-Sea Res., *15*: 327-337.

MENZEL, D. W., and J. H. RYTHER. 1970. Distribution and cycling of organic matter in the oceans. *In* D. W. Hood [ed.], Proc. Symp. Organic matter in natural waters. Occa. Pub. No. 1, Inst. Mar. Sci., Univ. Alaska.

MENZEL, D. W., and R. F. VACCARO. 1964. The measurement of dissolved organic and particulate carbon in seawater. Limnol. Oceangr., *9*: 138-142.

METCALFE, L. D., A. A. SCHMITZ, and J. R. PELKA. 1966. Rapid preparation of fatty acid esters from lipids for gas-chromatographic analysis. Anal. Chem. *38*(3): 514-515.

MEYRATH, J., and A. F. McINTOSH. 1963. Size of inoculum and carbon metabolism in some *Aspergillus* species. J. Gen. Microbiol., *33*: 47-56.

MIDDLETON, F. M. 1959. Report on the recovery of orthonitrochlorobenzene from the Mississippi River. U. S. Public Health Service, Dept. Health, Educ., Welfare, Cincinnati, Ohio. 12 p.

MIDDLETON, F. M., and A. V. de LAPORTE. 1956. A study of organic contaminants in boundary waters using carbon filter techniques, Lake Huron - Lake Erie, 1953-1955. Prepared for Int. Joint Comm., United States and Canada, on boundary waters. 34 p.

MIDDLETON, F. M., A. A. ROSEN, and R. H. BURTTSCHELL. 1959. Manual for recovery and identification of organic chemicals in water. U. S. Public Health Service, Dept. Health, Educ., Welfare, Cincinnati, Ohio. 48 p.

MILLER, W. W. 1968. Studies on glucose-6-phosphate dehydrogenase obtained from *Vibrio marinus*, an obligate psychrophile. M.S. Thesis, Oregon State Univ., Corvallis.

MIYAKI, Y., and K. SARUHASHI. 1956. On the vertical distribution of dissolved oxygen in the ocean. Deep-Sea Res., *3*: 242-247.

MIYAKI, Y., Y. SUGIURA, and Y. KATSURAGI. 1956. Radioactive fallout at Asahikawa, Hokkaido in April, 1955. J. Met. Soc. Japan, Ser. 2, *34*: 226-230.

MOLLITOR, A. 1937. Beiträge zur Untersuchung des Exkretsstoffwechsels und der Exkretion von *Eriocheir sinensis*. Zool. Jb. Allgem. Zool., *57*: 323-354.

MONOD, J. 1942. Recherches sur la croisance des cultures bacteriennes. 2nd ed., Hermann, Paris, 1958.

MOORE, B., E. S. EDIE, E. WHITELY, and W. J. DAKIN. 1912. The nutrition and metabolism of marine animals in relation to (a) dissolved organic matter and (b) particulate organic matter of sea water. Biochem. J., *6*: 255-296.

MORGAN, J. 1968. Metal organic complexes. Paper presented at Symp. Organic matter in natural waters. Inst. Mar. Sci., Univ. Alaska. Sept. 2-4, 1968.

MORITA, R. Y. 1966. Marine psychrophilic bacteria. Oceanogr. Mar. Biol. Annu. Rev., *4*: 105-121.

MORITA, R. Y. 1967. Effects of hydrostatic pressure on marine microorganisms. Oceanogr. Mar. Biol. Annu. Rev., *5*: 187-203.

MORITA, R. Y., and L. J. ALBRIGHT. 1965. Cell yields of *Vibrio marinus*, an obligate psychrophile, at low temperatures. Can. J. Microbiol., *11*: 221-227.

MORITA, R. Y., and S. D. BURTON. 1963. Influence of moderate temperature on growth and malic dehydrogenase activity of a marine psychrohpile. J. Bacteriol., *86*: 1025-1029.

MORITA, R. Y., and R. D. HAIGHT. 1964. Temperature effects on the growth of an obligately psychrophilic marine bacterium. Limnol. Oceanogr., *9*: 103-106.

MURTAUGH, J. J., and R. L. BUNCH. 1967. Sterols as a measure of fecal pollution. J. Water Poll. Control Fed., *39*: 405-409.

NATTERER, K. 1892-94. Denkschr. Akad. Wiss. Wien, *59*, 1st Reihe, 83; *60*, 2nd Reihe, 49; *61*, 3rd Reihe, 23.

NELSON, G. J. 1962. Studies on human serum lipoprotein phospholipids and phospholipid fatty composition by silicic acid chromatography. J. Lipid Res., *3*: 71-74.

NEUJAHR, H. Y. 1966. Transport of B-vitamins in microorganisms. II. Factors affecting the uptake of labelled thiamine by non-proliferating cells of *Lactobacillus fermenti*. Acta Chem. Scand., *20*: 771-785.

NEWELL, R. 1965. The role of detritus in the nutrition of two marine deposit feeders, the prosobranch *Hydrobia ulvae* and the bivalve *Macoma balthica*. Zool. Soc. (London), Proc., *144*: 25-45.

NICHOLSON, H. P. 1967. Pesticide pollution control. Science, *158*: 871-876.

NICOL, J. A. C. 1967. The biology of marine animals. 2nd ed. Interscience, New York. 699 p.

NICOL, J. A. C. 1967. Sensory organs and reception, p. 348-355. *In* J. A. C. Nicol [ed.], The biology of marine animals, 2nd ed. Wiley and Sons, New York.

NIELSEN, E. STEEMANN. 1958. The balance between phytoplankton and zooplankton in the sea. J. Cons., *23*: 178-188.

NIELSEN, E. STEEMANN. 1960. Productivity of the oceans. Annu. Rev. Plant. Physiol., *11*: 341-362.

NIELSEN, E. STEEMANN. 1965. On the determination of the activity in ^{14}C-ampoules for measuring primary production. Limnol. Oceanogr., *10*: R247-252.

NIGRELLI, R. F. 1958. Dutchmans "baccy juice" or growth-promoting and growth-inhibiting substances of marine origin. N.Y. Acad. Sci., Trans., Ser. II, *20*: 248-262.

NISIZAWA, K. 1938. Physiological studies on laminarin and mannitol of brown algae. I. Diurnal variation of their content in *Eisenia bicyclis*. Sci. Rep. Tokyo Bunrika Daigaku Sect., *B3*: 289-301.

NORTH, B. B., and B. C. STEPHENS. 1967. Uptake and assimilation of amino acids by *Platymonas*. Biol. Bull., *133*: 391-400.

ODUM, E. P. 1962. Relationship between structure and function in the ecosystem. Jap. J. Ecol., *12*: 108-118.

ODUM, H. T. 1951. The stability of the world strontium cycle. Science, *114*: 407-411.

OGURA, N. 1967. Studies of the ultraviolet adsorbing materials in natural waters. Ph.D. Thesis, Tokyo Metropolitan Univ., Tokyo. 101 p.

OLSON, J. S. 1963. Energy storage and the balance of producers and decomposers in ecological systems. Ecology, *44*: 322-331.

OPPENHEIMER, C. H., and C. E. ZOBELL. 1952. The growth and viability of sixty-three species of marine bacteria as influenced by hydrostatic pressure. J. Mar. Res., *11*: 10-18.

OSTROFF, R., and B. S. HENRY. 1939. The utilization of various nitrogen compounds by marine bacteria. J. Cell. Comp. Physiol., *13*: 353-371.

OXENDER, D. L., and H. N. CHRISTENSEN. 1963. Distinct mediating systems for the transport of neutral amino acids by the Ehrlich cell. J. Biol. Chem., *238*: 3686-3699.

PARK, R., and S. EPSTEIN. 1960. Carbon isotope fractionation during photosynthesis. Geochim. Cosmochim. Acta, *21*: 110-126.

PARKER, P. L. 1964. The biogeochemistry of the stable isotope of carbon in a marine bay. Geochim. Cosmochim. Acta, *28*: 1155-1164.

PARKER, P. L., C. VAN BAALEN, and L. MAURER. 1967. Fatty acids in eleven species of blue-green algae: geochemical significance. Science, *155*: 707-708.

PARKER, R. A., and M. I. OLSON. 1966. The uptake of inorganic phosphate by *Daphnia schødleri* Sars. Physiol. Zool., *39*: 53-65.

PARRY, G. 1960. Excretion, p. 341-366. *In* T. H. Waterman [ed.], The physiology of crustacea, v. 1. Academic Press, New York.

PARSONS, T. R. 1963. Suspended organic matter in sea water, p. 205-239. *In* M. Sears [ed.], Progress in oceanography, v. 1. Pergamon, Oxford and New York.

PARSONS, T. R., and R. J. LEBRASSEUR. In press. The availability of food to different trophic levels in the marine food chain. Proc. Symp. Marine food chains, Arhus, Denmark, 1968.

PARSONS, T. R., R. J. LEBRASSEUR, and J. D. FULTON. 1967. Some observations on the dependence of zooplankton grazing on the cell size and concentration of phytoplankton blooms. J. Oceanogr. Soc. Japan, *23*: 11-18.

PARSONS, T. R., K. STEPHENS, and J. D. H. STRICKLAND. 1961. On the chemical composition of eleven species of marine phytoplankton. J. Fish. Res. Bd. Canada, *18*: 1001-1016.

PARSONS, T. R., and J. D. H. STRICKLAND. 1961. On the production of particulate organic carbon by heterotrophic processes in sea water. Deep-Sea Res., *8*: 211-222.

PARSONS, T. R., and J. D. H. STRICKLAND. 1962. Ocean detritus. Science, *136*: 313-314.

PARSONS, T. R., and J. D. H. STRICKLAND. 1962. On the production of particulate organic carbon by heterotrophic processes in sea water. Deep-Sea Res., *8*: 211-222.

PENA, C. E. 1955. The influence of temperature on the growth of *T. utilis*. M.S. Thesis, Univ. Wisconsin. Univ. Microfilms, Ann Arbor, Michigan.

PERCIVAL, E. G. V., and S. K. CHANDA. 1950. The xylan of *Rhodymenia palmata*. Nature, *166*: 787.

PERCIVAL, E. G. V., and A. G. ROSS. 1949. Marine algal cellulose. J. Chem. Soc., 3041-3043.

PERLMAN, D. 1965. Microbial production of metal-organic compounds and complexes, p. 103-138. *In* W. W. Umbreit [ed.], Advances in applied microbiology, v. 7. Academic Press, New York.

PETERSEN, M. N. 1966. Calcite: rates of dissolution in a vertical profile in the central Pacific. Science, *154*: 1542-1544.

PETIPA, T. S. 1966. Relationship between growth, energy metabolism, and ration in *Acartia clausi* Giesbr., p. 82-91. *In* Physiology of marine animals. Akad. Nauk SSSR, Oceanogr. Comm.

PETRACEK, F. J., and L. ZECHMEISTER. 1956. Determination of partition coefficients of carotenoids as a tool in pigment analysis. Anal. Chem., *28*: 1484-1485.

PFEIFFER, W. 1963. Alarm substances. Experientia, *19*: 113-168.

PILKEY, O. H., and H. G. GOODWELL. 1963. Trace elements in recent mollusk shells. Limnol. Oceanogr., *8*: 137-148.

PILKEY, O. H., and J. HOWER. 1960. The effect of environment on the concentration of skeletal magnesium and strontium in *Dendraster*. J. Geol., *68*: 203-216.

PILPEL, N. 1968. The natural fats of oil on the sea. Endeavour, *100*: 11-13.

PINTNER, I. J., and L. PROVASOLI. 1963. Nutritional characteristics of some chrysomonads, p. 114-121. *In* C. H. Oppenheimer [ed.], Symp. Marine microbiology. C. Thomas, Springfield, Ill.

POMEROY, L. R., and F. M. BUSH. 1959. Regeneration of phosphate by marine animals, p. 893-895. *In* Mary Sears [ed.], Preprints Intern. Oceanogr. Congr., Amer. Ass. Adv. Sci., Washington, D.C.

POMEROY, L. R., and R. E. JOHANNES. 1968. Occurrence and respiration of ultraplankton in the upper 500 meters of the ocean. Deep-Sea Res., *15*: 381-391.

PRÁT, S., and F. POSPISIL. 1959. Humic acids with C^{14}. Biol. Plant., Acad. Sci. Bohemoslov., *1*: 71-80.

PRÁT, S., M. SMIDOVA, and A. L. CINCEROVA. 1961. Penetration and effect of humus substances (fractions) on plant cells. V. Int. Congr. Biochem. Abstracts of Commun. 329. Moscow.

PROVASOLI, L. 1961. Micronutrients and heterotrophy as possible factors in bloom production in natural waters, p. 48-56. *In* Trans. 1960 seminar on algae and metropolitan waters. Robert A. Taft Sanitary Engineering Center, Cincinnati, Ohio. Tech. Rep. W61-3.

PROVASOLI, L. 1963. Organic regulation of phytoplankton fertility, p. 165-219. *In* M. N. Hill [ed.], The sea, v. 2. Interscience, New York.

PROVASOLI, L., and K. GOLD. 1962. Nutrition of the American strain of *Gyrodinium cohnii*. Arch. Mikrobiol., *42*: 196-203.

PROVASOLI, L., and J. J. A. McLAUGHLIN. 1963. Limited heterotrophy of some photosynthetic dinoflagellates, p. 105-113. *In* C. H. Oppenheimer [ed.], Symp. Marine microbiology. C. Thomas, Springfield, Ill.

PROVASOLI, L., and I. J. PINTER. 1966. The effect of phenolic compounds on the morphology of ulva. Abstr. of Algae in the Pacific. 11th Pac. Sci. Congr. Tokyo. Fisheries, 7: 23.

PÜTTER, A. 1909. Die Ernährung der Wassertiere und der Stoffhaushalt der Gewässer. J. Fischer. Jena. 168 p.

PYTKOWICZ, R. M. 1965. $CaCO_3$ saturation in the ocean. Limnol. Oceanogr., *10*: 220-225.

PYTKOWICZ, R. M. 1968. Water masses and their properties at 160°W in the southern ocean. J. Oceanogr. Soc. Japan, *24*: 21-31.

RADTKE, L. D., and J. L. TURNER. 1967. High concentration of total dissolved solids block spawning migration of striped bass, *Roccus saxatilis* in the San Joaquin River, California. Amer. Fish. Soc., Trans., *96*: 405-407.

REDFIELD, A. C. 1942. The processes determining the concentration of oxygen, phosphate, and other organic derivatives within the depths of the Atlantic Ocean. Pap. Phys. Oceanogr. Meteor., *9*. 22 p.

REDFIELD, A. C. 1958. Preludes to the entrapment of organic matter in the sediments of Lake Maracaibo. *In* Habitat of oil. Amer. Ass. Petroleum Geol., Tulsa, Okla.

REDFIELD, A. C., B. H. KETCHUM, and F. W. RICHARDS. 1963. The influence of organisms on the composition of seawater, p. 26-77. *In* M. N. Hill [ed.], The sea, v. 2. Interscience, New York.

REID, J. L. 1965. Intermediate waters of the Pacific Ocean. Johns Hopkins Press, Baltimore. 85 p.

RICHARDS, F. A. 1957. Oxygen in the ocean, p. 185-238. *In* J. Hedgepath [ed.], Treatise on marine ecology and paleoecology. Mem. Geol. Soc. Amer., *67*.

RICHARDS, F. A. 1965a. Anoxic basins and fiords, p. 611-645. *In* J. P. Riley and G. Skirrow [ed.], Chemical oceanography. Academic Press, London.

RICHARDS, F. A. 1965b. Chemical observations in some anoxic, sulfide-bearing basins and fjords, p. 215-243. Proc. 2nd Int. Water Poll. Res. Conf., Tokyo, 1964.

RICHARDS, F. A., and B. B. BENSON. 1961. Nitrogen/argon and nitrogen isotope ratios in two anaerobic environments, the Cariaco Trench in the Caribbean Sea and Dramsfjord, Norway. Deep-Sea Res., 7: 254-264.

RICHARDS, F. A., J. D. CLINE, W. W. BROENKOW, and L. P. ATKINSON. 1965. Some consequences of the decomposition of organic matter in Lake Nitinat, an anoxic fjord. Limnol. Oceanogr., *10*: R185-R201.

RICHARDS, F. A., and A. C. REDFIELD. 1954. A correlation between the oxygen content of sea water and the organic content of marine sediments. Deep-Sea Res., *1*: 279-281.

RICHARDS, F. A., and R. F. VACCARO. 1956. The Cariaco Trench, an anaerobic basin in the Caribbean Sea. Deep-Sea Res., *3*: 214-228.

RILEY, G. A. 1951. Oxygen, phosphate, and nitrate in the Atlantic Ocean. Bingham Oceanogr. Coll., *13*(1), 126 p.

RILEY, G. A. 1963. Organic aggregates in sea water and the dynamics of their formation and utilization. Limnol. Oceanogr., *8*: 372-381.

RILEY, G. A., D. VAN HEMERT, and P. J. WANGERSKY. 1965. Organic aggregates in surface and deep waters of the Sargasso Sea. Limnol. Oceanogr., *10*: 354-364.

RILEY, G. A., P. J. WANGERSKY, and D. VAN HEMERT. 1964. Organic aggregates in tropical and subtropical waters of the North Atlantic Ocean. Limnol. Oceanogr., *9*: 546-550.

RILEY, J. P., and P. SINHASENI. 1958. The determination of copper in sea water, silicate rocks and biological materials. Analyst, *83*: 299-304.

RILEY, J. P., and G. SKIRROW [ed.]. 1965. Chemical oceanography, I. Academic Press, London. 712 p.

RINGBOM, A. 1963. Complexation in analytical chemistry. Interscience, New York, entire.

RISEBROUGH, R. W., R. J. HUGGETT, J. J. GRIFFIN, and E. D. GOLDBERG. 1968. Pesticides: transatlantic movements in the Northeast Trades. Science, *159*: 1233-1236.

RITTENBERG, S. C., K. O. EMERY, J. HÜLSEMANN, E. T. DEGENS, R. C. FAY, J. H. REUTER, J. R. GRADY, S. H. RICHARDSON, and E. E. BRAY. 1963. Biogeochemistry of sediments in experimental mohole. J. Sed. Petr., *33*: 140-172.

ROBISON, S. M. 1965. Studies on the effect of moderate temperature on *Vibrio marinus*. M.S. Thesis, Oregon State Univ., Corvallis.

ROCHE, P. M. 1966. The effect of copper on marine bacteria. M.A. Thesis, Boston Univ., Boston, Mass. 74 p.

RODHE, W. 1955. Can plankton production proceed during winter darkness in subarctic lakes? Verh. Int. Ver. Limnol., *12*: 117-122.

ROSEN, A. A., and M. RUBIN. 1964. Natural carbon-14 activity of organic substances in streams. Science, *143*: 1163.

ROSEN, A. A., and M. RUBIN. 1965. Discriminating between natural and industrial pollution through carbon dating. J. Water Poll. Cont. Fed., *37*: 1302.

RUBEY, W. W. 1955. Development of the hydrosphere and atmosphere, with special reference to probable composition of the early atmosphere, p. 631-650. *In* A. Poldervaat [ed.], Crust of the earth. Geol. Soc. Amer. Bull. Spec. Paper No. 62.

RUBEY, W. W. 1964. Geologic history of sea water, p. 1-63. *In* The origin and evolution of atmosphere and oceans. Wiley and Sons, New York.

RYAN, E. P. 1966. Pheromone: evidence in a decapod crustacean. Science, *151*: 340-341.

RYTHER, J. H. 1963. Geographic variations in productivity, p. 347-780. *In* M. N. Hill [ed.], The sea, v. 2. Interscience, New York.

RYTHER, J. H., D. W. MENZEL, E. M. HULBURT, C. J. LORENZEN, and N. CORWIN. In press. The production and utilization of organic matter in the Peru Coastal Current. ANTON BRUUN Reports, Southeastern Pacific Program.

SACKETT, W. M., W. R. ECKELMANN, M. L. BENDER, and A. W. H. BÉ. 1965. Temperature dependence of carbon isotope composition in marine plankton and sediments. Science, *148*: 235-237.

SARKANEN, K. V. 1963. Chapter 10. Wood lignins, p. 249-311. *In* B. L. Browning [ed.], The chemistry of wood. Wiley, New York.

SATOMI, M., and L. R. POMEROY. 1965. Respiration and phosphorus excretion in some marine populations. Ecology, *46*: 877-881.

SAUNDERS, G. W. 1957. Interrelationships of dissolved organic matter and phytoplankton. Bot. Rev., *23*: 389-410.

SCHLENK, W., Jr. 1949. Die Harnstoff-Addition der aliphatischen Verbindungen. Experientia, *5*: 204-220.

SCHLUNEGGER, U. P. 1966. Gas chromatographic separation of aliphatic oxygen-containing compounds dissolved in water. J. Chromatogr., *22*: 229-233.

SCHMALZ, R. F. 1967. Kinetics and diagenesis of carbonate sediments. J. Sed. Petr., *37*: 60-67.

SCHNITZER, M., and S. I. M. SKINNER. 1966. Organic-metallic interactions in soils: 6. Stability constants of Cu^{++}-, Fe^{++}-, and Zn^{++}-fulvic acid complexes. Soil Sci., *102*: 361-365.

SCHNITZER, M., and S. I. M. SKINNER. 1967. Organo-metallic interactions in soils: 7. Stability constants of Pb^{++}-, Ni^{++}-, Co^{++}-, Ca^{++}-, and Mg^{++}-fulvic acid complexes. Soil Sci., *103*: 247-252.

SCHUBERT, J. 1948. Use of ion exchangers for the determination of physical-chemical properties of substances, particular radiotracers. J. Phys. Coll. Chem., *52*: 340-350.

SCHUTZ, F. 1956. Untersuchungen über die Schreckreaktion bei Fischen. Z. Vergl. Physiol., *38*: 84-135.

SEIWELL, H. R. 1937. The minimum oxygen concentration in the western basin of the North Atlantic. Pap. Phys. Oceanogr. Meteor., 5(3). 24 p.

SEKI, H. 1965a. Microbial studies on the decomposition of chitin in marine environment. IX. Rough estimation of chitin decomposition in the ocean. J. Oceanogr. Soc. Japan, 21: 253-260.

SEKI, H. 1965b. Decomposition of chitin in marine sediments. J. Oceanogr. Soc. Japan, 21: 261-268.

SEKI, H., J. SKELDING, and T. R. PARSONS. 1968. Observations on the decomposition of a marine sediment. Limnol. Oceanogr., 13: 440-447.

SEKI, H., and N. TAGA. 1963. Microbiological studies on the decomposition of chitin in marine environment. I. Occurrence of chitinoclastic bacteria in a neritic region. J. Oceanogr. Soc. Japan, 19: 101-108.

SHAPIRO, J. 1957. Chemical and biological studies on the yellow organic acids of lake water. Limnol. Oceanogr., 2: 161-179.

SHAPIRO, J. 1964. Effect of yellow organic acids on iron and other metals in water. Amer. Water Works Ass., 56: 1062-1082.

SHAPIRO, J. 1966. Yellow organic acids of lake water: differences in their composition and behavior. Paper presented at Symp. Hung. Hydro. Soc. Budapest-Tihany. Sept. 25-28, 1966.

SHELDON, R. W., T. P. T. EVELYN, and T. R. PARSONS. 1967. On the occurrence and formation of small particles in sea water. Limnol. Oceanogr., 12: 367-375.

SHELDON, R. W., and T. R. PARSONS. 1967a. A practical manual on the use of the Coulter Counter in marine science. Coulter Electronics Sales Co., Canada. 66 p.

SHELDON, R. W., and T. R. PARSONS. 1967b. A continuous size spectrum for particulate matter in the sea. J. Fish. Res. Bd. Canada, 24: 909-915.

SHRIFT, A. 1966. Methionine transport in Chlorella vulgaris. Plant Physiol., 41: 405-410.

SIEBURTH, J. McN. 1965. Bacteriological samplers for air-water and water-sediment interfaces, p. 1064-1068. In Ocean science and ocean engineering, v. 2. Trans. MTS-ASLO Conf., Washington.

SIEBURTH, J. McN. 1965. Organic aggregation in sea water by alkaline precipitation of inorganic nuclei during the formation of ammonia by bacteria. J. Gen. Microbiol., 41: XX.

SIEBURTH, J. McN. 1967. Seasonal selection of estuarine bacteria by water temperature. J. Exp. Mar. Biol. Ecol., *1*: 98-128.

SIEBURTH, J. McN. 1968. The influence of algal antibiosis on the ecology of marine microorganisms, p. 63-74. *In* M. R. Droop and E. J. F. Wood [ed.], Advances in microbiology of the sea. Academic Press, London and New York.

SIEBURTH, J. McN. 1969. Studies on algal substances in the sea. III. Production of extracellular organic matter by littoral marine algae. J. Exp. Mar. Biol. Ecol., *3*: 290-309.

SIEBURTH, J. McN., and J. T. CONOVER. 1965. *Sargassum* tannin, an antibiotic which retards fouling. Nature, *208*: 52-53.

SIEBURTH, J. McN., and A. JENSEN. 1968. Studies on algal substances in the sea. I. Gelbstoff (humic material) in terrestrial and marine waters. J. Exp. Mar. Biol. Ecol., *2*: 174-189.

SIEBURTH, J. McN., and A. JENSEN. 1969. Studies on algal substances in the sea. II. Gelbstoff (humic material) formation in phaeophyte exudates. J. Exp. Mar. Biol. Ecol., *3*: 275-289.

SIEGEL, A., and E. T. DEGENS. 1966. Concentrations of dissolved amino acids from saline waters by ligand-exchange chromotography. Science, *151*: 1098-1101.

SILLÈN, L. G., and A. E. MARTELL. 1964. Stability constants of metal-ion complexes. The Chemical Society, Burlington House, London.

SILVERMAN, S. R. 1967. Carbon isotopic evidence for the role of lipids in petroleum formation. J. Amer. Oil Chem. Soc., *44*: 691-695.

SKOPINTSEV, B. A. 1957. The study of redox potential of the Black Sea waters [In Russian]. Gidrokhim. Materialy, *27*: 21-37.

SKOPINTSEV, B. A. 1960. Organic matter in sea water [In Russian]. Trudy Morsk. Gidrofiz. Inst., Akad. Nauk SSSR, *19*: 1-20.

SKOPINTSEV, B. A. 1965. Investigation of the water layer with oxygen minimum in the North Atlantic Ocean in the autumn of 1959 [In Russian]. Rez. Issled. Prog. Mezhd. Geofiz. Goda Mezhd. Geofiz. Komit, Presid. Akad. Nauk SSSR, *13*: 108-114.

SKOPINTSEV, B. A. 1966. Some aspects of the distribution and composition of organic matter in the waters of the ocean. Oceanology, *6*: 441-450. (Fish. Res. Bd. Canada Transl. No. 930.)

SKOPINTSEV, B. A., and S. N. TIMOFEEVA. 1960. The organic carbon in the waters of the northern part of the Black Sea [In Russian]. Dokl. Akad. Nauk SSSR, *134*: 688-690.

SKOPINTSEV, B. A., and S. N. TIMOFEEVA. 1961. New data on the content of total organic carbon in waters of the Atlantic and Black Sea [In Russian]. Pervichnaya Produktsiya Morei i Vnutr. Vod, *1961*: 60-66.

SKOPINTSEV, B. A., and S. N. TIMOFEEVA. 1962. Organic carbon content in the Baltic and North Sea, and in tropical and subtropical regions of the North Atlantic [In Russian]. Trudy Morsk. Gidrofiz. Inst., Akad. Nauk SSSR, *25*: 110-117.

SKOPINTSEV, B. A., S. N. TIMOFEEVA, and O. A. VERSHININA. 1966. Organic carbon in the equatorial and southern Atlantic and in the Mediterranean [In Russian]. Okeanologiya, Akad. Nauk SSSR, *6*: 251-260. Translated into English, Oceanology, *6*: 201-210.

SLATER, J. V., and J. W. TREMOR. 1962. Radioactive phosphorus accumulation and distribution in *Tetrahymena*. Biol. Bull., *122*: 298-309.

SLOAN, P. R., and J. D. H. STRICKLAND. 1966. Heterotrophy of four marine phytoplankters at low substrate concentrations. J. Phycol., *2*: 29-32.

SLOWEY, J. F., L. M. JEFFREY, and D. W. HOOD. 1959. Characterization of the ethyl acetate extractable organic material of sea water, p. 934-937. *In* Preprints Int. Oceanogr. Congr.

SLOWEY, J. F., L. M. JEFFREY, and D. W. HOOD. 1962. The fatty acid content of ocean water. Geochim. Cosmochim. Acta, *26*: 607-616.

SLOWEY, J. F., L. M. JEFFREY, and D. W. HOOD. 1967. Evidence for organic complexed copper in sea water. Nature, *214*: 377-378.

SMAYDA, T. J., and B. J. BOLEYN. 1965. Experimental observations on the flotation of marine diatoms. I. *Thalassiosira cf. nana, Thalassiosira rotula*, and *Nitzschia seriata*. Limnol. Oceanogr., *10*: 499-509.

SMAYDA, T. J., and B. J. BOLEYN. 1966a. Experimental observations on the flotation of marine diatoms. II. *Skeletonema costatum* and *Rhizosolenia setigera*. Limnol. Oceanogr., *11*: 18-34.

SMAYDA, T. J., and B. J. BOLEYN. 1966b. Experimental observations on the flotation of marine diatoms. III. *Bacteristrum hyalinum* and *Chaetoceros lauderi*. Limnol. Oceanogr., *11*: 35-43.

SMITH, A. E. 1952. The crystal structure of the urea-hydrocarbon complexes. Acta Cryst., *5*: 224-235.

SMITH, D. G., and E. G. YOUNG. 1953. On the nitrogenous constituents of *Fucus vesiculosus*. J. Biol. Chem., *205*: 849-858.

SMITH, D. G., and E. G. YOUNG. 1955. The combined amino acids in several species of marine algae. J. Biol. Chem., *217*: 845-853.

SMITH, S. V., J. A. DYGAS, and K. E. CHAVE. 1968. Distribution of $CaCO_3$ in pelagic sediments. Mar. Geol., *6*: 391-400.

SOCIETY OF AMERICAN BACTERIOLOGISTS. 1957. Manual of microbiological methods. McGraw-Hill, New York. 315 p.

SOLDO, A. T., and W. J. VAN WAGTENDONK. 1961. Nitrogen metabolism in *Paramecium aurelia*. J. Protozool., *8*: 41-55.

SOUTHWARD, A. J., and E. C. SOUTHWARD. 1968. Uptake and incorporation of labelled glycine by Pogonophores. Nature, *218*: 875-876.

STADNIKOFF, G. 1930. The origin of coal and oil. Enke, Stuttgart.

STANLEY, S. O., and R. Y. MORITA. 1968. Salinity effect on the maximal growth temperature of some bacterial environments. J. Bacteriol., *95*: 169-173.

STANLEY, S. O., and A. H. ROSE. 1967. Bacteria and yeasts from lakes on Deception Island. Roy. Soc. (London), Phil. Trans., *B.252*: 199-207.

STANLEY, S. O., and A. H. ROSE. 1967. On the clumping of *Corynebacterium xerosis* as affected by temperature. J. Gen. Microbiol., *48*: 9-23.

STARKEY, R. L. 1968. The ecology of soil bacteria: discussion and concluding remarks, p. 635-646. *In* T. R. G. Gray and D. Parkingson [ed.], The ecology of soil bacteria. Univ. Toronto Press, Toronto.

STEINHARDT, R. A., H. MORITA, and E. S. HODGSON. 1966. Mode of action of straight chain hydrocarbons on primary chemoreceptors of the blowfly, *Phormia regina*. J. Cell. Physiol., *67*: 53-62.

STEPHENS, G. C. 1963. Uptake of organic materials by aquatic invertebrates. II. Accumulation of amino acids by the bamboo worm, *Clymenella torquata*. Comp. Biochem. Physiol., *10*: 191-202.

STEPHENS, G. C. 1967. Dissolved organic material as a nutritional source for marine and estuarine invertebrates, p. 367-383. *In* G. H. Lauff [ed.], Estuaries. Amer. Ass. Adv. Sci. Pub. *83*.

STEPHENS, G. C., and R. A. SCHINSKE. 1961. Uptake of amino acids by marine invertebrates. Limnol. Oceanogr., *6*: 175-181.

STEPHENS, K., R. W. SHELDON, and T. R. PARSONS. 1967. Seasonal variations in the availability of food for benthos in a coastal environment. Ecology, *48*: 852-855.

STEVEN, D. M. 1959. Studies on the shoaling behavior of fish. I. Responses of two species to changes of illumination and to olfactory stimuli. J. Exp. Biol., *36*: 261-280.

STEWARD, W. D. P. 1963. Liberation of extracellular nitrogen by two nitrogen-fixing blue-green algae. Nature, *200*: 1020-1021.

STOFFEL, W., F. CHU, and E. H. AHRENS. 1959. Analysis of long chain fatty acids by gas-liquid chromatography: micro-method for preparation of methyl esters. Anal. Chem., *31*: 307-308.

STOKES, J. L. 1963. General biology and nomenclature of psychrophilic bacteria, p. 187-192. *In* N. E. Gibbons [ed.], Recent progress in microbiology. Univ. Toronto Press, Toronto.

STRAIN, H. H., M. R. THOMAS, and J. J. KATZ. 1961. Spectrum of eschscholtzxanthin and other carotenoid pigments. J. Org. Chem., *26*: 5061-5064.

STRANGE, R. E., and M. SHON. 1964. Effects of thermal stress on viability and ribonucleic acid of *Aerobacter aerogenes* in aqueous suspension. J. Gen. Microbiol., *34*: 99-114.

STRICKLAND, J. D. H. 1965. Phytoplankton and marine primary production. Annu. Rev. Microbiol., *19*: 127-162.

STUMM, W. 1967. Metal ions in aqueous solution, p. 520-560. *In* S. D. Faust and J. B. Hunter [ed.], Principles and applications of water chemistry. Wiley and Sons, New York.

SUESS, E. 1968. Calcium carbonate interaction with organic compounds. Ph.D. Thesis, Lehigh Univ., Bethlehem, Pa.

SUSHCHENYA, L. M., and N. N. KHMELEVA. 1967. Consumption of food as a function of body weight in crustaceans [Engl. trans.]. Akad. Nauk SSSR Doklady, Biol. Sci. Sect., *176*: 559-562.

SUTCLIFFE, W. H., E. R. BAYLOR, and D. W. MENZEL. 1963. Sea surface chemistry and langmuir circulation. Deep-Sea Res., *10*: 233-243.

SUTHERLAND, M. D., and J. W. WELLS. 1959. Anthraquinone pigments from the crinoid *Comatula pectinata*. Chem. Ind., *37*: 291-292.

SVERDRUP, H. U. 1938. On the explanation of the oxygen minima and maxima in the oceans. J. Cons., *13*: 163-172.

SVERDRUP, H. U., M. JOHNSON, and R. FLEMING. 1942. The oceans. Prentice-Hall, New Jersey. 1087 p.

SWINNERTON, J. W., and V. J. LINNENBOM. 1967a. Determination of the C_1 to C_4 hydrocarbons in sea water by gas chromatography. J. Gas Chromatogr., *5*: 570-573.

SWINNERTON, J. W., and V. J. LINNENBOM. 1967b. Gaseous hydrocarbons in sea water: determination. Science, *156*: 1119-1120.

SWINNERTON, J. W., V. J. LINNENBOM, and C. H. CHEEK. 1962. Determination of dissolved gases in aqueous solutions by gas chromatography. Anal. Chem., *34*: 483-485.

SWINNERTON, J. W., V. J. LINNENBOM, and C. H. CHEEK. 1964. Determination of argon and oxygen by gas chromatography. Anal. Chem., *36*: 1669-1671.

SWINNERTON, J. W., V. J. LINNENBOM, and C. H. CHEEK. 1968. A sensitive gas chromatographic method for determining carbon monoxide in sea water. Limnol. Oceanogr., *13*: 193-195.

SZEKIELDA, K. H. 1967. Some remarks on the influence of hydrographic conditions on the concentration of particulate carbon in sea water, p. 314-322. *In* H. L. Golterman and R. S. Clymo [ed.], Chemical environment in the aquatic habitat. N. W. Noord-Hollandsche Uitgevers Maatschappij, Amsterdam.

TAGA, N. 1955. Studies on the effect of copper upon the marine bacteria. I. The depressing activities of copper sulfate upon the development of bacteria in sea water. Jap. Soc. Sci. Fish. Bull., *20*: 280-285.

TATSUMOTO, M., and C. C. PATTERSON. 1963. The concentration of common lead in sea water, p. 74-89. *In* J. Geiss and E. D. Goldberg [ed.], Earth science and meteoritics. North-Holland Publishing Co., Amsterdam.

TAYLOR, F. J. 1960a. The absorption of glucose by *Scenedesmus quadricauda*. I. Some kinetic aspects. Roy. Soc., Proc., *B.151*: 400-418.

TAYLOR, F. J. 1960b. The absorption of glucose by *Scenedesmus quadricauda*. II. The nature of the absorptive process. Roy. Soc., Proc., *B.151*: 483-496.

TEICHMANN, H. 1957. Das Riechvermögen des Aales (*Anguilla anguilla*, L.). Naturwissenschaften, *44*: 242.

TESTER, A. L., P. M. VAN WELL, and J. J. NAUGHTON. 1955. Reaction of tuna to stimuli. I. Response of tuna to chemical stimuli. Spec. Sci. Rep. U.S. Fish Wildl. Serv., No. 130, part 1.

THIESSEN, R. 1925. Origin of the boghead coals. U.S. Geol. Surv. Prof. Paper 132-K: 121-137.

THOMAS, W. H. 1966. On denitrification in the northeastern tropical Pacific Ocean. Deep-Sea Res., *13*: 1109-1114.

THOMEN, H., and H. WACKERNAGEL. 1964. Zum Vorkommen von Keto-Carotenoiden in Crustaceen. Naturwissen, *51*: 87-88.

TIMMONS, C. O. 1962. Stability of plankton oil films to artificial sunlight. U.S. Nav. Res. Lab. Rep. No. 5774. 8 p.

TODD, J. H., J. ATEMA, and J. E. BARDACH. 1967. Chemical communication in social behavior of a fish, the yellow bullhead (*Ictalurus natalis*). Science, *158*: 672-673.

TOLBERT, N. E., and L. P. ZILL. 1956. Excretion of glycolic acid by algae during photosynthesis. J. Biol. Chem., *222*: 895-906.

TOLBERT, N. E., and L. P. ZILL. 1957. Excretion of glycolic acid by *Chlorella* during photosynthesis, p. 228-231. *In* M. Gaffron [ed.], Research in photosynthesis. Interscience, New York.

TRACEY, M. V. 1948. A manometric method for the estimation of milligram quantities of uronic acids. Biochem. J., *43*: 185-189.

TRASK, P. D. 1953. Chemical studies of sediments of the western Gulf of Mexico, Part II of The sediments of the western Gulf of Mexico. Mass. Inst. Technol. and Woods Hole Oceanogr. Inst. Paper *12*(4): 49-120.

TRY, K. 1967. Presence of the hydrocarbons pristane and phytane in human adipose tissue and the occurrence of normal amounts in patients with Refsum's disease. Scand. J. Clin. Lab. Invest., *19*: 385.

UREY, H. C. 1947. The thermodynamic properties of isotopic substances. J. Chem. Soc., 562-581.

UREY, H. C., H. A. LOWENSTAM, S. EPSTEIN, and C. R. McKINNEY. 1951. Measurement of paleotemperatures and temperatures of the Upper Cretaceous of England, Denmark, and the southeastern United States. Geol. Soc. Amer. Bull., *62*: 399-416.

UNRAU, A. M., and F. SMITH. 1957. A chemical method for the determination of the molecular weight of certain polysaccharides. Chem. Ind. (London): 330-331.

USSING, H. H. 1949. Transport of ions across cellular membranes. Physiol. Rev., *29*: 127-155.

VACCARO, R. F., and H. W. JANNASCH. 1966. Studies on heterotrophic potential in the sea: the use of specifically labelled glucose. Can. J. Microbiol., *13*: 1165-1173.

VACCARO, R. F., and H. W. JANNASCH. 1966. Studies on heterotrophic activity in sea water based on glucose assimilation. Limnol. Oceanogr., *11*: 596-607.

VACCARO, R. F., and H. W. JANNASCH. 1967. Variations in uptake kinetics for glucose by natural populations in sea water. Limnol. Oceanogr., *12*: 540-542.

VALLENTYNE, J. R. 1957. The molecular nature of organic matter in lakes and oceans, with lesser reference to sewage and terrestrial soils. J. Fish. Res. Bd. Canada, *14*: 33-82.

VALLENTYNE, J. R. 1962. Solubility and the decomposition of organic matter in nature. Arch. Hydrobiol., *58*: 423-434.

VAN UDEN, N., and R. CASTELO-BRANCO. 1961. *Metschnikowiella zobellii* sp. nov. and *M. krissii* sp. nov., two yeasts from the Pacific Ocean pathogenic for *Daphnia magna*. J. Gen. Microbiol., *26*: 141-148.

VINOGRADOV, M. E. 1962. Feeding of the deep-sea zooplankton. Rapp et Procesverb. J. Cons., *153*: 114-120.

VIRKAR, R. A. 1963. Amino acids in the economy of the sipunculid worm, *Golfingia gouldii*. Biol. Bull., *125*: 396-397. (Abstr.)

VOGEL, J. C. 1961. Isotope separation factors of carbon in the equilibrium system CO_2-HCO_3^--$CO_3^=$. Comitato Nazionale per L'energia Nucleare, Summer course on nuclear geology, p. 216-221. Laboratorio Di Geolgia Nucleare, Pisa.

VON FRISCH, K. 1938. Zur Psychologie des Fisch-Schwarmes. Naturwissenschaften, *26*: 601-606.

WAKSMAN, S. A., and C. L. CAREY. 1935. Decomposition of organic matter in sea water by bacteria. II. Influence of addition of organic substances upon bacterial activity. J. Bacteriol., *29*: 545-561.

WAKSMAN, S. A., D. D. JOHNSTONE, and C. L. CAREY. 1943. The effect of copper on the development of bacteria in sea water, and the isolation of specific bacteria. J. Mar. Res., *5*: 136-152.

WAKSMAN, S. A., and C. E. RENN. 1936. Decomposition of organic matter in sea water by bacteria. III. Factors influencing the rate of decomposition. Biol. Bull., *70*: 472-483.

WANGERSKY, P. J. 1952. Isolation of ascorbic acid and rhamnoside from seawater. Science, *115*: 685.

WANGERSKY, P. J. 1965. The organic chemistry of sea water. Amer. Sci., *53*: 358-374.

WANGERSKY, P. J., and D. C. GORDON, Jr. 1965. Particulate carbonate, organic carbon, and Mn^{2+} in the open ocean. Limnol. Oceanogr., *10*: 544-550.

WANGERSKY, P. J., and R. R. L. GUILLARD. 1960. Low molecular weight organic base from the dinoflagellate *Amphidinium carteri*. Nature, *185*: 689-690.

WATT, W. D. 1966. Release of dissolved organic material from the cells of phytoplankton populations. Roy. Soc. (London) Proc., B. *164*: 521-551.

WATTENBERG, H., and E. TIMMERMANN. 1936. Ueber die Sattigung des Seiwasser an $CaCO_3$, und die anorganogene Bildung von Kalksedimenten. Ann. D. Hydrogr. U. Mar. Meter., 23-31.

WEAR, R. G. 1966. Commensalism: polychaete and bivalve. Biol. Bull., *130*: 141-149.

WEBB, K. L., and R. E. JOHANNES. 1967. Studies of the release of dissolved free amino acids by marine zooplankton. Limnol. Oceanogr., *12*: 376-382.

WEBB, K. L., and R. E. JOHANNES. 1969. Do marine crustaceans release dissolved amino acids? Comp. Biochem. Physiol., *29*: 875-879.

WEBB, K. L., and L. WOOD. 1967. Improved techniques for analysis of free amino acids in sea water, p. 440-444. *In* Automation in analytical chemistry, Technicon Symposium 1966, v. 1. Mediad, White Plains, New York.

WEISS, A. In press. Organic derivatives of clay minerals, zeolites, and related minerals. *In* G. Eglinton and M. Murphy [ed.], Organic geochemistry: methods and results. Springer-Verlag, Inc., New York.

WENDT, I. 1968. Fractionation of carbon isotopes and its temperature dependence in the system CO_2-gas-CO_2 in solution and HCO_3-CO_2 in solution. Earth Planetary Sci. Letters, *4*: 64-68.

WETZEL, R. G. 1967. Dissolved organic compounds and their utilization in two marl lakes. J. Hungarian Hydrol. Soc. (Hydrológicai Közlöny), *47*: 298-303.

WEYL, P. K. 1961. The carbonate saturometer. J. Geol., *69*: 32-44.

WHITEHEAD, W. L., and I. A. BREGER. 1950. The origin of petroleum: effects of low-temperature pyrolysis on the organic extract of a recent marine sediment. Science, *111*: 335-337.

WHITTLE, K. J., and M. BLUMER. 1970. Interactions between organisms and dissolved organic substances in the sea. Chemical attraction of the starfish *Asterias vulgaris* to oysters. *In* D. W. Hood [ed.], Proc. Symp. Organic matter in natural waters. Occa. Pub. No. 1., Inst. Mar. Sci., Univ. Alaska.

WIESER, W., and J. KANWISHER. 1961. Ecological and physiological studies on marine nematodes from a salt marsh near Woods Hole, Massachusetts. Limnol. Oceanogr., *6*: 262-270.

WILEY, W. R., and W. H. MATCHETT. 1966. Tryptophan transport in *Neurospora crassa*. J. Bact., *92*: 1698-1705.

WILLIAMS, P. M. 1961. Organic acids in Pacific Ocean waters. Nature, *189*: 219-220.

WILLIAMS, P. M. 1965. Fatty acids derived from lipids of marine origin. J. Fish. Res. Bd. Canada, *22*: 1107-1122.

WILLIAMS, P. M. 1967. Sea surface chemistry: organic carbon and organic and inorganic nitrogen and phosphorus in surface films and subsurface waters. Deep-Sea Res., *14*: 791-800.

WILLIAMS, P. M. 1968. Stable carbon isotopes in the dissolved organic matter of the sea. Nature, *219*: 152-153.

WILSON, D. P. 1955. The role of microorganisms in the settlement of *Ophelia bicornis savigny*. J. Mar. Biol. Ass. U.K., *34*: 531-543.

WILSON, D. P., and F. A. J. ARMSTRONG. 1952. Further experiments on biological differences between natural sea waters. J. Mar. Biol. Ass. U.K., *31*: 335-349.

WILSON, D. P., and F. A. J. ARMSTRONG. 1954. Biological differences between sea waters. J. Mar. Biol. Ass. U.K., *33*: 347-360.

WILSON, R. F. 1963. Organic carbon levels in some aquatic ecosystems. Publ. Inst. Mar. Sci., Univ. Texas., *9*: 64-76.

WINBERG, G. G. 1956. Rate of metabolism and food requirements of fishes. Nauchnye Trudy Belorusskovo Gosudarstvennovo Universiteta imeni V. I. Lenina, Minsk, 253 p. F. E. J. Fry and W. E. Ricker [ed.], Transl. Ser. No. 194, Fish. Res. Bd. Canada.

WINDOM, H., J. GRIFFIN, and E. D. GOLDBERG. 1967. Talc in atmospheric dusts. Environ. Sci. Technol., *1*: 923-926.

WIRSEN, C., Jr. 1966. The effects of nickel on marine bacteria. M.A. Thesis, Boston Univ., Boston, Mass. 122 p.

WOOD, E. J. F. 1956. Diatoms in the ocean deeps. Pacific Sci., *10*: 377-381.

WOODWARD, H. P. 1968. Cited in R. L. Bates, The geological column. Geotimes, *13*(6): 46.

WOOSTER, W. D. 1967. Further observations on the secondary nitrite maximum in the northern equatorial Pacific. J. Mar. Res., *25*: 154-166.

WOOSTER, W. S., and M. GILMARTIN. 1961. The Peru-Chile undercurrent. J. Mar. Res., *19*: 97-122.

WRIGHT, R. T., and J. E. HOBBIE. 1965. The uptake of organic solutes in lake water. Limnol. Oceanogr., *10*: 22-28.

WRIGHT, R. T., and J. E. HOBBIE. 1966. Use of glucose and acetate by bacteria and algae in aquatic ecosystems. Ecology, *47*: 447-464.

WURSTER, C. F. 1968. DDT reduces photosynthesis by marine phytoplankton. Science, *159*: 1474-1475.

WURSTER, C. F., and D. B. WINGATE. 1968. DDT residues and declining reproduction in the Bermuda petrel. Science, *159*: 979-981.

YEMM, E. W., and E. C. COCKING. 1955. Determination of amino acids with ninhydrin. Analyst, *80*: 209-213.

YONGE, G. M., and A. G. NICHOLLS. 1931. Studies on the physiology of corals. IV. The structure, distribution and physiology of zooxanthellae. Sci. Rep. Gr. Barrier Reef Exped. 1928-29. Br. Mus. (Nat. Hist.), *1*: 135-176.

ZEUTHEN, E. 1947. Body size and metabolic rate in the animal kingdom, with special regard to the marine micro-fauna. Compt. Rend. Trav. Lab. Carlsberg, Ser. Chim., *26*: 17-161.

ZOBELL, C. E. 1941. Studies on marine bacteria. I. The cultural requirements of heterotrophic aerobes. J. Mar. Res., *4*: 42-75.

ZOBELL, C. E. 1963. The occurrence, effects and fate of oil polluting the sea. Int. J. Air, Water Poll., 7: 173-193.

ZOBELL, C. E., and D. Q. ANDERSON. 1936. Observations on the multiplication of bacteria in different volumes of stored sea water and the influence of oxygen tension and solid surface. Biol. Bull., *71*: 324-342.

ZOBELL, C. E., and C. W. GRANT. 1943. Bacterial utilization of low organic matter. J. Bacteriol., *45*: 555-564.